349
351

The Biotic Message

This book is dedicated to my mother and father

Doris Irene and William Hervey

— Dossie and Bill

THE
BIOTIC MESSAGE

Evolution versus Message Theory

———

Walter James ReMine

St. Paul Science　　• • •　　Publishers
Saint Paul, Minnesota

Publisher's Cataloging in Publication Data

ReMine, Walter James, 1952-
    The Biotic Message : Evolution versus Message Theory / by Walter James ReMine.
    -- St. Paul, Minn. : St. Paul Science, c1993.
    538 p. ; 26 cm.
    Includes index.
    Bibliography: p. 515-527.
    ISBN 0-9637999-0-8

    1. Evolution. 2. Creation. 3. Ontogeny. 4. Phylogeny. 5. Biology--Classification.
    6. Natural selection. 7. Genetic load. 8. Population genetics. 9. Life--Origin.
    10. Science--Philosophy. I. Title. II. Title: Evolution versus Message Theory.

    QH371.R284 1993   575.01   AACR2

    Library of Congress Catalog Card Number 93-92637

Printed and bound in the United States of America.
Printed on durable acid-free paper.

PRINTED ON 10% POST CONSUMER RECYCLED PAPER   PRINTED WITH SOY INK™

Printing: 10 9 8 7 6 5 4 3 2 1   99 98 97 96 95 94 93

Please turn to last page for ordering information.

But each organism can mean so much more to us. Each instructs; its form and behavior embodies general messages if only we can learn to read them. (Stephen J. Gould, 1980, p 11)

Since the time of Darwin, paleontologists have found themselves confronted with evidence that conflicts with gradualism, yet the message of the fossil record has been ignored. This strange circumstance constitutes a remarkable chapter in the history of science, and one that gives students of the fossil record cause for concern. (Steven M. Stanley, 1981, p 101)

Preface

Evolutionists broadcast a challenge to the world. They continually taunt the public with a question. They charge, "Why would a creator have designed life to look like evolution?" That question is the focus of this book. The solution, bold and ironic, is that the question itself is gravely mistaken.

Perception is key to this realization. This book offers a scientific solution conflicting little with any known data. Rather, it is a radically different way of *perceiving* the data. This book is therefore about perception. It is about the interpretation and meaning of life's message.

This is a science book about the modern creation/evolution debate, with emphasis on biological issues. I quote frequently. I have excluded quotation from anti-evolutionary literature, such as the books by Denton, Fix, Hitching, P. E. Johnson, and G. R. Taylor. I quote only twice from creationists, and then only to disagree. (These two cases are clearly marked.) Except for those two instances, I quote exclusively from committed evolutionists. I have concentrated on main-stream evolutionary literature, with special effort to survey all the anti-creation material.

In fact, this book is driven by the issues raised by modern anti-creationists. I quote from these sources to authenticate data or an opinion that I discuss. This is not to imply the quoted author would necessarily agree with the point I make. I quote no authors who would presently have the slightest favor for my views. This is a do-or-die reckoning of the debate. It leaves no middle ground. Whatever the outcome, I am convinced the debate will be irrevocably transformed. When the debate continues, as seems inevitable, it will be in new territory — with new visions, new analogies, new arguments.

This book has been written to be free of religious reference. I argue that life shows the marks of having been designed as a system, and therefore the term *designer* is appropriate, as it expresses the attribute demanded by the data. Furthermore, I use *designer* because, unlike most alternatives, it is devoid of commonplace religious meaning.

Evolutionists, however, are often eager to represent creation in the most extreme unscientific light, so they frequently infuse religion into their discussion of the subject. (I wish to depict their material the way it actually is, so I do not excise their religious references.) Evolutionists are not alone in this. Many creationists have the lamentable habit of inserting irrelevant religious references into their "scientific" discussion of creation.

In short, many evolutionists and creationists have had motives for injecting religion into creation. This practice, on both sides, has propagated confusion about where the science ends and religion begins. One of my tasks is to clear this up, and the first step is to reject the religiously loaded language so often found in discussions of creation. The second step is to clearly reaffirm *testability* as the accepted criterion for demarcating science from non-science. Surprisingly, by so doing I show that several concepts, previously thought religious, actually fall into the domain of science.

2

This book also argues that evolutionary theory is not science. Though my criticisms of evolution are central to a comprehension of message theory, they may be appreciated on their own merit. I hope they will be taken as a contribution to our understanding of evolutionary theory.

This book was motivated partly by a growing sense of frustration with many creationist authors. For well over a decade I waited for them to produce books scientifically stating their case as forcefully as I felt it could be made. The reader should not assume I align myself with the present body of creationist literature — on most occasions my disagreement with it is substantial. I have also been dismayed by evolutionists, who, for reasons of their own,[1] felt unmoved to respond to the creationists' legitimate arguments until prodded by multiple cases of serious legal action.[2] This is a sorry but perhaps realistic view of how "Science" often operates.[3] I believe science can only benefit from the dialogue on origins. I disagree with those nay-sayers who declare the sky will fall if we lend an ear to the creationists. An adversarial dialogue, responsibly undertaken, can only improve our science and understanding. Adversarial dialogue can be an efficient means of clarifying scientific issues.

I refer frequently to the writings of prominent anti-creationists including Cracraft, Eldredge, Futuyma, Godfrey, Kitcher, Mayr, McGowan, Montagu, Newell, Ruse, Strahler, and especially their foremost proponent here in the United States, Stephen Jay Gould. That is the way it must be if this book is to be taken seriously. The reader may feel my disagreement with these evolutionists implies disrespect — an impression I am eager to dispel. These scientists have taken time to address this important issue. Without their insight I could not have written this book. I have developed a personal feeling toward many of these authors. As people and as scientists, I would be deeply honored to be counted among their number.

---

[1] "[S]cientists themselves frequently act in ways that effectively suppress ideas with which they disagree. A conspiracy of silence is the scientific community's most effective weapon. .... For champions of orthodox views, the best response to an attack is initially no response at all. Only if the attacks begin to attract converts can powerful scientists be smoked out to defend themselves." (Hull, 1989, p 276)

[2] "Until the recent courtroom, schoolboard, and textbook triumphs experienced by creationists, anthropologists, like other scientists, held an almost Olympic disregard for creationist views." (Womack, 1982, p 27) "Until Spring 1981, most U.S. newspapers had given only sporadic attention to Creationism or creation-science." (La Follette, 1983a, p 191) "Until then [1982], I had shared the view of most scientists that the creationists were not to be taken seriously. 'Just ignore them, and their demands will soon be forgotten,' was the attitude of busy scientists ..." (Berra, 1990, p vii)

[3] Evolutionists charge that creationists have been politically motivated. Yet evolutionists are in no position to make any such disparaging complaint. It is now a fact of history that evolutionists did not enter the modern origins debate until *after* they were politically motivated by pending legislation. For many years evolutionists steadfastly refused to mount a meaningful public response to the creationists' arguments. Political interests finally spurred evolutionists to action.

Evolutionary biology textbooks err in various ways. Often they are storybooks that oversimplify the issues in favor of evolution and leave out the crucial details that would call evolution into question. Most commonly they embed the subject in irrelevant technical details that make the theory look "scientific."

My major goals in this book are: (1) to break new ground toward a scientific resolution of the controversy; (2) to provide thorough documentation[4] (an odious but necessary task in this controversy); (3) to avoid details that are unnecessary to illumination and resolution of the issues; and (4) to make the subject interesting and understandable to a wide audience. The first two goals often sharply conflict with the last two. I have had to make tradeoffs between these goals, and I hope I have done this agreeably.

Unlike evolutionary texts, this book avoids irrelevant details. The subject can be grasped by many general readers, but the subtlety of the pertinent concepts does occasionally require some patience. I cannot meet the goals of the book and still have easy, light reading end to end. In all, this book is for readers with a serious desire to resolve the origins controversy.

Many if not most of the arguments are new. The chapters have summaries to recount major points. These restatements serve a teaching purpose, and will help many readers get through the book (and revisit at a later date). The summaries can be skipped by those adroit readers who need no review. On the other hand, the reader can examine *only* the summaries and still find the book informative. Such a reader, however, will miss the arguments, the details, the documentation, and the excitement of the book.

Many of the issues cannot be fully appreciated in isolation, so the book is best read in sequence. Evolutionary illusions are so potent and entrenched that people have an immediate knee-jerk reaction against any idea of creation. Those illusions must be cleared away if message theory is to get a reasoned hearing. The book first clears away the philosophical illusions (in chapter 2), and then many theoretical and terminological illusions (in chapters 3 through 12). Only then can it fruitfully examine the empirical data of the fossil record (in chapter 13). Virtually the entire book is about evolutionary theory, in one way or another. Chapters 1 through 15 focus predominantly on evolutionary theory. They dismantle evolutionary foundations, clear away fallacies, and prepare the reader for an issue — nested hierarchy — whose central importance most pedestrians are only faintly aware of. Those chapters also teach about evolutionists and their theory, which is essential to understanding message theory. After chapter 15 the book focuses more intensely on details of message theory and a head-to-head comparison. Those chapters show that evolutionary theory has shaped the pattern of life (with a reverse impact). The book is sequenced so that issues can be maximally understood and appreciated at the time they are resolved.

---

[4] I always identify when I have added italics or parenthesis to a quotation. If I state nothing, then the reader may correctly assume the quote is authentic as it stands. Brackets [ ] always enclose words I have added or altered for the purpose of clarification. I give author/date with the quoted text, so the reader may know at a glance who said it and how recently it has possessed currency. (Outdated citation has previously been an issue in this controversy.) Page numbers are cited to aid research.

Chapter 1, *Evolution versus the Biotic Message,* gives a brief historical background of the issues, and the central question the book aims to overturn: Why would a designer create life to look like evolution? The chapter introduces message theory and the major themes of the book. It then solves the problem of imperfection — Stephen Gould's "panda principle."

The historian of science, Thomas Kuhn, warned that the philosophy of science is a subject largely ignored until there arises a clash between two great scientific viewpoints (known as paradigms). In such a clash, issues of subtlety suddenly loom enormous before us. To resolve these issues we must examine the philosophy of science more than scientists typically want to do. Chapter 2, *Naturalism versus Science,* lays the philosophical foundation for the book. It delineates the difference between science and non-science. It debunks many anti-creation arguments. It shows that theories of an intelligent designer and messages can be scientific. Finally, it shows that some statements about the supernatural can be testable science.

Chapter 3, *The Origin of Life,* contains some chemistry and probability. A reader's previous knowledge in these areas is helpful, but not required. A major conclusion is simple, yet surprising to many. In no way does evolution predict life's biologic universals; yet message theory does. This is opposite from what evolutionists have claimed.

Chapters 4, 5, and 6, *Survival of the Fittest, Inventive Natural Selection,* and *Darwinian Scenarios,* (and an appendix) cover much material, yet they accurately reflect the great diversity of defenses that evolutionists have made for Darwin's theoretical mechanism. A lengthy treatment is necessary to document this controversy, which in its modern form has already evaded both clarity and resolution for many decades. Evolutionists claim that "natural selection is a scientific explanation of life's biological design." These chapters dismantle that intricately crafted illusion.

Chapters 7, 8, and 9, *Population Genetics, Haldane's Dilemma,* and *The Neutral Theory of Evolution,* are the most difficult, and may be skipped without loss of continuity. They explain some tough genetic issues to the average person, while remaining true to the technicalities of this field. Some of the issues — such as Fisher's theorem, the cost of substitution, and the neutral theory — have been persistently elusive even to specialists. My contribution here is to clarify what has previously been murky. The chapters show that genetics has failed to support our evolutionary origins. It has failed to provide a clear picture of how evolution occurs at the genetic level. Yet evolutionary geneticists have not candidly acknowledged the difficulties.

Chapter 10, *Gradual-Intergradations and Phylogeny,* returns to message theory for discussion of some major predictions. Life was designed so two things would be absent: (1) gradual intergradations of life forms; and (2) phylogeny. This chapter lays out the battleground between evolution and message theory.

Chapter 11, *Modern Systematic Methods,* is a tutorial on methods for studying the pattern of life. Though this chapter gives some new insights, it is not especially controversial. Readers already familiar with the subject can skip this chapter without loss of continuity.

Chapter 12, *Evolutionary Illusions,* shows how words and imagery are used to create the illusion of ancestry. This is crucial reading for clarifying the origins debate.

Chapter 13, *The Fossil Record,* draws the three previous chapters together, showing that fossils are evidence for message theory, and against evolution. This chapter is largely documentary.

Chapter 14, *Punctuated Equilibria,* shows the modern evolutionists' theoretical response to the observational setbacks of the fossil record. The chapter exposes (for the first time) the purpose behind the punctuationists' curious emphasis on speciation.

Chapter 15, *Hierarchy Theory,* shows how modern theorists have shifted away from phylogeny, to life's nested hierarchy, as the major prediction of evolution. This chapter dismantles the illusions created by punctuated equilibria, hierarchy theory, pluralism, and anti-reductionism.

Chapter 16, *Nested Hierarchy and Convergence,* examines the pattern of life in morphology space. It shows that message theory predicts nested hierarchy and "convergence" — while evolution never did. Also, Darwin's Riddle is cleanly solved. This is a key chapter, though it cannot be fully appreciated without the groundwork laid earlier.

Chapter 17, *Embryology,* explains this classic body of evidence, especially von Baer's laws of development. It shows that Haeckel's (now defunct) recapitulation theory was an attempt to distort von Baer's laws into evidence for evolution, and that is why notions of recapitulation linger today. Contrary to the claims of evolutionists, embryology is major evidence against evolution, and for the biotic message.

Chapter 18, *Vestigial Organs,* shows that this body of evidence has dwindled to a vestige of its former self. Its remains are harmonious with message theory.

Chapter 19, *Molecular Evolution,* examines the evidence now available at the molecular level, showing that this most modern of evidences fully supports message theory. It shows how molecular cladograms and phenograms are compelling evidence against evolution's simplest and most powerful mechanisms.

Chapter 20, *Illusions of Fossil Sequence,* exposes evolutionary illusions about the fossil sequence.

Chapter 21, *Fossil Sequence and Message Theory,* explains life's pattern in time.

Chapter 22, *Biogeography,* gives a brief update on the pattern of life in geographical space.

Chapter 23, *Cosmological Issues,* looks briefly at side issues that extend beyond biology.

Chapters 24 and 25, *Discontinuity Systematics,* and *Systematics and the Origins Debate,* provide the foundation for a new field of biosystematics that will become a dominant research method for evolutionists and creationists alike. These chapters will primarily interest systematists, and may be skipped by most readers.

Chapter 26, *Conclusions,* summarizes major points and draws the book together.

My references to evolution (and its variants) refer to large-scale molecules-to-man transformation. This is surely what the words mean to most everyone, especially those people thoughtfully concerned with the debate. To fruitfully discuss the origins debate I need commonly understood words, and the word *evolution* is certainly appropriate. I have little patience with those quibblers who insist that since we are not identical to our parents we must therefore admit to the "fact of evolution."[5] Such misuse of the word belittles and misrepresents.

Thomas Kuhn notes that new insight frequently arises from researchers new to a field, because they bring their own diverse backgrounds and apply them in novel ways. That is the case here. My study of creation/evolution issues began haltingly twenty years ago, and laborious work on this book has been ongoing for eleven. Yet my graduate training and professional life have been in the fields of pattern recognition, signal processing, biomedical engineering, and radio communications. Of some concern has been the problem of how to recognize patterns and messages; and conversely, how to construct patterns and messages so they may be intelligibly discerned by an observer. From this background springs my recognition that life is a biotic message. Additionally, this background gave the impetus to apply pattern analysis in a more abstract way — at the level of theories themselves. This book is concerned with two levels of biological pattern: the pattern of the data, and the pattern of theories invoked to explain that data.

When this manuscript was nearly complete I had the opportunity to pause and ruminate. I asked myself, "Why was I the one to have written it?" If it contains real contributions, then why was I the one to commit them to paper? With reflection, I recognized there is an aspect of my background whose importance I had overlooked. I mention it here because some readers are keenly interested in the history of ideas: Where do scientific ideas come from? What factors help shape scientific thinking? To answer these questions I must be thoroughly candid about my own thinking. I must acknowledge that for many years I pursued the hobby of magic.

Let me explain. Magic is a psychological art. Magicians study the psychology of illusion, and the psychological techniques are often powerful. Imagine that a magician performs a given effect five or six times, each time with a visibly different handling, from a different angle and different hand position. The audience sees the same phenomenon each time. In turn from all angles. They see it as a thing of ephemeral beauty — the temporary suspension of natural laws.

---

5   Sidney Fox makes this argument. "The fact of evolution … can no more be denied than one can deny his own senses. Each of us need only examine human offspring and their parents to attain this inference." (Fox, 1984, p 209)

The audience views several repetitions of the same phenomenon and (consciously or unconsciously) forms hypotheses about how the trick is done. Yet the magician accomplishes the feat in a different way each time. The magician is secretly *shifting* between various techniques to show different perspectives. Each repetition of the trick is specifically optimized to destroy particular hypotheses. Each repetition is to be viewed only from a certain perspective. After five or six repetitions the audience has no hypotheses left, and the mind concludes that the observed phenomenon is "real." The combined impact of this can be quite strong.

Magicians learn many techniques and refine them. No subtlety of presentation is too small to be important. Yet no one subtlety can be relied on alone. The magician learns the importance of blending and orchestrating these techniques together (sometimes in rapid-fire succession) to achieve the overall effect.

So you ask, What does all this have to do with science? Magicians study illusion: it is their art form. For this reason they are good at dissecting the illusions of others. As you are probably aware, James "The Amazing" Randi is a magician who has built a respectable career debunking mystics, parapsychologists, and faith healers. (Houdini did likewise in his day.) Randi recommends that an experienced magician be part of any debunking team, since scientists simply are not trained in the art of illusion.

Evolutionary reasoning has been "out in the open" and available for all to see. It has been scrutinized by capable people on all sides. Surely if there were serious errors in it then they must reside deeper than anyone has previously suspected— or else at the level of illusion. This book must dismantle evolutionary illusions, precisely identify their source of apparent power, and dispel them. I did not know it at the time, but I was helped by my background in magic.

Then I realized this background had influenced the development of my own theory, the biotic message. I like to watch other magicians and admire their craft. Even if I know the trick, I can revel in the skillful way a magician systematically destroys all our hypotheses about how it is done. This is not easy — the audience has a lot of hypotheses. In this way, I developed a thought process from watching other magicians. You learn to recognize when another being is thwarting your naturalistic hypotheses. You learn to see it in detail as a methodical step-by-step process, undertaken consciously by another being to get us to acknowledge a presumably "impossible" phenomenon as real. You learn that seemingly inconsequential details of the presentation are, *in combination,* essential to its success. You learn that this coincidental combination of details cannot have been accidental, but is instead the result of serious premeditation by the presenter. You learn to see the presentation itself as an 'act of communication.'

In short, there is a relationship between a magician and the audience. Anyone seriously studying the art ends up being on both sides of that relationship enough to appreciate its peculiar dynamic. That dynamic, that act of communication, has striking parallels to the one identified in message theory. The theory poses a certain dynamic taking place between the sender and the receiver of a biotic message, and my experience enabled me to grasp it. In this way, my background provided fertile ground in which this unusual idea could grow.

We live in an era when virtually every scientific finding has an impact on political, philosophical, ethical, and religious views. This is true whether the finding is from fields as diverse as astronomy, cybernetics, ecology, evolution, medicine, or nuclear physics. The ideas in this book are no exception. They cast implications far outside the realm of science. Some of these implications are transparent, while many are not so clear and will require much insight from scholars in other fields. I'll not apologize for that. It is simply a fact of life — science has meanings far beyond the merely scientific.

Walter James ReMine
September 1993

Contents

1

Evolution versus the Biotic Message

Why would God create a pattern that appears to be the result of evolution? (Cracraft, 1983a, p 174)

Or is the Creator trying to trick us into believing in evolution? (Futuyma, 1983, p 199)

Have we been victims of a Divine practical joke? (Stanley, 1981, p 176)

Creation theory suffered a decisive blow in 1859 with Charles Darwin's publication of *The Origin of Species*. Evolution — the molecules-to-man explanation — transformed our view of life, and scientists expected creation would never recover.

Yet creation did not fall into disrepute due to the overpowering evidence for evolution as is commonly supposed, but because creation theory failed to cope with the issues. It lacked the key insight needed for scientifically explaining life's pattern. That insight was evolutionary theory itself.

Evolutionary theory is now fully ripened. Its meanings are clearer, but much of it is illusion. Evolutionists have been deeply mistaken about every major issue — including evolutionary theory. This strange circumstance constitutes an extraordinary chapter in the history of science.

We begin with a review of the origins debate.

In 1802, the creationist William Paley published the **argument from design**, showing that life must have had a designer. Paley reasoned that if we found a watch on the ground, an examination would reveal its intricate structure and organization. We could assess the accuracy, delicacy, and reliability of its workings. We would find many parts or 'contrivances' all arranged for a specific end of accurately telling the time. We would conclude the watch had a watchmaker, because such intricate design requires a designer. Paley argued that life itself shows greater marks of design, and therefore must have had a designer.

The concept is ancient, yet Paley succeeded in giving it voice in a world that only recently had come to terms with scientific methodology and expression. Simple in concept, yet powerful in persuasion, Paley's argument became widely accepted by scientists.

Darwin knew that evolutionary theory would have to resolve Paley's watch problem — the problem of design. Darwin aimed to accomplish this with several broad strategies. First, he offered potent arguments against a designer.

He developed the **argument from imperfection**. He noted that nature shows imperfect design that a capable engineer would not use. His favorite examples were the orchids, which contain reproductive structures that are imperfect designs, yet may be viewed as highly modified parts of ordinary flowers. He argued that a capable designer would not use such bad design.

Another example was vestigial organs, such as whale fins containing finger-like bones reminiscent of their alleged land-roaming ancestors. Fins could be better designed another way. Darwin argued that a designer would not knowingly use an inferior design. A capable designer would use the best-suited design in each case.

When creationists offered the argument from design, Darwin answered with the argument from imperfection — *Why would a designer intentionally use imperfect designs?* If design was evidence for a designer, then imperfect design must be evidence against. So, Darwin concluded a designer did not construct life.

Darwin also noted something curious about the relationship between design and purpose. Oftentimes the same design is not used for the same purpose in different organisms. So, he posed a riddle.

Darwin's Riddle: Why would a designer use similar designs for *different* purposes, and in other cases use different designs for the *same* purpose?

Darwin used this riddle as a powerful argument against creation. He argued that a capable designer: (1) would not need to experiment; (2) would not need to switch between alternate designs; (3) and would not knowingly use an inferior design. A designer would use the best design in each case. Therefore, since nature is not reasonably designed, there was no designer.

Darwin's Riddle, vestigial organs, and the problem of imperfection were potent arguments. They showed that nature contains 'bad' design. This seemed to contradict Paley's argument from design. Can good and bad design both be attributed to the same designer?

Darwin did not raise these problems only to leave them unanswered. Each living form possesses designs well-suited for its mode of living. These are called adaptations. These biological designs must be explained.

Darwin explained biological design with his theory of natural selection, also known as survival of the fittest. Members of a population have variation, and due to the struggle for existence, the best available varieties would survive, while those less suited to nature would perish. He said this process of variation and selection creates biological design.

Darwin also explained imperfection. He pointed out that natural selection has no forethought and cannot design organisms for some future role. He argued that imperfect design is expected from an undirected mechanism such as natural selection which modifies *available* structures only for an *immediate* use in nature.

Darwin said natural selection would be a major cause of descent with modification, so descendant organisms can be slightly modified from their ancestors. Darwin combined these ideas into a theory of common descent where organisms share similarities inherited from a common ancestor. Darwin argued that common descent would produce an abundance of shared similarities, as seen in nature.

15

Most importantly, Darwin explained the way characters are distributed throughout nature. Characters are the complex features, traits, and structures of organisms. Examples are feathers, hair, or a backbone.

Darwin noted that characters form a peculiar nested pattern: a nested hierarchy of similarities. Characters tend to form a pattern of subsets nested within subsets. For example, some organisms are vertebrates; of those some are tetrapods; of those some have an amniote egg; and of those some are hairy creatures with mammary glands—mammals. There are no non-vertebrates with an amniote egg. There are no non-amniotes with hair and mammary glands. A nested pattern of some type had been suspected since Aristotle (350 B.C.) and had recently been illuminated with greater precision by the classification work of creationist Carl Linnaeus.

This peculiar pattern needed explanation. Darwin explained it as the expected result of descent with modification because newly evolved characters are shared only with descendants, not with ancestors or other lineages. Therefore, newly evolved characters should form nested subsets within subsets, according to ancestry. This seemed a stunning corroboration of Darwin's theory.

In addition, Darwin examined the field of embryology. He saw that organisms as diverse as human, chicken, turtle, and fish all have quite similar embryos. Darwin argued that no reasonable engineer would design in this fashion.

Darwin noted the curious developmental pathways of embryology. Diverse organisms begin development looking very similar, and follow similar paths. The paths tend to diverge at a point corresponding to the organism's location in the nested hierarchy of life.

Darwin explained these curious developmental pathways. Embryological development, he said, is the remnant of common descent — the closer two organisms are in ancestry the more similar they are in embryological development, and the longer they share similar development before they diverge. Organisms far apart in ancestry diverge early in their development, while those close together diverge later. Development of the embryo reflects the pattern of common ancestry.

Finally, Darwin rounded out his position with significant observations of intermediate forms, biogeography, and fossil sequence.

Within Darwin's framework the observations of nature fell into place. The new evolutionary theory explained the bad and good design, the bewildering patterns of similarity and diversity, the nested hierarchy of characters, and the curious embryological pathways. These arguments, first persuasively stated by Darwin, are still used today.

New evidence was added to the theoretical structure Darwin had begun. The tree of life was traced, and despite thorough searching of sedimentary strata, no fossils were found out-of-sequence with evolutionary expectations. This seemed to be compelling evidence for evolution.

The new field of population genetics provided a deeper view into heredity and variation. Its theoretical developments seemed to corroborate evolutionary claims.

Modern research revealed the detailed structure of biomolecules, showing that all life shares biochemical similarities. The most renowned example is the universal use of DNA as the carrier of inheritance. These biologic universals seemed astonishing confirmation that all life arose from a common ancestor.

Scientists could now read the sequences of molecules within proteins and DNA. Yet again the data formed a tree-structured pattern of common descent. All this, and more, neatly supported evolutionary theory.

*

As their case improved, evolutionists became increasingly bold:

> One has to decide if the Creator was incompetent or had a strange sense of humour. (Halstead, 1984, p 253)

> Does the Creator take pleasure in fooling us? Does it amuse Him to watch us go wrong? Is it part of a test to see if human beings will deny their senses and their reason in order to cling to myth? Can it be that the Creator is a cruel and malicious prankster, with a vicious and adolescent sense of humor? (Asimov, 1984, p 189)

> Those who choose to believe that God created every biological species separately in the state we observe them but made them in a way calculated to lead us to the conclusion that they are the products of an evolutionary development are obviously not open to argument. All that can be said is that their belief is an implicit blasphemy, for it imputes to God appalling deviousness. (Dobzhansky, 1962, p 6)[1]

Why would a designer create life to look like evolution? What possible motive could a designer have to be misleading? Is the designer trying to trick us? This is now the evolutionists' standard argument.

This book responds by showing they do not truly know their own theory. Life was designed to look *unlike* evolution, and to see this, one must understand evolutionary theory deeply.

---

[1] As another example, Varisco (1982, p 23) charges that "Creationism assumes that a very mysterious Creator reveals his plans only to a few and that the same Creator plays jokes with his worshippers."

J. S. Clarke (1919) stated that "no-one carefully studying the subsequent evolution of the biological, sociological and historical worlds can reach any other conclusion than that such evolution was the inspiration of an exaggerated and glorified criminal lunatic." (as cited in Halstead, 1984, p 245)

This book offers a new scientific explanation called message theory, which claims that life was intentionally designed to communicate a message. It is unlike any other creation theory. It departs from previous theories and identifies the intentions of the designer. Life was made by no ordinary designer, but by one with unusual intentions. Identifying these intentions resolves the difficulties. Features of life that seemed inexplicable become understandable once the designer's goal is recognized.

That goal was consistently pursued by the designer. Throughout nature it guided design choices and shaped the pattern of life. The data admit to no other solution. The pattern is intricate, yet so consistent it could not result from thoughtlessness. The pattern was premeditated. It was designed intentionally to meet a single-minded goal. The designer's goal was a reasonable one, carried out in a reasonable way and with meticulous care.

Ironically, evolution is central to that goal. Life was designed to thwart evolutionary explanation. Creation theory failed in the 1850s because it lacked a key ingredient: a full-grown theory of evolution. In Darwin's day no one understood evolution, and over 130 years have since been necessary to thoroughly reveal it. By understanding evolutionary theory, we can now understand why life was designed in such a peculiar manner.

There was never anything wrong with Paley's argument from design. It is still a compelling argument. It was merely held back by its association with inadequate concepts. Message theory resolves the inadequacies that seemed insoluble before, thereby restoring Paley's argument to respectability.

The Art Gallery

Envision yourself in an art museum, as I was on the occasion I am about to describe. I was there with a relative, who happens to be an artist, to see an exhibit neither of us had seen before. We entered a large gallery, and she spotted one of the paintings on the far wall. She pointed and said, "There's a 'so-and-so'." Since I was unable to read the artist's signature at that distance, I asked how she knew. She assured me she could not read the signature and had no prior knowledge of the painting. When I walked up to the painting, I found that indeed she had correctly recognized the artist's work. She said this was not uncommon.

An artist uses brush strokes, composition, style, and coloring that are often unique to that artist. The chance combination of these features by any other painter would be most unlikely. The similarity of highly complex features is strong evidence that they derive from a common source, since similarity is unlikely to result just by chance. There must be some common cause for the similarity. In this case the common cause is the original artist.[2]

---

[2] Even the similarities in a work of forgery must be attributed to some ultimate common source — the original artist.

This same reasoning applies to life. Diverse life forms display strikingly similar characters. For example, there is the nearly universal use of: DNA as the carrier of inheritance; the expression of that information as proteins via an RNA intermediate; the genetic code; the use of left-handed amino acids in proteins; and the bi-layered phosphatide construction of cell membranes.[3] The biochemical similarities extend to proteins and to the cellular metabolism of the most diverse living beings. Adenosine tri-phosphate (ATP), biotin, riboflavin, hemes, pyridoxin, vitamins B_{12} and K, and folic acid are used in metabolic processes everywhere.[4] Furthermore, amino acid sequences of common proteins are similar among different organisms. For example, the protein cytochrome-*c* contains 104 amino acids, yet 64 of these are identical between yeast and horses.[5] Even more impressive is a protein, appropriately called *ubiquitin*, present in all organisms, tissues, and cells so far studied — and it has an absolutely identical amino acid sequence in each case.[6]

These similarities have been uncovered by the research of twentieth-century molecular biology, yet the unity of life was recognized long ago. Darwin (and Buffon nearly a century before Darwin[7]) saw the unity based on evidence from morphology, behavior, ecology, mimicry, and mutualism. There is a crisscrossing web of such factors uniting smaller groups together into a larger and larger whole.

> [P]lants and animals, most remote in the scale of nature, are bound together
> by a web of complex relations. (Darwin, 1859, p 124-125)

Before Darwin, the predominant creationist theory was the Great Chain of Being. Though it is no longer tenable, it did have some important insights. Central to that theory was a recognition that all life is linked together by a chain of similarities.

Even ancients such as Aristotle (350 B.C.) were aware of the vast unity of life. The unity of life could not possibly result from chance, nor from multiple sources, nor from multiple designers acting independently. Life must have come from some single common source. Evolutionists say "common descent." Creationists say "common designer."

Life could have looked like an art gallery with many artists — yet it does not. This is not happenstance. It is premeditated design. It is a major factor in message theory. All life is linked together by a complex web of similarities. Life looks like the product of a *single* designer. (This single designer can be a single being or design team.) Message theory says nature was intentionally constructed to look this way.

---

[3] Wilson, J. H., 1983, p 87-90

[4] Dobzhansky, 1973, p 23

[5] Gould, Luria, and Singer, 1981, p 680

[6] Margulis and Sagan, 1986, p 119

[7] Edey and Johanson, 1989, p 14

Message Theory

Did he create to mimic evolution and test our faith thereby? (Gould, 1984a, p 123)

Examine these numbers: ... 229, 233, 239, 241, 251, 257, 263, 269, 271, 277, ... There is something rather odd about them. They form a pattern, can you tell what it is?

They are all prime numbers: numbers divisible only by themselves and by 1. Yet the definition of a prime number only tells what it is, it tells nothing about the pattern that interrelates them. There is no pattern exactly interrelating them.

The prime numbers are 'unnatural' in the sense that there is no natural way they can be produced. An intelligent being can recognize them. Yet no known formula will generate them. No equation will 'derive' prime numbers from other numbers, nor can prime numbers be 'ancestors' for other prime numbers by some transforming formula.

Each prime number is separate and distinct — pristine. They are unrelated to each other except by possession of their common property — prime-ness. These numbers are all unified, yet they are simultaneously distinct and separate. These numbers have a property both simple and unique. They are the product of intellect, not natural processes.

For this reason prime numbers have figured into the search for extra-terrestrial intelligence (the SETI program) as part of radio messages transmitted into space. In 1974, Cornell University transmitted such a message from the Arecibo radio astronomy observatory in Puerto Rico. The signal was aimed at a cluster of stars in the constellation Hercules. Prime numbers have played a key role in SETI transmissions. The SETI researchers want a transmission to stand-out against the background of interstellar noise. They want it to draw attention to itself and decode easily. Prime numbers help meet this goal.

The purpose? These transmissions serve as a message to others that, "We are here." It is a longing we feel, an emotion we understand. I have chosen this as the central metaphor of message theory. We may dispassionately view life forms as objects to be studied and explained. Message theory claims these living objects contain a message written into their biology. Loosely interpreted, the message says, "I am here." I call it the **biotic message**.

The Central Claim of Message Theory:

Life was reasonably designed for survival and for communicating a message that tells where life came from. The biotic message says, "Life is the product of a single designer — life was intentionally designed to resist all other interpretations of origin."

Life was designed to 'speak' the biotic message, yet it was also designed for survival. Each living form is finely tuned to its environment, possessing characteristics well-suited for its mode of living. These adaptations would require skillful design, beyond our capacities.

Moreover, system design is more complicated than the mere functional design of each separate life form. The separate forms must work together, and function as a system. The system must be in ecological equilibrium so as not to perish due to collapse of the food pyramid. The system must be stable so a suitable equilibrium is restored after environmental perturbations. Also, there is concern for the disposal of prodigious quantities of waste and decomposition products. The constraints on system design are boggling. Rafts of ecology texts could be written on the subject. A designer who could accomplish these tasks would be a master.

Life was designed with two considerations in mind. Life was reasonably designed for survival, and life was also designed to convey the biotic message. The designer achieved these simultaneously. This required insuperable design capabilities.

Pause and make a list. List every other explanation of life you can think of. Think freely and use your imagination. Be expansive. For example, life might have been created by many separate civilizations. Or, life might have been created casually by many independent designers from a single civilization. Also list all the naturalistic (evolutionary) explanations you can think of. List Lamarck's theory (the inheritance of acquired characters). List Darwin's theory of evolution. Don't hold back, list everything you can.

Now, examine your list and ask yourself: How would you design life to *defeat* all those explanations? How would you design life to look like the result of a single designer? How would you achieve these goals while reasonably designing life for survival? These are not easy questions, yet life on earth shows an elegant solution.

*

Any message can be separated into three layers of information:

- The frame message

- The outer message

- The inner message

Take a message in a bottle washed up on a beach. The frame message is found when one discovers the sealed bottle, and notices it contains a dry piece of paper. It cries out for explanation, saying, "I am a message. Decode me if you can!" The marks on the paper make up the outer message. These might be hieroglyphics, or English, or Spanish, or something else. Suppose they are hieroglyphics. In this case the outer message would read, "I am a hieroglyphic message." The details of the outer message act as triggers to help decode the 'meaning' of the inner message. We are most familiar with the inner message: it is the meaning intended by the sender. The message might be a call for help, or a poem, or directions to buried treasure.[8]

---

[8]   Hofstadter, 1979, p 166-170

In the same way, the biotic message has three layers. We see the first layer when these life objects plaintively beckon to "Explain me, I am interesting. I am a message. Try to decode me!" — this is the frame message. Nothing in the world so arouses our curiosity as an explanation of life.

The biotic message was not written in English, Spanish, or hieroglyphics. It was written in a language both simple and international. Life shows a pattern of similarity and diversity. The pattern says, "I am a message written in the universal language of similarity and diversity" — this is the outer message.

The third layer, called the inner message, is seen when one uses the insights gained from the outer message to decode the meaning of the pattern. This is the layer that interests us. This layer is the biotic message. It reads: "I am a collection of life forms that could only have been created by a single designer."

From here we are interested solely in this inner layer of the biotic message. Let us divide it into two parts: the unifying message and the non-naturalistic message.

Biotic message =
Unifying message + Non-naturalistic message

The biotic message is the sum of the unifying and non-naturalistic messages.

The Unifying Message: "This system of living objects was constructed by a single source (e.g., a common designer)."

The unifying message can be sent by making all the objects very similar, such that they look like they were made by the same source. The drawback is that similarity is easy for evolutionary theory to explain.

The Non-naturalistic Message: "This system of living objects did *not* result from a naturalistic (evolutionary) process."

The non-naturalistic message can be sent by making all the objects very different, and a lot of objects with a lot of differences spells *diversity*. Diversity is difficult to explain naturalistically.

> The well-nigh inconceivable richness of kinds of organisms posed a serious challenge to the human mind, however. The western world was preoccupied with a search for laws ever since the scientific revolution in mechanics and physics. Yet, no aspect of nature was as unyielding to the discovery of laws as was organic diversity. (Mayr, 1982, p 141-142)

Diversity defeats simple naturalistic explanations. The drawback is that different designs look like creations from many separate designers.

There is a tension between the unifying message and the non-naturalistic message. They impose conflicting design constraints. Yet a judicious use of similarity and diversity allows both messages to be sent simultaneously. These countervailing requirements set up the tension between similarity and diversity that we see in nature.

Life forms are like the prime numbers: they are all unified, yet they are simultaneously unique and distinct. They have a non-naturalistic origin recognizable by intelligent beings.

*

Life was designed as a message, and messages have special requirements. Messages have senders, and (hopefully) receivers or observers. Life's designer is a biomessage sender.

A key element in all messages is perception. Since perception can go awry, an observer can misperceive a message in many ways. The sender must therefore anticipate this and design the message to avoid misperception. The message sender should design the message to convey itself reliably to the observer.

In turn, a message receiver should visualize the problems faced by the sender. The receiver should anticipate the problems posed by his own misperception, and understand how they have affected the design of the message.

Our task is to understand the biotic message and its perception. Throughout this book, we will see that the design choices made by the sender have been reasonable ones. To see life as a message is to see life in a new way.

Look at the unifying message. It says life was designed as a unified body of objects. Not one single species is an outlander. All organisms are tied together, intentionally, by a unity of design. All organisms are united by underlying similarity. A complex web of factors links all life. These similarities extend down to biomolecules. Biologic universals such as DNA/RNA, proteins, amino acids, and ATP join life together at the molecular level.

If you could find a single endemic living species dis-associated from the rest of life, then message theory would be refuted. What kind of species would this be? Perhaps a marine invertebrate based on silicon chemistry rather than carbon? Perhaps bacteria that uses a genetic molecule unlike DNA/RNA? Perhaps organisms made of crystallized clay? The possibilities are endless. If capable research into a living species failed to show its distinct unification with the remaining system of life, then message theory would be irrevocably wrong.

To some extent this type of prediction applies also to the fossil record. Unfortunately, an extinct fossil species inherently lacks the details that would readily show its unity with life. The biologic universals at the molecular level are missing, as are the soft organs, behavior, ecology, mimicry, mutualism, and the various juvenile stages of development. The fossilized hard parts are often fragmentary and incomplete. Some entire multicellular species are not even partially represented in the fossil record, and almost all single-celled organisms inherently leave no detailed fossils whatever.

For those reasons we must be cautious when evaluating the prediction for extinct organisms. The prediction cannot hinge on one, or even several fossil species, but must hinge on the overall pattern of life. If evolutionists could compellingly show that the overall pattern of life (living and fossil) is distinctly dis-united, then message theory would be wrong.

Message theory passes that test. Evolutionists do not claim that life is demonstrably dis-united. On the contrary, they claim the available data is compelling evidence that all life came from one common source (in their view, common descent from one ancestor).

Message theory would not be especially enlightening, however, if its sole statement were the unity of nature. Nature's unity has been known for millennia. Message theory embraces this unity, but its real challenge is to go further, and the needed insight is the non-naturalistic message. Life was designed to look unlike the result of natural processes — it was designed to look unlike evolution.

*

If I am to show the shortcomings of evolution, I must reveal its illusions and how they are accomplished. I must teach the illusions. This showing must be direct, vivid, and memorable. I must describe the mechanics clearly, as one would a magic trick: The magician uses steps A and B to misdirect the spectator and accomplish end C.

Yet evolutionary illusions are so thorough that evolutionists themselves are unaware. So I refer to an imaginary evolutionary theorist. The theorist is the magician who produces illusions in the mind. The illusions are achieved by selectively invoking concepts, ideas, and arguments. The theorist invokes concepts A and B to misdirect you and accomplish end C.

The central illusion of evolution lies in making a wide array of contradictory mechanisms look like a seamless whole. There is no single evolutionary mechanism — there are countless. Evolutionary theory is a smorgasbord: a vast buffet of disjointed and conflicting mechanisms waiting to be chosen by the theorist. For any given question, the theorist invokes only those mechanisms that look most satisfying. Yet, the next question elicits a different response, with other mechanisms invoked and neglected.

Evolutionary theory has no coherent structure. It is amorphous. It is malleable and can readily adjust to disparate patterns of data. Evolution accommodates data like fog accommodates landscape. In fact, evolutionary theory fails to clearly predict anything about life that is actually true. As a result this book will show that *evolution is not science.*

24

Yet evolutionary theory is the centerpiece of message theory. Evolutionary theory is itself data — *data of pivotal importance.* To experience message theory deeply you must see the evolutionary smorgasbord in its full breadth and power. Life was designed to oppose the smorgasbord. Life was designed to resist *all* naturalistic interpretations, not just Darwin's.

Darwin's 'decent with modification' is not the only entree at the evolutionary smorgasbord. There are many others to feast upon. The theorists gather around the buffet tables, singing the praises of their favorite entrees. These contrived and complicated dishes are highly prized because they would seem to complement the observed pattern of life. In all the hoopla, the theorists overlook many other edibles. Some entrees are neglected — neglected merely because they do not fit the observed pattern. Yet some of these neglected ones are simple, all-natural recipes quite suitable for consumption. Is this not curious? These neglected dishes at the evolutionary banquet have a special significance. For they hold the key to understanding why a designer should fashion Earth's peculiar pattern of life. Some of these simple all-natural recipes have a potent "pattern explaining" potential. They are simple, yet extremely powerful at explaining away data. To send the non-naturalistic message the designer must avoid creating a pattern that looks like these.

*

This book focuses on the evolutionary smorgasbord in two ways.

- Evolutionary theory is not science; it is a smorgasbord.

- Life was designed to thwart the smorgasbord. So, to understand life's design, you must understand the smorgasbord.

The classic evidences for evolution never were valid — because evolution never predicted them. They were merely used as evidence *against* a designer. Message theory resolves those problems, and turns them around. Life has a peculiar pattern that could not result from thoughtlessness. On point after point, message theory correctly predicts the details of life.

To illustrate this, we will next apply message theory to one of Darwin's major arguments.

The Argument from Imperfection

> [I]mperfections are the primary proofs that evolution has occurred (Gould, 1987a, p 14)

The argument from imperfection was developed by Darwin as a response to Paley's argument from design. Darwin showed that nature contains many examples of odd, non-optimal, imperfect design, and he argued that a capable designer would not use these bad designs. His favorite examples were the odd reproductive organs of orchids. He said such imperfect designs are unexpected from a capable designer, but are the expected result of evolution which modifies *available* structures for an *immediate* use in nature.

That argument is a favorite of evolutionists. Some of them, most notably Gould and Ghiselin, built it into an argument of considerable force.

> [I]deal design is a lousy argument for evolution, for it mimics the postulated action of an omnipotent creator. Odd arrangements and funny solutions are the proof of evolution — paths that a sensible God would never tread but that a natural process, constrained by history, follows perforce. (Gould, 1980, p 20-21)

> [Darwin began] inquiring just what sort of empirical consequences one would expect *if* God had structured each organic being according to the same kinds of standards that an engineer or craftsman might demand. The facts do not bear out the predictions, and insofar as it has a scientific basis, the argument from design is refuted. (Ghiselin, 1969, p 157-158)

> If there were no imperfections, there would be no evidence of history, and therefore nothing to favour evolution by natural selection over creation. (Cherfas, 1984, p 29)

The argument from imperfection is Gould's preferred class of evolutionary evidence. He has devoted many articles and books to promoting it, particularly *The Panda's Thumb*. He argues that odd and funny solutions (such as the panda's awkward thumb) are the major evidence of evolution. He calls this line of reasoning the panda principle.

Yet the argument from imperfection is not evidence for evolution. Neither perfection nor imperfection is evidence for evolution, since evolution is so vacuous it could accommodate both situations. Perfection is not immune from the facile just-so stories of natural selection, even Gould admits this.

> But perfection could be imposed by a wise creator or *evolved by natural selection*. (Gould, 1984a, p 122, my italics)

The argument from imperfection never was evidence for evolution, instead it was used as evidence *against* a designer.

Creationists traditionally responded to the argument by showing that the alleged "imperfect" designs are, in fact, sophisticated engineering feats that serve a useful, even optimal, purpose. They had notable success in this effort.

Additionally, creationists might argue in the following way. The problem does not begin and end with a single structure, such as the panda's thumb. If the panda had been designed with a perfect hand then we might wonder why the panda had not been given the motor capability necessary to fully mobilize it. If the motor capability was provided, then we might ask why the panda had not been given the creative intellect to fully apply it. Such a regress continues with this and other structures, and perhaps we would soon be suggesting that pandas should not have been made at all.

A system of life has many requirements. Not every organism needs the most perfect vision, wings, or hands. Not every organism can be at the top of the food chain. A system of life requires organisms with different capabilities and different positions in the overall scheme of things. Perhaps a system of life requires, for its survival, some organisms that are "imperfect"?

One could continue with this line of reasoning, with some success. It could help focus the debate, but it is implausible as a principal solution. It is difficult to argue that pandas, complete with their unusual thumbs, are needed for the system of life to survive.

No, the evolutionists have correctly identified a problem. There are just too many designs that are functional, maybe even highly so, but which are *odd* nonetheless. The problem of imperfection is real, and to solve it we must approach it directly.

Evolutionists have seen "odd arrangements and funny solutions" in nature and they insist these are paths a sensible designer would never tread. They are mistaken. Not only is it sensible, but message theory *absolutely requires it*, though at first it will seem paradoxical.

We expect a designer of life to create perfect designs. Yet this expectation itself constrains a biomessage sender to do the unexpected. A world full of perfect optimal designs would form an ambiguous message. In fact, it would not look like a message at all. It would provide no clues of an intentional message. It would look precisely as expected from a designer having no such intentions. Life's designer created life to look like a message, and therefore had to accept an astonishing design constraint: life *must* incorporate odd designs.

How can I be so utterly sure on this point? Because evolutionists have (unknowingly) said so. In fact, they insist on it. Every one of them — from Darwin, to Ghiselin, to Gould — has emphasized how unreasonable it is for a designer to have created such non-optimal, odd structures. We can rightfully conclude that if evolutionists had the wherewithal to create life, then they would independently go forth and create optimal perfect designs. We can conclude that a world of perfect designs would look precisely like the work of multiple designers acting independently. The biomessage sender created life to look *unlike* the product of multiple designers, and therefore had to use odd designs.[9]

---

[9] This is a second reason for odd design. A third reason is given later in the book.

It is not enough for a biomessage sender to merely include odd designs. All the designs together must form a pattern attributable only to a single designer. Life on earth has such a pattern.

Suppose we examined many separate handwritten documents. How would we recognize they all had the same author? Answer: By the overall pattern, especially the funny quirks and odd imperfections. It is the same with living organisms.

The quirks and imperfections play a key role in the pattern. They unite all organisms into a unified whole, while looking unlike the product of multiple designers. They give life the distinctive look of a single designer. They also make the pattern look like an intentional message, rather than an ordinary design effort.

The concept of "perfection" is loaded with different meanings. Anti-creationists thought of it solely as engineering elegance. Yet message theory indicates a slightly different standard is needed. Biological designs serve a dual role: (1) as instruments of survival; and (2) as conveyors of a message. There is some range between 'elegant engineering designs' and 'designs sufficient for survival.' Life's designer used this range to incorporate a message. In this sense, life's designs are neither imperfect nor non-optimal. They are more aptly described as odd and curious. The argument from imperfection falls down because it used the wrong concept of perfection.

This case illustrates several themes of this book.

- Evolutionary theory never did make a clear prediction on the matter, it just accommodated the data. It can adapt to both imperfection and perfection, since both explanations are available within the evolutionary smorgasbord. Imperfection never was evidence for evolution.

- Imperfection was erroneously used as evidence *against* a designer.

- The concept that *life is a message* resolves problems that seemed insoluble in the 1800s. Life was designed as a biotic message, it was designed to resist all other interpretations.

- Paley's argument from design is freed from its adversary (the argument from imperfection), and re-emerges as valid science.

Naturalism versus Science

Naturalism is the doctrine that mechanistic laws of nature are adequate to account for all phenomena. Belief in this doctrine grew with Newtonian physics, and received a major boost from Darwin. Many scientists now hold it as an unconscious assumption.

Some evolutionists are trying to build naturalism into science by redefining science to prohibit non-naturalistic explanations. They seek to disallow creation theory on that basis. By showing that creation is "unscientific by definition," they hope to ultimately win a quick victory in the origins debate.

Niles Eldredge attempts this approach.

> "If there is one rule, one criteria that makes an idea scientific, it is that it *must* invoke naturalistic explanations for phenomena, and those explanations must be testable solely by the criteria of our five senses. ....

> [S]cientists are constrained to frame *all* their statements in 'naturalistic' terms simply to be able to test them. ....

> It's simply a matter of definition — of what is science and what is not. By its very definition, scientific creationism cannot be science." (Eldredge, 1982, p 82, 87, and 88)

Eldredge says scientific ideas must use only naturalistic explanations. The problem is that he offers this as a *criterion of science,* for distinguishing between science and non-science. His effort is to make evolution "scientific" and creation "unscientific" by definition. His approach is fairly common.

Yet this redefinition of science is wrongheaded. Naturalism is not the criterion of science. Science does not begin by assuming all phenomena are naturalistic.

Instead, the basis of science is the search for the truth. It may place a premium on naturalistic explanations (since these are often valuable to us), but it is at its core a search for truth.

Suppose a police detective investigates a missing car. The detective is not restricted to consider only an intelligent being: a car thief. After all, the parking brake may have failed, the car rolled down a hill and off the road. This is a naturalistic explanation for the missing car, and it also must be considered. The detective, like the scientist, is searching for the truth.[1] What unites them is that their explanations must depend on empirical evidence: evidence observable with our five senses. But this dependence does not prevent them from recognizing the work of an intelligent being.

Historical sciences recognize intelligent design. Archaeology studies stone artifacts and can frequently tell whether they were created by natural processes

---

[1] "The evaluation of historical clues is not unlike a detective's reconstruction of a crime from circumstantial evidence" (Newell, 1982, p 57)

or intelligent beings. Archaeology even goes further, to understand the culture of these beings by studying their creations. There is no reason why an intelligent designer should be allowed into archaeology but not biology.

*

Examine the following explanation.

> The data is the handiwork of an intelligent designer who fashioned it in secret, without being seen by anyone, and who, with a purpose, specially placed it here.

Many feel this explanation is inherently unscientific,[2] yet they are mistaken. Piltdown Man involved precisely this idea.

Piltdown Man was a hoax. The perpetrator's identity is still uncertain, yet scientists deduced his *existence* no less. Scientists did not have to catch the hoaxer "in the act" to make his existence a fact. The details of the case made 'intelligent design' tenable and all naturalistic explanations untenable.

Around 1908 a group of scientists were digging near Piltdown, England in search of man's fossil ancestors. Several ancient-looking bones were found in the pit. The bones — known as Piltdown Man — included a cranium and mandible. The jaw was ape-like, containing two molar teeth, worn flat as commonly found in humans, but never in apes. Unfortunately, the jaw was broken in just the two places that might have determined its relationship with the skull: the chin region and the area of articulation with the cranium. For over forty years, scientists discussed Piltdown Man and its allotted position in pre-human evolutionary lineages.

In the 1950s, science eventually detected the hoax through three lines of evidence. First, when bones are buried underground, they readily absorb fluorine from the soil. A chemical test showed the bones contained only trace amounts of fluorine, proving they could not have been in the soil for long. Second, the tooth surfaces had unusual scratch marks, presumably from a file used to reshape the teeth. Third, the bones had a potassium bichromate stain, making them look old. Scientists considered these findings to be compelling evidence of intentional fraud.[3] Scientists later showed Piltdown Man had been fabricated from a human skull and an orangutan jaw.

Scientists also deduced information about the forger. The forger knew many things to include to be convincing, yet the forger's main skill was in knowing what to leave out.[4] The hoaxer skillfully left out the chin and the jaw joint — just the two structures that would have disclosed the hoax, had they been present. The hoaxer had an acute awareness of the scientific climate.

---

[2] Ronald Pine writes, "Thus any statement concerning the existence, nonexistence, or nature of a creator or creators is *not science by definition and has no place in scientific discussion or in science classrooms.*" (Pine, 1984, p 10, his italics) He is mistaken. For example, we can deduce the existence of the creator of the Piltdown Hoax.

[3] Gould, 1980, p 108-124

[4] Gould, 1980, p 112. I will later show that an important skill of life's designer was knowing what to 'leave out' of life in order to successfully send the biotic message.

30

This example shows how science can discriminate between an intelligent designer and naturalistic causes. It also shows that science can go further and deduce a designer's character traits and motives. Science does this based on the *pattern* of the data.

*

The Search for Extra-Terrestrial Intelligence (SETI) is a scientific research project to find other intelligent life in the galaxy. The project uses radio-telescopes to monitor thousands of radio-frequency channels from deep space. These signals might provide evidence of extra-terrestrial life. Extra-terrestrial civilizations might be recognized by the radio signals they transmit.

There is a difficulty. Random signals from radio-telescopes may eventually appear to have significance. The signal may correctly spell your grandmother's name or some other arcane information. This does not mean the signal had an intelligent source. The universe is full of radio noise sources pulsing, squawking, and humming. As an observer, you could be ignoring most noise as insignificant while identifying as "intelligent" those noise signals having a special significance to you.

In fact, many cases from the recent history of astronomy were first suggestive of extra-terrestrial intelligence, but on scrutiny proved to be natural phenomenon. When the well-known radio source CTA102 was first discovered, it was promptly declared to be non-naturalistic, originating from some extra-terrestrial intelligence. Later, when many such sources appeared, this idea was abandoned. The discovery of pulsars was similar. Cases like these caused SETI proponents to become more cautious.[5]

Yet SETI researchers still hope the data will someday be in their favor. They know science can discriminate between natural causes and messages, based on the pattern of the data. The SETI project is founded on this.

> It is not easy to state *a priori* how to distinguish messages from purely physical phenomena. But should the case really arise, we shall know how to answer the question: we should try to understand the message. (Freudenthal, 1985, p 220)

The SETI project is described as: "a valid scientific discipline," "perfectly proper science,"[6] and "The plan for SETI derives from the best and most effective of scientific traditions and procedures."[7] Active supporters of the SETI project include such notable evolutionists as Carl Sagan, Francis Crick, Stephen Jay Gould, David Raup, and Edward O. Wilson.[8] In the United States, funding for SETI has been provided by the National Academy of Sciences, the National Science Foundation, and NASA.[9]

---

[5] Sagan, 1973, p 143, 150-151

[6] Tarter, 1983

[7] Drake, 1982

[8] Sagan, 1982

[9] Sagan, 1973, p x-xi

With radiotelescopes tilted skyward, the SETI researchers are listening for signals from deep space. They are waiting for a message … and they are ready to receive it.[10]

Naturalism is not the criterion of science. Intelligent designers and messages can be legitimate science.

What is Science?

To be scientific, a theory must meet several criteria.

- A scientific theory must be explanatory: it must explain the empirical world. It must explain actual observations made with our five senses, often assisted by scientific instruments. Scientific theories are not works of fiction or fanciful imagination. They explain the real world around us.

- A scientific theory must have a self-consistent logical structure. It must not contradict itself.

These two criteria are basic. In fact, they are so basic we do not think of them. We want self-consistent explanations of our observations, and anything falling short is immediately severed from science. Seldom is there debate over the matter, so we rarely think about these criteria explicitly.

These criteria are also too easy. Most every legend, myth and religion qualify as explanatory and self-consistent. So people asked: What differentiates science from other things?

Sir Karl Popper identified the answer early in this century. He saw that **falsifiability** (also known as **testability**) distinguishes science from non-science. Scientists accepted Popper's insight, and falsifiability is now known as the criterion of science.

- A scientific theory must be falsifiable (or testable). It must be vulnerable to observations. We must, in principle, be able to envision a set of observations that would render the theory false.[11]

If an explanation is invulnerable to testing, then it is not science.

---

10 "At this very moment the messages from another civilization may be wafting across space, driven by unimaginably advanced devices, there for us to detect them—if only we knew how. …. *Or perhaps the messages are already here, present in some everyday experience that we have not made the right mental effort to recognize. The power of such an advanced civilization is very great. Their messages may lie in quite familiar circumstances.* …. *The message from the stars may be here already. But where?*" (Sagan, 1973b, p 224, my italics)

11 "Scientific claims must be testable; we must, in principle, be able to envision a set of observations that would render them false." (Gould, 1984b, p 130)

A scientific theory must be falsifiable, not false. The difference between falsifiable and false is like the difference between being vulnerable and being demolished.[12]

A scientific theory must have a clear logical structure that prevents it from bending and twisting to accommodate every observation. The structure provides the connection between a scientific explanation and its predictions. Because of the structure, a theory explains our observations while also predicting other related observations that we should *not* see. This is a key feature of a scientific theory. The theory ultimately predicts that we will *not* observe certain things. This makes the theory testable. The theory could be refuted by observations that contradict it.

A scientific theory must explain the things we see in terms which *deny* we will see certain things. This sets up an inner tension within scientific theories. A scientific theory cannot merely be explanatory. Nor can it merely deny certain observations. It must do both these in a logically unified manner.

For example, Copernicus explained that the planets revolve around the sun. This idea neatly explained the motions of planets across the sky. It also predicted that as the planets revolve they should appear to go through phases, like the phases of the Moon. Years later, Galileo sought to test this idea. He used a newly developed instrument — the telescope — enabling him to see the phases of planet Venus for the first time. Copernicus' explanation had made a clear prediction and survived the test, so it was scientific.

Unscientific explanations make no clear predictions and therefore can accommodate all possible observations. Since they cannot conceivably be refuted, they are not science.

> [T]here is another important criterion of a scientific theory which most scientists accept. This is Karl Popper's dictum that a theory be in principle 'falsifiable.' That is, a good theory doesn't merely explain everything; it specifically predicts that certain observations, if made, would prove the theory wrong. .... The nonscientific theorist lives within an impregnable fortress, safe from criticism, because *the hallmark of nonscientific theories is that they cannot be falsified. They are formulated vaguely, or invoke agents whose actions cannot be predicted, so that they 'explain' every possible outcome of a situation.* Whatever your personality or history may be, a good astrologer will find some conjunction of the planets that explains why you are this way, even though as a Sagittarius you're 'expected' to be the opposite. .... there is more to a good scientific hypothesis than corroboration; it must be falsifiable. (Futuyma, 1983, p 168-170, my italics)

Astrology is a classic example of a non-scientific explanation. It claims to predict human personalities and fortunes, yet no observations could conceivably refute it. It is so vacuous it can accommodate all observations, therefore it is not science.

---

[12] Kitcher, 1982, p 38

Science is Tentative

The criterion of falsifiability indicates science is tentative. Science never achieves absolute certainty. Science is not rigid and dogmatic. It is always questioning and searching for more complete answers.

In empirical science we can never absolutely prove a theory is true. We never attain perfect proof since we make *finite* observations. Because our observations are limited, we can only attain fine shades of *near* certainty. This point is subtle, but important. Science is tentative, always subject to possible refutation by further observations.

While science is tentative, it is not flimsy. Science can carry enough weight that we often speak of a given theory as a fact. A *fact* is something so thoroughly confirmed it would be perverse to withhold provisional assent.[13] For example, it is a fact that Piltdown Man was a hoax. This is as certain as any fact gets in science, yet ultimately it is still subject to possible falsification by further observations. That is what makes it science. Empirical science must always be subject to possible falsification, which is to say it must be testable.

Science is also tentative about falsifying a theory. It can be difficult to falsify a theory with all the finality we would like. No hypothesis *taken by itself* has observable consequences that can be tested. Rather, a hypothesis must be combined with other hypotheses in order to be tested. Hypotheses are tested in bundles.

Suppose a theory claims certain diseases are caused by microscopic germs. Suppose you wish to test this theory by looking for the germs with a microscopic. The test now depends on many theories of microscopes, light, lenses, and tissue. The outcome of this test now depends on this entire bundle of hypotheses. If the test fails and no germs are seen, then it is not always clear which of the hypotheses failed.[14] Thus, when a prediction fails, we are in a somewhat ambiguous situation. It is not always clear which of the hypotheses in the bundle is at fault.

Fortunately, while hypotheses are tested only in bundles, they can be tested within different bundles. We can combine hypotheses in many different ways to form bundles. By testing these various bundles we attain greater confidence in identifying false hypotheses.

Therefore, no observation ever guarantees falsification of a hypothesis (a point which Popper himself noticed early). In practice, theories can be difficult to falsify with all the clarity and finality we would like.

In summary, science is tentative about the proving and falsifying of theories. Though science is tentative, it is not flimsy. It can give results that warrant our confidence.

---

13 This excellent definition of "fact" is from Gould, 1984a, p 119.

14 "We can only test relatively large bundles of claims. What this means is that when our experiments go awry we are not logically compelled to select any particular claim as the culprit. We can always save a cherished hypothesis from refutation by rejecting (however implausibly) one of the other members of the bundle." (Kitcher, 1982, p 44, his parenthesis)

Double Standards

Today, Popper's criterion of falsifiability is accepted by most scientists. It is the weapon used to fight such non-science as astrology and occultism.

> [M]any anticreationists also accept Popper with no questions asked. Popperianism appears to be gospel among many scientists. Efforts by scientists to counter the nonscientific components of our culture, such as astrology and extrasensory perception, have typically been fought under the banner of falsificationism. (Kline, 1983, p 41)

Virtually all anti-creationists have explicitly endorsed testability as the criterion of science. They have further endorsed it by using it against creation. They have widely proclaimed that creation theories are not science because testability is an essential characteristic of science.[15] They convinced a federal court of this in the case of *McLean v. Arkansas*.[16] Finally, 72 Nobel Laureates, 17 State Academies of Science, and 7 other scientific organizations signed an *amicus curiae* brief to the U.S. Supreme Court in *Aguillard v. Edwards*,[17] endorsing testability as the criterion of science.[18]

Nonetheless, evolutionists often use a double standard: one standard for creation and another lesser standard for evolution. For example, Steven Stanley refers to creationism as "the 'Will of Allah' point of view: whatever happens is God's choice." He correctly categorizes this idea as unscientific because it is untestable.

> The 'Will of Allah' viewpoint is untestable, or irrefutable, and therefore unscientific. (Stanley, 1981, p 174)

Three pages later he defends evolution from a similar charge:

> [Creationists] claim that evolution does not represent a true theory (an irrelevant point; we are concerned with *credibility, not categorization*). (Stanley, 1981, p 177, my italics)

Stanley applies a criterion of testability to creation but he only demands "credibility," not testability, from evolution. Such double standards are common, and we will examine more of it later.

We must reject double standards, and assess creation and evolution by the same criteria.

---

[15] See National Academy of Sciences, 1984, p 8, 26

[16] See Overton, 1982, McLean v. Arkansas

[17] Aguillard v. Edwards, 1986, p 23

[18] McCollister (1989) has compiled resolutions, statements, and position papers from 30 scientific and 23 educational organizations. (The statements roundly condemn the creationism of the pre-1990s.) However, endorsements of testability appear on pages: 4, 7, 9, 11-12, 14, 17, 18, 19, 25, 30, 32, 34-36, 42, 47-48, 50-51, 52, 100, 103, 117, 125, 126-127, 128, 131, 137, 138, and 140. In many cases testability is used as a weapon against creation theory.

Labels

Some evolutionists argue that creation theory is unfalsifiable and also argue that it is falsified. For example, Norman Newell says:

> Creationism cannot be defined as a science because it is based on an inflexible presupposition, a conviction based on supposed cases and events that cannot be examined either directly or indirectly by scientific methods. (Newell, 1982, p 16)

Newell devotes much of his anti-creation book to an examination of creation science by scientific methods. His book shows that creation scientists do offer many testable explanations. Thus he seems to be contradicting himself. In reality, he used one broad label ("creationism") for more than one theory, and this results in his seemingly self-contradictory statements.

To usefully criticize a theory one should properly identify it and use the right label. In many cases this requires clarification.

Clarification is essential in the origins debate since evolutionists often apply evolutionary labels (erroneously) to non-evolutionary sciences. Labels such as *evolutionary theory* and *natural selection* are especially problematic. At one extreme they are mis-interpreted broadly to include all biological knowledge. At the other extreme they are mis-interpreted narrowly as population genetics. Such mis-labeling causes confusion, since many things claimed to be "evolutionary" are not, and can be endorsed by creationists.

Evolutionary theory is the naturalistic explanation of large-scale transformation (ultimately from molecules-to-man). Any theory shrinking from that claim is not evolutionary. This book will show that evolutionary theory is always either falsified or unfalsifiable, depending on whose version of the theory we are talking about.

The Blueprint Theory

The Blueprint Theory was an attempt by creationists to explain life's pattern of similarity and diversity. The theory says life's shared similarities are due to the designer's use of a common blueprint. The biology textbook developed by the Creation Research Society states the idea:

> He used a single blueprint for the body plan but varied the plan so that each 'kind' would be perfectly equipped to take its place in the wonderful world He created for them. (Creation Research Society, 1970, p 422)

The Blueprint Theory says similarities are the result of a common blueprint. But this gives the designer contradictory character attributes. Life clearly shows the designer has insuperable capabilities of creativity and imagination. Yet the designer is simultaneously said to lack these same qualities enough to require the re-use of old blueprints. The designer created everything from ants to zebras. Are we to believe this same designer was baffled when it came to creating a snout for the platypus? Are we to imagine the designer, in effect, shuffled through some desk drawers and in desperation finally found an old blueprint for a duck's bill?

More difficulties are added by the way the theory explains variation. The Blueprint Theory says some variations were designed to enhance survival of the created organisms, yet it also says the designer desired to show as much beauty, variety, and interest as possible, to prevent the world from being monotonous.

> [Some variation] is simply an expression of the Creator's desire to show as much beauty of flower, variety of song in birds, or interesting types of behavior in animals as possible. It would be a monotonous world if all roses looked alike, or if all birds sang like the meadowlark, lovely as the song of this bird is. (Creation Research Society, 1970, p 147)

> (These last two quotes are the only ones from creationists. All other quotations are from committed evolutionists.)

The Blueprint Theory explicitly states the designer intended to create as much variety as possible. This is hard to reconcile with the designer's obvious failure at meeting this goal. Life does not contain as much variety as possible. It falls way short.

> One of the most remarkable revelations of comparative anatomy, in fact, is how seldom truly novel structures are found. We can imagine cherubs and flying horses with wings sprouting from their shoulders; but the wings of vertebrates are always modifications of the front legs. As Darwin's colleague Milne Edwards expressed it, 'Nature is prodigal in variety, but niggard in innovation.' Take any major group of animals, and the poverty of imagination that must be ascribed to a Creator becomes evident. (Futuyma, 1983, p 62)

Contradictions are inherent in the Blueprint Theory for it says the designer used a common blueprint and simultaneously intended to create as much diversity as possible.

The Blueprint Theory is untestable. It allows that the designer could use a blueprint anywhere, anytime, or not at all. The theory makes no clear prediction about nature. It is at best unfalsifiable and at worst self-contradictory. In either case, it is not science.

The Blueprint Theory is the result of the following lamentable tendency among some creationists: If X is observed in nature then one speedily attributes it to the direct desires of the designer. The problem then arises (as it has here) when both 'X' and 'not X' (e.g., similarity and diversity) exist abundantly in nature, in which case one is forced to conclude the designer has directly self-contradictory intentions.

These problems are resolved by message theory, which identifies a specific self-consistent goal the designer had in mind. The designer created life as a biotic message: to look like the product of a single designer and unlike all other interpretations. Similarity and diversity both have a role in the biotic message. Similarity makes life look like the work of one designer, while diversity makes life difficult to explain by naturalistic processes. Similarity and diversity are the alphabet for the biotic message.

The Argument from Design

In 1802 the creationist William Paley published his famous argument from design. The concept was not new. Paley gave it new expression in a form suitable for science. It was a simple concept, yet it persuaded most scientists of that day.[19]

Since Darwin, the argument from design has been overshadowed by evolution. Scientists assumed that since evolution is right, Paley's argument must be wrong, but they were unclear about why.

The modern origins debate has brought this issue forward again, with many evolutionists claiming Paley's argument is unscientific or somehow improper. Modern evolutionists attack Paley's argument by using misdirection: they emphasize the irrelevant.

A common version involves crystals such as snowflakes.

> So if he [the creationist] can depart from his analogy when it comes to crystals, why not when it comes to life? Does one idea bother him more than the other? (Edwords, 1983, p 8)

Edwords draws parallels between 'design' in the human brain and in snow crystals. He tries to cast doubt on the entire argument from design by misapplying it to crystals.

Crystals do not demand an intelligent designer. Crystals — in this case snowflakes — show design only in the casual sense of the word. We say crystals have a "pretty design." Crystals are highly regular or *ordered*, yet they are actually quite elementary. The unifying design of snowflakes is so simple it is fully described in two words: hexagonal symmetry.

Evolutionists overemphasize *order*, and this misdirects our attention away from the real issues.

Another misdirection involves *complexity*.

> It is true that enzymes, and especially enzyme systems, are complex, but complexity is not a sign of 'directed' assembly. Complexity can be found in chaos even more quickly than in order. (Vogel, 1984, p 2)

Vogel uses the word complexity in an unusual way, making it useless in the discussion of design. If you pour a handful of sand onto a tabletop then Vogel's logic would say the resulting configuration is 'complex' because a description of the position and orientation of each sand grain would fill many volumes of text.[20] Vogel uses this logic to draw close parallels between the complexity of enzyme systems and chaos. The comparison is misplaced.

---

[19] Though Francis Crick believes (erroneously) that natural selection now overturns the argument from design, he acknowledges the design argument is powerful. "Had I been living 150 years ago I feel sure I would have been compelled to agree with this Argument from Design." (Crick, 1988, p 32)

[20] See (Edwords, 1983, p 9) for an example using a large snowfall instead of a handful of sand grains.

Design is concerned with a pattern of ordered complexity. It is neither simple and ordered (like a crystal), nor chaotic (like the random distribution of sand grains).

Another misdirection emphasizes cases where design is marginal or non-existent.

> [The design] argument depends on the supposed easiness of separating [designed] artifacts from natural objects. But it isn't always that easy. A person could conceivably smooth a stone in such a way that it was indistinguishable from one smoothed by a stream. How could anyone judge which was which? If a stone face in the side of a mountain [like Mount Rushmore] were carved crudely enough, it might be impossible to distinguish it from natural features. By the same token, some natural features bear an uncanny resemblance to human-made objects, often to the point that they have been mistaken for such. .... The appearance of 'marks of contrivance' can be deceptive and their absence proves nothing.[21]
> (Edwords, 1983, p 11)

Edwords points out several marginal cases of design in an attempt to cast doubt on the entire argument from design. But this merely emphasizes the irrelevant.

Obviously, the argument from design depends on the extent of the design. When the design is marginal so is the argument, but when extensive so is the conclusion: clear-cut design is clear-cut evidence for an intelligent designer.

The argument from design finds application throughout science. Therefore, some evolutionists try to erect various artificial criteria for the correct application of the argument. They claim the argument is incorrectly applied to life. For example, Hadow argues that tooling marks are needed to establish a designer.

> [The argument from design] works scientifically, though, because we can objectively study how people create now, and see if things suspected of being created by primitive humans carry these same 'tooling marks.' .... If there was a Creator, he left no 'tooling marks' on the molecules which have been distinguished from those left by natural processes. More importantly, we cannot observe the Creator at work in pre-living times or even place Him in a laboratory and have Him demonstrate His creating technique so that we can see what 'tooling marks' to seek, or how 'tooling marks,' if they exist in natural molecules, differ from those produced by natural processes. (Hadow, 1984, p 10-11)

Tooling marks are sometimes associated with design. If a sculptor chisels a marble statue then, strictly speaking, the design is entirely made of tooling marks in the marble. Yet, this is inadequate as a necessary criterion for the argument from design. The SETI researchers are waiting for radio signals showing the existence of extra-terrestrial intelligence. They are not looking for tooling marks in the radio signals. They are looking for 'pattern' and 'marks of contrivance'; they are looking for design.

*

---

[21] Thwaites attempts a similar argument. (Thwaites, 1983, p 17)

We can make everything from paper clips to computers, but we cannot make life. Modern research has abundantly confirmed Paley's view of the watch-like, ordered complexity of the simplest of living cells. Of all the objects known to man, life most warrants the argument from design. Paley's argument embodies strong evidence for a designer.

> **Paley's theory**: An intelligent designer is *necessary* for the origin of life from non-life.

Paley's theory is science because:

- It is explanatory: it explains the origin of life. An intelligent designer is demanded by the data.

- It is testable: it specifically predicts against certain observations — observations that would falsify it. If we could demonstrate the origin of life through natural processes then Paley's theory would be falsified.

If a testable hypothesis repeatedly passes rigorous testing, then it is elevated to the rank of scientific theory. Paley's argument for the origin of life has met this qualification. His challenge has been repeatedly assaulted by the best minds in science. Of all the widely-applicable testable theories in biology (and there are not many), Paley's is the most thoroughly tested.

*

In an attempt to rebut Paley's argument, Niles Eldredge misconstrues two of the essential characteristics of science.

> [Paley's analogy] 'proves' nothing. It could even be true — but it cannot be construed as science, it isn't biology, and in the end it amounts to nothing more than a simple assertion that naturalistic processes automatically *cannot* be considered as candidates for an explanation of the order and complexity we all agree we do see in nature. (Eldredge, 1982, p 134)

First, Eldredge complains that Paley's argument "proves" nothing. Yet, no scientific theory ever proves anything with finality. Scientific theories are always vulnerable to further observations.[22] The conclusions of science are always tentative; this is an essential characteristic of science.[23]

Second, his statement implies that creationists have closed minds and automatically cannot consider alternatives. It is a dexterous twist, and it appeals to one's prejudice. But Paley's theory does precisely what every scientific theory must do — it denies we will ever see certain observations. That is what makes it testable. It is science and it is biology.

Awbrey and Thwaites make a similar argument.

> A claim of intelligent design must be backed by experimental proof that such a feature could not result from natural selection. Inability to imagine such a result proves only that some humans have more limited imaginations than others. Only data can serve as evidence for or against an idea. (Awbrey and Thwaites, 1984, p 6)

Note their appeal to imagination and the suggestion that the argument from design proves only that creationists lack this mental faculty. They are using prejudice as a weapon of debate.

They demand "experimental proof" and that "only data can serve as evidence." These catch-phrases make their position *sound* scientific. Their remarks merely misdirect attention away from the untestability of the evolutionists' position.

*

In summary, evolutionists defend against Paley's argument from design by using misdirection, by emphasizing the irrelevant. Yet evolutionists confidently use the argument from design in archaeology, the Piltdown case, and the SETI project.

Paley's argument identifies evidence for a designer. It is explanatory, testable science — a point we will study more closely in the next chapter, *The Origin of Life.*

---

[22] Science does not require perfect proof. This point is recognized by evolutionists. "The point is that there can logically be no proof of evolution that enjoys apodictic certainty. That is to say, there is no definitive proof so conclusive, so finally conclusive, that it leaves no possibility of criticism and, if necessary, modification." "So I must emphasize this point: the acceptance of the hypothesis of evolution does not depend upon proofs." (Medawar, 1983, p 48 and 50)

[23] Judge Overton has ruled that one of the essential characteristics of science is: "Its conclusions are tentative, i.e., are not necessarily the final word." (Overton, 1982) However, Singleton notes that "many members of the scientific community espouse views of reality that go beyond the realm of testable scientific observation. The creationists are often correct in their assertion that evolution is presented with the aura of religious certainty rather than scientific tentativeness." (Singleton, 1987, p 340-341) "Evolution theory is frequently invoked beyond its explanatory power in both teaching and application. Evolution, or natural selection, is often used as a magic wand to explain a variety of molecular or physiological observations, where there is no apparent selection pressure operating." (Singleton, 1987, p 341)

Turning to the Supernatural

Though Paley's argument concludes that life had a designer, it does not say the designer was supernatural.[24] His theory is noncommittal about the supernatural. Nonetheless, the supernatural is an issue in the origins debate.

Many creationists invoke the supernatural unnecessarily. They propose a supernatural being whose unknown whims remove every empirical difficulty, thereby making their theories untestable. Creationists have a long tradition of this. Ironically, creationists themselves played a role in giving the supernatural a bad name in science.

The supernatural got a bad name by association. Most theories containing the supernatural happen to be untestable, and untestable theories are not science.

Some philosophers say science already accepts the supernatural, since 'intelligence' is already accepted within science. Creative intelligence, they say, is not derivable from matter and naturalistic processes, and therefore it contains an element of the supernatural.

A few evolutionists try to resolve this by redefining natural. Eugenie Scott uses this tactic.

> To be dealt with scientifically, "intelligence" must also be natural, because *all* science is natural. .... SETI is indeed a scientific project; it seeks *natural* intelligence. (Scott, E. C., 1990, p 18)[25]

She implicitly defines *natural* as 'whatever science deals with.' Her approach is common.[26]

Pressed to its logical conclusion, Scott's definition means that three hundred years ago DNA, microwaves, and neutrons were *un*natural because science did not deal with them. It means the natural world arbitrarily changes and expands as science advances. It means that what is unnatural now, may become natural in the future.

She is mistaken. The natural world is not defined by science, rather it is *observed* by science. The natural world has an objective reality independent of its discovery by science. The natural world exists on its own as an object of study. Thus, DNA, microwaves, and neutrons were part of the natural world three hundred years ago, they just hadn't been discovered yet.

---

[24] Smith, G. H., 1979, p 264

[25] Scott is mistaken. The SETI project does not seek natural intelligence only. If SETI researchers received a radio message from space they could not know whether the message sender was natural or supernatural.

[26] Some evolutionists try a slightly different approach. They define science as 'the study of the natural world.' But this approach does not conclude that "intelligence" is natural, as Scott has done. The only way she could have arrived at her conclusion was by defining natural as 'whatever science deals with.'

*

The essence of the natural world is twofold. If something meets both criteria, then it is part of the natural world: it is naturalistic.

- The natural world is empirical. It can be observed by the five senses, either directly or indirectly with the aid of equipment.

- The behavior of the natural world can be expressed by laws that are consistent through time and space. We recognize these natural laws by their repeatability. They are consistent from moment to moment and from place to place.

We cannot observe electrons directly with our eyes. Yet we observe them in other ways, and they always obey regular laws that are repeatable. So, electrons are naturalistic entities.

Radioactive decay is a natural phenomenon. It is observable, and though the exact moment of decay is not predictable, it rigidly follows repeatable laws.

Likewise, gravity is natural because we can observe its action as a repeatable phenomenon, though we do not yet completely understand it.

Intelligence is a more slippery phenomenon. It seems to defy the natural world. It does not rigidly obey laws. It is not a repeatable phenomenon. We cannot observe it with our five senses. We must 'observe' it inferentially with our minds. We observe its creations, such as a mathematical formula written on paper. Our marvelous human intelligence is enormously complex and often bewildering. No one has shown it is the result of natural laws operating on molecules and atoms. Is intelligence naturalistic or not? I regard this as an open question.

For our discussion, the supernatural is something that fails the definition of the natural world. Let us focus on cases where the supernatural cannot be observed, not even indirectly. We cannot see it or hear it. We cannot poke it to see how it reacts. We cannot measure it with instruments.

The issues are these: Can we show the existence of the supernatural without observing it in any way? Can the supernatural be a legitimate part of science? Can the supernatural have a testable scientific basis? My answer to all three questions is *yes*.

People assume that since we cannot observe the supernatural, we can never know anything about it. People assume that the supernatural has an entirely different sphere of influence from nature — the two spheres being separate and distinct — that we cannot scientifically learn anything about the supernatural. Edwords claims that "a smooth and complete argument from natural to super-natural ... cannot be made without the use of a *non sequitor*."[27] But there is evidence to the contrary, if we take any indication from the science of pure logic — mathematics.

---

[27]   Edwords, F., 1984, p 43

Science must be self-consistent. It must not contradict itself. This mandate is simple and often overlooked.

Yet logical self-consistency is not always easy. Logic can sometimes be treacherous and full of pitfalls. Science sometimes can have real difficulty maintaining consistency. This difficulty was first clearly seen within mathematics, which studies the fabric of logic.

The next five sections examine mathematical logic and its tumultuous history with self-contradiction. Logical self-consistency has had a major impact on modern mathematics. Entire fields have risen and fallen due to its simple, yet surprising, demand. The demand for self-consistency carries real force. It forces us to acknowledge the existence of things we cannot ever reach directly — a supernatural sphere if you will. It compels us to admit an abstract supernatural realm within mathematics.

The results are not confined to the abstract world of mathematics. We will turn our attention later to the physical universe and apply what we have learned to concrete examples. We will see why science is sometimes forced to cope with the supernatural: *Logical self-consistency demands it.*

Yet self-consistency is not good enough. Science must also be testable. I will show that the supernatural can have a testable basis. The supernatural can be scientific, when approached in the proper way.[28]

---

[28] Some anti-creationists agree the supernatural is not necessarily unscientific. John Wilson writes, "[I]t is not surprising that unnatural and supernatural phenomena are not represented in the realm of current science, *but that fact does not eliminate them from the province of science.*" (Wilson, J. H., 1983, p 100, my italics) Wilson is directly rebutting the idea that 'only natural phenomena are in the province of science.'

Paradox and Self-Reference

A paradox is an apparently valid argument that reaches self-contradictory conclusions. Understanding paradox and removing its contradictions is a time-consuming task for logicians. The cause of a paradox is often difficult to eliminate without also eliminating many useful logical statements.

The study of paradox has taught mathematicians some hard lessons. On some occasions entire fields of study had to be revamped to resolve paradoxes. The demand for logical self-consistency has had real impact.

Let us begin with a benign example: the Barber Paradox.

> In a certain village there is a man who is a barber. This barber shaves all and only those men in the village who do not shave themselves. Then we ask, Does the barber shave himself?

> Any man in this village is shaved by the barber if and only if he is not shaved by himself. Thus, the barber shaves himself if and only if he does not. We have a contradiction either way.[29]

The barber shaves himself only if he does not. This is a contradiction.

Paradox often acquires its self-contradiction because of self-reference. In this paradox the self-reference appeared when we asked whether the barber shaves himself. The paradox is resolved by recognizing an initial assumption was erroneous, and we then reject that assumption. In this case we conclude: There can be no such barber.

The barber paradox was easy to resolve, but this is not always the case. Sometimes a resolution requires that we reject some of our simplest, most common ways of thinking.

For example, Epimenides Paradox has caused us to alter our conceptions of true and false. Epimenides is famous for making the singular statement, "I am lying." Here is another version of his paradox:

THIS SENTENCE IS FALSE.

It is a true sentence if it is false, and it is a false sentence if it is true. It is a contradiction either way. The sentence is paradoxical because of self-reference: it is referring to itself. A similar paradox is created by a small 'loop' of self-reference:

THE FOLLOWING SENTENCE IS TRUE.

THE PREVIOUS SENTENCE IS FALSE.

Again we have a contradiction: each sentence must be both true and false. In this case, the loop of self-reference is only two sentences long, but we may easily

---

[29] Quine, W. V., "Paradox," *Scientific American*, April 1962

construct loops many sentences long. Such long loops of self-contradiction are more difficult to follow and detect. These examples are paradoxical due to their loop of logic which asserts "not true of self."

How are we to resolve these paradoxes? We cannot resolve them as in the barber paradox by saying, "There are no such sentences." On what basis are we to reject these sentences from our logic and keep other logical sentences instead? This paradox contradicts our common sense, the way we commonly think and reason. To resolve it we must alter the way we think.

In fact, logicians have done this. The logicians Bertrand Russell and Alfred Tarski suggested the following resolution to the paradox. Expressions such as "true", "true of", "false" and so forth can be used with subscripts numbered 0, 1, 2, 3, ... as follows.

Bill says: "Al's hat is purple."

Cindy says: "Bill's statement is $true_0$."

Deb says: "Cindy's statement is $false_1$."

Ed says: "Deb's statement is $true_2$."

These are grammatically correct statements of logic. Some of these statements indicate 'truth' (or falsity) — call these truth statements. The truth statements have subscripts numbered in sequential order. Each truth statement must have a subscript numbered 1 greater than the truth statement it refers to. If it does not, then it is ungrammatical.

With these subscripts in place we readily identify Epimenides statement as ungrammatical.

Epimenides says: "This sentence is $false_0$."

It is ungrammatical because its subscript is not 1 greater than the truth statement it refers to. We throw it out because it is a nonsense sentence. (Like a sentence composed only of verbs.) It is a sentence lacking the grammar necessary for a meaningful statement of logic. In the same way we can recognize, and throw out, long loops of self-reference.

By absorbing this 'subscript' method into our logic: (1) we can throw out nonsense sentences; (2) we can keep our useful sentences of logic; and (3) we can have a system of logic free of known self-contradictions. In the bargain we must accept an infinite hierarchy of truth and falsehood. We must accept a methodology difficult to apply in practice.

The subscript method is inconvenient and too impractical for common use. Also, it is rarely necessary for resolving contradictions. So, it is ignored in our everyday language. Yet logicians take this matter very seriously.

The simple demand of self-consistency has had serious impact on the exacting field of pure logic. We will see this demand has also affected geometry, set theory, and ordinary arithmetic.

Euclidean Geometry

The study of geometry was founded by Euclid in ancient Greece. Until well into the nineteenth century, mathematicians believed Euclid's geometry contained certain truths. They believed these truths were clear, universal, and not open to doubt. Euclid proved these truths using the axiomatic method still learned by secondary school students.

The axiomatic method begins with a few axioms or fundamental self-evident truths. It operates on these axioms using propositional calculus, a fancy name for our logical reasoning. This process proves a mathematical theorem: a non-obvious statement whose truth depends on the truth of the axioms. The process continues to operate on theorems and axioms, to prove new theorems.

The axiomatic method builds mathematical knowledge from the ground up. Axioms are the 'ground' — the most basic, self-evident truth. The girders, nuts, and bolts are our logical reasoning. The method creates a super-structure of theorems, built upon theorems — ultimately built upon a few axioms — all inter-connected by tight unassailable logic. Anyone examining this super-structure could find nothing wrong. The super-structure can be 'observed' in detail. It is as sound as the few axioms it is built on.

Euclid used this method in his geometry. He started with self-evident axioms and rigorously proved a body of knowledge which seemed objective and eternal. Scholars regarded geometry as the most reliable branch of knowledge. Geometry made up the foundation for other branches of mathematics such as calculus. This common solid foundation of geometry gave legitimacy to all branches of mathematics.

Until modern times, Euclidean geometry was the only geometry; we believed there could be no other. It studied the properties of space as we know it. Its theorems were corroborated by our intuition. It provided knowledge that was exact, timeless, and certain. At least that was how it seemed.

The nineteenth century proved differently. Several new developments showed our geometrical intuition is not always a reliable guide. One development was the discovery of non-Euclidean geometries (showing there is more than one thinkable geometry). Other shocks were the discoveries of space-filling curves and continuous nowhere-differentiable curves. These surprises ran contrary to intuition, thereby casting doubt on its adequacy. This doubt disturbed the foundation of geometry itself.

This loss of certainty in geometry upset the apple cart. All mathematical knowledge was constructed on the foundation of geometry, and no human knowledge had seemed more certain. Yet it had fallen into doubt.

A new solid foundation for human knowledge would have to be found, and mathematicians of the nineteenth century dedicated themselves to finding it. Dedekind and Weierstrass led the way. They turned from geometry to arithmetic as the foundation for mathematics.[30] They were determined to prove that arithmetic is a solid foundation.

---

[30] Davis, P. J. and Hersh, R., 1981, *The Mathematical Experience*, p 322-344

Just after the turn of the century their work suddenly took on increased importance. They were shocked by an unpleasant discovery from another field of mathematics. Intuitive set theory was shown to be inconsistent.

Consistency and Set Theory

A mathematical system is inconsistent when a theorem within that system can be proven to be both true and false: a self-contradiction. Also, if one such inconsistency exists in a system, then every theorem can be proven both true and false — the entire system collapses into contradictions. As disconcerting as this is, it has actually happened in the field of mathematics.

Toward the end of the nineteenth century, mathematicians were progressing in a field called intuitive set theory. Georg Cantor founded this branch of mathematics, and gave the following definition of a set:

Cantor's intuitive definition: A set is any collection into a whole of definite and separate objects of our intuition or our thought.

Cantor's definition was simple, transparent, and intuitively obvious. It agreed with our intuition. There seemed little to disagree with it. Nonetheless, it concealed snares.

In 1902, another mathematician, Gottlob Frege, fell into such a snare. Frege was ready to publish his enormous research. He had rebuilt arithmetic on the foundation of intuitive set theory. Frege then received a letter from the young British mathematician, Bertrand Russell. Russell had proved that Cantor's intuitive definition leads to inconsistencies — intuitive set theory is self-contradictory. Frege got the rug pulled from underneath him at the last minute. His work had been in vain.[31]

Russell accomplished his unsettling result by a short, yet subtle proof. He began with Cantor's intuitive definition of a set. All such sets may be divided into two groups, which we can call *normal* and *non-normal*. Normal sets are those not containing themselves as members. An example is the set of 'all books.' The set is not a book and therefore is not a member of itself. On the other hand, non-normal sets do contain themselves as members. An example is the set of all thinkable concepts. The set of 'all thinkable concepts' is itself a thinkable concept, and is therefore a member of itself. So far, we've only divided all sets into two groups: normal and non-normal. This is a perfectly legitimate thing to do.

---

[31] Frege acknowledged the letter from Bertrand Russell by adding this postscript to his treatise: "A scientist can hardly meet with anything more undesirable than to have the foundation give way just as the work is finished. In this position I was put by a letter from Mr. Bertrand Russell as the work was nearly through the press." (Cohen, P. J., and Hersh, R., "Non-Cantorian Set Theory," *Scientific American*, December 1967)

Now let N stand for the set of all normal sets. We then ask, is N itself a normal set?

> If N is a normal set, then N must contain itself because N was defined to contain all normal sets. However, if N contains itself, then by definition it is non-normal.

> If N is a non-normal set, then by definition it is a member of itself. However, if N is a member of itself, then it must be normal, because N was defined to contain only normal sets.

In short, N is normal if and only if N is non-normal. This is known as Russell's Paradox.

The problem was not caused by the definitions of normal or non-normal sets, nor by the definition of set N — These are all legitimate applications of Cantor's intuitive definition. The problem was caused by the intuitive definition itself.

The simple, intuitively obvious definition of a set had led to contradictions. Once again our mathematical intuition had let us down. Once again the contradiction had arisen from self-reference: sets that contain themselves as members. The intuitive definition allowed these to count as sets, and contradiction resulted.

There are infinitely many of these paradoxes. Russell's Paradox is only the lowest level of an infinite hierarchy of paradoxes involving sets and self-membership. His paradox involves a set which is a member of itself. Similar paradoxes result from a set which is a member of a member of itself; or a member of a member of a member of itself; and so on.

To resolve these paradoxes, we must reject the intuitive definition of a set. (Much as we rejected the barber in the barber paradox.) Instead, we need a definition which eliminates all the inconsistencies without eliminating useful concepts of sets.

Today, our rigorous definition of a set is not so intuitive. It is inconvenient and harder to apply in practice. For this reason it is typically not used in applied mathematics and science courses since it is rarely needed for resolving contradictions. Nonetheless, set theoreticians take this matter seriously. They cannot ignore it. The demands of logical consistency are too important.

In this way the simple demand of logical consistency has affected the fields of logic and set theory. Next we will see it has affected the way we look at arithmetic, geometry, and our very conception of knowledge itself.

Gödel's Incompleteness Theorem

Intuitive Set Theory was shown inconsistent. This caused a crisis in mathematics. After all, how could a branch of mathematics which was clear and intuitively reasonable also be inconsistent? How could our intuition have failed us so? Could such inconsistencies be lurking in other branches of mathematics?

To end these problems, mathematicians set out to prove the consistency of the various branches of mathematics. They eventually showed that Euclidean geometry, non-Euclidean geometry, and ordinary arithmetic are all interrelated — they are either all consistent or all inconsistent.

Mathematicians focused their effort on ordinary arithmetic (our simple concepts of addition, subtraction, multiplication and division). This was a good starting point, since arithmetic is the foundation for other branches of mathematics and science. Mathematicians set out to prove its self-consistency. This study was lead by mathematicians like Hilbert and Russell.

After nearly three decades the search ended in 1931, when Kurt Gödel published an unsettling proof. His proof had two profound conclusions.

First, Gödel showed that all efforts to prove arithmetic to be free from contradictions are doomed to failure. Arithmetic cannot be proven consistent. In fact, no system powerful enough to include arithmetic is capable of proving itself consistent.[32]

This was a shock, since people considered arithmetic to be so certain as to be beyond question. Call it what you will, when people have 'certainty' about arithmetic it is by some means other than proof. Bertrand Russell lamented this lack of certainty in mathematics:

> I wanted certainty in the kind of way in which people want religious faith. I thought that certainty is more likely to be found in mathematics than elsewhere. But I discovered that many mathematical demonstrations, which my teachers expected me to accept, were full of fallacies, and that, if certainty were indeed discoverable in mathematics, it would be in a new field of mathematics, with more solid foundations than those that had hitherto been thought secure. But as the work proceeded, I was continually reminded of the fable about the elephant and the tortoise. Having constructed an elephant upon which the mathematical world could rest, I found the elephant tottering, and proceeded to construct a tortoise to keep the elephant from falling. But the tortoise was no more secure than the elephant, and after some twenty years of very arduous toil, I came to the conclusion that there was nothing more that I could do in the way of making mathematical knowledge indubitable.[33]

Gödel's first conclusion was revolutionary, yet his second was even more astonishing. Gödel showed a basic limitation in the power of the axiomatic method. He showed that any mathematical system powerful enough to contain arithmetic within itself is essentially incomplete. Ordinary arithmetic (and any system powerful enough to contain it) is incapable of deriving (or proving) all of its true statements. This is called Gödel's Incompleteness Theorem.

---

[32] "Gödel showed that no system powerful enough to include ordinary arithmetic is capable of proving itself consistent, unless the proof uses rules of inference *from outside the system*, whose own internal consistency is as much open to doubt as is the consistency of arithmetic itself. In short, one monster is slain only by creating another; the proof is never completed." (Nagel, E., and Newman, J. R., "Gödel's Proof," *Scientific American*, June 1956)

[33] Russell, B., *Portraits of Memory*

For millennia, mathematicians had relied on the axiomatic method. They believed any mathematical statement that is true could be proven to be true. They believed all mathematical knowledge was within reach of the axiomatic method. Given enough effort, the super-structure of interconnected theorems would extend to include all mathematical truth. They believed the truthhood of any theorem could be 'observed' by scrutinizing this super-structure.

Gödel destroyed this comforting notion. He showed there exists mathematical truth that can never be proven true. There exists truth forever out of reach of the axiomatic method. There exists truth we can never 'observe' to be true by examining a superstructure of reasoning. Ordinary arithmetic (and anything powerful enough to contain it) is incomplete: it can never prove all its true statements.

This is curious. How could Gödel show the existence of unprovable truth? How could Gödel show the *existence* of truth that can never be observed to be true? This is like proving the existence of the supernatural.

Gödel accomplished this feat in a remarkable way. First, he proved that arithmetic cannot be proven to be consistent. Then he proved arithmetic is either inconsistent or incomplete — one or the other must be true.

Thus, mathematicians faced a dilemma. Most branches of mathematics (and our everyday reasoning) are built on the foundation of arithmetic. Thus, if arithmetic was inconsistent then so were all these others too. The whole structure of mathematics and logic would collapse into self-contradictions. To avoid self-contradiction, mathematicians were forced to acknowledge that arithmetic is incomplete. Logical self-consistency demanded it.

Some true theorems can never be proven true. Scientists now call these "Supernatural Theorems."[34] One example seems to be a conjecture made by Christian Goldbach.

Goldbach's Conjecture: Every even number is the sum of two primes.

Every time we try a specific even number it fulfills Goldbach's Conjecture. Yet no one has succeeded in proving it for all even numbers. Mathematicians now suspect Goldbach's Conjecture is a supernatural theorem.[35] Gödel had proved that such supernatural theorems exist.

---

[34] Hofstadter, 1979, p 454. As described in Douglas Hofstadter's book, *natural* theorems are derivable from a formal system, and *supernatural* theorems are statements which, though not derivable, are theorems of that formal system nonetheless. In mathematical language more precise than I have used, he has written an illuminating book.

[35] Two mathematical statements (the Paris-Harrington and Friedman theorems) have been proven to be undecidable statements in Peano arithmetic in accordance with Gödel's Incompleteness Theorem. (Kolata, G., Science, Vol. 218, Nov. 19, 1983, p 779-780)

Science and the Supernatural

Self-reference is a surprisingly involved concept, fraught with dangers, contradictions, and inconsistencies. Gödel used this idea. Since mathematics was trying to prove itself consistent, it was undertaking the business of self-reference. By understanding this self-reference, Gödel revealed the inherent paradox and proved a remarkable result. Mathematicians had believed that any statement of a formal mathematical system could be proven either derivable or underivable: true or false. Those days are gone forever.

Gödel's proof is only one modern result showing the limitations of science. Earlier this century many scientists believed any problem could, in principle, be solved by computer. They believed that given enough time a powerful computer could solve any problem. Alan Turing overturned this idea. He used the idea of self-reference to solve the Halting Problem. This showed there are interesting questions that have definite answers (such as a simple yes or no) but whose answers are forever unsolvable (uncomputable).

Imagine a computer with an infinite memory. No matter how powerful and fast the computer, no matter how long the computer runs, there are some problems that can never be computed. We can prove the answers exist, but we can never know what they are. If a computer were given one of these problems it would never halt with the answer. It would go on computing forever, or until it broke. It would never reach the answer. Yet the answer exists, and may be quite simple (like a yes or no).

There have been many similar results in this century which have altered our concept of what is knowable by finite means. They have changed our concept of knowledge, and they have a profound impact on our vision of science. They eliminate the notion that everything may, in principle, be known by the scientific method.[36] Rudy Rucker explains:

> "The thinkers of the Industrial Revolution liked to regard the universe as a vast preprogrammed machine. It was optimistically predicted that soon scientists would know all the rules, all the programs. But if Gödel's Theorem tells us anything, it is this: Man will never know the final secret of the universe.
>
> Of course, anyone can *say* that science does not have all the answers. What makes Gödel's achievement so remarkable is that he could rigorously *prove* this, stating his proof in the utterly precise language of symbolic logic." (Rucker, 1982, p 158)

---

[36] Wills (1989, p 160) argues (mistakenly) that, "in science, if a question can be posed, no matter how far-fetched, it can eventually be answered." Gödel's Incompleteness Theorem and many similar results from this century have overthrown this naive notion.

Rucker notes that scientists are in a position somewhat like Kafka in *The Castle*.

> "Endlessly we hurry up and down corridors, meeting people, knocking on doors, conducting our investigations. But the ultimate success will never be ours. Nowhere in the castle of science is there a final exit to absolute truth.
>
> This seems terribly depressing. But, paradoxically, to understand Gödel's proof is to find a sort of liberation. For many logic students, the final breakthrough to full understanding of the Incompleteness Theorem is practically a conversion experience. ... more profoundly, to understand the essentially labyrinthine nature of *the castle* is, somehow, to be free of it." (Rucker, 1982, p 165)

Douglas Hofstadter notes that all the results dependent on self-reference — the fusion of subject with object — have been limitative results.[37]

> Gödel's Incompleteness Theorem, Church's Undecidability Theorem, Turing's Halting Theorem, Tarski's Truth Theorem — all have the flavor of some ancient fairy tale which warns you that 'To seek self-knowledge is to embark on a journey which ... will always be incomplete, cannot be charted on any map, will never halt, cannot be described. (Hofstadter, 1979, p 697-699, his ellipsis)

Many scientists feel science can only study the natural and can never hope to determine anything about the supernatural, the natural and supernatural spheres being separate and unbreachable. Evidence from mathematics suggests something to the contrary. Gödel has shown that supernatural spheres bear a special relationship to their subordinate natural spheres, and that this relationship may be fruitfully studied. Gödel proved the existence of unprovable truths (supernatural theorems). So, scientists might prove the existence of 'causes and effects' they are forever unable to study directly (i.e., supernatural agents).

Studies of mathematics and logic have shown the hidden hazards of self-reference. Self-reference changed our conceptions of sets, arithmetic, consistency, solvability, computability, and "true" and "false."

Evolutionists claim that science must understand nature in terms of nature. This is a task of self-reference. Precisely because of this self-reference, we can expect paradoxes and contradictions. When science tries to 'explain nature by reference to nature' it is sailing through dangerous and uncharted waters. Next I will show the inconsistencies and self-contradictions are visible even now.

---

[37] In addition, there is Heisenberg's uncertainty principle, which states that measuring one quantity renders impossible the simultaneous measurement of a related quantity.

Thermodynamics and the Big Bang

A collection of scientific theories can mean more than the sum of their parts. The collection can have surprising consequences not visible in any single theory alone. For example, the laws of Thermodynamics, the Big Bang, and Paley's argument from design are among our most thoroughly tested science, and none of them says anything about the supernatural. Yet anyone subscribing to them is forced to acknowledge the supernatural. There is nothing unscientific about it.

The First Law of Thermodynamics says mass-energy is conserved. This means the universe is a closed system — no mass-energy can get in or out.

The Second Law of Thermodynamics is more complicated. In the origins debate we typically hear of it as the universal tendency toward disorder or "entropy." There is another aspect of this law. The Second Law says that in a closed system, energy always distributes itself so it is no longer available to do useful work, and this will happen irreversibly.

Imagine a closed system of two rooms: a cold empty room next to a room full of hot steam. The non-uniform distribution of mass-energy — known as disequilibrium — provides energy that is available to do work. This is called the available energy or free energy.

Imagine a steam engine in one of the rooms with pipes connected so that the hot steam powers the engine and the exhaust is then expelled into the cold room. The engine can then drive many devices to accomplish useful tasks. As the steam engine runs, the hot room gets colder and the cold room hotter. When the two rooms reach the same temperature the engine can no longer run (no matter how efficient it may be, no matter what temperature the rooms). The system has reached equilibrium. All the mass-energy is still present. It has merely distributed itself so it can no longer do work. The available energy is now gone from the system forever. This process is irreversible. It is a one way process that happens automatically.

In a closed system the available energy can never spontaneously increase. The cold room will never get colder and the hot room hotter. If we had a refrigerator we could cool one room while heating the other, but the energy for that would have to come from outside the system.

The loss of available energy happens automatically. If we open a door connecting the two rooms, they quickly reach the same temperature. The available energy is lost without ever performing useful work.

The First and Second Laws of Thermodynamics are among the most thoroughly tested in all science. The classical interpretation reads them at face value to mean the universe is winding-down irreversibly toward a heat death where all the mass-energy is still present but unavailable to perform work. These laws indicate the universe is not a perpetual motion machine.

The Big Bang is a theory with similar implications. The universe began as a supermassive, infinitesimally small point. It then exploded to produce the universe we see today. The observed red-shift of distant galaxies indicates they are receding from us at a rapid rate. The 2.736 K microwave background radiation from space is interpreted as the pale remnants of the big bang explosion. As predicted by the Big Bang theory the radiation is highly uniform in all directions and has precisely the spectrum of a blackbody radiator. In addition, the theory gives reasonably accurate predictions of the observed abundances of the light elements.[38] These are the main evidences for the Big Bang.[39]

The Big Bang, the First and Second Laws of Thermodynamics, and Paley's Theory are the best that science has accomplished in these fields. Independently, they say nothing about the supernatural, but taken together they have unshakable implications. They tell us a supernatural agent has performed a creative act in the universe. We can imagine designers who create other designers, until one of them creates life, but looking backward in a Big Bang universe eventually reaches a dead end. At some point an intelligent designer was required who could transcend (get around, survive through, not be bothered by) the Big Bang. Such a being would qualify as supernatural by most anyone's reckoning.

This conclusion is a logical consequence of a collection of explanatory, scientific theories. Its legitimacy could be refuted by falsifying any of those theories. Because it is explanatory, logically self-consistent, and testable, it is science.

Note the similarities with Gödel's Theorem. Gödel's Theorem provides both a precedent and a model for how interesting statements about the supernatural can be derived in science. As you recall, Gödel showed that a collection of simple axioms from arithmetic can force us to accept the existence of true theorems which lay *outside* the system. We cannot ever prove the truth of such theorems directly, but we are forced to accept their existence nonetheless. We must do this for no other reason than that logical consistency demands it. In this way, science can and must come to grips with the supernatural. A collection of scientific theories can present unanticipated consequences not inherent in any theory taken separately. Thermodynamics, the Big Bang (or any finite age theory), and Paley's theory imply the existence of a supernatural agent.

This caused a dilemma for evolutionists, and they dealt with it in a peculiar way. First, they searched among the theories and selected one to throw out: Paley's theory. Second, having thrown out a legitimate scientific theory for the origin of life, they have not replaced it with a scientific alternative. Third, as justification they claim (erroneously) that science must deal only with the natural. We must be honest here. From among several options for resolving this dilemma, evolutionists have selected naturalism.[40]

---

[38] Some theorists dispute the ability of Big Bang theory to accurately predict the light elements.

[39] There are other evidences that were once said to support the Big Bang. For example, observational data obtained in the 1950s show that radio sources then were brighter or more numerous than at present. This observation is incompatible with previously held concepts of a steady-state universe. (Munitz, 1981, p 153-154) Olber's Paradox (the riddle of the dark sky at night) was traditionally interpreted as evidence for the Big Bang. These evidences have fallen into some disfavor.

[40] As a play on words, I call this "Natural" selection. Evolutionists select naturalistic mechanisms from their theoretical smorgasbord. To solve any problem from nature, they merely scan the smorgasbord of naturalistic possibilities and select those items

The fourth and final leg of the evolutionists' argument is their claim that creationists are being unscientific. They say creationists have only taken one problem (the origin of life) and turned it into a more difficult one (the origin of a supernatural agent).[41]

The origin of a supernatural agent is a classic problem. The classic answer is:

> Perhaps there is no origin to be explained — perhaps the entity in question is, in some sense, timeless (or without origin).

This is a logically sound answer to a problem that evolutionists have fueled as a live issue. Moreover, evolutionists have no basis for complaint about it — they previously used it for their explanations of life and the universe.[42] They would still use this explanation today, if only the data would cooperate.

> To explain the origin of the DNA/protein machine by invoking a super-natural Designer is to explain precisely nothing, for it leaves unexplained the origin of the Designer. You have to say something like 'God was always there', and if you allow yourself that kind of lazy way out, you might as well just say 'DNA was always there', or 'Life was always there', and be done with it. (Dawkins, 1986, p 141)[43]

> [I]t is perfectly possible that the universe is infinitely old and therefore requires no Creator. (Sagan, 1979, p 336)

Evolutionists would gladly claim that life (and the universe itself) did not have an origin and just always existed, but the data resists such a claim. The Big Bang and Thermodynamics are the obstacles preventing evolutionists from trivially 'explaining away' origins.

---

that seem most appropriate. They are limited only by the breadth of the smorgasbord, and it is vast. While their approach is perhaps understandable, it is not a scientific theory. Evolutionists are not committed to science. They are committed to "natural" selection, and it is a major subject of this book.

[41] For examples, see Edwords, 1986, p 42; Shapiro, 1986, p 119; Scott, A., 1986, p 126; Strahler, 1987, p 512-513; Arduini, 1988, p 37-38; Young, 1985, p 127; Sagan, 1979, p 336-337; Underwood, 1876, p 44; DeWiel, 1983, p 87-88; Shotwell, 1987, p 379; Zindler, 1990, p 10; Bakken, 1987, p 2; Saladin, 1988, p 47; Smith, G. H., 1979, p 259 & 269; Johnson, B. C., 1981, p 49 & 63.

[42] For example, De Maillet (1748) proposed that life and the universe did not have origins. A similar theory for the origin of life was advocated by the materialist philosopher La Mettrie. (For discussion see Bowler, 1984, p 65) And in the mid 1870s (before big bang cosmology) B. F. Underwood argued for an eternal universe so "We are not therefore in need of a creator." (Underwood, 1876, p 45)

[43] Dawkins affirms the idea again in his book. "If we are going to allow ourselves the luxury of postulating organized complexity without offering an explanation, we might as well make a job of it and simply postulate the existence of life as we know it!" (Dawkins, 1986, p 316-317)

Even if Paley's theory were removed, the evolutionists' problems do not go away. The Big Bang indicates the universe is not infinitely old. The universe could not have continually oscillated in size without violating the law of gravitation and general relativity (or without requiring an unknown force.)[44] The universe could not regenerate its available energy without violating the Second Law of Thermodynamics. Yet, the universe could not originate itself without violating the First Law of Thermodynamics. Even without Paley's theory, these scientific theories and laws point to a supernatural agent.

> Many people do not like the idea that time has a beginning, probably because it smacks of divine intervention. .... There were therefore a number of attempts to avoid the conclusion that there had been a big bang.[45] (Hawking, 1988, p 46-47)

To resolve this dilemma, evolutionary cosmologists have proposed many untestable speculations, for which the field is now notorious.[46] Their ideas often break the Laws of Thermodynamics and gravity, the theories of general relativity, quantum mechanics, and the Big Bang.[47] Ironically, evolutionists suggest breaking (or bypassing) some of the best established scientific theories and laws in order to maintain their devotion to naturalism.

Somehow they feel they are being more scientific.

*

---

[44] The idea of an oscillating universe has serious problems.

> "Some physicists are troubled by the notion of beginnings. That's why the open universe theory, in which the universe begins with a big bang and expands indefinitely, isn't in favor. But a closed universe — one that eventually collapses — might expand and collapse again and again, thus posing no question about beginnings. .... Trouble is, physicists have had a terrible time finding evidence that the universe will one day stop expanding and start collapsing." (*Discover*, 1986)

There are further problems with the oscillating universe idea.

> "The trouble is that even if there were enough matter to stop the expansion, there is no known physical theory that could lead to a new expansion. All that we know would lead us to expect the universe to collapse into a cosmic black hole from which it could never escape. The oscillating universe theory is thus not really a theory at all but a speculation based on wishful thinking." (Abell, 1985, p 236)

[45] Hawking (1988, p 47-48) continues: "The proposal that gained widest support was called the steady state theory. .... Another attempt to avoid the conclusion that there must have been a big bang, and therefore a beginning of time, was made by two Russian scientists, ... in 1963."

[46] The untestability of modern cosmological theories is documented in John Boslough's book (1992).

[47] The classic example was the steady-state theory of Gold, Bondi, and Hoyle, which rejected the Big Bang cosmology and claimed that matter/energy is constantly being created (conveniently for the theory, at a level much too low to test) in contradiction to the First Law of Thermodynamics.

This book shows that evolutionists hold several double standards: one standard for creation, and another lesser one for evolution. Here is another example. Evolutionists demand that creation theory provide answers about ultimate origins. They demand an explanation of the ultimate origin of a supernatural agent. It is one of their favorite attacks on Paley's argument from design.

- Paley's argument from design together with the Big Bang immediately indicates the existence of a supernatural agent. Evolutionists then *demand* an explanation for the ultimate origin of the supernatural agent.

They impel creation theory to its logically consistent conclusion, then they try to tell us that to do so is unscientific. Why? Because "Science does not deal with questions of ultimate origins." (Gould, 1987e, p 21) Here it is in action:

> [C]reationists can't explain life's beginning, while evolutionists can't resolve the ultimate origin of the inorganic components that later aggregated to life. But this inability is the very heart of creationist logic and the central reason why their doctrine is not science, while science's inability to specify the ultimate origin of matter is irrelevant because we are not trying to do any such thing. We know that we can't, and we do not even consider such a question as part of science. (Gould, 1987e, p 21)

Hidden in Gould's argument is the double standard that creationists must explain ultimate origins, while evolutionists need not.[48]

Gould's argument uses this double standard together with an *ad hoc* criterion of science. Gould often writes articles on the philosophy of science. In these articles he repeatedly endorses testability, but nowhere does he defend 'ultimate origins' as a criterion of science. He spontaneously pulls it from a hat, to use against creationists. It has the sound of plausibility, but it is without foundation. Theories of ultimate origin got a bad name by association, because most of them happen to be untestable, and untestable theories are not science.

While we're on the subject of ultimate origins, we need to set the record straight. Evolutionists *do* make incredible claims about ultimate origins. They do it, in a concealed way, with the anthropic principle.

---

[48] As another example of an evolutionist using 'ultimate origins' as a double standard see Young, 1985, p 126-127

The Anthropic Principle

Naturalism tends to display its most doubtful doctrines in a way that conceals their true nature. This is done by presenting the doctrines in a confusing manner. Often, the doctrines are misleadingly presented as tautologies or truisms whose truth is obvious and could not be doubted by anyone. This is the case with the anthropic principle, whose real meaning is quite unlike the way it is presented.

Historically, scientists had long known that planet Earth is a peculiar place, having many rare properties necessary for life. Earth's distance from the Sun and nearly circular orbit keep it at a temperature suitable for life. Earth has abundant water and an average temperature that happens to lie within the narrow range where water is liquid. This is rather special, even compared to the planets on either side. If the axis tilt had been smaller, then more of the Earth would be lost to cold polar ice caps or hot equatorial deserts. If the tilt had been greater, then substantial portions of the Earth would have six months of darkness followed by six months of light, and few places would be habitable. The Earth's magnetic field and ozone layer filter out lethal radiation. Other special features of Earth are its mass, density, radius, spin rate, weather system, atmospheric pressure, and chemical makeup. If these features had been substantially different, then life as we know it would not have been possible.

Evolutionists always responded to this candidly. They said there are countless other planets unlike Earth, and Earth happened by chance to have the properties necessary for life. Therefore, they concluded, the universe has no special favor toward the Earth or life.

In recent decades this explanation was upset when new evidence showed the universe itself has numerous peculiar properties necessary for life. For example, if the electric charge of the electron had been only slightly different, then stars would be unable to burn hydrogen and helium.[49] If the relative strengths of the nuclear and electromagnetic forces were slightly different, then carbon atoms could not exist in nature and therefore humans could not exist.[50]

> If the rate of expansion one second after the big bang had been smaller by even one part in a hundred thousand million million, the universe would have recollapsed before it ever reached its present size. (Hawking, 1988, p 121-122)

> The cosmos threatened to recollapse within a fraction of a second or else to expand so fast that galaxy formation would be impossible. To avoid these disasters its rate of expansion at early instants needed to be fine tuned to perhaps one part in 10^{55} (which is 10 followed by 54 zeros). (Leslie, 1989, p 3)

Fundamental parameters — the strengths of the nuclear weak force, nuclear strong force, electromagnetism, and gravity; the expansion rate of the universe; and the charge and masses of fundamental particles — all had to be finely tuned to extraordinarily tight tolerances. Remarkably, the values of these fundamental

---

[49] Hawking, 1988, p 125

[50] Barrow and Tipler, 1988, p 5

parameters seem to have been finely adjusted to make life possible.[51] How could these highly improbable details be explained? The universe appears to have been specially designed for life by a rational mind. Many people read the evidence in precisely this way.[52] The universe itself seemed to be important evidence for an intelligent designer.

Naturalism was confronted by this new data.

> Over many years had grown up a collection of largely unpublished results revealing a series of mysterious coincidences between the numerical values of the fundamental constants of Nature. The possibility of our own existence seems to hinge precariously upon these coincidences. (Barrow and Tipler, 1988, p xi)

> [W]e have found Nature to be constructed upon certain immutable foundation stones, which we call fundamental constants of Nature. .... The fortuitous nature of many of their numerical values is a mystery that cries out for a solution. (Barrow and Tipler, 1988, p 31)

Evolutionists responded by inventing the anthropic principle. The principle is intended to explain the universe's highly peculiar properties that are necessary for our survival. The idea is presented like this:

> [T]he anthropic principle ... can be paraphrased as 'We see the universe the way it is because we exist.' (Hawking, 1988, p 124)

> [T]he universe has the properties we observe today because if its earlier properties had been much different, we would not be here as observers now. The principle underlying this method of cosmological analysis has been named the anthropic principle. (Gale, 1981, p 154)[53]

So, the universe has the properties necessary for our survival *because if it did not, then we would not be here to observe it.* The anthropic principle is typically presented in this way — emphasizing man's role as an observer.

---

[51] Leslie, 1989, p 2-6; Hawking, 1988, p 125

[52] For example, Freeman Dyson (1979, p 245-253) examines the evidence that the universe has highly improbable properties that operate to our favor. He reads this as evidence that "mind plays an essential role" in the functioning of the universe. (p 251) He gets mystical about it, rather than coming right out and claiming it as evidence for a designer. Nowhere does he mention the anthropic principle, rather he correctly refers to his discussion as an argument from design.

Gould (1985, p 392-402) disagrees with Dyson's mysticism. However, he mis-labels Dyson's discussion and proceeds to argue against what he mistakenly believes to be the "anthropic principle." This is unfortunate, since Gould got the labeling exactly backwards. Correctly understood, the anthropic principle is naturalism's *response* to the highly improbable features of the universe cited in Dyson's argument from design.

[53] "The anthropic principle states that the fact of our existence may serve as a valid explanation in fundamental physics." (Rosen, J., 1985, p 335)

"The Anthropic Principle is a consequence of our own existence." (Barrow and Tipler, 1988, p 27)

Sometimes the concept is given an esoteric twist to add interest: The universe is the way it is *because we are observing it*. This misleadingly sounds as though 'observation' affects the universe somehow.

The anthropic principle has been widely advertised in recent years. Many articles promote it in the science journals: *Scientific American, Nature, Science,* and *American Scientist* to name a few.[54] Entire books are devoted to the subject.[55] It was promoted by renowned cosmologists such as Stephen Hawking. Theorists highly praise the idea.

> I will stick my neck out and state that I really feel that AP [the anthropic principle] is the closest we will ever come to an ultimate explanation. (Rosen, J., 1985, p 338)[56]

Nonetheless, the anthropic principle is not science. Evolutionists created the illusion that it is.

The illusion hinges on a key factor. The anthropic principle is actually defined many different ways — it has many formulations. These formulations are in three distinct categories, each with its own strength and downfall. The illusion is created by shifting between these formulations to avoid your objections and meet your expectations of science.

The anthropic principle is typically formulated as a tautology. A **tautology** has the appearance of being explanatory, but is not. A tautology is a statement which, due to its circular form, is true by definition. A simple example is "All tables are tables."

A tautology is always true and cannot ever be untrue (as long as the words are so defined). Since a tautology is a circular definition of words, it is only about words. It is not about the empirical world. It explains nothing about our observations.

Tautologies masquerade as though they convey knowledge and information, when in fact they convey none. An example is when the doctor says, "Your father's deafness is caused by hearing impairment." Tautologies are forbidden from scientific theories because they are neither explanatory nor testable. The anthropic principle is typically formulated this way:

> **The tautological anthropic principle**: The universe has survivable (and observable) properties *because* we survive (and observe).

---

[54] For example, tutorial articles are: Gale, 1981; Rees, 1987; Rosen, 1985 & 1988. Articles endorsing it in some sense are: Carr and Rees, 1979; Barrow and Silk, 1980; Trimble, 1977; Maddox, 1984; Weinberg, S, 1987; Silk, 1986; Fracassini *et al*, 1988; Tipler, 1982. Also see Barrow and Tipler, 1988, p 25 footnote #27 for an additional bibliography.

[55] The major book on the subject is Barrow and Tipler's, "The Anthropic Cosmological Principle" (1988). It has also been handled in a more popular way in Hawking's "A Brief History of Time," (1988), and in Leslie's 1989 book appropriately titled, "Universes."

[56] Joe Rosen feels the anthropic principle is "among the most important fundamental principles around, even, let me dare venture, *the most basic principle we have*." (1985, p 335, his italics)

The tautological anthropic principle sounds explanatory but is not. Why do we survive? Answer: Because the universe has survivable properties. Why do we know the universe has survivable properties? Answer: Because we survive. It is a circular argument. Does our survival *cause* the universe to have survivable properties? Yes, in a trivial linguistic sense, it 'causes' it to be true by definition.

The tautological anthropic principle is not science on two counts: it is neither explanatory nor testable.[57] Moreover, it focuses your attention on man's existence as an observer, and this misdirection keeps you focused on the wrong issue. The real focus of the anthropic principle is the existence of other universes.

To be explanatory the anthropic principle requires the existence of countless other universes (or other incarnations of this universe) where natural laws and properties are unlike they are here. This is the concealed assumption that evolutionary cosmologists often avoid mentioning.

When stated clearly the reasoning behind the anthropic principle is straight-forward — resulting in a second formulation:

1) Naturalism assumes that nature has no inherent special favor towards life or our existence.

2) Yet observation shows the universe actually has *highly improbable properties* necessary for life and our existence.

3) Points #1 and #2 create a conflict, and this conflict is resolved by the metaphysical anthropic principle.

The metaphysical anthropic principle: There are an infinitude of *other* universes having properties *unlike* the known universe; almost all those other universes are unsuitable for life; therefore 'nature' (all this infinity of universes) on the average has no special favor toward life or humankind.[58]

The metaphysical anthropic principle is the naked, unadorned, unconfused formulation; the only one having any explanatory power. Though it is typically hidden, it is the formulation evolutionists use when they explain the peculiar properties of the universe.

Correctly understood the principle is uncomplicated. Why does the universe have such highly improbable properties? Answer: It's just a matter of random chance — there are countless other universes lacking those properties.

---

[57] My search of mainstream literature (Science Citation Index 1989) revealed only two authors who emphatically denounced the anthropic principle as non-science. Pagels (1985, p 37) denounced it quite explicitly by correctly citing it as untestable. William Press (1986, p 316) is somewhat less explicit as to why it is not science.

[58] The line of reasoning in the anthropic principle (#1 through #3) cannot be hurt by further observations. It is invulnerable. The facts established in point #2 may well be refutable, but if they were refuted it would come as an enormous relief to evolutionists — the evolutionary position is untestable.

The argument tries to 'dilute' nature's design by adding other universes that lack design. The more improbable the observed designs are, the more 'other universes' must be added to make the dilution effective. Thus, the argument claims that *on the average* nature has no design, no inherent favor toward life or humankind. The argument claims the fortuitous design of the universe is simply the result of random chance.

*

Evolutionists often avoid giving the metaphysical formulation. They avoid it because 'other universes' are metaphysical, unobservable entities that immediately smack of non-science.

So they often state their argument indirectly. They imply the existence of other universes by mentioning a "selection effect."

> Observers will reside only in places where conditions are conducive to their evolution and existence: such sites may well turn out to be special. Our picture of the Universe and its laws are influenced by an unavoidable selection effect — that of our own existence. (Barrow and Tipler, 1988, p xi)

Obviously there can be no 'selection' unless there are various alternatives to select from. In this case the selection is on a cosmic scale including all we observe. The alternatives therefore must be entities other than the observable universe.

Occasionally, the theorists will directly speak of "alternative worlds" and "the existence of many possible universes."[59] One theorist, Pantin, stated the principle quite directly by making an analogy with natural selection at the level of universes.

> [If] we could know that our Universe was only one of an indefinite number with varying properties, we could perhaps invoke a solution analogous to the principle of Natural Selection; that only in certain universes which happen to include ours, are the conditions suitable for the existence of life, and unless that condition is fulfilled there will be no observers to note the fact. (Pantin, 1965, from Barrow and Tipler, 1988, p 19)

The anthropic principle is misnamed, which helps conceal its true nature. The name misdirects your attention onto man. It should be called the Many Universes scenario.[60]

*

---

[59] For example, Barrow and Tipler, 1988, p 19

[60] Some theorists refer to the anthropic principle as the "Multiple Worlds hypothesis" or "World Ensemble hypothesis." This is an improvement, but still not as direct as it could be. Moreover, it is not a hypothesis, because it is not testable.

A few theorists use a special approach to avoid any mention of 'other universes.' They change the definition of universe. In their definition, a universe must contain intelligent observers: *By definition* it cannot be a universe unless it contains observers.[61]

It is like the classic conundrum over the definition of sound: If a tree falls in the woods and no one is there to hear it, does it make a sound? Some people argue that by definition it cannot be a sound unless someone is there to hear it. In the same way, these theorists argue that: It cannot be a universe unless someone is there to observe it. Therefore, they argue, *this* universe may well be the only universe. In this way, these theorists invoke the anthropic principle and simultaneously avoid invoking alternative universes.

The counter-argument is direct. To follow the metaphor, we *are* in the woods and we *do* hear the sound. We *are* in this universe and we *do* see its highly unique properties that operate to our favor. These facts must be explained. The problem will not go away by force of redefining the words. The explanation provided by the anthropic principle absolutely requires, in some disguised form or another, a concept of 'other universes' unlike our own. By redefining and narrowing the word "universe," the theorists blur the very word that is most critical to their concept. They cannot communicate their explanation while simultaneously denying the words required by that explanation.

*

The anthropic principle is stated as a tautology to get people to accept it, if only as an harmless "true" proposition. The real explanatory power comes from the metaphysical formulation. Theorists shift back and forth between these formulations to create their illusion. The concept is 'always true' and not open to serious doubt (when stated as the tautological formulation) and it is explanatory (when stated as the metaphysical formulation).

Its proponents need the latitude to shift between these formulations. They achieve this flexibility by failing to give a precise statement of the principle.

> Although the Anthropic Principle is widely cited and has often been discussed in the astronomical literature there exist few attempts to frame a precise statement of the Principle; rather, astronomers seem to like to leave a little flexibility in its formulation ... (Barrow and Tipler, 1988, p 15)

The principle is often mis-presented as a deep esoteric mystery. Also, the principle is often stated in two different forms (the *weak* and the *strong* anthropic principles) though there is no general agreement about what these are. These confusing factors create additional cover for the theorists to shift back and forth.

---

[61] This approach is reflected in what Wheeler called the Participatory Anthropic Principle: "Observers are necessary to bring the Universe into being." (Barrow and Tipler, 1988, p 22)

Stephen Hawking shows how this shift can take place:

> According to this theory, there are either many different universes or many different regions of a single universe, each with its own initial configuration and, perhaps, with its own set of laws of science. In most of these universes the conditions would not be right for the development of complicated organisms; only in the few universes that are like ours would intelligent beings develop and ask the question: "Why is the universe the way we see it?" The answer is then simple: If it had been different, we would not be here! (Hawking, 1988, p 124-125)

He begins with a good discussion of the metaphysical anthropic principle, with its many alternative universes having properties unlike ours. Then, in the second half, he shifts the focus to our existence as observers and gives the classic tautological formulation — the universe is the way we see it *because* "If it [the universe] had been different, we would not be here." The tautology captivates his readers since they automatically accept it as true, and it sounds explanatory. In actuality it explains nothing and may by removed without loss. All the explanatory power is derived from the 'other universes.' Yet Hawking gives his readers the erroneous impression that the tautological formulation is where the explanation resides. With this misperception in place, Hawking then goes back to remove the 'other universes' from his explanation, as if they had no real importance.

> [I]n what sense can all these different universes be said to exist? If they are really separate from each other, what happens in another universe can have no observable consequences in our own universe. We should therefore use the principle of economy and cut them out of the theory. (Hawking, 1988, p 125)[62]

In this way, Hawking gives the mistaken impression that the anthropic principle: (1) is an explanation of the universe's design; (2) is true; and (3) does not necessarily require other universes.

*

For another example of the shift, we turn to Barrow and Tipler's definitive book, *The Anthropic Cosmological Principle.* They offer many tautological and metaphysical formulations. Yet there is one place where they clearly set the principle apart from other text and define it. Presumably this definition must take the heat of close scrutiny, so they word it carefully to avoid any obvious pitfalls.

> *The observed values of all physical and cosmological quantities are not equally probable but they take on values restricted by the requirement that there exist sites where carbon-based life can evolve and by the requirement that the Universe be old enough for it to have already done so.* (Barrow and Tipler, 1988, p 16, their italics)

---

[62] Hawking also makes confusing references to the *weak* and the *strong* anthropic principles. These confusing factors further conceal the shift.

On close examination, most of the anthropic principle has been left unstated and implicit. It is ambiguous. It can be read in several different ways. That is key to their presentation.

For instance, the metaphysical formulation is concealed so well it hardly seems present. Absent are the references to 'other universes' or 'selection.' In their place is a vague reference to cosmological quantities that are not fixed but "take on [alternative] values." Surely most readers would not readily detect 'other universes' on reading such a definition.

Likewise, the tautological formulation is well concealed. This is because the explanation is left unstated and implied. Their statement does not say what is being explained. If we fill that in, then we end up with a tautology, like this: The observed cosmological quantities are suitable for our existence because they are restricted by the requirement that we exist.

At this point we need a third category, called a **lame formulation**. A lame formulation fails to even attempt to explain the problem it is claimed to explain. If one takes Barrow and Tipler's definition precisely as it stands, then it is lame. It does not attempt to explain the peculiar features of the universe. Suppose you ask, Why is the sky blue? By analogy, Barrow and Tipler's answer would be: The observed color of the sky is restricted by the requirement that it be blue. Their formulation simply does not explain the problem.

In short, Barrow and Tipler's central definition has concealed the tautological and metaphysical formulations by avoiding any direct attempt at being explanatory. This is why the definition appears to withstand these two criticisms, and why critics can stare at it a long time without finding obvious fault.

Ambiguity serves the purpose of allowing theorists to shift effortlessly away from any single line of criticism. If you argue it is tautological, they can shift to either a metaphysical or lame formulation. If you argue it is lame, they can shift to either a tautological or metaphysical formulation. This ability to shift back and forth is key to the illusions about the anthropic principle.

Summary

Testability is rightly known as the crucial criterion of science. Evolutionists and major scientific organizations have thoroughly endorsed it.

Yet evolutionists often misapply testability in an effort to defeat creation theory. They also try to redefine "science" and "natural" to favor that goal. The result has been mistakes and double standards.

Science is capable of deducing a designer's existence, character, and motives, as seen in the examples of archaeology and the Piltdown case. It can identify and decode messages, as proposed in the SETI project. Science does this based on the pattern of the data. A designer and a message can be part of testable scientific theories.

The argument from design is valid scientific reasoning, used throughout science and our daily living. William Paley merely applied it to life. Of all the things known in the universe, life most warrants the argument from design.

Paley's argument forms the basis for a scientific theory of life's origin. It is explanatory, general, and the most frequently tested theory in biology. Paley's theory says a designer was necessary for the origin of life, but it does not say the designer was supernatural.

Yet, Paley's theory, the Big Bang, and the Laws of Thermodynamics, in combination point to a logically consistent conclusion: a supernatural agent has performed a creative act in the universe. Though this argument points to the supernatural, it is empirically testable. It could be discredited by falsifying Paley's theory, the Big Bang, or the Laws of Thermodynamics. Because the argument is explanatory, logically consistent, and empirically testable, it has a place in science.

There is a precedent for this in mathematics. Kurt Gödel showed that a collection of simple self-evident axioms can, in combination, demand that we acknowledge the *existence* of true 'supernatural' theorems whose truth can never be proven directly. That conclusion is required solely because logical self-consistency requires it. When approached the proper way, the supernatural can be scientific.

Message theory, like Paley's theory of life, does not presuppose the existence of supernatural causes.

*

Evolutionists would like to solve the origin of life in a simple way. They would like to say that life always existed. But the Big Bang and the Laws of Thermodynamics refute it. So evolutionists pursue other alternatives. They do not yet have a scientific explanation for the origin of life.

Evolutionists have not falsified Paley's theory. Nonetheless, they throw it out, solely because it conflicts with their philosophical commitment to naturalism. The evolutionists' rejection of science begins there.

The naturalistic explanations for the origin or regeneration of the universe contradict our most firmly established scientific theories and laws. Evolutionary cosmologists regularly negate our best science, solely because it conflicts with naturalism.

The Earth has many features that seem finely designed for life. Evolutionists claimed this is the result of chance because there are an infinitude of other planets unlike Earth. Their explanation is not scientific because there is no conceivable observation that would falsify it.

In recent decades, evidence has emerged showing that the universe itself looks like it was designed for life. This conflicted with naturalism. So, evolutionists tried to explain away the design of the universe.

- Evolutionists argue there are an infinitude of other universes unlike this one, therefore, on average, nature has no special favor toward our universe or toward life. Our universe just happened by chance to have the right features for life.

That idea — called the anthropic principle — has been widely promoted by evolutionary cosmologists like Stephen Hawking. It is not science because we cannot test 'other universes.' Its unscientific nature was hidden by shifting it between various formulations.

*

The rigid commitment to naturalism contains an inherent contradiction: a preference to do damage to natural laws rather than accept any element of the supernatural. Naturalism demands that any inconsistency be resolved by *altering* the theories which gave rise to it, thus causing theorists to despoil the very natural law they profess to be safeguarding. In the name of naturalism, they willingly jettison our most thoroughly tested natural laws. In this way, naturalism can be downright anti-naturalistic.

We arrive at the supernatural by respecting our best scientific theories and laws — Logical consistency then compels us to infer the supernatural. This situation need not lead us to have a closed mind, or to stop probing for deeper comprehension of nature's mysteries. No theory ever urges that. Science is tentative. We understand that theories are tested; sometimes discredited and replaced. This is our search.

The Origin of Life

> [F]ar from there being a million ways in detail in which evolution could have got under way, there seems now to have been no obvious way at all. The singular feature is in the gap between the simplest conceivable version of organisms as we know them, and components that the Earth might reasonably have been able to generate. This gap can be seen more clearly now. It is enormous. (Cairns-Smith, 1985, p 4)

Spontaneous generation was widely believed just two centuries ago. This idea held that life could arise spontaneously from non-living matter such as mud, hay, or decaying meat. Organisms such as flies, beetles, mice, and frogs were included in the great list alleged to arise in this manner. Spontaneous generation captured the endorsement of such intellects as Descartes, Thomas Aquinas, Francis Bacon, Galileo, and Copernicus.[1]

Two developments in the nineteenth century contradicted the idea of spontaneous generation. In 1802 Paley's argument from design was published, soon achieving wide acceptance. This was followed in the 1860s by Louis Pasteur's famous experimental disproof of spontaneous generation. Pasteur showed that sterilized sealed jars of nutrient do not spontaneously produce life. The life alleged to originate by spontaneous generation was merely arising from pre-existing life.

These advancements eventually eliminated the belief in vitalism and biochemical predestination. These philosophies had postulated that matter has an innate tendency, drive, or *vital force* to produce life.

With the rise of modern physics and Darwinism, scientists turned toward a mechanistic philosophy of nature. They became aware that laws of nature are indifferent to life and have no special workings in favor of life. This was a major step in our understanding of nature. This also subtly strengthened creation theory by eroding the foundation of alternative worldviews. One by one, the alternatives to an intelligent designer were being eliminated.

Yet, theorists were buoyed up by the wave of Darwinist enthusiasm. They viewed chance as the major factor in life's origin. Chance is the modern orthodoxy. The rest seemed just a detail to be filled-in by research.

---

[1] Shapiro, 1986, p 17

Primitive Atmosphere and Primordial Soup

In 1924 Oparin proposed the sequence of events in the origin of life: first cells, then enzymes, and finally genes. Oparin suggested the first protocell began by the accumulation of more and more complicated molecules within an oily liquid called coacervate droplets. The evidence for this was never good, though it was widely accepted because it conformed with the philosophy of naturalism.

> The Oparin picture was generally accepted by biologists for half a century. It was popular not because there was any evidence to support it but rather because it seemed to be the only alternative to biblical creationism. (Dyson, 1985, p 31)

*

A major obstacle to naturalistic theories is our atmosphere.

Chemists categorize the chemical effect of atmospheres into a range, from oxidizing, to neutral, to reducing. These are terms for the ability of atmosphere to remove (oxidize) or add (reduce) electrons to an atom, ion, or molecule. Our atmosphere contains abundant free oxygen. We have an oxidizing atmosphere.

By the 1920s, Oparin and Haldane knew our oxidizing atmosphere would forbid the naturalistic origin of life. So, they dutifully suggested that the primitive earth atmosphere contained *no* free oxygen.

> The first step towards life is the chemical generation of 'organic' compounds: that is, compounds containing carbon. Such compounds react very readily with oxygen. In an atmosphere containing oxygen, they would not last very long. The origin of life, therefore, requires the absence of free oxygen. (Maynard-Smith, 1986, p 111)

They assumed a strongly reducing atmosphere, since this is the most favorable to formation of organic molecules. Thus was born the myth of the primitive reducing atmosphere.

*

In 1953 Stanley Miller conducted his classic prebiotic experiment to simulate the origin of organic molecules. His experiment used a reducing atmosphere claimed at the time to represent the primitive earth. The experiment produced detectable quantities of amino acids. The public was told his experiment demonstrated how earth naturally originated the molecules of life. Many similar experiments were done, and the results have been exaggerated.

> Yet the initial promise has not been maintained. Miller's experiment has hardly been improved on. Even the simpler molecules are produced only in small amounts in realistic experiments simulating possible primitive earth conditions. What is worse, these molecules are generally minor constituents of tars: it remains problematical how they could have been separated and purified through geochemical processes whose normal effects are to make organic mixtures more and more of a jumble. With somewhat more complex molecules these difficulties rapidly increase. (Cairns-Smith, 1985, p 90)

But all such 'molecules of life' are always minority products and usually no more than trace products. Their detection often owes more to the skill of the experimenter than to any powerful tendency for the 'molecules of life' to form. (Cairns-Smith, 1985, p 44)

In sum the ease of synthesis of 'the molecules of life' has been greatly exaggerated. It only applies to a few of the simplest, and in no case is it at all easy to see how the molecules would have been sufficiently unencumbered by other irrelevant or interfering molecules to have allowed further organisation to higher-order structures of the kinds that would be needed. (Cairns-Smith, 1985, p 44)

Prebiotic experiments begin with a few molecule types, said to represent the primitive earth. Typically, a reservoir of these is provided. The experiments include an energy source such as electric spark, heat, acoustic shock, or ultraviolet light. The energy source is required to drive the chemical reactions that produce organic molecules, but it also destroys these just as effectively. Therefore, the apparatus includes hardware called a cold trap to catch and safekeep the organic molecules. Another feature is a subtle yet effective pump, gently circulating material through the experiment's glassware tubing. The hardware is specially arranged so that organic molecules formed near the energy source are immediately circulated to the cold trap for safekeeping.

Some critics argue that the reservoir ingredients at the beginning of the experiment are unnaturally pure. Many commonplace natural compounds and their by-products would interfere with the desired results. These interfering compounds have been unnaturally excluded from the experiment by the researcher. Other critics point out that the arrangement and proximity of the various pieces of apparatus is unnatural and not to be expected from nature. The neat flow from energy source to cold trap is unlikely to have a commonplace natural version that operates as efficiently. These factors artificially elevate the yield of organic molecules in the prebiotic experiments.

The prebiotic experiments also produce an abundance of unwanted compounds that would detrimentally effect the next stage of biosynthesis. These unwanted compounds cannot be ignored out of existence. They cause a legitimate problem for the proponents of prebiotic origins.

*

There are also problems with the primitive reducing atmosphere. The lack of free oxygen would have left the upper atmosphere without an ozone layer to filter out ultraviolet rays from the sun. These rays would directly destroy most exposed organic matter since they can penetrate tens of meters beneath the ocean surface. Ocean currents would periodically circulate even the deep water and expose its organic contents to destruction.

Ultraviolet rays would also have a destructive effect indirectly. The ultraviolet sunlight converts surface minerals into materials that will destroy organic molecules even more effectively than will oxygen gas.[2] Ultraviolet light also

---

[2] Cairns-Smith, 1985, p 43

breaks apart water vapor into oxygen and hydrogen. The hydrogen, due to its light weight, escapes into space leaving the oxygen behind. Scientists now believe this mechanism can be a substantial source of atmospheric oxygen, rivaling production by plant photosynthesis. This mechanism would have rapidly oxidized the atmosphere, thereby destroying organic molecules.

Furthermore, even a strongly reducing atmosphere would itself have been destroyed by sunlight. Geologists now realize that a methane and ammonia atmosphere would have been destroyed within a few thousand years by chemical reactions caused by sunlight.[3]

In addition, the geological evidence indicates the primitive atmosphere was not reducing.

> Since the atmosphere interacts with the chemicals on the surface of the earth, the chemical composition of the earliest sedimentary rocks should give us some clues to the composition of the early atmosphere. Some of those rocks suggest that they were formed under reducing conditions. This was taken to support the hypothesis that the atmosphere then was reducing. This also has recently been called into question. Even today some sediments are reducing — stinking muds, for example — in spite of all the oxygen in the air around us. Such conditions are usually produced by the anerobic decay of organic materials in the mud. It is now claimed that if *all* the available rocks of a given age are considered, then, when averaged, the evidence suggests that the atmosphere in the past was rather like what it is today. Unfortunately, this only takes us back to 3.2 billion years ago. Before that the evidence is too sparse, because too few suitable rocks are available to us. (Crick, 1981, p 75-76)

> No geological or geochemical evidence collected in the last 30 years favors a strongly reducing primitive atmosphere, ... Only the success of the laboratory experiments recommends it. (Kerr, 1980, p 42)

> The Urey-Miller experiment yielded amino acids under conditions then believed to be early geological. This belief has not stood the test of time. The change in belief gradually occurred as the opinion became more widespread that the reactant atmospheres employed had not been geologically valid and because it strained the imagination to suppose that laboratory apparatus could simulate structures in the geological realm. (Fox, 1988, p 26)

This evidence has forced theorists to revise their model. They now believe the primitive atmosphere was nitrogen, carbon dioxide, water vapor, and a small amount of hydrogen. This would be nearly neutral, with only a slight reducing power.

Prebiotic experiments have not shown favorable results for such an atmosphere. They yield smaller quantities and fewer varieties of organic molecules. The simplest of all the amino acids — glycine — is virtually the only one produced by such experiments, and only in trace amounts.

---

[3] Shapiro, 1986, p 111-112

Stanley Miller and others have attempted to prepare amino acids under the new conditions. The ratio of hydrogen to carbon dioxide is a crucial variable. When this falls below 1 ... only glycine is produced, in trace amounts, but no other amino acid.[4] (Shapiro, 1986, p 112)

Other researchers also acknowledge difficulties.

[I]t seems now that the early atmosphere of the Earth was dominated by nitrogen and carbon dioxide. This would have made the synthesis of organic molecules much more difficult than under the methane-dominated [strongly reducing] atmosphere that had previously been imagined. (Cairns-Smith, 1985, p 42)

*

Just a few decades ago, scientists believed organic molecules collected in the oceans and formed a primordial soup, thick with nutrients "like a chicken broth." Now theorists doubt the existence of a primordial soup.

There is growing doubt about the idea that the primitive oceans would have been full of organic molecules. (Cairns-Smith, 1985, p 42)

But the expected rush of new developments has not been forthcoming. Rather, doubt has been cast on two of the basic premises, the reducing atmosphere and the prebiotic soup. Scientific unity has fragmented, and very unusual ideas have moved to the center of public attention. (Shapiro, 1986, p 278)

In summary, prebiotic experiments once offered tantalizing hints of the origin of life. Scientists now find these experiments of little help. Scientists doubt the existence of a primitive reducing atmosphere or a primordial soup. They are doubting the abundance of prebiotic organic molecules.

*

Other fields of exploration also have failed to support evolutionary expectations. Only a few decades ago, the Moon, Venus, Mars, and Jupiter were suspected to harbor life. Now, our space research has demolished those hopes. There is no evidence for life on any other body in the solar system, and few scientists even hold a hope for it.

Mars is a notable case, since it was the most likely candidate for life. As the two Viking spacecraft neared the planet, Carl Sagan predicted we might find life forms the size of a squirrel. These spacecraft carried equipment so sensitive that if placed at any location on Earth (for example hot, dry deserts, or the coldest mountain tops, glaciers, or poles) they would have readily detected life. Their failure to detect life on Mars is considered conclusive evidence that Mars is barren.

*

---

[4]   Miller himself has acknowledged the difficulty of justifying a high ratio of hydrogen to carbon dioxide (a ratio greater than 1) due to the escape of hydrogen into space.

If time were infinite, then evolutionists would simply claim life always existed. The Big Bang puts a serious crunch on that notion.

So, the origin of life must be explained within the available time, at most 20 billion years. The limited time allows probability to make powerful scientific arguments against evolution. These disprove the chance origin of anything resembling known life.

> Although the idea was entertained at one time, it is now considered highly unlikely that a chance assemblage of randomly synthesized prebiotic molecules could have been the source of the first bacteriumlike organism. The odds are overwhelmingly against it. Even these simplest of organisms are amazingly complex biological machines that must be immensely more sophisticated than the transitional forms that are thought to have bridged the gap between nonliving and living matter. (Wilson, J. H., 1983, p 89)

> [T]he simplest known organisms are far too complex to form spontaneously. (Shapiro, 1986, p 132)

> How did the first one-celled creatures arise? They are too complex to form by spontaneous generation, and so must also be the products of evolution from even simpler beings. (Shapiro, 1986, p 155)

The Misuse of Probability

> Why do we seem so singularly unable to grasp probability? (Gould, 1991d, p 21)

Evolutionists commonly overlook or distort probability science. This practice is now second-nature in genetics, cosmology, and the origin of life.

They overlook probability by automatically *assuming* there is enough time available to overcome any problem. They underestimate how quickly probability can become an obstacle, even on a cosmic time scale.[5]

For example, the college-level introductory biology text by Gould, Luria, and Singer states:

> [I]s life ... a product of chance — some fundamentally 'lucky' event that happened only because so much time was available? (Given enough time, you will eventually flip 100 heads in a row, however improbable it might be in any one trial.) (Gould, Luria, and Singer, 1981, p 689, their parenthesis)

---

[5] Andrew Scott naively suggests that with the help of modern technology mankind could search "through the entire repertoire of nucleic acids and proteins of differing nucleotide and amino acid sequence". (Scott, A., 1986, p 189) He shows a blissful unawareness of the magnitude of the problem. There are too many possible sequences to search them all, even helped by a universe full of supercomputers. This is not unusual. Evolutionists commonly underestimate the magnitude of problems relative to the available time. They mistakenly believe that evolution itself tried most protein and nucleotide sequences.

Their statement is no accidental slip of the pen. They emphasize it three times in their book.[6] Yet it is so misleading we must conclude they failed to seriously think about the matter. They are uncritically reciting the evolutionary anthem: give chance enough time and it can do anything.

Their statement is misleading on the time-scale of the universe itself. If you flipped an honest coin once a second continuously around the clock, then you would require 200 thousand billion times the maximum estimated age of the universe to flip a trial of 100 heads.[7] This is no exaggeration. On average it would require that much time. This narrative description explains the extremely low probability in terms we can humanly grasp. Narrative description is the best way to obtain perspective on these low odds.

*

Though probability is often overlooked through simple neglect, the distortions of probability are deeper and more serious. Some evolutionists directly assault probability science to brush it aside as insignificant or unreliable. This is an assault on science itself.

For example, Stephen Gould attempts to eliminate probability science from the study of origins.

> [A] probability cannot even be calculated for a singular occurrence known only after the fact (whereas probabilities could be attached to predictions made at the beginning of a sequence).[8] (Gould, 1991c, 324, my italics)

> [T]he actual result of evolution is the only sample we have. We cannot compute a "probability" or even speak in such terms. Any result in a sample of one would appear equally miraculous when you consider the vast range of alternative possibilities. But something had to happen. We may only talk of odds if we could return to the beginning, list a million possible outcomes, and then lay cold cash upon one possibility alone. (Gould, 1991c, p 319, my italics)

---

[6] The other repetitions are: "give us enough time, and we will eventually flip 100 heads in a row with an honest coin." (p 592) and "no one expects to throw 100 heads in a row the first time, but given enough trials, it will eventually happen." (p 693)

[7] Here is a brief math review. The probability of flipping a coin heads is ½. The probability of flipping two heads in a row is $½ \times ½ = ¼$. The probability of flipping 100 heads in a row is $(½)^{100}$. (This is one-half taken to the 100th power, or one chance in 2^{100}.) In general, the probability of N heads in a row is one chance in 2^N.

We convert these probabilities to a base of 10, since this is the numbering system commonly used in science. In this case, $2^N = 10^M$, we know N and we wish to know M. Solving for M gives: $M = N \times LOG_{10}(2) = N \times 0.301$

So, the chance of flipping N heads in a row is one in $10^{0.301 \times N}$. For N=100 the probability is 1 in 1.3×10^{30}. Use formulas like this throughout this chapter.

[8] Former President Jimmy Carter wrote to Gould with a correct argument: one chance in ten, a thousand, or even a million may be a credible occurrence, but eventually an improbability can be too small to be plausible — there are real limits to what chance can accomplish in this universe. Gould responded with the argument cited above.

It is one thing to argue that a particular probability has been computed inaccurately. It is quite another to argue, as Gould does, that probability science *inherently* cannot be applied to singular events.

Gould is deeply mistaken, as our common experience shows. A dead body, a broken-out window pane, a smudge of blood, a missing fireplace poker — without any eyewitnesses, simple unrepeatable data like this together with a probability argument can defeat all claims that it was the result of "chance." It can even show that the death was not from accidental or natural causes, but resulted from intentional "design" by an intelligent being. It can even point the finger at the perpetrator, who may be imprisoned for life (or worse). Even without super-accurate computations, the probability argument (and its companion the argument from design) can be that compelling. Gould is flatly wrong when he says probability science cannot be applied to singular events from the past.

Gould's error goes further. Elsewhere he argues (quite correctly) that "postdictions" (modern jargon for scientific predictions about past events) *can* be applied to singular events from the past.[9] Thus, Gould's position is self-contradictory on its face.

Gould's error goes deeper still, for he was arguing in favor of *evolutionary* postdiction. In actual practice, evolutionary postdiction is not scientific, it is merely flexible just-so storytelling that accommodates the data after the fact. Thus, for studying the past, Gould indicates that probability is unscientific, but just-so storytelling is scientific. In effect, Gould forged a complete reversal of proper science.

It is remarkable that evolutionary scientists stand by silently while other evolutionists (often their leaders) propagate errors that normally would not be tolerated for a minute. Apparently the errors are tolerated because they promote evolution. Stripped of all references to evolution the errors would not stand — evolutionists themselves would readily dismantle them. The evolutionists' distortions of probability are an example of this.

*

Science rarely deals in pure logic. Science is a tentative enterprise undertaken by finite beings with finite observations. Empirical facts are never established with perfect, formal certainty. Instead, a fact is something so thoroughly confirmed it would be perverse to withhold provisional assent.[10]

For example, it is a fact that a tornado sweeping through a junkyard will not assemble an airplane, a house, or a watch. For the scientist it would be perverse to insist otherwise.

Yet some evolutionists do insist otherwise. They insist that no probability is ever too small to bar evolution. One example is from Robert Steiner's vociferous anti-creation article in *Reason* magazine. A creationist had argued that the odds against forming even the simplest protein molecule by random chance were far greater than 10^{67} to one. Steiner responded:

---

[9]   Gould, 1992e, p 18

[10]   This excellent definition of "fact" is from Gould, 1984a, p 119.

"So what? Think of anything that has in fact occurred; if you look back far enough, the probability of the occurrence of the sequence of events necessary for that event to have occurred is infinitesimal.

Shuffle a normal pack of playing cards. The probability of arriving at the precise arrangement of cards at which you in fact arrive is one in 8-followed-by-67-zeros. That is, the occurrence of [the random origination of a simple protein molecule] is eight times *more likely* than the arrangement of cards you arrived at by one simple shuffle of the pack.

Imagine your four grandparents at their time of birth. With all the choices and chances in life, not the least of which is the number of live sperm that never fertilized an egg, what is the probability that two generations later you would *at this exact moment* be reading this article? And yet, here you are." (Steiner, 1981, p 31)

In his effort to get around the creationists' argument, Steiner attempts to cast doubt on the validity of probability science. His argument is built on errors.

- Given that something has in fact occurred, what is the probability of the occurrence of the sequence of events necessary for that event to have occurred? It is exactly 1 — absolute certainty — not "infinitesimal" as suggested by Steiner.

- Shuffle a deck of cards. What is the probability of arriving at the precise arrangement of cards at which you in fact arrive? It is exactly 1 — absolute certainty. You will always arrive at the arrangement at which you in fact arrive — it is impossible to do otherwise. The probability is not one in 8×10^{67} as suggested by Steiner.

- Given your four grandparents, what is the probability that two generations later they would give rise to you? It is 1. If it were not so then they would not have been *your* four grandparents, thereby breaking the starting assumption. The probability is not infinitesimally small as suggested by Steiner.

- What is the probability that you would *at this exact moment* be reading these words? Again it is 1 — absolute certainty — not infinitesimal as suggested by Steiner.

Steiner argues that highly improbable outcomes can often occur, but in each of his examples the outcome is *guaranteed* by his premises. The outcomes are already present within his starting assumptions, yet he erroneously calculates extremely low probabilities. This creates the confusion on which his argument thrives. By misapplying probability theory he attempts to discredit its validity.

On a deeper level, his argument can be understood this way. The universe has an infinitude of 'possibilities' that never occur. There are an infinitude of possible babies who are never born because their necessary sperm and egg never met. There are an infinitude of progeny your grandparents might have fostered, but did not. There are an infinitude of things other than these words you could be looking at right now, but are not. There is an unspeakably large number of possibilities that never occur. Contrary to this, Steiner wants to convince you that most anything will occur given time. So he focuses on things known to have occurred, rather than on the *overwhelming* infinitude that do not, and this skewed focus distorts your perspective.[11]

People have difficulty comprehending very small probabilities. Our delicate perspective on these matters is easily distorted, and Steiner's argument takes advantage of this fact.

To regain perspective let us discuss one of his examples. One would think mankind has mastered a deck of cards by now, but we fall miserably short. Give a deck a thorough random shuffling. You now possess something unique in all the universe.[12] No one is remotely in a position to arrive at that same sequence by random means. Imagine there were 10 billion people on earth, each shuffling a deck once a second around the clock. Imagine they are being helped by one billion-billion (1×10^{18}) similarly sized extra-terrestrial civilizations. Imagine this activity is occurring continuously over the maximum estimated age of the universe (20 billion years). All this mad shuffling is done by beings slavishly devoting their lives to the task. Yet it would require over

$$10,000,000,000,000,000,000,000$$
$$(= \text{ten thousand billion-billion} = 10^{22})$$

such universes before we could expect your card sequence to be duplicated by chance.

*

Another type of distortion is made by Rosenberg:

> The hypothesis that an organism, in a given environment, has a given level of fitness is like the hypothesis that a given die is a fair one. This latter hypothesis is consistent with any finite sequence of outcomes of rolling the die, even 10^6 straight '2's. *No finite number of outcomes of rolling the die can refute the hypothesis.* (Rosenberg, 1985, p 158, my italics)

---

[11] Another example of this erroneous argument occurs in Milner's *Encyclopedia of Evolution* (1990, p 51). "From a statistical perspective, any individual human being is the highly improbable result of an unlikely sequence of events. .... Once his parents did meet and procreate, the chances of the one particular egg being fertilized by the one particular sperm that formed his genetic combination are exceedingly slim. If one were to calculate the probability for the existence of that unique individual, the chances would be almost infinitesimal. Each of us is the very improbable, highly unlikely result of a unique history — and yet here we all are. .... This paradox of the extremely unlikely being not only possible, but inevitable, is one aspect of chance in evolution." Erroneous arguments like that are common. For example, see Saladin, 1988, p 38-39 & 69; and Hewitt, 1988, p 298-299.

[12] There are 8×10^{67} (52 factorial) possible sequences to a deck of 52 cards. There are 52 possibilities for the bottom card of the deck. Once that card is in place there are 51 cards left, so there are then 51 possibilities for the second card. This leaves 50 possibilities for the third, and so on. The total number of possible sequences for the deck is therefore the product of all these or $52 \times 51 \times 50 \times \ldots 3 \times 2 \times 1 = 52$ factorial.

Rosenberg claims that one million straight 2's is consistent with a die being fair. This feat has a probability of one in $10^{778,150}$, a chance so minuscule it would strain our ability just to describe in humanly meaningful terms, even on the scale of the universe.

Rosenberg is wrong. One million straight 2's would refute the 'fair die' hypothesis with all the certainty we could humanly hope for in science.

Empirical science is not about absolute, perfect certainty — it is about shades of *near* certainty. The difference is subtle yet important, as this case illustrates so well. Rosenberg distorted the way probability is applied in testing theories, thus implying that no theory is testable.

Why does he make that distortion? The answer is revealing. A later chapter will show that natural selection is not science because it is not testable. Darwinians sometimes try to defend natural selection by assaulting the criterion of testability itself. Rosenberg is making such an attempt in association with his argument.

He does this as follows. He discusses the 'fair die' hypothesis as a rather simple scientific hypothesis. He discusses the difficulty of falsifying the hypothesis and then exaggerates that difficulty in an attempt to allow scientific status for natural selection. He attempts to lower all science to the level of untestability so natural selection looks good by comparison.

*

Evolutionary philosophy is now so pervasive that it distorts fields well outside biology. One case is Stephen Hawking's recent book on cosmology, *A Brief History of Time*. Hawking unknowingly purveys the evolutionary distortions of our times.

For example, he misinterprets the probabilities involved in the Second Law of Thermodynamics. He has the reader imagine two boxes: one containing oxygen and the other containing nitrogen. The boxes are joined together and the intervening wall is removed. As predicted by the second law, the gases will mix throughout the box. What is the probability the oxygen gas will randomly move back to its half the box?

> The probability of all the gas molecules in our first box being found in one half of the box at a later time is many millions of millions to one, *but it can happen*. (Hawking, 1988, p 103, my italics)

Hawking claims it can happen.

Hawking didn't supply exact details, so we have to assume them as his reader would. Assume the two original boxes are small, about shoebox size (5 liters). Each box would contain approximately $N=1.3\times10^{23}$ molecules.[13] Later, each oxygen molecule would have a fifty percent probability of being in a given half of the available space at a given instant in time. Therefore the probability that all N

---

[13] This assumes typical temperatures and pressures. The necessary equation here is Avogadro's Law. At STP (standard temperature and pressure) 22.4 liters of any gas contains 6.02×10^{23} molecules.

oxygen molecules would randomly move back into half the box is one chance in 2^N. Let me write this figure out for you.[14]

It is one chance in $10^{40,000,000,000,000,000,000,000}$

The number would be a 1 followed by forty thousand billion-billion zeros. Hawking's casual argument has misrepresented the facts. It is a *fact* the gases will not separate by chance.

*

Hawking also recites the classic myth about the horde of typing monkeys, "very occasionally by pure chance they will type out one of Shakespeare's sonnets."[15]

This notion is unsound, yet it beguiles the public by playing on the human difficulty of comprehending very small numbers. That is why narrative descriptions are so important.

The monkeys could not randomly type merely the first 100 characters of *Hamlet*. If we count only lowercase letters and spaces (27 characters in all), then the probability of typing the 100 characters is one chance in 27^{100} (one chance in 1.4×10^{143}).

If each proton in the observable universe were a typing monkey (roughly 10^{80} in all[16]), and they typed 500 characters per minute (faster than the fastest secretary), around the clock for 20 billion years, then all the monkeys together could make 5×10^{96} attempts at the 100 characters. It would require an additional 3×10^{46} such universes to have an even chance at success. We scientifically conclude that the monkey scenario cannot succeed. For the scientist it would be perverse to insist otherwise.

Christopher Wills acknowledges this fact. Then he tries to change the argument to favor evolution.

> But if we set an unimaginably large number of universes full of monkeys to work, sooner or later one of them will succeed. (Wills, 1989, p 243)

Wills changes the argument by invoking *an unimaginably large number of universes.* This 'infinitude of universes' is the fundamental assumption of the anthropic principle and the reason why many evolutionists — such as Stephen Hawking — take such liberties with probability. It is not science. It is the evolutionists' attempt to arbitrarily protect their worldview from the intruding facts of science.

---

[14] We convert probabilities to a base of 10, since this is the numbering system commonly used in science. Here is an example conversion from a base of 2 to a base of 10. Let $2^N = 10^M$ and we wish to know M. Then $M = N \times LOG_{10}(2) = N \times 0.301$

[15] Hawking, 1988, p 123

[16] Boslough, 1992, p 155; Kimura, 1983, p 238

The Probability Arguments

Probability arguments follow three steps:

1)   Model the chance origin of a biological feature;

2)   Calculate the odds;

3)   Attempt to describe the odds

Step 2 is a straightforward probability calculation. Step 3 is needed because the odds are so small they defy our common understanding. We lack the verbal superlatives to express such small chances. Narrative description is needed to counter the abuses of probability by evolutionists. We need to regain honest perspective about very small probabilities.

Steps 2 and 3 are typically not controversial. Evolutionists usually attack the argument at Step 1 by claiming an invalid assumption has been made.[17]

John Wilson provides an example of how evolutionists debate probability arguments. He frames the issue as follows:

> One such argument focuses on the ten enzymes involved in glycosis, a primary metabolic pathway by which glucose is converted to pyruvic acid in almost all contemporary organisms. The random, undirected polymerization of these enzymes from a mixture of the twenty amino acids is calculated to occur with a rough probability of 10^{1000}. Even with relatively fast rates of polymerization and a billion-year time scale, it is argued, the likelihood that even one copy of each of these enzymes would be spontaneously produced is infinitesimal. The overall likelihood is not much improved even if only one of the ten enzymes is considered, and, of course, it becomes preposterously small for the thousand or so different enzymes in a typical bacterium. In the face of such overwhelming odds, how can evolutionists continue to assert the plausibility of life arising from nonlife? (Wilson, J. H., 1983, p 95-96)

---

[17] "[A major error is the] assumption that the first catalysts had to be as complex and large as those of today. The first catalysts were inefficient by modern standards. The pace of life in general was not the same then as it is today. Moreover, the polypeptide catalysts were doubtless smaller than are most contemporary enzymes." (Doolittle, 1984, p 161)

"There is only one possible conclusion: the statistical argument is invalidly applied to the origin of life because it makes invalid assumptions about the chemical building blocks of life." (Root-Bernstein, 1984a, p 12)

"Such impossibility arguments are awfully difficult to make in science because they depend so heavily on initial assumptions. It takes a rather arrogant person to claim that he has constructed an air-tight impossibility argument for something. Such a person says that he knows all the boundary conditions for a particular situation. I, for one, tend to go with the ideas of people who are willing to admit that we don't know everything." (Thwaites, 1983, p 14)

How does Wilson respond to that:

> *No evolutionist seriously proposes that even a single contemporary enzyme was polymerized prebiotically.* Thus the probability estimates advanced to date by creationists are simply irrelevant to the evolutionists' arguments. (Wilson, J. H., 1983, p 96, my italics)

First he makes a complete concession to the creationists' probability arguments and then, in the next sentence, he says these are "simply irrelevant."

*

Amino acid molecules can link-up or polymerize, forming a polymer known as a polypeptide. Each amino acid molecule counts as one unit in the total length of the polypeptide.

Proteins are polypeptides having special construction and characteristics. Functional proteins from known life are roughly a hundred to a thousand units in length. We will take 100 units as the minimum length likely to give a biologically functional protein. This assumption gives an advantage to evolution, since most of life's proteins are much longer than 100 units.

There are many thousands of kinds of amino acid. The 20 kinds found in life are called proteinous amino acids. Many of the proteinous amino acids have never been detected in prebiotic experiments. In fact, most kinds occurring in prebiotic experiments are *non*-proteinous.

This causes a puzzle for evolution. Gould asks, "Why only a few [20] amino acids in organisms, when the [primordial] soup must have contained ten times as many?"[18]

Is it possible the first life had only the 20 proteinous amino acids by chance? Let us calculate the probability. Assume one-tenth the amino acid units in the soup are proteinous (as suggested by Gould), and assume these bond into polypeptides as often as the non-proteinous amino acids (as is the case experimentally). Then the probability that a 100 unit polypeptide will contain *only* proteinous amino acids is one chance in 10^{100}.

This is too small to have occurred in this universe by chance. Evolutionists respond to this fact by claiming (without evidence) that the reliance on proteinous amino acids is not necessary for life.

*

---

[18] Gould, Luria, and Singer, 1981, p 689

Amino acid molecules occur in right-handed and left-handed forms. These forms are mirror images of each other,[19] and have identical chemical properties. In prebiotic experiments the two forms occur in equal portions.

Amino acids polymerize without preference for either handed form — the two forms join together with equal facility. Yet, protein from known life uses only left-handed amino acids.[20]

Biochemists have not found a realistic process to create this situation, so some suggest it happened by chance. We can calculate the chance. What is the probability that a randomly polymerized 100 unit polypeptide would contain only left-handed forms? — it is one chance in 2^{100} (or one chance in 10^{30}). This would be a most unlikely event. Evolutionists respond to this by claiming (again without evidence) that the reliance on left-handed amino acids is not necessary for life.

*

When amino acids bond together in prebiotic experiments they do so in several different ways using α, β, γ, or ϵ-links as the molecular bonds. In origin-of-life experiments, the α-links are largely out-numbered by the other types. Yet, all protein from known life uses *only* α-links.

What is the possibility that this situation arose by chance? Assume the probability of an α-link is as great as one half. What is the probability a 100 unit polypeptide will contain only α-links? It is one chance in 2^{99} (or approximately one chance in 10^{30}). Evolutionists respond to this by claiming (again without evidence) that the reliance on α-linked amino acids is not necessary for life.

*

So far we have discussed cases where *one* polypeptide is produced. If L polypeptides are required for life, then the probabilities must be taken to the L-th power.

For example, the probability that ten randomly polymerized 100 unit polypeptides will each use only α-links (as in known life) is no better than one chance in 2^{990} (one chance in 10^{298}).

The probability that ten randomly polymerized 100 unit polypeptides will each use only left-handed amino acids (as in known life) is one chance in 2^{1000} (one chance in 10^{301}).

Chance cannot account for the origin of these features.

These are the probabilities of originating just ten polypeptides with characteristics found in life. Another difficulty is getting them to exist at the same place at the same time. This adds substantial improbability to the problem.

*

---

[19] The exception is glycine, where the two forms are identical.

[20] There are rare exceptions. For example, the cell membranes of certain bacteria possess a few right-handed amino acids.

Probability has been a potent force in constraining evolutionary speculations. As a result, here is a summary of the most optimistic evolutionary views relating to proteins:

- Polypeptide molecules in the first organism[21] had to be shorter than those from known life.

- The first organism had to contain less than a few tens of polypeptide molecules (orders of magnitude fewer than the number of proteins occurring in known life forms).

- The polypeptides in the first organism were not predominated by left-handed amino acids, nor by proteinous amino acids, nor by α-linked amino acids — all contrary to known life.

- The first organism did not incorporate any of the catalytic pathways from known life.

As the facts intrude on the evolutionists' worldview, they have sought to protect it with an impregnable assumption. They claim there are innumerable other possible life forms unlike any known life — there are other possible proteins, other possible arrangements, other possible simpler organizations suitable for life.[22]

Evolutionists use the same basic argument for biomolecules, life, the Earth, and the universe itself. When a design is too improbable to form by chance, they claim there are an *infinitude* of other biomolecules, life forms, planets, or universes *unlike* ours.

---

[21] Evolutionists commonly make origin-of-life arguments based on a model of the mycoplamas as 'the simplest known life forms.' However, the mycoplasmas "are only quasi-independent, since they must live in very close association with animal or plant cells in order to survive." (Wills, 1989, p 167) Thus, the mycoplasmas are not self-sustaining, and so are not suitable as models for the first life on earth. Bacteria are the simplest known *self-sustaining* life.

[22] For example Futuyma, 1983, p 223; Raup and Valentine, 1983, p 2981

Stripping Down the First Organism

Probability science succeeded in stripping down the first organism. Bit by bit, evolutionists were forced to reject biological designs as too improbable for the first life form.

They now suggest the first life had a membrane totally unlike anything known, or perhaps none at all.

> Fatty acids, which are the main constituent of the phosphatides in biological membranes, also have proved to be difficult to synthesize under plausibly prebiotic conditions. .... The difficulty in synthesizing fatty acids is an additional reason for suggesting that contemporary membranes were a later evolutionary addition. Perhaps the first life forms made use of ... alternative molecules in their membranes (Wilson, J. H., 1983, p 93)

> Modern cell membranes include channels and pumps which specifically control the influx and efflux of nutrients, waste products, metal ions and so on. These specialised channels involve highly specific proteins, molecules that could not have been present at the very beginning of the evolution of life. .... It seems likely, therefore, that the macro-molecular constituents of the earliest forms of biological organisation stayed together by some sort of self-aggregation, perhaps stuck to mineral surfaces, in a form that permitted ready access to nutrients in the 'external environment'. The development of a continuous membrane probably occurred relatively late, after complex metabolic pathways had evolved. (Orgel, 1982, p 151)

Some of the proteinous amino acids have never been produced under simulated prebiotic conditions. So, evolutionary theorists suggest these amino acids were not present in the first life.

> [This] suggests that primitive proteins may have been composed of fewer varieties of amino acids than are modern proteins. Perhaps the missing amino acids had to await the development of biological processes for their synthesis. (Wilson, J. H., 1983, p 92)

The polymerization of protein molecules is a problem for the evolutionists. Amino acids do not readily bond together to form peptides when water is present. Thermodynamics dictates that the opposite should tend to take place. In the presence of water, peptides and proteins tend to break down into amino acids.

> [T]he mechanism of prebiotic polymerization is a gap in the evolutionists' account of the origin of life. (Wilson, J. H., 1983, p 95)

The prebiotic formation of sugars is likewise a problem.

> Sugars are particularly trying. While it is true that they form from formaldehyde solutions, these solutions have to be far more concentrated than would have been likely in primordial oceans. and the reaction is quite spoilt in practice by just about every possible sugar being made at the same

time — and much else besides. Furthermore the conditions that form sugars also go on to destroy them. Sugars quickly make their own special kind of tar — caramel — and they make still more complicated mixtures if amino acids are around. (Cairns-Smith, 1985, p 44)

Genes are hereditary material made of sequences of nucleotide bases. Genes and enzymes are each so difficult to form prebiotically that a hypothetical first organism could not reasonably have contained them both. Yet they are both essential to known life. Shapiro acknowledges the difficulty.

Genes and enzymes are linked together in a living cell — two interlocked systems, each supporting the other. It is difficult to see how either could manage alone. Yet if we are to avoid invoking either a Creator or a very large improbability, we must accept that one occurred before the other in the origin of life. But which one was it? We are left with the ancient riddle: Which came first, the chicken or the egg? (Shapiro, 1986, p 135)

These factors have forced evolutionists ever further from the domain of known life. They now suppose the first organism was nothing more than a single, simple, replicating molecule.

Advocates of the ruling theory disagree passionately on an important detail: the chemical identity of the first self-replicating molecule. The majority supports the nucleic acids, the carriers of heredity today. A vocal dissenting minority prefers the proteins, another important contemporary class of biochemicals. Most recently, a radical faction has suggested that clay minerals, which usually suggest pottery to us rather than reproduction, played this vital initial role. (Shapiro, 1986, p 31)

Evolutionists suggest three possibilities for that first molecule: nucleic acid; protein; or crystalline clay. I discuss each in turn.

The Nucleic-Acid First Theory

The idea that life first originated as nucleic acids is called the nucleic-acid first theory. A major difficulty with the theory, however, is the problem of error rate, sometimes known as error catastrophe.

The genome of an organism is its genetic material. This DNA is made of paired nucleotides or bases, representing the smallest unit of genetic information. Imagine a population of asexual organisms having an average of ten offspring before dying. If the population is to be maintained without steady genetic deterioration, one of the ten must have the same genetic information as the parent. The other nine can have mutations causing them to perish. If no offspring is without mutation, then the genetic information will deteriorate.

Take a numerical example. Suppose the organism has a genome size of 10,000 bases, and these are each replicated with an error rate of 1 in 1,000, that is a chance of 0.001. The chance a given replicated base is correct is then 0.999, and that all 10,000 bases are correct is $0.999^{10,000}$ (or 1 in 22,000). With only ten offspring, there would be little chance any offspring would be identical to its parent. If the population is to survive, then the error rate must not be greater than 1/10,000 (one divided by the genome size).

Modern organisms have an error rate of approximately 1 in 10^{10} due to a three stage process that requires specialized enzymes. The first process aids in selecting which of the four nucleotides is added onto the daughter strand. The second process involves proof-reading enzymes and the third process takes place after synthesis and corrects errors that escape the first two processes. But the first organism could contain none of these processes, so the error rate was approximately 1 in 10 and certainly greater than 1 in 100. According to Maynard-Smith:

> This has brought us to the catch-22 of the origin of life. The first replicating molecules had to manage without informed enzymes, and hence had to put up with error rates greater than 1 in 100. *This limited their genome sizes to 100 bases or less.* To improve on this, they had to code for a replicase enzyme, and also for a primitive protein-synthesizing machinery. That cannot be done with as few as 100 bases. So, if you cannot increase your genome size you cannot code for an enzyme, and if you cannot code for an enzyme you cannot increase your genome. (Maynard-Smith, 1986, p 117-118, my italics)

Thus, the hypothetical first organism had to be less than 100 nucleotides. In known life this could code for a polypeptide less than 33 units long. This places severe (if not fatal) constraints on the ability of such a minuscule genome to code for useful functions.

There are more problems with the nucleic-acid first theory. As acknowledged by Cairns-Smith and Shapiro, there are "appalling difficulties", "massive objections", and "intractable problems"[23] in the idea that the earth ever manufactured nucleotides.

---

[23] (Cairns-Smith, 1985, p 56 and 73) and (Shapiro, 1986, p 281) respectively. See also (Scott, A., 1986 p 88-93) for similar sentiments.

[N]ucleotides and lipids, which are crucial to our present system [of life], are absent from the class of 'ubiquitous' molecules. Nucleotides and lipids have yet to be made under conditions that are realistic simulations of primitive Earth conditions. Nucleotides and lipids are much too complicated and particular for this to be surprising. They have all the appearance of molecules specially contrived for particular purposes. (Cairns-Smith, 1985, p 45)

The formation of sugars in plausible conditions and their incorporation into nucleosides have not been achieved. Until this problem is solved or bypassed, it remains a weakness in theories of abiotic nucleic acid synthesis. The origin of nucleosides and nucleotides remains, in our opinion, one of the major problems in prebiotic synthesis. (Leslie Orgel, as quoted in Shapiro, 1986, p 188)

[T]he formation of nucleosides and nucleotides ... remains a major obstacle in prebiotic synthesis. (Wilson, J. H., 1983, p 93)

We cannot say that the pre-biotic synthesis of nucleotides is impossible. We know only that if it happened it happened by some process which none of our chemists has been clever enough to reproduce. (Dyson, 1985, p 24)

Many introductory biology texts will confidently tell you that simple nucleic acids have been shown to form and replicate themselves under prebiotic conditions, but such reports are simply wrong.[24] (Scott, A., 1986, p 89, my italics)

[N]ucleic acids first has for thirty-five years had virtually no experimental backing (Fox, 1988, p 53-54)

RNA and its components are difficult to synthesize in a laboratory under the best of conditions, much less under plausible prebiotic ones. For example, the process by which one creates the sugar ribose, a key ingredient of RNA, also yields a host of other sugars that would inhibit RNA synthesis. .... Once RNA is synthesized, it can make new copies of itself only with a great deal of help from the scientist. (Horgan, 1991, p 119)

Finally, nucleotides are unstable in solution and tend to break down (hydrolyze) relatively quickly back into their components. These difficulties with nucleotides caused evolutionary theorists to postulate other means of storing hereditary information.

Determined efforts have failed to turn up pathways suitable for the production of abundant supplies of nucleotides on the early earth. Consequently, the first life forms probably stored their genetic information in some chemical system simpler than nucleic acids. (Shapiro, 1986, p 186)

---

[24] "We have had even less success in explaining the origin of the vital gene-protein link. The theories are woefully vague and inadequate and the experimental evidence is virtually nil." (Scott, A., 1986, p 88)

Proteins or Clay

Some evolutionists say the first organism was only "protein" or a "proteinoid" material. These terms are misleading, since evolutionists are referring to polymerized amino acids, not protein. Biological protein has special handedness, bonding, sequence, and types of amino acids. Protein is not merely a random amalgamation of amino acids.

Robert Shapiro wrote a book proposing a protein-first origin of life. His concept is more accurately described as a conviction that the nucleic-acid first theories are unrealistic. But he gives few hopeful details about his protein-first idea. In fact, after examining both the nucleic-acid first and the protein first theories, Shapiro laments:

> [S]elf-replicating systems capable of Darwinian evolution appear too complex to have arisen suddenly from a prebiotic soup. This conclusion applies both to nucleic acid systems and to hypothetical protein-based genetic systems. (Shapiro, 1986, p 207)

A major problem with protein-first theories is that protein cannot replicate.

*

Freeman Dyson wrote a book on the origin of life, suggesting that collections of proteins can somehow "metabolically reproduce." He explicitly tries to get around the problem of error catastrophe.

> The model overcomes the error catastrophe by abandoning exact replication. (Dyson, 1985, p 52)

He speculates that the "metabolism" of a collection of "proteins" might be extremely tolerant of errors. He suggests, without evidence, that these "metabolic cycles" as he calls them, might tolerate *25 percent replication error each generation.*[25]

It is doubtful whether amino acid polymers could "reproduce" with the 75 percent accuracy that Dyson suggests. He acknowledges his concept is not supported by experimental evidence.

> The major obstacle that we face in constructing a realistic theory is the fact that we have no experimental information about possible metabolic cycles that are substantially simpler than the very complicated cycles we see in modern organisms. The primeval metabolic cycles must have been simpler than the modern ones but we do not know what they were. *We do not even have plausible candidates for the rudimentary enzymes which must have been the ultimate ancestors of modern enzymes.* (Dyson, 1985, p 44, my italics)

*

---

[25] It is questionable that such a high error rate would even qualify to be called replication.

Origin-of-life theorists jettison every function of a cell except replication. They cling to replication as though it contained some magic ingredient that solves all the problems. The reason is clear: They wish to hand the problems over to natural selection.

Theorists have difficulty stretching their hypothetical first organism to within reach of natural selection. Dyson, on the other hand, is stretching natural selection to reach the first organism.

He does this by presuming the Darwinian mechanism will operate as long as *something* (virtually anything at all) results from a chemical reaction. The original molecules are then said to have "replicated," and natural selection operates on the 'daughter molecules' (whatever they may be). In a move that would surprise most evolutionists, Dyson gives up highly precise replication as a requirement for Darwinism. His concept shows the remarkable flexibility of natural selection theory.

*

The difficulties with nucleic acids and proteins caused some theorists to propose even wilder scenarios. Graham Cairns-Smith claims the first replicating organism contained *no organic molecules at all*, but instead was made of micro-crystalline, inorganic, mineral clay. His concept is a radical move away from organic molecules and the prebiotic experiments previously felt to supply them. The main factor driving his theory is the substantial evidence against other naturalistic theories.

*

Some evolutionists have stepped forward to flatly admit the difficulties in the idea that life originated naturally.

> In truth, the mechanism of almost every major step, from chemical precursors up to the first recognisable cells, is the subject of either controversy or complete bewilderment. (Scott, A., 1985, p 30)

> [E]very [origin-of-life] scenario offered by the materialist [theorists] of any school is invalid since they conflict with biological or mathematical facts.[26] (Yockey, 1986, p 44)

---

[26] In intimate association with this citation Yockey gives a definition of "materialist creationist" which virtually no creationist or evolutionist would endorse. In his usage it is someone who believes that life had a materialistic, naturalistic origin. His usage is confusing so I have substituted the word "theorists" in the citation.

Francis Crick (co-winner of the Nobel prize for the discovery of DNA) is well-acquainted with the complexities of cell replication. Crick felt sufficiently moved by the problem to write a book suggesting the theory of directed panspermia — the notion that <u>life did not originate on earth but instead was sent here as bacteria from outer space</u>. Recognizing that our knowledge is incomplete, he compares the origin of life to a miracle.

> An honest man, armed with all the knowledge available to us now, could only state that in some sense, the origin of life appears at the moment to be almost a miracle, so many are the conditions which would have had to have been satisfied to get it going.[27] (Crick, 1981, p 88)

Crick's notable coworker, Leslie Orgel, also supports directed panspermia. According to *Scientific American*, "Orgel, says ... directed panspermia, was 'sort of a joke.' But he notes that it had a serious intent: to point out the inadequacy of all explanations of terrestrial genesis."[28]

There are others proponents of directed panspermia. For example, Sir Fred Hoyle (the renowned British astronomer) and his colleague Chandra Wickramasinghe began their careers as ardent evolutionists. Yet their research led them to disavow naturalistic mechanisms for the origin of life or for evolution. They have written several books proposing their own theory of directed panspermia. They feel subsequent evolution was due to the absorption of genes raining down on earth from outer space.[29]

---

[27] This was not a new position for Francis Crick. He stated essentially the same thing ten years earlier. "A rational man, having only the information we have at the present day, might reasonably conclude that the origin of life is a miracle, but this again reflects our ignorance on the subject." (Crick, as quoted in Sagan, 1973, p 52)

[28] Horgan, 1991, p 125

[29] Hoyle and Wickramasinghe, 1981

Biologic Universals

Biologic universals are the biochemical and biological similarities that unify life. These had been a classic evidence for evolution.

> [T]he finding of the same genetic code in microbes, plants, and animals (except for minor variations in intracellular organelles) spectacularly confirms a strong evolutionary prediction. (Davis, 1985, p 256)

> The unity of life is no less remarkable than its diversity. Most forms of life are similar in many respects. The universal biologic similarities are particularly striking in the biochemical dimension. .... What do these biochemical or biologic universals mean? They suggest that life arose from inanimate matter only once and that all organisms, no matter how diverse in other respects, conserve the basic features of the primordial life. (It is also possible that there were several, or even many, origins of life; if so, the progeny of only one of them has survived and inherited the earth.) But what if there was no evolution, and every one of the millions of species was created by separate fiat? However offensive the notion may be to religious feeling and to reason, the antievolutionists must accuse the Creator of cheating. They must insist that He deliberately arranged things exactly as if his method was evolution, intentionally to mislead sincere seekers of truth. (Dobzhansky, 1973, p 23, his parenthesis)

This was one of evolution's major illusions. Evolution does not predict biologic universals.

- First, evolution does not predict that life would arise precisely once on this planet.[30] If there were two or more unrelated systems of life, then evolutionary theory would effortlessly accommodate that situation. (This is parenthetically acknowledged by Dobzhansky.)

- Second, even if life originated precisely once, then evolutionary theory would still not predict biologic universals. Shortly after life's origin, nothing prevented life from branching and leading separate lineages to higher life forms entirely lacking the known biologic universals.

- Third, evolutionary loss and replacement processes could prevent biologic universals. If one organism is a distant ancestor to another, then nothing in evolution predicts the two must share similarities. If evolution were true, then distant ancestors and descendants (as well as sister groups) can be totally different.

---

[30] In fact, Freeman Dyson's theory for the origin of life specifically claims that "life had a double origin" (Dyson, 1985, p 27). According to his theory the first origin was for protein life and the second was for nucleic-acid life which then became parasitic on protein life.

Evolution never did predict biologic universals, it merely accommodated them.[31]

In fact, evolutionists are on the horns of a dilemma. They have rejected each of the biologic universals. They insist that *other* life forms must have existed on this planet. They postulate the earthly existence of life bearing no resemblance to anything known today:

> life without DNA,
> life without predominantly left-handed amino acids,
> life without predominantly α-bonded amino acids,
> life without the twenty proteinous amino acids,
> life without ribosomes,
> life without the genetic code,
> life without RNA,
> life without the bi-layered phosphatide construction of cell membranes,
> life without any membrane of any kind,
> life without any enzyme known today,
> life without protein,
> ... the list goes on.

Cairns-Smith is quite direct: "To conclude, the unity of biochemistry does not refer to the start of evolution but to a much later stage."[32] Shapiro insists that we may yet find living organisms on earth that contain protein but no DNA or RNA of any kind.

> Much more dramatic and to the point would be the discovery of living relics, survivors of the original protein-based system that are alive and functioning on our planet today. Microbiologists often deny the possibility of such a discovery, maintaining that such creatures would already be known, if they existed at all. But this need not be the case. .... Somewhere on this planet, perhaps in localities depleted in phosphate, survivors from the era of protein life may yet persist. (Shapiro, 1986, p 293)

Cairns-Smith is even more emphatic about the existence of crystalline clay organisms.

> Evolution did not start with the organic molecules that have now become universal to life: indeed I doubt whether the first organisms, even the first evolved organisms, had any organic molecules in them at all. (Cairns-Smith, 1985, p 107)

---

[31] Francis Crick writes, "Such an astonishing degree of [biochemical] uniformity was hardly suspected as little as forty years ago". (Crick, 1981, p 47) Historically the discovery of biologic universals was followed, *virtually immediately*, by their rejection from the presumed hypothetical first organism. They were too complicated to have been in the first organism. Thus, at no time did evolutionary theory truly predict biologic universals.

[32] Cairns-Smith, 1985, p 91

He believes "it is quite possible" that crystalline clay organisms "are indeed all around us."[33]

*

Origin-of-life theorists rejected the biologic universals, while main-stream evolutionists claimed biologic universals as a major prediction of evolution. This contradiction existed for decades, yet it was successfully hidden. The contradiction went unnoticed because evolutionists artificially separated the origin of life from its subsequent evolution — as though the two were unrelated problems.[34]

This 'false separation' was their strategy at the Arkansas creation-science trial (Act 590), as noted by the judge.

> Although the subject of origins of life is within the province of biology, the scientific community does not consider origins of life a part of evolutionary theory. The theory of evolution assumes the existence of life and is directed to an explanation of *how* life evolved. (Overton, 1982, part IV(B))

This false separation concealed the contradiction, so evolutionists continued to present biologic universals as evidence in their favor.

*

Dobzhansky said the designer of life must be accused of cheating because "He deliberately arranged things exactly as if his method was evolution, intentionally to mislead sincere seekers of truth." Dobzhansky was mistaken.

Nowhere is his error greater than on this very issue: the unity of life. Message theory says all life was constructed to look like the unified work of a single designer. This prediction is fulfilled in biologic universals and the unity of every living being.

Evolutionary theory does not predict anything either way about biologic universals. It is compatible with any outcome. It is completely flexible on the matter.

Despite this unrestricted flexibility, evolutionists have been forced to retreat. Science (together with probability arguments) shows that nothing resembling known life could have directly originated naturalistically. Evolutionists want to protect naturalism, so they claim the first life forms were unlike anything known.

So where are those alternative life forms? Why haven't they been found? Message theory predicts they will never be found because they never existed. Message theory is an explanatory, testable theory. It is science. Evolutionary theory is falsified or unfalsifiable — either way it is not science.

---

[33] Cairns-Smith, 1985, p 100

[34] For example Gould, 1987e, p 18; Christensen, 1984, p 67; Scott, E. C., 1990, p 16

Biochemical Predestination

In the 1960s, evolutionists felt life's origin occurred about 4 billion years after the Earth formed. Recent fossil evidence pushes back the earliest appearance of life, so there is less time available for the origin of life. The new evidence indicates life appeared on Earth rather quickly, at most a few hundred million years after the crust solidified from a molten state.[35] A few hundred million years — not 4 billion — is the maximum time available for life's origin on Earth.

As the available time decreased, the probability arguments became even more compelling. Evolutionists are now caught in a serious time squeeze. Stephen Gould misreads that message and asserts that life was "chemically destined to be."

> … I don't know what message to read in this timing but the proposition that life, arising as soon as it could, was chemically destined to be, and not the chancy result of accumulated improbabilities. (Gould, 1990, p 6)

That idea — known as biochemical predestination — is becoming popular as evolutionists abandon the idea that life arose by chance.[36]

The original idea of biochemical predestination was thrown out in the nineteenth century because it relied on mystical forces, incompatible with the mechanistic view of nature that emerged after Newton and Darwin.

The modern revived version claims that life was destined to arise by "self-organization" due to the inner structure of naturalistic processes.[37] It claims unknown processes for the origin of life, while somehow claiming they are "naturalistic." It merely replaces the old unknown mystical forces with new unknown "naturalistic" forces. Either way, it is not science.

Evolutionists are not moving toward science, they are moving away from science. They retreat as science advances.

---

[35] Gould, Luria, and Singer, 1981, p 693; also Gould, 1990, p 6

[36] Conventional evolutionists still argue that the origin of life is predominantly the result of chance. Yet Gould (1992d, p 119) says that "no scientist has used that argument for 20 years, now that we understand so much more about the self-organizing properties of molecules and other physical systems." Gould is mistaken. Though he embraces biochemical predestination, most evolutionists have not. Most still feel that chance is the essential, key ingredient in the major steps leading to life. The experiments that show "self-organization" of molecules are woefully inadequate to explain life, and are typically irrelevant to the situation on Earth, since they require conditions that did not plausibly exist here. Nonetheless, evolutionists are moving toward biochemical predestination because they are desperate for answers — the probability arguments show that 'chance' is inadequate.

[37] An example of extreme speculation on biochemical predestination is given by Berra, "Is new life still being evolved from nonliving components today? Unlikely, but *because of the nonrandom, self-ordering properties of amino acids, the new life may be indistinguishable from the old life.*" (Berra, 1990, p 80, my italics)

Summary

The classical prebiotic experiments assume conditions that scientists now doubt existed on Earth. Scientists doubt the existence of a primitive reducing atmosphere and an abundant primordial soup.

Exploration by spacecraft and radiotelescopes has failed to support evolutionary expectations of extraterrestrial life. We remain the only known life in the universe.

The Big Bang indicates that life cannot be infinitely old. So, the origin of life must be explained within a limited time. The limited time makes probability a powerful weapon against evolutionary speculation. The evolutionists' use of an 'infinitude of other universes' (the anthropic principle) is an unscientific attempt to protect naturalism from the facts.

For decades, biologic universals were claimed as evidence of evolution, yet evolutionary theory never predicted them; it merely accommodated them. In fact, the evidence has forced evolutionists to retreat. They now tacitly acknowledge that no major feature of known life could have directly originated through known processes aided by chance. They now claim that numerous life forms *without* the biologic universals must have existed on this planet. The absence of such life forms is compelling evidence against that claim.

Evolutionists are squeezed between the advance of science and their commitment to naturalism. That squeeze caused evolutionary thinking to splinter in many directions. Now, evolutionists suggest the first life was crystalline clay, or came from Space, or that life was somehow biochemically predestined to occur. Now, informed Nobel laureates refer to the origin of life as a miracle.

One by one, the alternatives to an intelligent designer have been eliminated from science, beginning with the broadest, simplest, and most testable. As this happened, evolutionary theorists moved onward to their less desirable alternatives. As science advances, the evolutionists retreat, revamping their claims accordingly as they go. They are not moving toward science. (After, all, evolutionary theory is so flexible it offers little guidance.) Rather, the theorists move away from science, since they must keep their 'claims' one step ahead of being falsified.

Evolutionary theory never predicts anything. It is a vast smorgasbord that theorists accommodate to the data. Is evolutionary theory falsified? Or unfalsifiable? Either way, it is not science.

Paley's theory for the origin of life is confirmed by modern science. The watch-like design in the simplest of living organisms demands a designer. In addition, message theory says life was designed to look like the work of a *single* designer. The biologic universals serve this purpose beautifully. All life is united intentionally by design, and biologic universals make this unity unmistakable. Message theory predicts that no life will be found substantially unlike known life. Message theory is testable science.

4

Survival of the Fittest

Adaptations are complex biological designs, such as eyes, hair, and wings. We must account for these. Nothing else in the universe tugs so strongly at us for an explanation.

> The complexity of living organisms is matched by the elegant efficiency of their apparent design. If anyone doesn't agree that this amount of complex design cries out for an explanation, I give up. (Dawkins, 1986, p ix)

The creationist, William Paley, said adaptations are like the complex designs of a pocketwatch and demand an intelligent designer. His reasoning — known as the argument from design — cannot easily be ignored. The argument from design was widely accepted by scientists in the 1800s.

Darwin knew evolutionary theory would need to solve the problem of adaptation.

> The main task of any theory of evolution is to explain adaptive complexity, that is, to explain the same set of facts which Paley used as evidence of a Creator. (Maynard Smith, 1972, p 82)

> No evolutionary theory can be considered successful unless it contains an explanation for adaptation. (Minkoff, 1983, p 171)

Darwin proposed natural selection as a naturalistic explanation of adaptation. Also known as survival of the fittest, it is the central mechanism of Darwinism: the theory of common descent or descent with modification.

> Darwinian evolution explained the intricate design in animals that had so amazed Paley. (Wilson, D. B., 1983b, p 15)

The twentieth century embellished the theory with the new science of population genetics, calling it neo-Darwinism. Yet the essence of the theory is unchanged. Its central strengths and weaknesses remain as they were in Darwin's day.

Evolutionists proclaim that Darwin's theory is a scientific solution of biological adaptation. This chapter will show their claim to science is mistaken. Natural selection is actually defined many different ways. The theory has many formulations, each with its own downfall. The illusion that 'natural selection is science' is created by shifting between the formulations to meet any objection.

Tautology

A **tautology** is a definition masquerading as higher knowledge. A tautology is a statement true by virtue of its logical form alone. Because of its redundancy it is true by definition. A simple example is "All hats are hats."

We sometimes use tautologies for emphasis, for poetic effect, or for humor. Common examples are, "Boys will be boys" and "Enough is enough."

Though tautologies are sometimes amusing, they are not science. Science tries to explain effects in terms of their causes. As cause and effect are different, the two sides of a causal explanation cannot be the same. In a tautology the cause and effect are the same. Therefore there is no explanation. A tautology gives the appearance of being explanatory when, in fact, it is not. An example is when the doctor says, "Your father's deafness is caused by hearing impairment." This is a major objection to tautologies: they do not explain anything.

Another objection is that tautologies are not falsifiable. They are always true, in all possible universes, by definition. There is no conceivable observation that could refute a tautology. Tautologies are not testable.

> Tautologies are fine as definitions, but not as testable scientific statements — there can be nothing to test in a statement true by definition. (Gould, 1983b, p 142)

Tautologies give the mistaken appearance of conveying knowledge. Yet they are neither explanatory nor testable, so they are not science. They are dangerous because they masquerade as knowledge, while conveying no useful information.

Tautologies are most dangerous when they are unobvious and thereby escape our detection. In such cases we must unmask the tautology by plugging in the definitions of the words. Then the circular definition of a tautology becomes clearer.

*

The tautology objection is a classic argument against Darwinism.

> The charge of tautology, if true, would be a devastating indictment of the claim that evolutionary theory is acceptable as science. (Caplan, 1985, p 25)

Natural selection is often formulated as a tautology. Natural selection is survival of the fittest, and the tautology hinges on the word *fittest*. When the fittest are identified by their survival then there is a tautology. We ask, who are the fittest? We are told, the survivors. We ask, who will survive? We are told, the fittest. Natural selection is then "the survival of the survivors." It is a tautology.

*

The tautology problem causes evolutionists to disagree among themselves about how natural selection should be formulated.

Gould writes, "Natural selection is defined by Spencer's phrase 'survival of the fittest', ..."[1] In later editions of *The Origin of Species,* Darwin himself endorsed this definition.

---

[1]   Gould, 1983b, p 141

Michael Ruse calls Spencer's phrase "a disastrous qualification which led straight to all of the silly arguments about selection being tautological."[2]

Ernst Mayr calls Spencer's phrase "rather unfortunate," but adds, "Repeated attempts were made in the ensuing years [since Darwin] to find a better term than either natural selection or survival of the fittest, but none was successful."[3]

> The inability of Darwinists to persuasively describe and defend their theory as scientific has, over the years, done much to discredit the theory in the eyes both of other scholars within the academy and among the general public.[4] (Caplan, 1985, p 25)

*

Thomas Bethell attacked natural selection as a tautology, and Gould acknowledges there is some truth to the charge.

> Although I will try to refute Bethell, I also deplore the unwillingness of scientists to explore seriously the logical structure of arguments. *Much of what passes for evolutionary theory is as vacuous as Bethell claims.* Many great theories are held together by chains of dubious metaphor and analogy. Bethell has correctly identified the *hogwash surrounding evolutionary theory.* (Gould, 1983b, p 141, my italics)

*

John Maynard Smith acknowledges that natural selection is often formulated tautologically.

> It therefore seems to me absurd to argue that the theory is tautological, *though I readily admit that it is often formulated tautologically.* (Maynard Smith, 1972, p 88, my italics)

*

Even more surprising is the admission by Waddington that natural selection is a tautology. This is together with his sorely mistaken suggestion that when clearly formulated a tautology can have "enormous power as a weapon of explanation."

> Natural selection, which was at first considered as though it were a hypothesis that was in need of experimental or observational confirmation, turns out on closer inspection to be a tautology, a statement of an inevitable although previously unrecognized relation. It states that the fittest individuals in a population (defined as those which leave the most offspring) will leave the most offspring. Once the statement is made, its

---

[2]   Ruse, 1982, p 331

[3]   Mayr, 1982, p 519

[4]   Caplan then tried to defend natural selection by giving a derivation of natural selection. In the section, *Derivations of Natural Selection,* I show that such an approach fails to establish natural selection as science.

> truth is apparent. This fact in no way reduces the magnitude of Darwin's achievement; only after it was clearly formulated, could biologists realize the enormous power of the principle as a weapon of explanation. (Waddington, 1960, p 385)

*

Singleton defends natural selection by arguing that tautologies are not really so bad.

> [A]ll tautologies are not meaningless; indeed many logical arguments are compelling because of their tautological nature. (Singleton, 1987, p 331)

Singleton has misunderstood the problem. He is correct that tautologies are compelling — they are totally compelling. They are *always true*, by definition. The problem is that they masquerade as useful knowledge when they contain none. They pretend to explain, but they are void of explanation. They do not reveal anything about the empirical world. They are neither testable nor explanatory, therefore they are not science.

*

Natural selection says, "the adapted individuals will survive." If adaptation and survival are synonymous, then natural selection is a tautology. To demonstrate an absence of tautology, evolutionists must show that adaptation and survival are different concepts. They must show that adaptation can be measured *independently of survival.* In a direct rebuttal to the tautology objection Norman Newell writes:

> Adaptation and survival are different concepts. The comparative utility of a trait within a particular environmental context can be assessed and *the way in which this trait spreads or diminishes in a population is* a test of the pressure of natural selection and *a measure of adaptation.* (Newell, 1982, p 167, my italics)

He claims that adaptation and survival are different concepts. Yet he next says the way a trait survives (spreads or diminishes) in a population is a measure of adaptation. The two concepts are then the same. Contrary to Newell's intention, he has provided a tautology.

*

Douglas Futuyma also unintentionally gives a tautology.

> Natural selection is merely the replacement of the less able by the more able. Able at what? At survival and reproduction. (Futuyma, 1983, p 211)

Replacement in his context is just a different word for survivorship. So, we may substitute *survivorship* into his statement along with his definition of *able.* His statement then becomes, "natural selection is merely the survivorship of the less able to survive by the more able to survive." With this we see he has given a tautology.

*

100

Robert Chapman gives a definition that leads to tautology.[5]

> The ability of an organism to leave more surviving progeny is termed evolutionary fitness [T]. (Chapman, 1983, p 109)

Natural selection claims to identify the survivors. Which progeny survive? Chapman's answer: The progeny of those organisms who leave more surviving progeny. That is a tautology.

*

Philip Kitcher gives the following example.

> [O]ne may see, for example, that a certain pair of alleles drastically reduces the chances of survival. So, for all practical purposes, it may be possible to assign selective values to allelic pairs .... When we can specify values of fitness that is because it is possible to hold constant the variables on which fitness generally depends. (Kitcher, 1982, p 20)

Kitcher says that under precise conditions (not commonly met in nature) we may specify values of fitness (selective values) based on the chances of survival. Nonetheless, the fitness values are completely determined by measuring the 'chances of survival.' He measures fitness by measuring survival. This definition of fitness turns natural selection into a tautology.

Tautological fitness is when fitness is defined as survival, thereby making natural selection a tautology. Tautological fitness is measurable, in a sense, since survival can be measured. Theorists are often using tautological fitness when they say fitness is measurable. Kitcher did that in his example.

*

In summary, when natural selection is a tautology, it is not science because it is neither explanatory nor testable. Nonetheless, it can mislead us in three ways:

1) It masquerades as an explanation when it is not.

2) It is 'always true' (by definition) and thereby captures our confidence.

3) Tautological fitness is observable and measurable, therefore it seems like empirical science.

---

[5] Robert Chapman states, "Evolutionary fitness may have nothing to do with physical strength or other characteristics that we usually associate with the term fitness." His statement is odd. (Evolutionists generally say fitness has *everything* to do with the characteristics of the organism.) Yet it does follow directly from his tautological definition of fitness.

Fitness — the Special Definition

A way out of the tautology objection is with a special definition. A special definition is when a theory (or keyword) is specially defined for each case.

Special definitions are made by redefining *fitness* for each given case, resulting in a **special definition of fitness.** In one instance fitness is 'cryptic coloration.' In the next it is 'high speed.' In the next it is 'small size.' In the next it is 'aggressive behavior,' and so forth. Most everything has been used in special definitions of fitness. Each instance of organism and environment receives its own special definition.

Special definitions are not tautologies. Yet a theory made of more than one definition (and especially contradictory definitions) is not science. A theory cannot be tested when redefined for every case. Special definitions are a multitude of disjointed, conflicting explanations masquerading as a single, unified theory.

Here is an example from Kitcher.

> Naturalists can watch predators at work. They can record the relative numbers of captures involving well-camouflaged moths and those that stand out from their surroundings. Moreover, they can eliminate other possible reasons for differential reproductive success. For example, it is possible to show that protective coloration makes no difference in fecundity, survival of larvae, or ability to mate. Thus they confirm the claim that the success results from the protection afforded by cryptic coloration. (Kitcher, 1982, p 59)

At Kitcher's last sentence, fitness is defined to mean 'cryptic coloration.' This concept is definite, measurable, explanatory, testable, demonstrable, and non-tautologous. It seems to have all the good things one could want in science. Yet, it is a special definition given specially for this case. His concept is false for most other organisms and environments.

*

Futuyma discusses a case where a bacterial colony has acquired a mutation giving it resistance to (i.e., survivability in) the antibiotic streptomycin.

> If the bacteria encounter streptomycin, the mutation is clearly adaptive; if they don't, it isn't. (Futuyma, 1983, p 137-138)

Futuyma uses two distinct special definitions of *adaptive*: one if the bacteria encounter streptomycin and another if they do not.

*

Warren Dolphin seems to advocate special definitions.

> Natural selection is only definable within the context of an organism, a trait, and an environmental component. (Dolphin, 1983, p 27)

*

In summary, special definitions are non-tautologous, explanatory, testable, and true for a narrow special case. Yet they have two drawbacks:

1) They are false for the general case.
2) They do not unify our understanding of nature in the manner claimed of natural selection.

Metaphysical Fitness

There is an alternative to tautologies and special definitions — metaphysics.

Metaphysical explanations rationalize the empirical world, but they are untestable. Therefore they are not science. Classical myths and religions are typically metaphysical. Their untestability arises because the essential ideas are unempirical, or lack firm coherent structure.

Astrology is a metaphysical theory. It claims to identify an intimate relationship between planetary motion and human personality. Yet it provides no coherent structure to that relationship. Astrology is flexible to interpretation and cannot be tested.

If you claim to disprove astrology, then the proponent may always say, "No you haven't falsified astrology, because you didn't apply the ideas correctly. You didn't consider all the proper phases of the right moons; the rising and setting of the correct stars; or the precession of the Earth." In this way, the proponent of a metaphysical theory may always protect it from being inconvenienced by the facts. Astrology does not have enough structure to hold it accountable to test.

*

Metaphysical fitness is when *fitness* is a combination of countless factors. Fitness is large size for combat, but it is also small size for hiding. Fitness is high-speed for catching and escaping, but it is also slow-speed for energy conservation. Fitness is genes that replicate faster than other genes, but it is also genes that replicate only as needed, to conserve genetic material. Fitness is sending out millions of seeds, but it is also sending out only a few specialized seeds. All these and more are heaped onto *fitness* making it less like a special definition or tautology. In the end, fitness becomes an unmeasurable quantity. The concept is esoteric. It is not empirical.

*

Darwin usually enunciated natural selection as a metaphysical explanation.

> Owing to this struggle for life, *any variation, however slight* and *from whatever cause proceeding,* if it be *in any degree profitable* to an individual of any species, in its *infinitely complex relation to other organic beings and to external nature,* will tend to the preservation of that individual, and will generally be inherited by its offspring. The offspring, also, will thus have a better chance of surviving, for, of the many individuals of any species which are periodically born, but a small number can survive. I have called this principle, by which each slight variation, if useful, is preserved, by the term of Natural Selection, in order to mark its relation to man's power of selection. (Darwin, 1859, p 115, my italics)

We cannot possibly investigate "infinitely complex relations" between an organism and its environment. Darwin repeats this phrase often in his writings. He felt the idea of infinite steps and complexity strengthened his argument.[6] It did make his concept explanatory; the problem is it made his concept untestable.

---

[6] Brady, 1979, p 600-620

Darwin frequently made an analogy between natural selection and artificial selection. Because of the analogy he did not have to define fitness (or "beneficial variation" as he often called it). To a pigeon breeder, a pigeon's fitness is whatever the breeder defines it to be. If breeding for large size, then fitness is large size. If breeding for bright coloration, then fitness is bright coloration. By using the analogy of artificial selection Darwin could discuss his concept without providing a useful definition of fitness.[7] By avoiding a definition of fitness Darwin's artificial selection analogy obscured the true nature of his theory.

*

Suppose your data falsifies natural selection. The proponent may say you have not falsified it at all, it was your misapplication of the concept that resulted in error. Suppose you have kept accurate measurements of one hundred important organism features and environmental factors. With these measurements you show the unfit organisms survived instead of the fit. To all this the proponent may reply, "Aha! In your calculation of fitness you obviously left out many important features and factors." To be helpful, the proponent may offer a list of these, with examples where each is quite important.

In fact, that has happened.

Mayr wrote, "one can never assert with confidence that a given structure does not have selective significance."[8]

Simpson remarked, "The fallibility of personal judgements as to the adaptive value of particular characters, most especially when these occur in animals quite unlike any now living, is notorious."[9]

Dobzhansky stated it even stronger, concluding, "[No biologist] can judge reliably which characters are neutral, useful, or harmful in a given species."[10]

These evolutionists have highlighted the metaphysical, unfalsifiable nature of natural selection. The context of their statements is significant. In each case these evolutionists are defending the theory against the charge that non-adaptive structures and trends actually exist in nature. They are defending against the charge that the theory is in error. They defend by saying that no one can reliably determine fitness. These examples show how Darwinians protect their theory by invoking its metaphysical, unempirical, unfalsifiable nature.

*

In summary, a metaphysical formulation of natural selection is explanatory and non-tautologous. The problem is it is not testable, and therefore it is not science. This arises because metaphysical fitness is not empirical.

---

[7] The lack of definition continues to this day: "[T]he fact is that there is a major problem in the foundations of evolutionary theory which remains unsolved, and which continues to give life to the debate. The definition of fitness remains in dispute, and the role of appeals to fitness in biologists' explanations is a mystery." (Mills, and Beatty, 1984, p 37)

[8] Mayr, 1963, p 190

[9] Simpson, 1953, p 278

[10] Dobzhansky, 1975, p 376-378

Lame Natural Selection

There is an alternative to tautology, special definition, and metaphysics. This fourth group is called lame formulations. **Lame formulations** are sometimes legitimate scientific theories, but they have a downfall: They do not attempt to solve the problem they are claimed to solve. They get their name from their inability to carry the claims made on their behalf.

Lame formulations do not even try to solve the problem of design and adaptation. This was the central problem Darwin set out to solve with natural selection. (So, strictly speaking, lame formulations are not natural selection.)

Lame formulations typically use some concept of **differential survival**: which is just *differences* in survival. Some organisms survive and some do not. Differential survival is an observed fact of nature, but it is lame:

- Differential survival fails to mention adaptation, therefore it cannot explain adaptation.

- Adaptation cannot be explained by saying, "Some organisms live and some die, and the result is adaptation." Differential survival fails to identify the survivors, therefore it lacks the key factor of Darwin's explanation.

*

Ayala provides an example.

> Natural selection can be defined simply as *the differential reproduction of alternative genetic variants,* determined by the fact that some variants increase the chances of survival and reproduction of their carriers relative to the carriers of other variants. (Ayala, 1982, p 88)

Ayala's definition is merely: Genetic variants cause differential survival. There is no explanation of adaptation here.

*

Futuyma gives a similar approach: Differential survival of different variants.

> Natural selection, … is merely a name for any consistent difference in survival or reproduction between genetically different members of a species. (Futuyma, 1983, p 116)

Biological design was not explained.

*

Lewontin offers another version.

> [It is] the Darwinian view that evolution is the conversion of variation between individuals into variation between populations and species in time and space. (Lewontin, 1974, p 12)

*

Evolutionists often argue against the tautology objection by giving a lame formulation.

> But Darwin never spoke in [tautological] terms, arguing only that some variations would confer 'advantage' and that others would be 'injurious'. In fact, if we define natural selection as the *differential contribution of heritable variations to the next generation,* all of Darwin's claims on behalf of selection would be just as valid, even without reference to the 'fittest'. (Minkoff, 1983, p 82)

> The most frequent criticism is that the principle of natural selection is a tautology. .... Our conclusion is that this criticism is trivial because it is due to semantic confusion. Rewording the principle as: 'some genetic variants in a population alter the probability [PC] of survival of descendants' eliminates the problem because such an assertion can be falsified. (Riddiford and Penny, 1984, p 33)

*

Formulations that do not provide direction to evolution are lame. So, this problem would seem to be cured by *defining* natural selection to have direction. SeWall Wright tried this approach.

> Selection is here defined as any process in a population that alters gene frequencies in a *directed* fashion [without mutations or immigration]. (Wright, 1969, p 28, my italics)

Wright's formulation is still lame because it does not identify *which* direction. His concept cannot explain adaptation. It does not even try.

*

In summary, lame formulations can sometimes be science, but they do not explain adaptation. They fail to address the central problem Darwin set out to solve. Differential survival is the most common lame formulation.

Equivocation

Equivocation is when the meaning of words is shifted. Many false arguments use equivocation to convince an audience. Equivocation makes natural selection slippery and provides its apparent scientific power. If natural selection were consistently either tautology, or special definition, or metaphysics or lame, then it would not have lasted so long in the scientific arena.

Natural selection seems like powerful science because 'fitness' is shifted to mean different things. Fitness can appear in three different ways.

- Fitness — one-half a tautology

- Fitness — a special definition

- Fitness — the metaphysical, unmeasurable quantity

By using these definitions 'survival of the fittest' appears as:

T   Tautology — These are undeniably true in all cases, and measurable. Problems: They are not explanatory and not testable.

SD   Special Definition — These are measurable, explanatory, testable, non-tautologous, and true for a particular case. Problems: They are false for the general case; they do not unify nature; they are many disjointed, conflicting theories masquerading as a single unified theory.

M   Metaphysics — These are non-tautologous, explanatory, and perhaps true. Problems: They are unempirical, and untestable.

Alternatively, all references to *fitness* and *adaptation* may be abandoned. Natural selection then appears as:

L   Lame — These are perhaps scientific in every way. Problem: They do not even try to explain adaptation.

The illusion is achieved by shifting between T, SD, M, and L. In this way natural selection can appear to have all the good qualities one could want in science: empirical, measurable, explanatory, general, testable, non-tautologous, and true. This shift can happen rapidly during a book or lecture. Once we understand the principle, watching natural selection in action is like watching the three-shell game at the carnival. One never knows which of the walnut shells the pea will be under next.

Proponents of natural selection have many options during a debate. These options depend on which version (T,SD,M,L) they are using when challenged.

I   If they use T and you object that it is not explanatory, then they may switch to either SD or M, which are both explanatory.

II   If they use SD and you object that it is falsified by a different particular case, then they may switch to another version of SD (one that is not specifically falsified by your particular case) or they may use option III.

III   If they use SD and you object that it is falsified for the general case, then they may switch to either T or M, which are not falsified for the general case (they are 'always true' and 'unfalsifiable' respectively).

IV   If they use M and you object that it is not empirical, then they may switch to either T or SD, which are both empirical.

IV   If they use SD and you object that it provides no unification of nature, then they may switch to either T or M, which are both quite general and unified.[11]

V   If they use either T or M, and you object that it is not testable, then they may switch to SD, which is testable.

VI   If they use either T, SD, or M, and you object for any above reason, then they may switch to a version of L that meets your objection.

VII   If they use L and you object that it does not even attempt to explain adaptation, then they may switch to M or SD, which at least make an attempt. Or they may switch to T, which pretends to be an explanation.

In this way the proponent of natural selection always seems to meet any objections.

This is a bit complicated, but I have found (from many exasperating conversations) that if I do not point out all the angles, then the result is just a more vigorous carnival shell game.

*

In summary, the scientific stature of natural selection is an illusion. The illusion is created by shifting back and forth between various formulations: tautology (T), special definitions (SD), metaphysics (M), and lame formulations (L). Each of these formulations has something that seems like science, but none of them scientifically solves the problem of adaptation and design.

---

[11] Kitcher claimed that natural selection is a unified problem-solving strategy. (Kitcher, 1982, p 46-48) He is mistaken. It is never simultaneously a unified and problem-solving explanation of adaptations.

Speed Shift

The process of shifting back and forth between formulations is eased by using vague and ambiguous keywords that allow the shift to occur without drawing attention. The most notorious of these are words like *fitness, favorable, advantageous, beneficial,* and *adaptive*. These undefined keywords are ready to assume the identity necessary to snatch a formulation from the jaws of a particular line of criticism. These ambiguous keywords are the major method for shifting between formulations.

*

Often a shift occurs by stating different formulations one right after another. This rapid-fire technique creates confusion that conceals the shift. Here is an example from McGowan.

> [S]ome [individuals] are better able to survive than others, and we call these the fittest [T]. This year's criteria for fitness may not be the same as next year's because environmental conditions fluctuate [SD,M]. (McGowan, 1984, p 24)

*

Alternatively, a shift can be concealed by misdirection. Misdirection is achieved by over-emphasizing peripheral issues. The misplaced emphasis takes your vision off the central issue — Is natural selection science? The misdirection is especially effective when ambiguous and confusing.

The most common example of misdirection is the **reproduction conundrum** (denoted as RC). An evolutionist can misdirect by emphasizing reproduction, as though it were a special key to understanding natural selection. It brings to mind technical issues about DNA, genes, and conjugation, that are only peripheral to the central problems with natural selection (T,SD,M,L).

The misdirection is particularly effective when it is ambiguous by using terms like *reproduction* and *reproductive success*. These terms can mean anything from 'high birth rate' (which is a special definition of fitness) to 'population growth rate averaged over many lifecycles' (which is tautological fitness). The reproduction conundrum does not solve the problems. Instead its ambiguity creates further avenues for evasive maneuvering.

For example, Singleton argues against the tautology objection by using the reproduction conundrum (RC). The result is not clarity but confusion.

> First, most scientists today do not define fitness in terms of survival but rather in terms of reproductive success [RC], that is, in terms of leaving one's genes behind in a gene pool. (Singleton, 1987, p 331)

Singleton's statement can be read as T, SD, or M. It is so ambiguous it contains all three. The reproduction conundrum (RC) creates this ambiguity. His emphasis on *genes* and a *gene pool* misdirects readers toward technical issues only peripheral to the problems.

*

Another source of misdirection is the **probability conundrum** (denoted as PC). It misdirects attention by overemphasizing statistics and probability, as though these were a special key to understanding natural selection. It brings to mind mathematical issues that many people find confusing, if not inscrutable. Yet these issues are only peripheral to the problems with natural selection.

For example, "the probable survival of the probable survivors" is still a tautology despite the reference to probability. Also, "the probable survival of those with cryptic coloration" is still a special definition. The reference to probability does not solve the problems.

*

Mayr incorporates all the above factors in his defense of natural selection. His discussion is an excellent example of the rapid-fire, shell game phenomenon.

> Darwin ... has therefore been accused of tautological (circular) reasoning .... To say that this is the essence of natural selection is nonsense! To be sure, those individuals that have the most offspring are by definition the fittest ones [T!]. However, this fitness is determined (statistically) [PC] by their genetic constitution [M]. Let it be clearly understood that what really counts in evolution is not survival but the contribution [T,SD,M] made by a genotype to the gene pool of the next and subsequent generations. Reproductive success [RC] rather than survival is stressed in the modern definition of natural selection. A superior genotype has a greater probability [PC] of leaving offspring than has an inferior one [T,SD,M]. Natural selection, simply, is the differential perpetuation of genotypes [L]. Most of the objections raised against natural selection and its role in evolution become invalid and irrelevant as soon as the typological formulation of natural selection is replaced by one based on the probability [PC] of reproductive success [RC]. (Mayr, 1963, p 183)

*

In summary, shifting between formulations is aided by various factors.

- Vague and ambiguous keywords, such as *fitness favorable, adaptive, advantageous,* and *beneficial,* allow the shift to occur without drawing attention.

- Rapid shifting between formulations can create confusion that conceals the shift.

- Over-emphasis of peripheral issues can misdirect attention, thereby concealing the shift. The reproduction conundrum (RC) and the probability conundrum (PC) are examples. The misdirection is especially effective when it uses ambiguous terms like *reproduction* and *reproductive success.*

Lamarck's Theory

Other than natural selection, the most influential evolutionary mechanism was that of the Frenchman, Jean Baptiste Lamarck. Lamarck's theory was popular from the 1800s through the 1940s. Its central mechanism was Lamarckian inheritance also known as the inherited effects of the use and disuse of parts. The theory claimed that traits acquired (or lost) during life can be inherited into future generations.

The classic example was the giraffe's neck. Giraffes stretch their necks to reach the treetops to eat, and this stretching slightly lengthens their neck. Lamarck's theory suggested this acquired characteristic is inherited by offspring. Over many generations this would have a cumulative effect, so each generation would tend to have longer necks. Supposedly the giraffe eventually got its long neck this way.

Lamarck's theory began its gradual downfall in 1885 when Weismann published his hypothesis of the "continuity of the germ plasm." His hypothesis says that the cells responsible for reproduction (the germ cells) are separate from the body cells (the soma) from early in life, and nothing that happens to the body cells can be communicated to the germ cells for transmission to the next generation.

We now have a sound basis for rejecting Lamarck's theory. First, many sensitive experiments failed to demonstrate it. Second, our modern knowledge of DNA and cell physiology confirms Weismann's hypothesis in detail. We now understand the specific mechanisms preventing the communication of acquired information from the body cells to the DNA of germ cells. Weismann's hypothesis is now well established, despite many attempts to overturn it. These results are incompatible with Lamarck's theory. So, Lamarck's theory is falsified, at least in its classic form, though some evolutionists still actively seek it.

*

Lamarck's old discredited theory is curiously pertinent today. Some evolutionists use Lamarck's theory to argue that natural selection is testable. The argument does not make sense since the two theories are separate. Yet it is a common argument.

Futuyma tries this approach. He feels natural selection would be falsified if Lamarck's theory were shown to be true.

> The neo-Darwinian theory of evolution is also clearly falsifiable because we can postulate theories which, if true, would render neo-Darwinian theory superfluous. The most obvious alternative theory is the Lamarckian one. If it were true that modifications acquired during the life of an organism could become hereditary, many features of organisms would evolve by the direct influence of the environment, and natural selection would not play a major guiding role in adaptation. (Futuyma, 1983, p 172)

111

Futuyma argues that if another evolutionary mechanism (such as Lamarckian inheritance) were 'true,' then natural selection would be 'false,' so natural selection must therefore be falsifiable.

Futuyma is attempting to swap roles with his opponent. He suggests that to disprove natural selection we must prove another evolutionary mechanism. It would then fall on the anti-evolutionist to prove evolution.

Futuyma is mistaken. Natural selection is untestable all on its own, and other rival theories (such as Lamarck's) do not change that status.

*

Gould uses a similar argument.

> 'Survival of the fittest' is not a tautology. It is also not the only imaginable reading of the evolutionary record. It is testable. It had rivals that failed under the weight of contrary evidence and changing attitudes about the nature of life. It has rivals that may succeed, at least in limiting its scope. (Gould, 1983b, p 144)[12]

Natural selection is not made falsifiable by the fact that you do or do not believe it over other explanations. Astrology is not made falsifiable by the fact that physics, physiology, and psychology have 'succeeded in limiting its scope.' Neither success nor failure of rivals changes the status of an unfalsifiable theory.[13]

*

---

[12] At the Nobel Conference XVIII, Sir Peter Medawar acknowledged that he does not know a way to test Darwinism. Stephen Jay Gould then responded, "I can think of ways that would falsify Darwinism on a very broad scale .... If it turned out that mechanisms of heredity, when elucidated, allowed for a Lamarckian mode of transmission, it would have effectively disproved Darwinism — not that Darwinism wouldn't have operated ..." (as recorded in Hamrum, 1983, p 115)

[13] A demonstration of Lamarckian inheritance would not falsify natural selection. Instead it would cause evolutionists to initiate more of their interminable discussion concerning, "Which mechanism has the dominant effect?" Natural selection is unfalsifiable, and the presence or absence of Lamarckian inheritance would not change that fact.

John Maynard Smith argues that a genetic demonstration of either Lamarckist effects, inertial effects, or teleological effects would refute natural selection.[14] Thus, he feels we may falsify natural selection by demonstrating another evolutionary mechanism. This is a no-lose proposition for evolution. Maynard Smith is attempting to swap roles with an opponent.

> I concluded that there were several kinds of observational evidence which could in principle falsify the neo-Darwinian theory. However, much the most effective way of falsifying the theory would be to falsify the genetic theory on which it is based, and in particular to falsify the Weismannist assumption, popularly but loosely expressed by saying that acquired characters are not inherited. (Maynard Smith, 1972, p 1-2)[15]

Maynard Smith is mistaken. Natural selection is compatible with both Weismann's hypothesis and Lamarck's. In fact, "a correct theory of genetics is not a prerequisite for a Darwinian theory of evolution."[16] Evolutionists had created a counterfeit test to make natural selection seem like testable science.

*

Darwin himself embraced Lamarckian inheritance. Darwin was so strongly convinced of its importance that he discussed it for an entire section of chapter V of the *Origin of Species*.

> I think there can be little doubt that use in our domestic animals strengthens and enlarges certain parts, and disuse diminishes them; and that *such modifications are inherited*. (Darwin, 1859, p 175-179, my italics)

Darwin repeatedly affirmed the inheritance of acquired characters.[17] He described how the constant milking of cows leads to an inherited increase in the size of the udder.[18] His belief in this mechanism continued through his later editions and letters. We now know such ideas are mistaken.

Darwin's acceptance of Lamarckian inheritance shows he did not consider it anti-Darwinian. Even Weismann did not see any inherent conflict between natural selection and Lamarckian inheritance.[19]

*

---

[14] Maynard Smith, 1972, p 86

[15] Maynard Smith expresses his same argument today. (For example see his interview in Wolpert and Richards, 1988, p 135)

[16] Brandon, 1984, p 61; also Mayr, 1977, p 325; Mayr, 1991, p 82

[17] Mayr, 1982, p 691

[18] Cited and discussed by Mayr, 1982, p 691-693

[19] Mayr, 1991, p 119

There is more to this issue. Why is Lamarckian inheritance absent from nature? It requires only a simple mechanism. It is compatible with natural selection. It is sufficiently plausible that some evolutionists still actively pursue it.

> We cannot simply dismiss this theory [Lamarckism] as false, for two reasons. First, it is not so obviously false as is sometimes made out. Secondly, it is the only alternative to Darwinism as an explanation of the adaptive nature of evolution. (Maynard Smith, 1989, p 8)

Suppose an animal fractured a bone, and the body responded by augmenting bone tissue at that point. This elevated construction of specific bones could be passed on to offspring by Lamarckian inheritance, thereby offering increased protection from similar injury.

Suppose an organism got a disease, and the body responded immunologically or by making increased levels of certain proteins. These responses could be passed on by Lamarckian inheritance, perhaps to be culled further by natural selection.

Lamarckian inheritance would be a powerful additional mechanism of evolution. Why isn't it here in abundance?

This is an enigma for evolution. Theorists offer countless scenarios for the origin of adaptation. With a sweep of the hand they explain complex features like the eye, consciousness, the genetic code, sex, and the metamorphosis of the butterfly. They leave the indelible impression that if something even minutely benefits evolution, then it will evolve. Lamarckian inheritance could benefit evolution in a major way, and it is so simple a mechanism. *Why isn't it everywhere?*

That problem was concealed by the following logic. Evolutionists said that natural selection explains the data better than Lamarckian inheritance.[20] They also claimed (erroneously) that natural selection would be falsified if Lamarckian inheritance were shown to be true. This created the impression that only one of the mechanisms could operate in nature. So, evolutionists were not concerned by the absence of Lamarckian inheritance. They just didn't see it as a problem. The problem was hidden by faulty logic.

*

---

[20] "The third way of refuting the theory of the inheritance of acquired characters is to show that the phenomena that are claimed to *require* the postulate of an inheritance of acquired characters can be explained equally well or better on the basis of the Darwinian theory. Much of the evolutionary literature of the 1920s, 30s, and 40s was devoted to this third approach." (Mayr, 1982, p 700-701)

Message theory predicts that Lamarckian inheritance should be, at the very most, only a minor part of life's pattern. Message theory says life was designed to convey a biotic message — it was designed to thwart all alternative interpretations. Since Lamarckian inheritance is a simple, plausible mechanism, it seriously threatens the goals of the biomessage sender. The biomessage sender took special care to assure its undoing, by making life unlike Lamarckian inheritance.

*

The major evidence *for* natural selection historically has been the refutation of all competing evolutionary theories,[21] such as Lamarck's theory.[22]

> Nothing strengthened the theory of natural selection as much as the refutation, one by one, of all the competing theories, such as saltationism, orthogenesis, an inheritance of acquired characters, and so forth.[23] (Mayr, 1982, p 840)

This is significant. Natural selection is the only major evolutionary mechanism that is not now falsified — and natural selection is unfalsifiable.

*

In summary, the status of an unscientific theory is not affected by the presence or absence of rivals. The presence of Lamarckian inheritance would not change the status of natural selection. Natural selection remains untestable either way.

Lamarckian inheritance is a simple, plausible mechanism, with real benefit for evolution. Accordingly it should be everywhere, and its absence is a serious problem for evolutionists. That problem was concealed by faulty reasoning.

The broad absence of Lamarckian inheritance is a straightforward prediction of message theory.

---

[21] "Natural selection is credited with seemingly miraculous feats because we want an answer and have no other." (Wesson, 1991, p *xii*)

[22] In the falsificationist view, it is a good sign for an explanation when alternatives are refuted, however such a circumstance does not make the explanation scientific.

[23] Provine correctly points out that the so called "evolutionary synthesis" of the 1930s and 1940s was "scarcely a synthesis at all." It was not characterized by extraordinary new discoveries, concepts, or theories, nor even by agreement on the detailed mechanisms of evolution in nature. Rather, its major feature was the final elimination from biology of all the "purposive" (or purposeful) mechanisms of evolution (such as aristogenesis and *élan vital*) that had been common and popular before 1930. Thus, it was not a synthesis, but a *constriction* of evolutionary theory. Thereafter, evolutionists relied on natural selection, and this more constricted view "hardened" during the late 1940s and 1950s. (Provine, 1988, p 53-62) The motives for that hardening are given by Mayr.

Summary

Formulations of natural selection fall into four groups: tautologies, special definitions, metaphysics, and lame formulations (T, SD, M, L).

- Tautologies are not testable scientific explanations. They are definitions masquerading as explanations.

- Special definitions are a multitude of conflicting explanations masquerading as a single unified theory.

- Metaphysical explanations are not testable, therefore they are not scientific.

- Lame formulations do not even address the problem of adaptation, therefore they cannot solve it.

None of these formulations scientifically solves the problem of adaptation and design.[24]

The illusion that "natural selection is science" was created by shifting back and forth between formulations. The shifting was concealed by various factors:

- Vague and ambiguous keywords (like *fitness*)

- Rapid shifting between formulations

- Over-emphasis of peripheral issues, like reproduction and probability

Evolutionists erroneously read the absence of Lamarckian inheritance as evidence for natural selection. Lamarckian inheritance is a simple, plausible, evolutionary mechanism. It would be a powerful aid to evolution. Its absence is actually a puzzle in evolutionary theory. Moreover, the broad absence of Lamarckian inheritance is a straightforward prediction of message theory. Life was designed to resist all naturalistic explanations of origin, so the absence of Lamarckian inheritance is completely understandable to creationists.

---

[24] A few evolutionists have tried to dispose of testability and redefine science, so as to allow natural selection to count as science. Those attempts have not been successful. (See appendix for details.)

5

Inventive Natural Selection

Before Darwin, the creationists embraced an idea like survival of the fittest to explain the maintenance (not the origin) of healthy populations. In this mode, survival of the fittest eliminated the defective organisms, thereby preventing, or at least slowing, the accumulation of heritable defects in natural populations. This mechanism would preserve the good design of organisms. In this way a relationship between biological design and survival was not foreign to creationists.

Moreover, creationists explained the origin of biological design in a straightforward way: Organisms have 'designs for survival' because they were in fact designed for survival. Once again, creationists recognized a relationship between design and survival.

If survival of the fittest is compatible with creationist views, then why should anyone object to it? The answer puts it in perspective. Survival of the fittest is not the main objection to evolutionary theory, it is only the most fundamental. Since we had to begin our analysis with basics, we began with survival of the fittest. The previous chapter was a warm-up for larger issues. It focused on survival of the fittest: the explanation of why organisms live and die. The idea in itself is harmless.

Yet evolutionists claim that survival of the fittest *creates* adaptation. They say this mechanism operates in a simple way.[1] First, mutation creates new heritable variations, and then survival of the fittest operates on these to create new adaptations. I call that idea *naive natural selection.*

> **Naive natural selection** assumes that survival of the fittest (acting with reproduction and mutation) is *sufficient* to account for the adaptations of life.

This chapter will show that naive natural selection is insufficient to account for adaptation. In reality, evolution requires a vastly more dynamic creative process. I call that process *inventive natural selection,* since it is said to invent adaptations where they did not exist before.

> **Inventive natural selection** is the essential evolutionary mechanism for the origin of life's adaptations. The mechanism includes survival of the fittest (acting with reproduction and mutation) *plus many other mechanisms and assumptions.*

---

[1] Evolutionists often present natural selection as a simple idea. "Natural Selection is a remarkably simple idea" (Ghiselin, 1969, p 46) "[Darwinism] is, indeed, a remarkably simple theory; childishly so" (Dawkins, 1986, p xi) Yet this chapter will show that natural selection, even in its simplest barest essentials, is so convoluted it is not testable, and so not science.

Inventive natural selection is what separates evolutionary theory from any previous creationist concept. Inventive natural selection is the issue between evolution and creation. It is the mechanism of interest. It is what evolutionists ultimately mean by the term "natural selection," so that is how I will use the term henceforth.

This chapter focuses on inventive natural selection. For the sake of discussion we will even assume that survival of the fittest is true, that it actually operates in nature. Yet we can still show that natural selection is not science: it makes no predictions and is untestable.

Moreover, major illusions have been created by shifting back and forth between naive and inventive natural selection. The public was unaware because both had been called "natural selection." This chapter will dismantle these deepest illusions of the Darwinian mechanism.

The Inevitability of Adaptation

Evolutionists claim that adaptation is virtually inevitable. They say natural selection will produce new complex adaptations, given time and the basic resources. They claim that on earth (perhaps throughout the universe) the evolution of major adaptations is essentially unavoidable.

> If the assumptions basic to the theory of natural selection hold true, and if some unknown factors do not intervene, it follows deductively that evolution must occur. (Ghiselin, 1969, p 65)

> So the supposed difficulty in observing the formation of 'an entirely new form of life' has no significance. Given the small changes we see, sufficient time, and the absence of any force to prevent the accumulation of these small changes, evolution on larger and larger scales becomes inevitable. This is due mostly to the combination of mutation and natural selection. (Edwords, 1983, p 11)

> If there ever were, or are now, or ever will be biological entities that satisfy the parent-of relation, anywhere in the universe, then they will evolve in accordance with this theory (or else the theory is false). (Rosenberg, 1985, p 152, his parenthesis)

> But as of the 1980s many scientists are becoming convinced that evolution is not an accident, but occurs necessarily whenever certain parametric conditions are fulfilled. (Lazlo, 1987, p 29)

> The theory of natural selection not only predicts evolutionary change: it also says something about the kind of change. In particular, it predicts that organisms will acquire characteristics that make them better able to survive and reproduce in the environment in which they live. (Maynard Smith, 1989, p 4)

> According to modern textbook descriptions, the appearance of self-replicating entities seems almost as inevitable as the allegedly ubiquitous existence of thermodynamically and compositionally hospitable planets. Subsequent evolution proceeds inevitably in response to selective pressures in a competitive environment with limited resources. Again the result appears almost inevitable: advanced states of sentient, mobile, and manipulative beings, characterized by opposing thumbs and introspective temperaments, disposed to contemplate the events which led to their own existence. And thus, here we are today — it seems almost inescapable. (Levy, 1985, p 5)

Evolutionists are mistaken. Natural selection makes no predictions whatever. It does not predict that adaptations are inevitable, nor even possible. Next we see why.

Uphill Evolution

Imagine that evolution is like a long hill increasing from lower to higher fitness. Natural selection is said to take organisms away from disorder at the bottom of the hill and move them up the hill toward higher fitness and adaptation.

Let me describe this with imagery. Suppose a battalion of soldiers is evolving their way up the hill. When a soldier dies he disappears, and he is more likely to die if he is at the downhill edge of the battalion. The fittest soldiers (furthest up the hill) survive the best, due to survival of the fittest. Also, when a soldier reproduces, he 'multiplies' into two soldiers, and with each slight beneficial change (due to beneficial mutation) a soldier takes a slight step up the hill. This represents how evolution is said to occur: the beneficial is retained and accumulated; the harmful is selected out and removed. The battalion of soldiers marches its way up the hill, inch by inch, step by step — or so evolutionists would have us believe.

Evolutionists reason as follows. Since survival of the fittest, reproduction, and mutation are all facts of nature, the soldiers will inexorably move up the hill toward greater adaptation. Thus, the evolution of higher adaptations is virtually inevitable, they say. This is how evolutionists typically present their theory to the public.[2] It is a major illusion of evolutionary theory. It is naive natural selection.

Naive natural selection overlooks a key factor. As the soldiers are marching up the hill, marbles are rolling down toward them. The marbles represent the effect of harmful biological change (ultimately caused by mutation). The soldiers are then carried backward on a 'conveyor belt' of harmful mutations, while at any given time "the fittest survive" and each soldier is still making uphill steps.[3]

The soldiers are not necessarily marching up the hill, even if we assume they are making uphill steps. The soldiers' net motion depends on a complex balance of forces, upward versus downward. The soldiers can be slipping downhill despite survival of the fittest. Thus, we can assume survival of the fittest is true, without necessarily surrendering to an evolutionary worldview.

There is yet a deeper error with naive natural selection.

---

[2] "[N]atural selection is a process analogous to hill-climbing, in which the best phenotype is reached by a series of steps, each step leading to a type that is fitter than the previous one." (Maynard Smith, 1989, p 7)

[3] A species slowly slipping backwards down the fitness hill is not just a curiosity. I make this concept more concrete, in the chapter Haldane's Dilemma, by analyzing the human species.

The Fitness Terrain

Let us assume the soldiers succeed in moving uphill due to survival of the fittest. Evolution is still not inevitable. Naive natural selection assumes that adaptations are created by a march continually up an inclined slope. In reality, the evolutionary soldiers are not on an inclined slope. They are on a landscape, with hills and valleys, crevasses and mountains. The *contour* makes evolution vastly more complicated.

To aid visualization, let us use Sewall Wright's idea of adaptive topography or **fitness terrain**. As before, imagine a terrain where higher altitude represents higher fitness and adaptation. The directions (east/west and north/south) represent variation in the traits of the organism. The east/west direction might represent the thickness of the fur, with easterly directions being ever thicker fur and westerly directions being thinner fur. The north/south direction would represent another characteristic. Real organisms would be represented by a multi-dimensional terrain, but Wright's model of two-dimensional organisms serves to give us insight.

Each organism is represented by a point on the fitness terrain. The point occurs at a location representing the traits of the organism. The fitness of the organism is then given by the altitude of the terrain at that point. In this way, a population is represented by a cluster of points. As a population evolves, its cluster of points moves along the fitness landscape.[4]

Suppose that when the population comes to a hill, survival of the fittest moves the population up the hill to higher fitness. This hill may only be a small local hill, in which case the population gets stuck on top by survival of the fittest. *Thus, survival of the fittest can prevent evolution from occurring.* Small hills can be traps, preventing the evolution of new adaptations.

> Any population on a submaximal fitness peak is destined to stay there because natural selection will not carry the population down into any of the surrounding valleys and thus, perhaps, into the domain of attraction of a higher fitness peak. The population is simply 'stuck'. (Hartl, 1980, p 335-336)

In the same way, crevasses, canyons, and valleys can form barriers. They can block evolution because survival of the fittest does not allow the population to evolve downward. If the evolutionary paths to new adaptation require prolonged decreases in fitness, then survival of the fittest cannot create adaptation. So, we can assume survival of the fittest is true — and even predominates over other forces — without necessarily surrendering to an evolutionary worldview.

---

[4]   See also Templeton, 1982, p 24-27, or Eldredge and Tattersall, 1982, p 40-43

Naive Natural Selection

As just shown, there are two simple errors in naive natural selection.

- Naive natural selection assumes that survival of the fittest dominates over opposing forces and carries evolution ever upward to higher adaptation.

- Naive natural selection assumes that evolution is a march up a uniform fitness incline, with no significant barriers in the terrain.

There are countless examples of naive natural selection. Evolutionists *always* use it when they argue that natural selection is scientific. They also use it to convince the public that evolution is plausible, if not inevitable.

I offer two examples. To show how evolution works, Ruse uses the familiar analogy of a monkey, sitting at a typewriter, randomly striking the keys. He admits the impossibility of the monkey typing even a portion of *Hamlet* by such random means. Then Ruse says a selection process makes the typing of *Hamlet* seem more possible.

> Suppose, however, that every time the monkey strikes the 'right' letter, it records; but, suppose also that 'wrong' letters get rubbed out (literally or metaphorically!) And suppose the elimination of the wrong letter is the full consequence of a 'mistake': one does not lose what has already been typed. .... The Darwinian's point is that evolution of life occurs in this sort of way. Natural selection allows the successes, but 'rubs out' the failures. (Ruse, 1982, p 308)

Ruse makes the error of naive natural selection. He has unconsciously assumed that evolution is upward, ever upward — due to survival of the fittest. An error in his Shakespeare-monkey analogy is his assertion that "one does not lose what has already been typed."

*

A second example of naive natural selection is Richard Dawkins' book, *The Blind Watchmaker*. The book tries to show that natural selection can blindly construct elegant adaptations. The imagery and arguments of naive natural selection appear throughout. His book is founded on that error.

For example, Dawkins presents the evolution of the eye as a transition of many small intermediate steps "X." He says the transition is plausible if you merely divide it into countless small steps.

> By interposing a large enough series of Xs, we can derive the human eye from something ... *very* different from itself. We can 'walk' a large distance across 'animal space', and our move will be plausible provided we take small-enough steps. .... You might feel that 1,000 Xs is ample, but if you need more steps to make the total transition plausible in your mind, simply allow yourself to assume 10,000 Xs. And if 10,000 is not enough for you, allow yourself 100,000, and so on. (Dawkins, 1986, p 77-78)

Dawkins subtly models evolution as a march up a fitness slope — where many slight small improvements would take organisms up the hill. His discussion only makes sense when interpreted as naive natural selection, since a series of small 'improvements' is no help in getting unstuck from a local fitness hill.

*

In summary, naive natural selection emphasizes survival of the fittest and models evolution as a march continually up a fitness incline. That notion is the basis for most public presentations of evolutionary theory. Naive natural selection is responsible for the threefold illusion that evolution is: (1) simple in concept, (2) virtually inevitable, and (3) scientific.

More Equivocation

Inventive natural selection, even in its simplest essentials, is thoroughly tangled. It depends on a balance of countless forces — uphill versus downhill — and on the fitness terrain: its contour, its peaks and canyons, and the way it warps and deforms. These matters are all unknown, and the theory itself provides no means to predict them. Natural selection is untestable, if not incomprehensible. It is not science.

The illusion that natural selection is scientific was created by shifting to a naive version of the theory. When evolutionists defend "natural selection" as science, they use the term in its *naive* sense to focus on survival of the fittest. They defend survival of the fittest alone. All their defenses take that approach — as shown in the previous chapter.

Evolutionists do not defend inventive natural selection as testable science. *They do not even try.* I cannot find a single instance where evolutionists attempt to defend it as testable. All their defenses fall back on naive natural selection.

Inventive natural selection is essential to evolution. It is the distinctive Darwinian mechanism, yet it is seriously under-represented in the evolutionists' public presentations. This curious situation gives us cause for concern.

*

Yet there are situations where evolutionists shift emphasis. Let me give an example. Evolutionists have promoted naive natural selection so extensively that many people think evolutionary theory entails *progressivism,* the idea that evolution is always upward. Creationists rightly attacked the theory on that basis. They pointed out that humans are poorer at seeing, smelling, running, tracking, and pulling than are the alleged ancestors. This argues against naive natural selection.

Philip Kitcher responded by saying, "According to Creationists, evolutionary theory is committed to progressivism."[5] He then deftly turns this situation around. He charges that creationists have distorted evolutionary theory and misled the unwary public.

> [The Creationists'] criticism rests on a distortion of evolutionary theory. ....
> Creationists foist off on evolutionary theory some assumptions that are
> clearly false. Then they proclaim that the theory makes some false predic-
> tions .... [T]he connections alleged by Creationists are likely to sound
> natural enough to people who have only a superficial acquaintance with
> evolutionary theory. .... [The creationists' arguments] are well adapted to
> deceive the nonspecialist's eye. (Kitcher, 1982, p 74-75)

---

[5]   Kitcher, 1982, p 71-75

Kitcher rebuffs the creationists' argument: (1) by shifting away from naive natural selection; and (2) by pinning the misrepresentations of evolutionary theory onto creationists. Kitcher has it backwards. Evolutionists created naive natural selection. They fostered it as a way to sell evolution, and they profited from it.[6] Kitcher's attempt to blame it on creationists is misplaced.

The Fitness Bag

Natural selection is not a simple unified thing. It is a smorgasbord of disjointed, conflicting mechanisms. From the smorgasbord, evolutionists select whatever mechanisms they think appropriate to explain the origin of a given biological design.

We must now survey the smorgasbord. We must inventory the mechanisms, and place them in relationship one to another. By making this inventory, we will see that natural selection has no internal structure to test. The theory invokes all manner of conflicting mechanisms and is compatible with any of their outcomes.

To help inventory the mechanisms, we will group them into "bags." Let us start with survival of the fittest by putting all its causes into a bag called the *fitness bag*. Into this bag we place all the things contributing to survival of an individual: cryptic coloration, bright coloration, high speed, low speed, large size, small size, and all the many causes of survival. This is the fitness bag. We will be adding other bags shortly.

---

[6] Gould (1990a, p 3-4) laments that most people in the United States feel that evolution means *inevitable, predictable, progressive,* transformation. He seems unaware that evolutionists fostered that idea. He suggests the idea resulted because of our culture and "our hopes for solace in the world we know."

Levels of Selection

There is a modern controversy over the unit of selection: the fundamental entity selected by survival of the fittest. Classical Darwinian theory focuses on the individual organism as the unit of selection, that is, *individual* organisms partake in the struggle for existence and are selected based on their ability to survive.[7] That process of individual selection could not create traits that benefit the survival of anything other than the individual.

Yet some common traits work to the detriment of the individual, and therefore cannot be explained by the classical Darwinian analysis. These are called altruistic traits because they harm the individual, while helping someone or something else.

For example, there are cases where organisms seem to limit their own individual reproduction for the good of their whole species. This altruism is contrary to individual selection and cannot be directly explained by classical Darwinism. This problem of altruistic traits has caused evolutionary theorists to split into factions. There are now major rivals to individual selection: "group selection" and "gene selection."

Group selection argues that sometimes *groups* of organisms are units of selection. Gene selection argues that genes themselves are units of selection, and individual bodies are merely carriers of the genes.

*

Wynne-Edwards, a group selectionist, argued that animals regulate their own population size by assessing the limitations of their environment and regulating their own reproduction accordingly. His theory contradicted individual selection since it required that many individuals altruistically limit their own reproduction *for the good of their group*. In his theory, groups survive better if they regulate their populations by the altruistic acts of group members. The altruistic behavior is then inherited by succeeding generations. Wynne-Edwards gave many more examples of his theory.

Darwinians attempted a two part counter-attack on group selection. First, Darwinians reinterpreted Wynne-Edwards stories of group selection as stories of individual selection. For example, in many flocks of birds the first individual to sight a predator utters a warning cry which causes the flock to scatter. Group selectionists had said this behavior placed the crier at risk yet aided the group. Darwinians offered over a dozen different scenarios that interpret crying as beneficial for the crier.

> The cry may put the flock in random motion, thus befuddling the predator and making it less likely that he will catch anyone, including the crier. Or the crier may wish to retreat to safety but dares not break rank to do it

---

[7] According to Stanley (1981, p 200), "Darwin did not restrict selection to the level of the individual." Stanley also says the subtitle of Darwin's famous book — *On the Preservation of Favoured Races in the Struggle for Life* — speaks of selection above the level of individuals.

126

alone, lest the predator detect an individual out of step. So he cries to bring the flock along with him. As the crier, he may be disadvantaged relative to flockmates (or he may not, as the first to safety), but he may still be better off than if he had kept silent and allowed the predator to take someone (perhaps himself) at random. (Gould, 1980, p 88-89)

The Darwinians were merely countering Wynne-Edwards' group selection story with their own individual selection story.

Darwinians also posed a second strategy against group selection. They argued that acts of altruism are not truly altruistic, but are instead really just selfish acts to propagate the individual's genes through surviving kin. This, they argued, is just another form of individual selection. Darwinians called this "kin selection," and claimed it is distinct from group selection.[8]

For example, your siblings possess half your genes because they are derived from the same parents. For you to die in saving two siblings is to pass on 100% of yourself through *their* reproduction. Analysis like this led to Haldane's famous saying that he would give up his life to save two siblings or eight cousins.

Darwinians had a field day with their scenarios. They retold stories of group selection in terms of either individual selection or kin selection.[9] Nonetheless, these alternatives did not yield a resolution.

> *These alternatives do not disprove group selection*, for they merely retell its stories in the more conventional Darwinian mode of individual selection. The dust has yet to settle on this contentious issue but a consensus (perhaps incorrect) seems to be emerging. *Most evolutionists would now admit that group selection can occur* in certain special situations (species made of many very discrete, socially cohesive groups in direct competition with each other). (Gould, 1980, p 88-89, my italics)

*

Kin and group selection try to explain behaviors that work to the general detriment of the individual. The individual is said to perform its self-sacrificial act only because the behavior has been inherited. The individual behaves "altruistically" because the behaviors are programmed into it. Genes are essential in this process because they code for the behavior (or they code for the capacity by which the behavior is culturally transmitted). The gene is the common denominator between group selection and kin selection. The organism does not intentionally act for the benefit of its group, or its kin, or even itself — the individual ultimately acts for the benefit of genes. This focus on genes inspired another alternative to classical Darwinism.

---

[8] Kin and group selection are different only in degree, not in essential style.

[9] "[K]in selection has broadened the range of permissible stories, but it has not alleviated any methodological difficulties in the process of storytelling itself." (Gould, 1978, p 531)

These theorists assaulted Darwinism by arguing that genes, not individuals, are the unit of selection. They said a body is merely a gene's way of making more genes. Richard Dawkins is a major proponent of this view, known as gene selection.

> We are survival machines — robot vehicles blindly programmed to preserve the selfish molecules known as genes. .... they swarm in huge colonies, safe inside gigantic lumbering robots ... They are in you and me; they created us, body and mind; and their preservation is the ultimate rationale for our existence. (Dawkins, 1976, p ix, 21)

The theory of gene selection says genes (not bodies or groups) are ultimately selected, that genes are the fundamental unit of selection.[10]

Gene selectionists apply their theory to many problems in nature.[11] There are two types of problems for which gene selection seems to predominate: (1) altruistic behavior; and (2) selfish DNA.

Gene selectionists argue that altruistic behavior is ultimately controlled by genes. When an individual risks itself to aid a relative, it is really just genes coming to the aid of other copies of the same genes. *The genes are acting for their own survival* — they are merely using bodies as intermediaries.

The presumption that genes control altruistic behavior gave rise to a conjecture known as the green beard effect. Suppose a certain gene has only two effects:[12]

1)   It gives some identifiable trait X.

2)   It causes the organism to behave altruistically toward any other individual possessing trait X.

Dawkins explains that if such genes exist, then they should increase in the population. If trait X is a green beard, for example, then eventually many people would sport a green beard and behave altruistically toward anyone else with a green beard. Dawkins doubts the likelihood of this, nevertheless he acknowledges that according to evolutionary theory it is theoretically possible.[13]

---

[10] Dawkins, 1976, p 12

[11] The evolutionary explanation of altruistic behavior is dependent on the genetic makeup of the species. Haploidy, diploidy, and haplo-diploidy each has its own effect on the problem. Gene selectionists therefore argue that the problem is most easily understood when approached at the level of the gene. They like to cite explanations that are awkward when approached at the level of the individual or group.

[12] Modern genetics has shown that most genes are pleiotropic, that is, they have more than one effect on the organism.

[13] Dawkins, 1986, p 206-207. See also Dawkins, 1976, p 96

The green beard scenario seems outlandish and unfamiliar at first. But it is actually quite similar to classic sexual selection, where male peacocks sprout large colorful tails to which females are "attracted." These scenarios offer explanations for bizarre traits that often *reduce* the functioning of the organism. According to these scenarios, the strange traits develop because they elicit a favorable response from other organisms.

Selfish DNA is a name for highly repetitive DNA where the same sequence occurs many times in a row. These repetitions are believed to be essentially useless. The phenomenon was a problem for classical Darwinism because such useless junk-DNA should be eliminated by selection.

Gene selection explained selfish DNA as follows. Suppose a particular gene has no effect other than a tendency to cause replication of itself within the organism. This would cause the gene to multiply within the genome of the organism. The gene is merely playing the Darwinian game at the level of the DNA. The gene is furthering its own survival by replicating itself. In a sexually reproducing species, such junk-genes would increase in the population. In this way, selection can actively cause junk-DNA to increase. This increase will be counteracted only when it causes a harmful effect at another level.

*

At one level a trait can increase survival, while at another level the same trait can decrease survival. So there is a 'tug-o-war' between the two levels. It is quite enigmatic. For example, Gould endorses "complex ties of feedback,"[14] "positive and negative interaction between levels," and many levels of structural hierarchy, "including genes, bodies, demes, species, and clades."[15]

Now we need a fitness bag for each of seven levels — genes, bodies, kin, groups, demes,[16] species[17] and clades.[18] Each bag is filled with conflicting causes (including sexual selection and green beard effects). Each bag is also in conflict with the other bags. The fitness bag at the level of genes is in conflict with the fitness bag at the level of bodies, for example. So, imagine we place these discordant fitness bags into a still larger bag called "Multi-Leveled Selection." Here we have metaphysics multiplied.

---

[14] Gould, 1983a, p 175

[15] Gould, 1982b, p 384-385. "My plea for a recognition of selection at levels other than bodies is not a negation of Darwinian theory but an attempt to enrich it." (Gould, 1983a, p 175)

[16] Demes are isolated sub-populations of a species.

[17] Selection at the level of species — called species selection — is where entire species survive or go extinct based on the traits of the species. This mechanism gets special emphasis in the theory of punctuated equilibria.

[18] Clades are collections of similar species.

All academic evolutionists subscribe to selection at multiple levels.[19] Yet they argue with each other. They argue about which mechanism is the most plausible for a given case, and which mechanism predominates in nature. This situation is typical of evolutionary theory.

> The major questions in evolutionary biology now tend to be of the form, 'All right, factors x and y both operate in evolution, but how important is x compared to y?' (Futuyma, 1983, p 42)

> Evolutionary biology is so complex that attempts in the near future to build syntheses around the framework of rigid, all-inclusive generalizations or laws will continue to be self-defeating and will lead to disputes and confrontations that generate more heat than light. (Stebbins, 1982a, p 14)

Evolutionary theory is a smorgasbord. It has no structure, and it does not say which mechanisms predominate in nature. Rather, predominance is determined by seeing which mechanisms must be invoked to 'explain' the data.

*

The various levels of natural selection all suffer the same problem. Every level is tautology, special definition, metaphysical, and lame. Natural selection is an idea. We can discuss its many curiosities, but we cannot test it.

In recent years, evolutionary theorists have reformulated natural selection[20] in terms of "individual survival" and "survival of the fittest individual" — where "individual" is now an abstract term for genes, bodies, kin, groups, demes, species, or clades. That peculiar use of words merely conceals the difficulties. It obscures the fact that there are many opposing mechanisms operating simultaneously. It creates the false impression that evolutionary theory has firm structure.

---

[19] "[N]o level of selection has theoretical primacy over the others." (Williams, M., 1984, p 95)

[20] Some evolutionists have extended the term *natural selection* to all levels above and below organisms. For example, Gould, 1982b, p 386.

Neutral Evolution

Not all biologic traits affect survival. Some traits have no measurable effect on survival and are said to be neutral. Neutral traits survive and perish by chance, like the flip of a coin. There is no reason for their survival or extinction.

Neutral traits can spread throughout a population — simply by chance. Then these traits may later disappear from the population — again by chance. This is called neutral evolution. The term confuses many people, since adaptation and large-scale evolution cannot be explained by the chance comings and goings of neutral traits.

Some traits are neutral (having no effect on survival), while others are selective (having an effect on survival).

- If 'good and valid reasons' have been found for the survival (or lack of survival) of a trait, then the situation is said to be the result of selection.

- If the existence of such reasons seems unlikely, then there is always the option that the trait survives (or not) precisely because it has *little or no* effect on survival.

Thus, all traits are either selective or neutral, and evolutionary theory can flexibly accommodate them.

Nonetheless, evolutionists debate each other over the relative predominance of selection versus neutrality. The dispute is already several decades old, and is now focused at the molecular/genetic level. Neutralists argue that most genetic change has resulted from the chance origin and extinction of neutral genes. Selectionists argue that most genetic change is the result of real differences in gene survival.

As always, the debate cannot be settled on theoretical grounds, because evolutionary theory does not say which mechanism should predominate. Rather, evolutionists are trying to settle the matter by seeing which mechanism best 'explains' the data.

*

Neutrality can apply at all levels: genes, bodies, kin, groups, demes, species and clades. It can even apply between levels. A given trait might be neutral at some levels, and advantageous or harmful at other levels. We will discuss the neutral evolution debate more in the genetics chapters, but for now we must get another bag, label it "Neutral Evolution" and place inside it all the mechanisms of neutral change.

Chance

How can evolution go from a local fitness peak to the other side of a fitness canyon? This is a central dilemma of inventive natural selection.

One solution is pure chance. Supposedly, massive mutations sometimes happen to take an organism to the other side of the fitness canyon in one *large* step. This is called evolutionary saltation. It is a brute force approach that evolutionists avoid when they can. Saltation was a popular idea through the 1950s.

For example, the evolutionary geneticist, Richard Goldschmidt, proposed the theory of hopeful monsters. The theory suggested that the key events in evolution are the birth of mutated "monsters" that have unusual characteristics. Most of these monsters would soon die, but occasionally some would survive to form a new unusual species. The theory is often caricatured (imprecisely) as the idea that one day a reptile laid an egg and a bird hatched out.

Some evolutionists embellished the idea as follows. They argued that the mutated monster is due to *one or two* mutations having a large effect. It is really the same old Saltation theory plus the words "one or two." These theorists supposed that the mechanism is more likely if they claim few mutations are involved.

In reality, the fitness terrain is not limited by the theorists' claims. The larger the canyon, the more difficult it is for evolution to get across. Sudden, substantial increases in biological complexity are too improbable to be explained by mutations. In addition, a massively mutated monster probably would not find a mate with which it would be interfertile.

> The origin of species appears to depend on a complex and diverse series of processes. It can never be accomplished in a single event by one all-encompassing mutation, as some geneticists formerly thought possible. (Stebbins, 1982, p 96)

Academic evolutionists no longer openly endorse saltation to any significant extent. They suggest other mechanisms for getting unstuck from local fitness peaks.

Warping the Fitness Terrain

Some evolutionists suggest that the fitness terrain is not fixed and stable, rather it deforms. The paleontologist G. G. Simpson says the fitness terrain is "more like a choppy sea than a static landscape."[21] Daniel Hartl explains the idea:

> There are several ways out of the dilemma for populations 'stranded' on submaximal fitness peaks. The environment may change, for example, causing changes in fitness of the various genotypes and a consequent alteration in the adaptive topography surface. *What was a peak may become a*

---

[21] Cited by (Eldredge and Tattersall, 1982, p 41) and (Eldredge and Cracraft, 1980, p 256)

valley and any population in such a valley will evolve; if, after awhile, the environment should revert back to what it was originally, the population may have evolved far enough from where it was originally to find itself in the domain of attraction of a higher fitness peak. To assume that such fortuitous changes of environment will regularly occur is, of course, overoptimistic. (Hartl, 1980, p 336, my italics)

Hartl says the fitness terrain can deform so a peak becomes a valley (and a valley becomes a peak). Thus, a population stuck on a fitness peak can suddenly be down in the valley and begin evolving upward again.

Hartl says such fortuitous changes are "overoptimistic." However, there is a different reason evolutionists do not sell this mechanism more than they do. Natural selection relies on the fitness terrain for guidance. If the fitness terrain is bobbing up and down like a choppy sea, then nothing can guide evolution. If a peak becomes a valley (and vice versa) in an indiscriminate way, then natural selection becomes a random process.

*

The *scope* of the fitness terrain presents a special problem. The microscopic terrain is different from the larger macroscopic terrain. The situation in a narrow microscopic patch of terrain does not necessarily apply to a wider macroscopic portion of the same terrain. For example, the microscopic terrain may be bobbing up and down "like a choppy sea," yet the macroscopic terrain can still present effective barriers to evolution. The microscopic or macroscopic terrain can dominate the process of natural selection.[22]

Once you allow the fitness terrain to warp, then many bizarre phenomena become conceivable. For example, survival of the fittest can actively work to *destroy* adaptations. Suppose a population is at the top of a macroscopic fitness mountain. A sharp microscopic wave can pass through the area, rising up one side of the macroscopic mountain it can catch the organisms on its crest. Survival of the fittest would keep the population at the crest of the wave. As the wave passes down the other side of the mountain it would carry the population along. The species would *surf* its way to extinction.

There are countless ways the fitness terrain can warp, and most of them are not helpful to evolution. The theorists have avoided the unhelpful possibilities and say virtually nothing about them. There are two scenarios they endorse: the Stationary hypothesis and the Red Queen hypothesis.[23]

---

[22] The balance of forces between the microscopic and macroscopic terrain depends on the *steepness* of their slopes. If the microscopic terrain has sharper, steeper slopes, then it dominates over the macroscopic terrain. For example, a *sharp* microscopic wave could carry a population up one side of a macroscopic mountain, and down the other side.

[23] Some evolutionists mistakenly conclude that these are the only two plausible alternatives. For example, Lewin, 1985, p 399.

The Stationary hypothesis assumes:

1) The *environment* controls how and when the fitness terrain warps. As the environment changes, the fitness terrain warps.

2) The terrain warps *much slower* than species can adapt. (Without this assumption natural selection would be a random process. If the terrain is rapidly bobbing up and down, then the terrain would be unable to guide the origin of adaptations.)

The stationary hypothesis suggests that a species sits on a fitness peak and waits for the environment to alter the terrain. The species adapts as the terrain deforms, so the species stays near the moving peak. The model says, "in an undeviating environment evolution would grind to a halt, to be kicked into gear only when external conditions alter."[24]

The Red Queen hypothesis assumes:

1) The fitness terrain remains stable except in the immediate area of a species. The *presence of species* causes the fitness terrain to deform.

2) The terrain can warp faster than species adapt, but (because of assumption #1) there is a feedback mechanism that keeps the terrain from doing so.[25] Ultimately, it is the evolving species itself which deforms the fitness terrain.

3) As a species adapts its way toward a fitness peak, the peak moves *away from* the species (not downward, sideways, or toward the species). The species then is always trying to catch-up to the retreating peak. (The Red Queen hypothesis gets its name from the Alice in Wonderland character who says "it takes all the running you can do, to keep in the same place." The model assumes that a species chases its local fitness peak.)

According to the Red Queen hypothesis, as the species evolves toward a fitness barrier the barrier conveniently moves out of the way. This is precisely the goal of the Red Queen model. The model assumes the terrain warps in a favorable way to eliminate barriers in the fitness terrain.

---

[24] Lewin, 1985, p 399

[25] The Red Queen model contains an implicit feedback system, and feedback systems frequently have stability problems. In a Red Queen model this could cause the fitness peak to oscillate back and forth past (or even orbit around) the species.

The Red Queen model illustrates some complexities of natural selection.

I.   If a local microscopic peak retreats from the species, then will a macroscopic fitness mountain oblige so easily? Will fitness peaks, large and small, all scatter before the approaching species? If they do, then the overall terrain contour could not offer any guidance in constructing adaptations. The species merely evolves in any direction and the overall terrain (large and small) compensates by moving out of the way. In such a case, any direction is as good as any other, and nothing can direct the origin of complex adaptations.

II. On the other hand, if the macroscopic terrain remains stable, then there are still problems.

    A.   If the macroscopic terrain dominates the process, then it can present effective barriers to evolution.

    B.   If the microscopic terrain dominates the process, then a different sort of problem can arise. A species can chase its local microscopic peak up one side of a macroscopic mountain *and just as easily down the other side.* It is as if the only thing in the terrain is the one local microscopic peak, and that peak can go anywhere. Any direction is as good as any other, and there is nothing to guide the building of adaptations.

Proponents of the Red Queen model avoid talking about these problems because it only highlights the untestability of their idea.

*

Most evolutionary theorists endorse both mechanisms — the Stationary hypothesis and the Red Queen Hypothesis — and debate among themselves about the relative 'predominance' of the two mechanisms in nature. Evolutionary theory itself offers no guidance on the matter.

> Theory alone cannot make a choice between the two models because the values of certain variables in the mathematical formulations are simply not known … (Lewin, 1985, p 399)

So evolutionists seek to resolve the matter by selecting those naturalistic mechanisms that seem to fit the data.

> [T]he choice between Red Queen and Stationary models will have to depend *primarily on paleontological evidence* (John Maynard Smith in Lewin, 1985, p 399, my italics).

Once again, evolutionary theory has no structure, makes no predictions, and provides no answers. Rather, evolutionary theorists adapt their theory to fit the data.

*

In summary, if the fitness terrain warps, then the possibilities are endless, and many of them do not help evolution. Evolutionists have selected those that comply with their worldview — giving the mistaken impression: (1) that evolutionary theory has real structure; (2) that nature has some inherent tendency to make evolution easy; and (3) that evolution is virtually inevitable.

The Stationary hypothesis and the Red Queen hypothesis rely on peculiar deformations of the fitness terrain. They also use conflicting assumptions. One says the fitness terrain warps faster than species can adapt; the other says slower. One says the environment causes the fitness terrain to deform; the other rejects that idea. One relies on a questionable feedback mechanism; the other assumes that the fittest terrain *inherently* warps in ways that favor evolution. Such peculiar assumptions are needed to keep the warping from getting out of control.

Harmful Causes

There is one theoretical mechanism for getting evolution unstuck from a local fitness peak while the fitness terrain is fixed and rigid. The mechanism requires harmful causes to pull the population down from its fitness peak. The population undergoes deleterious change (due ultimately to mutations). The population decreases in fitness and goes down from its local peak to the bottom of the canyon. Then neutral evolution takes the population along the canyon floor to the other side of the canyon. *Only then* is survival of the fittest allowed to increase again, causing the population to rise up the other side of the fitness canyon. (This is known as the Shifting Balance hypothesis and will be examined in the chapter on Population Genetics.)

This solution requires mechanisms that *oppose* and *overpower* survival of the fittest. Harmful causes are actively required. So, we must get a bag, label it "Harmful Causes," and fill it with all the mechanisms that cause genetic damage.

*

In summary, evolutionists propose three scenarios for getting unstuck from fitness peaks.

- Raw chance, due to mutation: the Saltation hypothesis.

- Deformations of the fitness terrain: the Stationary Hypothesis and the Red Queen Hypothesis.

- An active role for harmful mechanisms: the Shifting Balance hypothesis.

Even if these mechanisms succeed on a microscopic portion of the terrain, that does not mean they can succeed over a macroscopic portion of the same terrain. The wider, deeper, and steeper the fitness canyon the more likely these mechanisms are to fail.

Evolution by Natural Selection

Evolutionary theorists have cooked up a vast smorgasbord of conflicting mechanisms. For any biological problem they proceed around the smorgasbord and help themselves to those tidbits that look most appealing. They take a main course here, a side dish there, a little garnish perhaps. In this way they serve up a steaming hot plate of evolutionary mechanisms intended to satisfy the appetite for answers. When asked if they would like a portion of the *other* mechanisms they respond politely, "No thank you please." When pressed they answer, "Those other mechanisms do not go well with these." But what if we serve up their entire concoction on a plate. Can they sort out the mess to yield a digestible meal?[26]

Evolutionary theory really includes every conceivable naturalistic mechanism. It is a hurricane of discordant causes all acting and counteracting in opposition, in an indeterminate manner.[27] Why should anything significant result from such a process?

At this charge, the theorists become oddly empirical. Pointing emphatically at examples from nature they exclaim, "See, look at the melanic moths! Look at the snails!" *But examples from nature are unable to provide structure to a theory that effectively has none.*

Take all the various evolutionary "bags" — the fitness bag, the multi-leveled selection bag, the neutral evolution bag, the harmful causes bag, all the mechanisms that warp the fitness terrain, plus chance — and place them inside a larger bag called "The Theory of Evolution by Natural Selection." This is not science. A scientific theory is not comprised of the unstructured invocation of everything under the sun.[28] The evolutionary mechanism is without form and void.

Yet that does not stop evolutionary theorists. To explain a particular case, they reach into the bag and *select* those *natural* causes that seem to apply. This is "*Natural*" selection at its most sublime.

---

[26] "Superficially, it looks as if we know less now about how evolution works than we did, say, even ten years ago. This is because as recently as a decade ago there was something approaching unanimity in the evolutionary ranks. Today, though chaos is too strong a word, there is definitely dissent in the ranks." (Eldredge, 1982, p 52)

[27] Some evolutionists claim that the scientific status of evolutionary theory is demonstrated by its useful role in guiding research. They are mistaken. "It might be thought … that evolutionary arguments would play a large part in guiding biological research, but this is far from the case. It is difficult enough to study what is happening now. To try to figure out exactly what happened in evolution is even more difficult. Thus evolutionary arguments can usefully be used as hints to suggest possible lines of research, but it is highly dangerous to trust them too much. It is all to easy to make mistaken inferences unless the process involved is already very well understood." (Crick, 1988, p 36)

[28] The bags do not provide structure to the theory, they merely provide labels and a classification for all the causes.

137

The Fine-Scale Theory

John Maynard Smith sought to show that natural selection is testable science, so he offered a test.

> [I]f someone discovers a deep-sea fish with varying numbers of luminous dots on its tail, the number at any one time having the property of a prime number I should regard this as rather strong evidence against neo-Darwinism. And if the dots took up in turn the exact configuration of the heavenly constellations, I should regard it as an adequate disproof. (Maynard Smith, J., 1969)

His test may be reinterpreted simply. Perhaps if we lived in a topsy-turvy world then survival of the fittest would be refuted. Perhaps if nature grossly violated our concept of good engineering design, then we would all be forced to reject natural selection theory. Perhaps we would reject natural selection if we found a cow with a built-in refrigerator. Or a horse with a built-in saddle. Or how about an air-conditioner elephant? Or a bookshelf bear? Maynard Smith indicates that if survival of the fittest is true then such organisms should not survive.

Critics of Maynard Smith's test argue that it would be like testing Newtonian mechanics by trying to see whether objects fall *upward,* or whether planets move in *squares* instead of ellipses. They argue that this is simply not how Newtonian mechanics (or natural selection) are applied in practice. They argue that to 'test' a theory at such ridiculous extremes is really not to test it at all. They argue that to wait for far-fetched occurrences is not a real test — no one operating without benefit of the theory expects such bizarre occurrences anyway.[29]

That line of criticism is convincing, yet I will add another. I will assume that Maynard Smith has identified a testable version of survival of the fittest, then I will show that it does not help evolutionists.

I call Maynard Smith's idea "wide-scale survival of the fittest" because it is different from the *fine-scale* version essential for natural selection. Simply put, the wide-scale theory paints a picture of nature with an extremely broad brush — It is unable to paint with the level of fine detail required by evolutionary theory.

Evolutionists require a fine-scale theory that can predict the *slight-small differences* in survival based on *highly reified[30]* assessments of design. They require a fine-scale theory that can predict the subtle balances between helpful and harmful causes, between advantageous and deleterious designs. Evolutionists require a fine-scale theory that can predict the contour of the fitness terrain: the steepness of its slopes, the depth and width of its canyons, and how it deforms on the scope and scale of interest. Whenever evolutionists make claims for natural selection (by telling one of their notorious just-so scenarios) they pretend to possess such knowledge.

---

[29] Even creationists always expected that a designer would create life reasonably for survival.

[30] Reification is the highly doubtful process of converting abstract concepts (such as intelligence) into a single number.

Even if wide-scale survival of the fittest were scientific, it is unable to provide the necessary precision. It is far too blunt an instrument. It has woefully too little innards to fill the requirements of evolutionary theory. The sterile repetition of the words "survival of the fittest" just will not do — and the fact that a bookshelf bear would not survive is no help in explaining the origin of bears.[31]

Summary

Inventive natural selection is the distinctive evolutionary mechanism — essential to Darwinian theory. Evolutionists presume it creates new adaptations by somehow traversing the hills and valleys of the fitness terrain. But they do not attempt to defend it as testable science. Rather, for the defense they shift back to the naive version — survival of the fittest. Then they might offer some tautology to help expunge all doubt.

When challenged, they shift between various formulations. They use naive natural selection to convince the public that evolution is simple, testable, and virtually inevitable.

When opponents point out that such continually uphill evolution is refuted by the data, evolutionists effortlessly shift away from naive natural selection. Then they charge that the opponent has a poor understanding of evolutionary theory.

In short, evolutionists merely shifted away from criticism, then focused their arguments (and your attention) in a direction that seemed to overcome the criticism. This phenomenon occurs at several levels.

Biological adaptation by natural selection is not inevitable, nor is the theory scientific. It had merely lent support to the philosophy of naturalism.[32]

---

[31] The Darwinian is somewhat like the student who constantly makes massively inaccurate measurements and errs by retaining excessively too many significant digits. Most any prediction may be forthcoming, but *no theory is ever at risk*, because any discrepancies may, in after-thought, always be attributed to inaccurate measurements. The previous chapter (Survival of the Fittest) may be read as documentation of the evolutionists' wholesale failure to provide a testable basis for their fine-scale theory. That shortcoming, together with the many other complexities, makes natural selection thoroughly metaphysical.

[32] "The importance of Darwinian theory does not lie in its predictive strength, for, as we have seen, the nature of its key explanatory concept, fitness, precludes such strength. *The importance of the theory lies in the freedom it provides biologists to view natural phenomena as just that, as natural, and not as the creation of an artificer with designs for natural phenomena.*" (Rosenberg, 1985, p 173, my italics)

6

Darwinian Scenarios

Imagine a room, and the door says, "Evolutionary Theory." You wish to know more, so you enter within. The room is as big as a convention hall, and crammed with theorists — everywhere, as far as the eye can see. Each theorist is shouting at you, and each is shouting something different. All is contradictions. Nothing is clear.

Visitors react to this differently. One sums up simply, "I see nothing here." Another visitor responds more precisely, "I see evolutionary theory says everything, so it says nothing." Yet the evolutionist says, "I see an explanation of life! Evolution is a fact! We are merely debating the details."

In this way, the real evolutionary theory is unseen, behind closed doors. It is different from the way evolutionists present it to the public. Evolutionists examine the data from nature. Then, armed with this knowledge, they enter the big room containing the real evolutionary theory, where they confer with the shouting theorists. Eventually the evolutionist emerges and presents "evolutionary theory" to you. Low and behold, it matches the data. On the surface all seems fine. To recognize the error we must understand evolutionary theory more deeply. We should go to the big room, and see for ourselves.

There is a difference between what evolutionary theory really says and what evolutionists _claim_ it says. The two are not the same. Evolutionary theory says little, if anything, of consequence. It does not predict that new adaptations are inevitable, nor even possible. Such claims are made by evolutionists, not by natural selection, population genetics, or any mechanism in evolution.

This chapter focuses on Darwinian scenarios: the many stories and claims made for natural selection. We can start with no better example than the phenomenon called convergence.

Convergence

A marsupial tasmanian wolf (a recently extinct animal from Australia) is remarkably like a dog, yet this similarity was not inherited from a common ancestor. These two wolf-like animals allegedly arose from structurally quite different ancestors, and evolved toward similar body designs. Evolutionists call this convergence, and examples are common in nature.

Whales are a well-known example. Whales are mammals with strikingly fish-like bodies, said to be the result of evolutionary convergence. Whales allegedly arose from land-roaming quadrupeds who returned to the sea.

Even more impressive are the ichthyosaurs: extinct aquatic reptiles with fins on their backs and tails, and with fore and hind paddles for swimming. They look like porpoises. Yet they are said to have arisen from four-legged land-roving reptiles.

Darwin shuddered when thinking about the origin of the eye, yet modern evolutionists say these evolved more than forty separate times.[1] For example, squids and octopi have eyes similar to the eyes of vertebrates, including features such as lens, retina, and musculature. The eyes are said to have originated separately and converged toward the same design.

> "The theory of natural selection has always recognized that there may well be two or more different 'solutions' to the same engineering problem. Take eyes, for example. Many animal groups have developed eyes independently. .... Yet squids and octopi, far more closely related to arthropods and annelid worms (as judged, for example, on patterns of intricate similarity of the larval development in all three groups), nonetheless have eyes far more similar to ours than to the compound eyes of fleas and shrimp. Also lacking a hard outer skeleton around their heads, squid and octopus eyes are also built along pinhole-camera principles and, superficially at least, look very much like vertebrate eyes. Multiple solutions there may be, but there is always a limit, *usually a rather small number of designs that can accomplish the same biological function.*
>
> Thus theory predicts that natural selection will favor, say, two or three equally viable 'solutions' to a functional biological problem." (Eldredge, 1982, p 70, 71)

Eldredge describes the evolutionary explanation of convergence:

1) There are *only a few* good solutions to any functional biological problem.

2) Natural selection can *find* those few good solutions and create them.

The explanation pretends to possess an intimate knowledge of the fitness terrain and the many forces acting on it — a knowledge that neither evolutionists nor their theory actually have. Evolutionary theory does not predict any adaptations, much less convergent adaptations.

---

[1] Mayr, 1982, p 611

141

Yet evolutionists claim that convergence is somehow inevitable.

> [E]xtensive convergence is virtually inevitable. (Gould, Luria, and Singer, 1981, p 710)

Again, there is a difference between what evolutionary theory says (which is nothing coherent), and what evolutionists claim the theory says (which they conveniently choose to match the data). Evolutionary theory is flexible to whatever problem is at hand.

Here is an example.

> Thus we should expect to see *many* different genetic solutions to *any* adaptive problem. (Futuyma, 1983, p 126, my italics)

> Indeed *many* of the environmental problems have *only a limited number* of genetic solutions ... (Newell, 1982, p 198, my italics)

Futuyma is explaining the plentiful existence of adaptive *variation* (called diversity). Newell is explaining the plentiful existence of adaptive *similarity* (called convergence). Therefore, they selected different explanations from the evolutionary smorgasbord. The two explanations happen to contradict each other.

The major "adaptation" in evolution is the way evolutionists adapt their theory to fit the data. Evolutionary theory can be easily adapted because it is untestable: its bonds are few, its flexibility is great. It is bent and molded by the needs of evolutionary storytelling.

This is not just an issue about evolution. It is a key factor needed to grasp message theory. To understand the motivation behind the designed pattern of life, one must first understand the incredible flexibility of evolutionary theory. That bears repeating: the *flexibility* of the theory(s) of evolution is key to understanding why the pattern of life was designed as it was.

Later we will see that "convergent" traits are common in nature because they serve a purpose in the biotic message. Specifically, they look *unlike* evolution. The human-like eye of the octopus, the fish-like bodies of whales and ichthyosaurs, the duck-like bill of the platypus — these are all visible clues that life was designed by a single designer. Yet they are especially difficult to explain convincingly by evolution.

Comparing Scenarios

When Darwin first published his theory, no one understood it well. So critics challenged it by saying, "Evolutionary theory cannot explain trait X." Trait X was the metamorphosis of the butterfly, or the origin of the eye, for example. Evolutionists handled these matters by disappearing into the big room for awhile, returning later with a Darwinian scenario to explain trait X.

This line of debate continued back and forth for decades. Meanwhile, evolutionary theorizing developed, and today's evolutionists have an abundance of scenarios to explain virtually any circumstance. So, the situation is clearer now than in Darwin's time.

The theory that evolutionists present to you seems explanatory. The problem is that it is untestable. You can experience this by comparing evolutionary scenarios one to another. When you compare scenarios, you can see the contradictions that are not visible in any scenario taken alone. Any single scenario can seem reasonable by itself, but when taken together the inconsistencies are seen.

Thus, you can get key insights into the real evolutionary theory without going to the big room yourself. You need only compare the scenarios that evolutionists bring out from the big room. By comparing scenarios you can see that evolutionary theory has nothing clear to say about nature.

Next we discuss some examples.

*

Supposedly, natural selection examines organisms precisely and eliminates inferior varieties. With its excellent vision, natural selection is said to create adaptations of subtly and perfection.

Mimicry is when an organism imitates something else — insects that look like twigs or leaves, for example. Natural selection is said to create mimicry by eliminating those individuals that do not look exactly like a twig or leaf in exquisite detail.

Natural selection is said to have superb vision, even down to the level of proteins, to create convergence at the molecular level. Accordingly, no detail is too small to be seen by natural selection.

Natural selection is said to see a tooth inside an organism and eliminate those individuals whose molars lack the proper shape. This is alleged to have caused many examples of convergence in mammalian molars.

Nonetheless, natural selection was unable to see and eliminate mammal-like reptiles in the midst of having their jaw bones radically displaced into the middle ear (allegedly to form the delicate mammalian hearing apparatus).

This disparity between what natural selection can and cannot see is incongruous.

A classic case is the whales, beautifully adapted to an aquatic life. Allegedly, the whales evolved from four-legged mammals who returned to the sea. The waters were already full of advanced predators and competitors. Imagine the difficulties as these land-roving animals lost their legs and underwent a total body transformation. The transformation would change their pelvis, their thermal insulation, their eating, breathing, sight, hearing and navigation apparatus.

Evolutionists claim natural selection could not eliminate these misfits. By all rights, such animals should have been wiped out soon after they entered the sea.

Moreover, evolutionists claim this awkward transition occurred many times independently. (For example, in whales, seals, and ichthyosaurs.)

*

Evolutionists imply that natural selection is intensely powerful and helplessly weak, both fantastically precise and indefinitely vague. The ambiguity of survival of the fittest provides the flexibility required by their storytelling. Survival of the fittest is so ambiguous it can be bent to the needs of evolutionary stories. When evolutionists tell their scenarios, they pretend to possess an insuperable knowledge of the fitness terrain. No one actually has such knowledge, and their theory does not provide it.

Yet, there is room for doubt. We can doubt the evolutionary story, and the doubt is generated by the evolutionary story itself, with its inconsistent claims. This is another clue that Darwinism is not science.

*

Darwinism is a Story

Correctly understood, evolutionary fitness is metaphysical and cannot be measured. Fitness is made up of countless factors about organisms and environments. Many factors cannot be accurately measured because they are complex. Things like intelligence, for example, are quite difficult to measure. Even a single well-defined parameter — such as fertility — can be practically impossible to measure to the accuracy required by evolutionary theory. We lack the stamina required by such measurements.

> The problem is that natural selection theory says that very small selection coefficients, of the order of 1 per cent or less, are effective in causing evolutionary change, yet the demonstration of such small differences in fitness is simply not possible in experiments. It has been calculated that a 1 per cent difference in fertility between two genotypes could be shown with 95 per cent confidence only if the fertility of 130,000 females of each type were measured. If the fertility of 380 females of each type were measured, the investigator has only an even chance of detecting a much larger difference in fertility, of 10 per cent. So selection theory is trapped in its own sophistication: it asserts that small differences in fitness are effective agents of evolutionary change, yet differences of that order are not detectable in practice.[2] (Patterson, C., 1978, p 69)

Thus, evolutionary theory typically depends on differences of one percent. Yet differences this small cannot usually be measured in practice.

*

---

[2] For more details see Lewontin, 1974, p 240-241

Kitcher admits we cannot make many evolutionary predictions about the future because almost any small change could have endless ramifications.

> "*If* we knew enough about the ways in which environments will change, *if* we knew enough about the genetics of organisms … *then* perhaps we could predict the future evolutionary path of the primates. But the supposition that we do — or should — know enough is clearly absurd. ....
>
> When [evolutionary biologists] try to solve the problem of how a species will evolve, almost anything is potentially relevant. A small environmental change could transmit a shock wave through the entire ecosystem, imposing unanticipated demands on the species under study. Important questions ramify endlessly."[3] (Kitcher, 1982, p 79)

We have abundant data about living organisms and environments, yet Kitcher says we cannot make evolutionary predictions about the future.

Nonetheless, from meager fossil data, evolutionists fearlessly give explanations of how various organisms arose. We cannot possibly measure the multitude of factors from the fossil past to check the validity of their scenario. Darwinism is a story.[4] It is not testable science.

Preadaptation

The incipient stages of an adaptation are the key stages of its evolution. Typically these are the earliest, poorly formed steps. These have always been a focus of skepticism and debate.

The eye is clearly a useful benefit to survival, yet this does not explain its evolution. In its incipient stages the eye would be poorly formed and of little use. The classic question is: What good is five percent of an eye?

Theorists sometimes use preadaptation to explain the evolution of incipient stages. According to this idea, the incipient stages were not used for their final perfected purpose. Rather, the incipient stages were preadapted for another use, and then later switched over to their ultimate function.

If evolutionists cannot explain the evolution of the eye, then they suggest preadaptation, and shift to an explanation of something else.

> How can a series of reasonable intermediate forms be constructed? Of what value could the first tiny step toward an eye be to its possessor? ....

---

[3] I cite Kitcher here because he seems to be the only anti-creationist who has seriously tried to defend Darwinian scenarios as science. His cited statement is evidence against his claim.

[4] Many places in Gould's book, *Wonderful Life,* acknowledge that one can easily invent evolutionary stories after the fact. Here is one example. "[Birds might easily have become the dominant carnivores,] but mammals finally prevailed, and we do not know why. We can invent stories about two legs, bird brains, and no teeth as necessarily inferior to all fours and sharp canines, *but we know in our heart of hearts that if birds had won, we could tell just as good a tale about their inevitable success.*" (Gould, 1989, p 297, my italics)

> With preadaptation, we cut through the dilemma of a function for incipient stages by accepting the standard objection and admitting that intermediate forms did not work in the same way as their perfected descendants. *We avoid the excellent question, What good is 5 percent of an eye? by arguing that the possessor of such an incipient structure did not use it for sight.* (Gould, 1973, p 104 and 107, my italics)

Evolutionists take their explanation as far as credulity will allow, then they imbue the trait with a different function and continue with their explanation, to further test credulity. Your credulity is being tested — not their theory.

*

Preadaptation builds on the central illusion from naive natural selection. It presumes that evolution is a march ever up a fitness incline. When theorists employ preadaptation they argue that each evolutionary step is an improvement in function (but not necessarily the same function). Thus, their explanation subtly conveys the imagery of naive natural selection. That is why the explanation has traditionally been so common.

In reality, preadaptation need not aid evolution. On the contrary, preadaptation could *prevent* evolution. Preadaptation can create small local hills in the fitness terrain, and species could get stuck on these hills forever. Why should the eye ever have evolved if its earliest structures were preadapted *for another useful purpose?* Why should the feather have evolved into a perfect instrument for flight if its earliest forms had *another useful role?*

*

Gould tries to defend preadaptation.

> [T]he principle of preadaptation simply asserts that a structure can change its function radically without altering its form as much. (Gould, 1973, p 108)

Yet his statement shows the untestability of natural selection. We cannot determine the fitness of a structure if, without altering its form much, it "can change its function [and thereby its effect on survival] radically." Gould suggests that mere slight changes in a trait can radically affect its survival. Thus, no one can know the fitness terrain well enough to apply evolutionary theory.

*

Preadaptation is used to explain cases where we do not possess specimens of the preadaptation, rather we must imagine the preadaptation.

For example, the earliest feathers in the fossil record are fully developed and well-formed. We have reptile scales and we have feathers, but we do not have organisms with partially formed feathers. We do not have a precursor that had another preadapted function. Unmistakable preadapted structures have not been found. They are hypothetical.

We cannot evaluate the fitness of organisms for which we possess specimens. Therefore, we cannot evaluate preadaptive structures that exist only in the minds of evolutionists. We cannot test a theory that employs structures and functions invented by evolutionists for each separate case.

146

Darwin's Challenge

Darwin sought to give his theory a scientific footing. So, he offered a challenge, to test his theory. He said that if the theory failed the challenge, then his theory would be disproved. Darwin asserted that species do not altruistically serve another without any gain for themselves. Futuyma explains Darwin's challenge and how it has fared.

> "If the theory of natural selection is true, though, organisms should have adaptations that serve purely for the survival and reproduction of the individuals who bear them, not for the good of any other individual or species. Darwin laid down the challenge in *The Origin of Species*: 'If it could be proved that any part of the structure of any one species had been formed for the exclusive good of another species, it would annihilate my theory, for such could not have been produced through natural selection.'
>
> How has Darwin's challenge fared? No one has ever found a case of a species altruistically serving another, without any gain for itself. Consider those relationships between species, such as pollination, in which some altruism seems at first glance to be involved. Flowers produce nectar to induce animals to help them reproduce. Plants that don't need animals, such as wind-pollinated pine trees and grasses, don't produce nectar. In fact, some plants deceive animals, and save themselves the energy that goes into making nectar. Many kinds of orchid flowers, for example, are shaped and colored so as to look like flies or bees. Pollination occurs when a male fly or bee 'thinks' it sees a female and come in to copulate — with a flower." (Futuyma, 1983, p 123)

Futuyma says that if natural selection is true, then we should not find species altruistically serving another without any gain for themselves. He gives the example of flowers and nectar. He says flowering plants are not altruistic, rather they get pollinated by insects in return for nectar.

Futuyma (apparently unknowingly) gives a counterexample in his own discussion of the common dandelion. The dandelion produces nectar and a brightly colored flower without any gain for itself. The common dandelion is asexual, and reproduces without pollination. The flower and nectar do not help the dandelion. They only help the insects.

> Most of the species of dandelions reproduce sexually, and have nectar and bright yellow petals that attract insects for cross-pollination. But the particular species of dandelion that grows in everyone's lawn is an anachronism: it reproduces entirely asexually, and does not need to be pollinated. Yet it still has nectar and yellow petals to which insects come, though they serve no function. (Futuyma, 1983, p 127)

Darwin's challenge seems overturned with this example. Nonetheless, evolutionists answer it by claiming that the dandelion's nectar and flower were not 'formed for' the exclusive good of the insects, these were 'formed for' the benefit of the dandelions, who later lost the use for these traits.

147

Darwin's challenge does not test evolutionary theory because Darwin himself insisted that natural selection is not the only force acting on organisms.

> In spite of Darwin's claim, a single instance of a structure in one species that serves the exclusive good of another would not annihilate 'evolutionary theory.' Even if it could somehow be shown that a structure contributed nothing to the organisms that possessed it, the legitimate conclusion is that natural selection is not the *sole* directive force in evolution — but Darwin repeatedly claimed that he never thought it was! (Hull, 1989, p 269)

*

Darwin's challenge at first sounded like a specific way to test his theory. In the end, the challenge is empty. It does not test his theory, it tests Darwinian ingenuity. Darwin's challenge merely tests the ability of evolutionists to provide a scenario.

Riddiford and Penny's Challenge

Riddiford and Penny want to show that natural selection is science. So they provide a challenge. They claim that an elephant could not evolve a complex "bird's nest" structure on its back.

> An organism that would be consistent with creationism, but not with natural selection is as follows. It could be an elephant with a complex structure on its back that acted only as a nest for a fish-eating bird, or any other bird that gave no benefit to the elephant. There are countless examples of this type that would be 'good design' but are prohibited by natural selection. (Riddiford and Penny, 1984, p 25)

The frustrating thing about natural selection is that its theorists can refuse to be ingenious at the necessary places. They take a structure *known not* to exist, then they say natural selection predicts it *could not* exist.

This sudden lack of imagination is too convenient. Darwinism easily 'explains' the impossible bird's nest. I suspect the explanation would go like this:

Perhaps the alluring ornament increased reproductive success by attracting the opposite sex.

Perhaps the ominous structure increased the elephant's ability to compete with the same sex. Just one shake and the odoriferous source of chirping would scare off opponents.

Perhaps the structure was initially preadapted for another function.
  Perhaps the accommodating structure served as an external place for the elephant to store food and water.
  Perhaps the convoluted structure served as a heat exchanger.
  Perhaps the unique structure benefited the group by providing a means of recognizing kin from outsiders.
  Perhaps the endearing structure resulted from a "green beard" effect.

Perhaps the behavior of the bird was a benefit. The chirping of the bird would alert the elephant to approaching predators, and the continual 'flitting about' would lead the elephant to food and water across long distances. Perhaps this helpful bird is now quite extinct and has been replaced by one quite uncooperative.

Perhaps the useless structure is now maintained in the elephant because it has side-effects (due to pleiotropy) that have become quite necessary.

Riddiford and Penny's challenge is easily answered with an evolutionary scenario. This is no trivial point. It is a major theme of this book. Most any circumstance can be accommodated by evolutionary scenarios.

*

Riddiford and Penny's challenge did not test evolutionary theory. It tested the ability of evolutionists to refrain from giving a scenario.

Lost Features

According to evolutionists, our primate ancestors had an acute sense of smell, far sharper then we now have. So, evolutionists say we lost our keen sense of smell.

Kitcher describes how we lost it.

> One ability that is clearly less developed in humans than in our mammalian ancestors is our sense of smell. ... Homo sapiens has lost a characteristic that was beneficial to our progenitors. *Yet this does not shake the foundations of evolutionary theory. It is not difficult to construct an evolutionary scenario that will show how we might have lost olfactory acuity. Here is one possibility.* In a forest environment, detection of objects by smell seems to be far less reliable than it is on the open plains. Hence, among the arboreal animals from whom we descend, there may have been selection for an alternative method of recognizing the threats and promises of the environment. Vision has become our dominant sense. As our ancestors perfected their ability to gain information by sight, *perhaps they no longer found it necessary to expend resources on developing an elaborate olfactory system.* So our sense of smell is less acute than was that of the early mammals from whom we began. (Kitcher, 1982, p 73-74, my italics)

Kitcher gave one possibility for how we lost an acute sense of smell: perhaps the resources spent developing the olfactory system did not result in sufficiently increased survival, so it was dropped.

Thus, there are Darwinian scenarios to explain why well-developed, functioning features (like a keen sense of smell) have been lost. Yet there are other scenarios to explain why useless non-functioning features have been kept (such as the dandelion's nectar and flower). Darwinian scenarios can be adapted to virtually any circumstance.

Repeated Evolution

Ruse is eager to show that Darwinism is testable science, so he offers a test. He argues that species cannot evolve again a second time.

> "[O]nce an organism has gone extinct, it can never return. There is no possibility of a second chance, given so undirected a phenomenon as natural selection. ....
>
> [U]nlike Lamarckian evolution, Darwinian evolution cannot repeat itself. The dodo is gone forever. Suppose one found a whole set of fossil mammals in the geological record, back about four billion years old, and then nothing until the mammals come back. Darwinism would be false."
> (Ruse, 1982, p 37 and 137)

Ruse says that if a species evolved again a second time, then Darwinism would be false. Ruse feels this is a test of Darwinism.

Perhaps he is unaware that Darwinism would fail the test. In fact, Schafersman gives an example.

> [E]volution does not assume or require nonrepeatability, and modern evolutionary theory certainly allows it. ... in fact, there exist documented examples of repeated or 'iterative' evolution of homeomorphs from the same and different lineages. These cases occur, for example, in the planktonic foraminifera; the repeated homeomorphs are said to be absolutely indistinguishable except by position in the stratigraphic record;
> ... (Schafersman, 1983, p 228)

Schafersman contradicts Ruse.

Evolutionary theory is so undirected that theorists can conform it to any data. If theorists view the data in different ways, then they can easily give contradictory "explanations." The statements by Ruse and Schafersman are examples.[5]

---

5   Gribbin claims that a 'easy clean perfect reversal' has occurred. (This feat is indicated by the theory proposed by him and Cherfas for the evolution of chimps from a somewhat human-like ancestor). "Whatever the small genetic changes needed to accomplish the anatomical reshufflings that produced the upright ape, they could surely have been *equally easily reversed*. .... In our defense, we would counter that perhaps *the reversion has been absolutely perfect*, that perhaps the genetic changes that produced early man from an ape were *cleanly reversed* to produce early chimps and gorillas from man." (Gribbin and Gribbin, 1988, p 195-196, my italics)

Cellulose and Herbivores

Cellulose, nature's building block, is the main structural ingredient of higher plants and their cell walls. Cotton and wood are 90% and 50% cellulose, respectively. Higher plants typically use cellulose with bonding agents such as sap, resins, minerals, and lignin (wood is 20 to 30% lignin). At least one-third of all vegetable matter is cellulose. It is a carbohydrate and the most abundant organic compound in nature.

Despite its abundance, no multicellular animals have the enzymes necessary to digest cellulose. Cellulose has no function in the human diet except as roughage. Horses, cows, and other herbivores can utilize cellulose because their digestive tracts can retain it long enough for microorganisms to accomplish the digestive process. Termites and other destructive insects digest cellulose with the help of protozoa or bacteria in their guts. The symbiont digests the vegetable material, and then the animal digests the symbiont.

This has become an issue in the origins debate. Sonleitner notes that herbivores — animals that eat only plants — lack the enzymes necessary to efficiently digest the major components of plants: cellulose and lignin. He argues that this is evidence against an intelligent designer.

> [Since creation theory] asserts that intelligent designers did this, and made all organisms out of the same basic substances so that the food chain would work, *why did they make plants out of cellulose and lignins and then forget to endow the herbivores with enzymes to digest those materials?* (Sonleitner, 1991a, in his overview of section 6, my italics)

> [A] really intelligent designer would have endowed the panda with enzymes to digest cellulose and lignin. As it is, the panda's digestion is only 17% efficient [at assimilating its major food source, bamboo] ... (Similarly the intelligent designer would have given cows such enzymes instead of the complex stomach and complex bacterial fermentation process that they actually have!) (Sonleitner, 1991a, in his excursion chapter 5)

> Design proponents attempt to explain biochemical similarities as a requirement for efficient functioning of the food chain. The designer must have forgotten this requirement when it forgot to endow most of its herbivorous designs with an enzyme to digest cellulose and lignin, making herbivore digestion very inefficient and complicated. (Sonleitner, 1991a, in his excursion chapter 6)

A theory is especially potent when it can take critical objections and turn them into corroborating evidence. Message theory can do that to Sonleitner's argument.

It is reasonable that a designer should make key parts of plants difficult to digest. From a human point of view, we are glad that cellulose is a poor food source for most organisms, considering that it is the major material we use to clothe and house ourselves. We use it to make everything from baseball bats, to boats, to books, and for fires as a ready source of energy. Fortunately, fruits and vegetables come in a sturdy natural 'peeling' of cellulose that protects them from rapid decay.

More significantly, such design provides ecological balance to the system of life. We are recently concerned about the loss of tropical rain-forests, so imagine what would happen if many higher animals[6] could efficiently devour forests and convert these into progeny. In the short term those species would prosper, but the long-term result would be a catastrophe for the system.

Plants have little mobility and limited defenses from animals. Therefore, a designer should take steps to protect the plant world from limitless overgrazing. The inability of multicellular animals to efficiently digest bulk plant mass is a reasonable step toward providing ecological balance to the system of life.

Moreover, this design serves the goals of the biotic message by creating an enigma for evolution. Cellulose and lignin are the most abundant organic substances on earth, and they are a ready food source. Enzymes for digesting these would be extremely valuable to an organism. Why were the enzymes not inherited widely? According to evolutionists, the enzymes were somehow not inherited nor even 'converged on' by any multicellular animals.

> It is easy to give [natural selection] credit for countless incredible adaptations, but *this makes it the more surprising that the process has failed to endow animals with many seemingly accessible capacities. For example, no multicellular animal is known to have the ability to digest the most abundant organic substance, cellulose. The necessary enzyme, cellulase, cannot be difficult to manufacture. Bacteria, fungi, and protozoa have it,* but it does not fit in the metazoan genome. (Wesson, 1991, p 89, my italics)

The widespread absence[7] from metazoans of the digestive enzymes is a puzzle for evolution. The absence benefits the system of life, but selection cannot look ahead to ensure designs that benefit the system. Natural selection favors the individual, or perhaps the group or the species, but hardly the system. Moreover, the absence clashes with the abundance of convergence in nature's pattern. Why is convergence so abundant elsewhere, yet here it is prohibited? This shows, once again, that evolutionary theory has no coherent structure for understanding nature.

Taken altogether this situation is actually potent evidence for message theory.

---

[6] Many microorganisms have enzymes for digestion of plant mass, yet they pose little danger to a living forest ecosystem. A living forest has physical and biochemical deterrents, and microorganisms lack the physical strength, teeth, and jaws needed to bypass them.

[7] The absence is complete, so far as is known.

Social Darwinism

Soon after Darwin published his theory, people began to apply it to issues outside science. Darwinism in nature was interpreted as a bloody battle of one against all: nature — red in tooth and claw.

> I think 'nature red in tooth and claw' sums up our modern understanding of natural selection admirably. (Dawkins, 1976, p 2)

Evolutionists explained many acts of nature as beneficial to evolution. Anything furthering survival and reproduction was given a Darwinian interpretation.

> [T]here are good biological reasons why [rape] frequently occurs. If a male animal is prepared to attempt rape on occasion, then he is more like [sic] to reproduce than otherwise. (Ruse, 1985, p 67)

Darwinism was also transferred to the realm of human relations, sometimes with chilling implications.

> Even the infanticide practiced by various peoples at various times serves the cause of Darwinian fitness, rather than acting as a curb on population. There is no point in keeping alive babies who could not be supported for long. Killing babies who could not be safely reared gives a better chance of survival to those who are left, and infanticide in hard times can mean that more children grow up in the end. (Colinvaux, 1978, p 16-17)

> Infanticide is killing surplus babies for whom there would be too few resources in order that others might survive. It is the mechanism of culling inherent in our sexual behavior and our Darwinian breeding strategy. Infanticide confers fitness.[8] (Colinvaux, 1978, p 216)

Even obscure Darwinian doctrines had a large impact on social policies. The concept of genetic throwback, for example, was used to explain criminal behavior. The criminal was said to be a "genetic throwback" to an earlier, primitive man or ape who possessed little moral fiber or an outright lust for blood. Consequently, many administrators, employers, and jurists believed they could identify criminals by their ape-like physical appearance. A perceived "genetic throwback" was used to identify a criminal mind. The shape of the head or eyes, pointed ears, and even epilepsy became signs of moral degeneracy.

> In later years, Lombroso [the major proponent of the genetic throwback interpretation of criminality] awarded special prominence to epilepsy as a mark of criminality; he finally stated that almost every "born criminal" suffers from epilepsy to some degree. The added burden imposed by Lombroso's theory upon thousands of epileptics cannot be calculated; they became a major target of eugenical schemes in part because Lombroso had explicated their illness as a mark of moral degeneracy. (Gould, 1981, p 134)

---

[8]   These two quotes on infanticide are from an otherwise fine evolutionary ecology text.

Social Darwinism grew from the application of Darwin's theory to human morality. Survival and reproduction were elevated above all else as the ultimate moral justification. Accordingly, anything benefiting "well-being and reproductive success" was validated. Selfishness was not merely acceptable, it was desirable. Through evolutionary selfishness, the elimination of the unfit would cause humans to evolve ever higher. Accordingly, "do the other fellow down with impunity," and "every man for himself" were used mercilessly, if not self-righteously. Social Darwinism was employed in politics, economics, individual lives, and in the movements of entire nations.

Darwinism was getting a bad name.

Some evolutionists tried to separate Darwinism from this ethical morass. Darwinism, they insisted, is a scientific theory and therefore is neutral concerning ethical problems. They said nature has no moral lessons to teach us, and moral answers "do not, and cannot arise from the data of science." (Gould, 1983a, p 43)

> [N]ature contains no moral messages framed in human terms. (Gould, 1983a, p 42)

> Nature has no automatically transferable wisdom to serve as the basis of human morality. (Gould, 1987f, p 225)

> If nature is nonmoral, then evolution cannot teach any ethical theory at all. The assumption that it can has abetted a panoply of social evils that ideologues falsely read into nature from their beliefs — eugenics and (misnamed) social Darwinism prominently among them. (Gould, 1983a, p 44, his parenthesis)

They argued that nature is non-moral, and without an intrinsic moral sense.

These evolutionists were headed for a collision with the modern emergence of sociobiology. Sociobiologists say nature has a lot to say about morality — nature created human morality.

Sociobiology

Evolutionists offer special explanations for altruistic social behavior in animals, especially the social insects. They say the behavior is not genuinely altruistic, instead the behavior is programmed into the organism and maintained by gene, kin, or group selection. All evolutionists endorse such explanations of social behavior in non-humans.

Some evolutionists apply these same explanations to human social behavior. This field, called sociobiology, has far reaching implications. Gone are the days when evolution merely implied social Darwinism with nature red in tooth and claw. Now, evolutionary sociobiology is challenging our most basic ideas of morality, ethics, love, human freedom, human autonomy, and illusion.

Sociobiologists say that human altruism does not really exist.

> Real, honest-to-God altruism simply doesn't occur in nature .... Evolutionary biology is quite clear that 'What's in it for me?' is an ancient refrain of all life, and there is no reason to exclude *Homo sapiens* (Barash, 1979, p 135 & 167)

They argue that altruistic behavior is programmed into us by various forms of selection.

> [K]in selection is thought to be responsible for a great deal of the altruistic behavior which we show towards the people around us, for instance, our children and so forth. (Ruse, 1985, p 61-62)

They say our sense of morality has been programmed into us by evolution.

> [E]volutionists today argue that the human sense of morality is something which is a product of evolution, no less than the hand or the eye. Our sense of morality is an adaptation. We survive and reproduce more efficiently with it, than we do without it. (Ruse, 1985, p 62)

Sociobiology is no mere quirk. It is popularized in many books and widely-read international science magazines. For example, E. O. Wilson is a distinguished Harvard professor, and Micheal Ruse is the only philosopher of science who represented evolutionists at the 1982 Arkansas creation-science trial. These two renowned sociobiologists stated their case in *New Scientist* magazine. They argue that ethics itself is an illusion.

> Nature, therefore, has made us believe in a disinterested moral code, according to which we *ought* to help our fellows. (Ruse and Wilson, 1985, p 51)

> As evolutionists, we see that no justification [for morality] of the traditional kind is possible. Morality, or more strictly our belief in morality, is merely an adaptation put in place to further our reproductive ends. Hence the basis of ethics does not lie in God's will — or in the metaphorical roots of evolution or any other part of the framework of the Universe. In an important sense, ethics as we understand it is an illusion fobbed off on us by our

156

genes to get us to cooperate. It is without external grounding. Ethics is produced by evolution but not justified by it, because, ... it serves a powerful purpose without existing in substance. (Ruse and Wilson, 1985, p 51-52)

[E]thics is a *shared* illusion of the human race. (Ruse and Wilson, 1985, p 52)

Suppose that, instead of evolving from savannah-dwelling primates, we had evolved in a very different way. If, like the termites, we needed to dwell in darkness, eat each other's faeces and cannibalise the dead, our epigenetic rules would be very different from what they are now. Our minds would be strongly prone to extol such acts as beautiful and moral. And we would find it morally disgusting to live in the open air, dispose of body waste and bury the dead. (Ruse and Wilson, 1985, p 52)

Sociobiologists assert that humans have no free will, particularly concerning moral choices.[9]

[M]odern science directly implies that there are no inherent moral or ethical laws, no absolute guiding principles for human society. .... The individual human becomes an ethical person by means of only two mechanisms: deterministic heredity interacting with deterministic environmental influences. .... [F]ree will, as traditionally conceived, the freedom to make uncoerced and unpredictable choices among alternative possible courses of action, simply does not exist. (Provine, 1988, p 65)

[T]he evolutionary process cannot produce a being that is truly free to make choices. (Provine, 1988, p 66)

[W]e humans are just complex machines without free will that have been poorly programmed for moral behavior. (Provine, 1988, p 71)

Evolution provides no foundation for ethics and no deep meaning in life. Julian Huxley's dream that evolution could provide the basis for ethics and give meaning to life is just that — a dream. (Provine, 1988, p 72)

According to sociobiology, even our freedom is an illusion programmed into us by evolution, because such an illusion is adaptive.

Moreover, sociobiology calls into question our basic ability to reason and sense.

My human senses, my human powers, are themselves products of natural selection. Therefore, everything I am saying could be totally mistaken. My claims could be simply things I believe, because I am a more efficient reproducer if I believe them, rather than otherwise. (Ruse, 1985, p 57)

---

[9] In fact, the sociobiologist, B. F. Skinner, has repeatedly argued that the prevalent *belief* in free will has contributed its share to human misery. (As noted by Hull, 1989, p 278)

Sociobiology claims that human "self-sacrifice" is ultimately driven by a genetic predisposition toward evolutionary selfishness. Yet humans honestly believe they are being altruistic, loving, and self-sacrificing. How does sociobiology resolve this dilemma between what humans believe they are doing and what the theory claims they are actually doing?

> The resolution of the dilemma may be self-deception. The best liars are said to be those who delude themselves into believing their own lies; in the same way, the best social animals — the best altruists — may be those who delude themselves into believing that they are acting solely for the good of others. We provide crutches for our altruistic tendencies in the form of morality or religion. (Gribbin and Gribbin, 1988, p 127)

> Many people — probably most people — are reluctant to accept that even acts of self-sacrifice and saintliness are part of our genetic makeup. This is interesting in itself, and some sociobiologists argue that the capacity for self-deception, to convince yourself that you are not really acting to maximize your own success, may be a trait that has been selected for together with the altruistic way of life. (Gribbin and Gribbin, 1988, p 127)

> Why should humans be thus deceived about the presumed objectivity of moral claims? The answer is easy to see. Unless we think morality is objectively true — a function of something outside of and higher than ourselves — it would not work. If I think I should help you when and only when I want to, I shall probably help you relatively infrequently. But, because I think I *ought* to help you — because I have no choice about my obligation, it being imposed upon me — I am much more likely, in fact, to help you. And conversely. Hence, by its very nature ethics is and has to be something which is, apparently, objective, even though we now know that, truly, it is not. .... Morality is an ephemeral product of the evolutionary process, just as are other adaptations. It has no existence or being beyond this, and any deeper meaning is illusory (although put on us for good biological reasons). (Ruse, 1989, p 268-269)

In short, sociobiologists claim our belief in our own altruism is mere self-deception, genetically programmed to get us to cooperate more fully with evolutionary selfishness. Ghiselin's famous saying (1974) boldly compares altruism with hypocrisy: "Scratch an 'altruist,' and watch a 'hypocrite' bleed."

Sociobiologists tell why humans pair up for raising children.

> A romantic will tell you that it is because we fall in love, and that love is forever. But, of course, *love is something that has evolved*, over countless generations, as a form of pair bonding. It has evolved, and persists, because it has proved to be a success in evolutionary terms .... *Any inherited tendency for people to 'fall in love' will therefore spread through the population.* We begin to see why 'falling in love' will spread through the population by looking at examples of other mammals (Gribbin and Gribbin, 1988, p 140-141, my italics)

They claim our sense of love is programmed into us by evolution.

Some evolutionists now suggest that genetic engineering may be used to improve humans in the ethical and moral realms.

> Gene splicing (recombinant DNA/RNA) and cloning should allow humanity to seed this universe with new forms of plants and animals as well as our own kind. Our species would thereby spread the sparks of life and consciousness throughout the dark abysses of endless space and eternal time. Human hope with *visionary science may elevate and transform us not only physically and intellectually but also, more importantly, perhaps even in the ethical and moral realms.* There could be an eventual holistic transformation of humanity as the cosmic primate into a higher being worthier of the challenges and rewards of its sidereal destiny. (Birx, 1991, p 268, my italics)

This trend continues in the modern eugenics movement, with its foreboding call for "applied genetics." Edey and Johanson endorse this (in the final pages of their book *Blueprints*) as a way out of world crises.

> There is a way out of this. It is not more weapons, more treaties, more garbage, more chemicals, or more smog. It is better people. Perhaps the next step in our evolution as a species will be for us to *recognize that natural selection of our emotions has been too slow, and that we must speed things up, to keep pace with our culture, through applied genetics.* (Edey and Johanson, 1989, p 390, my italics)

Many evolutionists have found sociobiology to be both repugnant and politically dangerous. The two groups of evolutionists are now embraced in bitter conflict. The sociobiologists, include E. O. Wilson, Ruse, Alexander, Barash, van den Berghe, and Gribbin. Their critics include Kitcher, Lewontin, and Gould.

*

Next we examine how the critics argue against sociobiology. Their arguments are virtually identical to arguments creationists make against evolution. Except these are made by evolutionists against other evolutionists.

The critics argue that human sociobiology has "grave effects" and "political clout," that it is "potentially damaging to the cause of social justice."[10]

> [Sociobiology is] a mass of unfounded speculation, mischievous in covering socially harmful suggestions with the trappings and authority of science. (Kitcher, 1985, p 8)

Because of the serious political effects the critics plead for a higher standard of evidence.

> If the costs of being wrong are sufficiently high, then it is reasonable and responsible to ask for more evidence than is demanded in situations where mistakes are relatively innocuous. (Kitcher, 1985, p 9)

---

[10]   Kitcher, 1985, p 435; Gould, 1978, p 532; and Kitcher, 1985, p 7 respectively.

159

Besides political arguments, there are also emotional arguments. In an article in *New Scientist* magazine, Gould tries to rebut sociobiology. He concludes his argument with an emotional appeal to meaning, hope, and essence.

> "And I remembered the visceral reaction I had experienced upon hearing the four brass choirs, finally amalgamated with the 10 tympani in the massive din preceding the great *Tuba mirum* — the spine tingling and the involuntary tears that almost prevented me from singing. I tried to analyse it in the terms of Wilson's [sociobiology] conjecture — reduction of behaviour to neurobiology on the one hand and sociobiology on the other. And I realised that this conjecture might apply to my experience. .... But I also realised that these explanations, however 'true', could never capture the meaning of that experience.

> And I say this ... merely to assert that the world of human behaviour is too complex and multifarious to be unlocked by any simple key. I say this to maintain that this richness — if anything — is both our hope and our essence." (Gould, 1978, p 533)

Critics of sociobiology also use moral arguments. The critic derives a prediction about behavior based on sociobiology. The critic then points out that the predicted behavior is grossly contrary to our common moral sense. The critic concludes that sociobiology must therefore be in error. Kitcher uses such an argument involving rape and another involving overpopulation.[11]

There are also scientific arguments. Critics of sociobiology argue that it is unfalsifiable.

> The combination of direct selection, kin selection, and reciprocal altruism provides the sociobiologist with a battery of speculative possibilities that guarantees an explanation for every observation. The system is unbeatable because it is insulated from any possibility of being contradicted by fact. If one is allowed to invent genes with arbitrarily complicated effects on phenotype and then to invent adaptive stories about the unrecoverable past of human history, all phenomena, real and imaginary, can be explained. (Lewontin et al, 1984, p 261-262)

Some critics make the serious charge that sociobiology is not testable, and simultaneously acknowledge that evolutionary theory has the same fault.

> The point about models is that they must be testable and refutable. The trouble with the sociobiologist's models is that they become a closed world — there is no sort of situation to which one cannot get a fit granted enough suppositions about genes for this or that piece of behaviour and some other genetic properties like dominance or partial expressivity. .... The charge that the sociobiological world is 'closed' to possible experimental refutation, *whilst serious*, does not make sociobiology unique. Many fields of science operate within paradigms — general overarching theories — which

---

[11] Kitcher, 1985, p 430-431

are so comprehensive and adaptable to 'new' facts that they are not capable of refutation in the classical sense of philosophy of science — *evolutionary theory itself is an example.* (Rose, 1980, p 166, my italics)

Kitcher points out that evolutionists have been applying a double standard.

> [S]ome of those [evolutionists] who insist on the methodological purity of evolutionary theory lambaste sociobiology as unfalsifiable and thus condemn it as pseudoscience. *There results the undeniable impression that a double standard has been applied.* (Kitcher, 1985, p 58, my italics)

For every argument evolutionists make against sociobiology, there is a parallel argument that creationists make against evolution.

*

Philip Kitcher (1985) wrote the most exhaustive criticism of human sociobiology to date. The following is a sample of the many objections he makes. Observe that his arguments (against sociobiology) run parallel to mine (against evolution).

> [T]here are ample opportunities for sociobiologists to employ language that is vague or ambiguous, to slide back and forth between claims about individual animals, to extend the application of a concept that makes sense only in a narrow context. (p 241-242)

> However, to understand it is one thing. To see if it is plausible is quite another. (p 29)

> The central issue in the sociobiology controversy is whether there is a firm ladder that will take pop sociobiologists where they want to go. (p 35)

> [I]t would be rash to assume that we already know how to identify all the critical factors. (p 26)

> The real problem is that certain explanations, in which some but not all of the relevant evolutionary factors are considered, are heralded as complete, and the rest of the factors are invoked only when things go wrong. Theorists consider the problem of sexual strategies in one place, the problem of division of labor in another, the problem of foraging elsewhere. It is then pointed out that difficulties with favorite analyses can be overcome by considering some neglected factor. (p 154)

> If we could expose one error underlying all the faulty analyses of human social behavior, then it would not be necessary to proceed, as I have done, by examining example after example. Unfortunately, sociobiology is a motley. Not only is there no single monolithic theory to be scrutinized, but the individual Darwinian histories offered by pop sociobiologists may be flawed in any of a number of different ways. There is a family of mistakes, and in distinct examples distinct members are implicated. (p 241)

Because there is no single locus of theoretical controversy, we are forced to examine the conclusions case by case. Sometimes the analyses are flawed in one way; sometimes a number of different errors combine. My aim has been to identify a surfeit of suspects. Each suspect is guilty some of the time, no suspect is guilty all of the time, and each grand conclusion about human nature involves at least one guilty suspect. (p 243)

[W]e should resist the idea of sociobiology as a unitary theory, something that must be accepted or rejected as a whole and that can only be called into question by abandoning large parts of contemporary biology. (p 10)

*

Those are some ways that evolutionists make emotional, moral, political, or scientific arguments against sociobiology. The following exercise is enlightening: If you replace the references to sociobiology with references to "general evolution," then you will likely have a statement found in creationist literature.

Anti-Reductionism

Reductionism is discussed with increasing frequency in scientific literature. The discussion is often confusing because the term is used in conflicting ways.

Actually, it would be difficult to find a more ambiguous word than the word "reduce." When one studies the reductionist literature, one finds that the term "reduction" has been used in at least three different meanings.[12] (Mayr, 1982, p 59)

The confusion of the term obscures significant issues.

Scientific theories are sometimes interconnected, where one theory is really just a special case of a more general, more expansive theory. This relationship is not always seen, and may lay undiscovered for some time. When the relationship is discovered we reduce one theory into the other. This process is called theory reduction. The less general theory is called the secondary theory and the more general theory into which it is reduced is called the primary theory.

Reduction expands our knowledge by identifying the structure that interrelates theories. Reduction simplifies science by unifying many specialized theories into a more comprehensive whole. It extends the explanatory power of science by showing how fewer theories can explain more of nature. Therefore, reduction complies with the goals of science.[13]

---

[12] The three different meanings Mayr cites are not identical to the ones I discuss. However, other workers (e.g., Caplan, 1988) have also noted the many conflicting definitions of reductionism that appear in the literature.

[13] Ayala, 1985, p 65

162

The history of science has seen many cases of reduction. Sometimes entire branches of science have been reduced. For example, much of thermodynamics was reduced to statistical mechanics by the realization that the temperature of a gas indicates the mean kinetic energy of the molecules. Much of chemistry became reduced to physics when it was discovered that the valence of an element is determined by the number of electrons in the outer orbit of the atom. The theories of quantum mechanics and general relativity succeeded in unifying and reducing large branches of physics and astronomy.[14] Even pure mathematics has cases where branches of study were reduced.

Theory reduction is highly desirable to achieve. However, it need not be achieved — it is not a criterion of science.[15] It is merely a desirable side effect of our advance in knowledge. If a branch of science resists reduction, we are perhaps disappointed, but not outraged.

*

Sometimes theorists attempt an invalid theory reduction, usually as the result of over-simplification. Invalid reduction is met with criticism that can be recognized by words like emergence, non-reducible properties, and emergent properties. Suppose a scientist claims to have reduced apples down to atomic theory. An opponent might argue like this: "The theory is mistaken. Apples cannot be reduced to atomic theory because apples have emergent properties that cannot be reduced. Apples have non-reducible properties."

I make the distinction between valid and invalid theory reduction so the reader is not confused by the literature. In one case, being a reductionist is "good" (when successful and valid), and in another case it is "bad" (when unsuccessful and invalid).

Many evolutionary writers use the word reductionist in the negative sense, as though it meant "second-rate scientist." They are blaming the wrong culprit. The issue is not whether to be a reductionist. The issue is whether a given attempt at theory reduction is valid. Successful theory reduction is an occasion to be highly prized.

Yet many evolutionists have ulterior motives for disparaging reductionism.

*

---

[14] Ayala, 1985, p 65

[15] A few philosophers of science argue that precise "theory reduction" is rare at best, rather they describe the event in different terms. Nonetheless, their arguments do not alter my conclusions, because they acknowledge: (1) that the reduction event is valuable, and (2) that it is not a requirement or criterion of science. Thus, these philosophers agree on the two points essential to my argument.

Reductionism is a criticism that evolutionists use against sociobiology — they charge that sociobiologists are (unsuccessful) "reductionists!"[16] The rhetoric of the sociobiology debate goes like this:

> The critic of sociobiology argues: Human behavior is "too complex and multifarious" to be reduced.[17]

> The sociobiologists counterargue: The critic is resorting to obscurantism and mysticism. The critic is drawing an arbitrary line saying, "Thus far with evolutionary theory, but no further." If evolutionary theory can be applied to brains, hearts, and animal behavior, then why not human behavior too? The critic is allotting some "mysterious essence" to human behavior; some "emergent non-reducible property" to the human mind.

> The critic of sociobiology argues: The criticisms are not founded in obscurantism and mysticism. There are valid scientific objections to the theory.

All that should sound curiously familiar. As already said, the evolutionist who criticizes sociobiology is like a creationist. In the above dialog, merely replace the sociobiologists with "evolutionists," and replace the critic of sociobiology with "creationist." This replacement yields rhetoric remarkably like the creation versus evolution debate.

*

Evolutionists have strategic motives to embrace anti-reductionism. Evolutionists use anti-reductionism in their attempt to alter the philosophy of science.

They say the philosophy of science should be amended to fully accept evolutionary theory. Their justification begins like this: Evolution is a fact, therefore evolutionary theory must be science. So, if the status of the theory is in doubt, then the philosophy of science must be amended to accommodate the infraction.

Ernst Mayr, for example, wants evolution and all its consequences built right into the philosophy of science.

> It is high time that the consequences of the Darwinian revolution be fully incorporated into philosophy. It is time that it be realized how much more important the Darwinian revolution was than any recent revolutions in the physical sciences. The changes in the theories of physics ... have no effect on the personal philosophy of the man in the street. It is quite different with the Darwinian revolution, which profoundly altered everybody's view of nature and of himself. This is the reason a philosophy of science based exclusively on the principles of the physical sciences is insufficient and incomplete. .... it is so important that the findings of biology, in all their consequences, should be built into philosophy. (Mayr, 1985, p 60)

---

[16] Often the critic of sociobiology sounds like this: "Human behavior at both the individual and cultural levels of organization has emergent properties not reducible to the maximization of inclusive fitness axiom of sociobiology." (Barkow, 1980, p 192)

[17] Gould, 1978, p 533

Evolutionists acknowledge that evolution has yielded little, if any, theory reduction. They account for this in the following way.

- They say evolution is pluralistic: it has a multitude of processes operating at cross-purposes with complex ties of feedback. This pluralism prevents theory reduction.

- They say evolution is a hierarchy theory: it has a hierarchical multi-level framework. So, new properties emerge at each level of theory. Genes have properties that atoms do not; organisms have properties that genes do not; species have properties that organisms do not. These emergent properties make evolutionary theory irreducible.

Evolutionists want to alter the criterion of science to accommodate their theory, and they identify "reductionism" as the culprit. They say science should move away from a reductionist philosophy, and accept biological theories of evolution. These evolutionists endorse anti-reductionism.

Much of their discussion is confusing, so I will summarize it.

- Evolutionists speak of theory reduction as a demand, requirement, or criterion of science: they call this "reductionism." (They are mistaken. No one endorses theory reduction as a demand, requirement, or criterion of science.)

- Having built a straw-man, the evolutionists then attack it. They point out how unreasonable it is to demand the reduction of all theories down to the level of atoms. They point out that evolutionary systems have emergent properties that cannot be reduced. They say this is because evolutionary theory is pluralistic and hierarchical.

- They conclude that science should move away from a reductionist philosophy and accept anti-reductionism, particularly the non-reducible theories of biology and evolution.

In short, evolutionists want to change the philosophy of science, and to accomplish this they must assail the present one. So, they create a straw-man version to attack — "reductionism." By defeating reductionism they presume to show that anti-reductionism is the correct philosophy of science. Their argument is built on this error.

There is another reason they attack reductionism. For an explanation to be scientific it must be reduced to a testable theory. This is the requirement that evolutionists want to get around. Evolution is metaphysical and cannot be reduced to a testable theory. Therefore, evolutionists attack the idea that it must be reduced.

Anti-reductionists do not directly attack testability, instead they attack "reductionism" — it is just different language to accomplish the same end. Anti-reductionism provided a concealed means to assault testability. This is the primary reason anti-reductionism is so frequently embraced by evolutionists.

*

A recent book has a particularly appropriate title — *Evolution at a Crossroads: The New Biology and the New Philosophy of Science*. The book is a collection of articles that consider altering the philosophy of science to better include evolutionary theory. Many authors do not hide the fact they are out to tamper with the canons of science.

For example, Mayr calls for an "autonomous biology": a philosophy of science enlarged to include evolutionary biology.

> It is now perfectly obvious that biological phenomena and processes cannot be completely reduced to processes found in inanimate matter. This again justifies the validity of a call for an autonomous biology.[18] (Mayr, 1985, p 58)

Mayr continues his attempt to redefine science in his book *Toward a New Philosophy of Biology*. It is an extended campaign at using anti-reductionism (including its forms of pluralism and hierarchy theory) as a covert anti-falsificationism. He stresses that, in biology, clear predictions are often not possible.[19]

> In biology, the pluralism of causations and solutions makes prediction probabilistic, if it is possible at all. (Mayr, 1988, p 19-20)

Then, he tries to alter the philosophy of science to make a lack of prediction acceptable.

> [T]he ability to predict is not a requirement for the validity of a biological theory. (Mayr, 1988, p 19-20)

Thus, Mayr arrived at 'prediction' — an issue far afield from theory reduction in which he couches his argument. Here, he is covertly attacking the criterion of testability by deflating the value of prediction. Prediction is necessary for testability, yet Mayr argues that biological theories should be released from that requirement.

Once the confusion is unraveled, a response to Mayr becomes clear: If some biological phenomena can be reduced (perhaps down to atomic theory) then fine — if not, then it may be a disappointment but it does not call for a redefinition of science.

*

---

[18] Depew and Weber (the editors of that book) point out the implications of Mayr's position. "Mayr himself recommends not a renewed search for more powerful and applicable laws, but a retreat from the philosophical demand for them." (Depew and Weber, 1985a, p 232)

[19] "[P]redictions in biology are so often impossible." (Mayr, 1985, p 56) and "[T]here are very few generalizations in biology that can be designated as laws" (Mayr, 1985, p 53)

Evolutionists embrace the criterion of testability (if only to use against creationists), but they also try to deflect the criterion when applied to evolution. Anti-reductionism provided the cover to attain these contradictory goals. Anti-reductionism provided a way of maintaining a double standard: one for creation (and the physical sciences), and a less restrictive standard for evolution.

Depew and Weber contemplate altering the philosophy of science for the specific purpose of influencing the creation/evolution debate. In the most flowery scientific prose they write:

> [T]he persistence of natural theological discourse, and perhaps even of residual tendencies to vitalism, together with the desirability of confuting these, might suggest that it is advisable to retain some attachment to reductionistic ideals. These ideals, whether they are given methodological, theoretical, epistemological, or ontological import, are still powerful tools for deconstructing attempts at non-natural explanations. But this may be to take these residual phenomena too seriously, if the effort diminishes our recognition that our knowledge [of evolutionary biology] is most perspicuously encoded in a fully naturalistic, but definitely nonreductionistic, conceptual matrix. (Depew and Weber, 1985a, p 255)

I decode their statement as follows:

> The desirability of refuting modern creationism suggests the use of reductionistic ideals. These ideals have been powerful tools for this in the past, and they still are. But this should not be taken too seriously because evolutionary biology is definitely nonreductionistic.

This is an example of the double standards used by evolutionists.

*

In summary, theory reduction is highly desirable to achieve. Yet the rhetoric of anti-reductionism is confusing. Anti-reductionism provides unfamiliar, confusing language by which to assault the canons of science. It supplies a shrouded way to argue against testability.

Evolutionary theory is metaphysical, and cannot be 'reduced' to testable science. So, evolutionists attacked the idea that it must be reduced. Anti-reductionists are really covert anti-falsificationists. They are trying to alter the criterion of science to allow evolutionary theory to count as science. This is why anti-reductionism is so frequently endorsed by evolutionists.

Summary

There is a difference between what evolutionary theory says and what evolutionists *claim* it says. The two are not the same. Evolutionists arrive at their claims by using "Natural" selection. First, they examine life, then from their theoretical smorgasbord they select whatever natural mechanisms they need to 'explain' what they see.

Evolutionary fitness is metaphysical. We cannot adequately measure the fitness of *living* organisms. So, we cannot possibly evaluate the fitness of fragmentary fossil material from ages past, or "hypothetical organisms" and "preadaptations" that exist only in the minds of evolutionists. Darwinism requires a measurement precision it is utterly unable to provide. Since natural selection is untestable, evolutionists fearlessly make many claims in their scenarios.

According to Darwinian scenarios, natural selection eliminated an acute functioning sense of smell in humans, yet it was unable to eliminate the useless flower of the dandelion, or the four-legged forerunners of whales, seals, and ichthyosaurs as they struggled to return to a sea full of advanced predators and competitors. Such conflicting scenarios show that Darwinism is a story that does not warrant our confidence.

Evolutionary theory does not predict convergence. Evolutionists merely *claim* that extensive convergence is virtually inevitable. They do this because "convergence" is abundant in nature. Their claim conflicts with the complete absence from metazoa of simple enzymes for digesting the world's most abundant organic compounds: cellulose and lignin. This peculiar circumstance is fully explained by message theory.

Evolutionists want to show that Darwinism is testable, so they offer various "challenges." In truth, the challenges are empty. They test the ingenuity of Darwinists, at giving scenarios (as in Darwin's challenge), or refraining from giving scenarios (as in Riddiford and Penny's challenge). As another example, Ruse resolutely claims that evolution cannot be repeated — Schafersman says it can, and gives evidence for it.

Social Darwinism raised selfishness to the level of virtue. Sociobiology then lowered altruistic ideals to the level of hypocrisy.

Sociobiologists argue that human "altruism" is not truly altruistic, but instead is programmed by evolutionary selfishness. They say the same about morality, ethics, love, and human freedom. They say these are all illusions, programmed into us so we cooperate more fully with evolutionary goals. They say we are not truly free, and our thoughts, emotions, and morality are not truly ours — evolution has created us totally. They say evolution programmed us with self-deception (including religion) to prevent us from fully experiencing the painful truth. Some sociobiologists now suggest that ethical and moral behavior can be genetically engineered into future generations. The implications of Sociobiology are stunning.

Many evolutionists find Sociobiology repugnant. They have risen to challenge Sociobiology and drive it from the realm of scientific respectability. Curiously, they use the same arguments that creationists use against evolution. The parallel between these two debates is striking.

Many evolutionists endorse anti-reductionism as a new extended philosophy of science. Anti-reductionism served a strategic purpose. Evolution cannot be 'reduced' to a testable theory, so evolutionists attacked "reductionism" to get around the requirement of testability. Anti-reductionists are really covert anti-falsificationists.

7

Population Genetics

Population genetics studies the mechanisms of genetic change in populations. For evolutionary purposes the most crucial mechanism is **differential survival** because of its unique ability to produce non-random genetic change. In population genetics, "survival" is measured by population growth, (which includes all the effects of reproduction and viability). Thus, differential survival is merely a differential population growth. Differential survival has some ultimate cause, but population genetics is not too concerned with what that cause is. Differential survival — by whatever cause — is a central focus of population genetics.

This chapter examines population genetics and its relationship to evolutionary theory. We begin by reviewing terminology for those readers unfamiliar with genetics.

Terminology

A genome is an organism's entire set of DNA. In higher organisms the DNA is arranged on chromosomes. Some organisms are haploid, they have only one of each chromosome. Most organisms are diploid, they have a pair of each chromosome — their basic chromosome number is doubled.

A gene is the functional unit of DNA. It is nominally the hereditary material necessary to control the synthesis of one protein or enzyme. Typically, we name a gene after the protein for which it codes. Such as the hemoglobin gene, which codes for the hemoglobin molecule used in blood.

An allele is a variant of a gene. For example, there are several variants of the hemoglobin gene. The one causing sickle-cell anemia is called the sickle-cell allele. (The terms *gene* and *allele* are often used interchangeably.)

Diploid organisms have two of each gene. This pair of alleles determines the genotype. If the two alleles are the same, then the genotype is a homozygote. If the two alleles are different, the genotype is a heterozygote.

Population genetics uses a parameter known as the selective value, or fitness. (The term *fitness* will be avoided here, because it is confusing and misrepresentative.) These terms describe the magnitude of the differential survival, and are typically expressed as a number ranging from 0 to 1, indicating the relative survival rate. Selective values of 0 and 0.5 are lethal and 50% survival, respectively.

Genotypes are denoted by pairs of letters. Suppose a population has two hemoglobin alleles called S and A. There are three ways these can pair-up in an organism: SS, AA, and SA. The genotypes SS and AA are homozygotes, and the genotype SA is a heterozygote. Selective values are associated with each genotype. The survival of each allele, S and A, is ultimately determined by the selective values of the allele *pairs*: SS, AA, and SA.

A gene locus is the location or site of a gene on the chromosome. Loci is the plural of locus.

Population genetics is interested in allele *frequencies*. The frequency of an allele can vary between 0 and 1, meaning zero percent and 100 percent respectively. If the sickle-cell allele has a frequency of 0.25, then twenty-five percent of the hemoglobin genes in the population are of the sickle-cell type.

A gene can spread through a population until it has a frequency at or near 1 (100 percent). The gene is then said to be fixed in the population; it has reached fixation.

*

One way a gene spreads is by migration. This occurs when an organism from a sub-population immigrates into another group and mates. A stream of immigrants results in gene flow from one sub-population to another. The gene flow mixes the populations' genes together, so the population is genetically homogeneous. Gene flow causes the sub-populations to lose their genetic distinctiveness and blend into one large, genetically unified population.

Geneticists simulate migration by using a two-dimensional "stepping stone" model. The model assumes sub-populations are distributed over a two-dimensional area and exchange migrants only with their nearest neighbor groups. The results are notable. If sub-populations exchange merely one individual per generation with a neighboring group, then the entire population becomes genetically homogeneous.[1] This surprisingly small migration is enough to unify sub-populations. Just a little migration can genetically transform many small sub-populations into one large unified population. This seemingly innocent mechanism is used in much evolutionary storytelling.

Population Genetics is not Natural Selection

Natural selection and population genetics are distinctly separate bodies of theory. Natural selection can be discussed, debated, and shown to be unscientific, without any detailed discussion of genetics. The fatal problems with natural selection have little to do with genetics, (as shown in previous chapters.)

Moreover, the central mechanism of natural selection — survival of the fittest — is not within population genetics. Survival of the fittest is intended as a general theory of survival. It claims to predict the magnitude of differential survival based on biological design. Population genetics does not claim to make that prediction.

Population genetics predicts the genetic *consequences* of differential survival. For example, population genetics does not tell which alleles will survive until you first tell population genetics about the differential survival of the allele pairs.

Will one of the alleles be eliminated from the population while another allele becomes fixed? If so, how many generations will this require? Or will the various alleles remain in the population and move to stable equilibrium frequencies? If so, what are the equilibrium frequencies? These are the types of questions answered by population genetics. These questions can be asked, and answered, without ever referring to survival of the fittest.

---

[1]   Kimura and Ohta, 1971, p 153-154; Maynard Smith, 1989, p 160-161

Population genetics begins where survival of the fittest ends. Population genetics tries to *interface with* (not encompass) survival of the fittest. The interface is unachievable because survival of the fittest is metaphysical.

In fact, if survival of the fittest were false it would not undermine population genetics — the two are entirely independent. Imagine that the 'unfit' organisms and genotypes survive better than the 'fit.' If this proposition were true, it would not alter population genetics in the slightest. Even the predictions would remain identical and every bit as accurate. This is because population genetics depends only on differential survival — not survival of the fittest.

*

When a critic says natural selection is not science, evolutionists claim population genetics as their most broad counter-example. To maintain this illusion, they try to entangle natural selection within population genetics. Terminology creates the illusion:

- Population genetics uses a parameter called *fitness* — defined in terms of survival. This gives the erroneous impression that 'survival of the fittest' is within the machinery of population genetics. This also provides avenues for tautology. When *fitness* and *survival* are the same — as they are in population genetics — then *survival of the fittest* is a tautology.

- Population genetics is about 'differential survival of genotypes,' and evolutionists call this "natural selection." This gives the erroneous impression that natural selection is within the machinery of population genetics. This also provides avenues for lame formulations. (Differential survival is lame because it does not try to explain adaptation.)

- Population genetics uses the term *selection* as a shorthand for either "natural selection" or "differential survival." This one word — selection — can lead to either tautology or lame formulations. This ambiguity gives further latitude for evasive action.

These terminologies lend themselves to the various forms of confusion documented in the previous chapters. If we exclude this misuse of terminology, then population genetics is scientific and its findings impinge with equal validity on both sides of the origins debate.

*

Summarized simply: population genetics is science; natural selection is not — the two are separate. All the theorems and results of population genetics can be stated without any reference to survival of the fittest or natural selection.

Tautology Revisited

Kitcher gives an example of natural selection from population genetics.

> "It is not easy to formulate the idea that 'the fittest survive' if we try to provide a principle about *organisms*. On the other hand, if we want a principle about *genes*, then we can obtain detailed mathematical results about the relations between fitness and the representation of genotypes. The task of mathematical population genetics is to work out the mathematical intricacies of the ways in which the distributions of genetic combinations will vary in a sequence of populations, according to the relative fitnesses of the relevant allelic pairs. Consider a simple example. Suppose that at a locus, there are two alleles, A and a. The allelic pairs AA, Aa, aa have relative fitness 0.9, 1.0, and 0. It is a theorem of population genetics that the lethal allele a will persist in the population at a frequency of 0.09. ....
>
> Mathematical population genetics articulates precisely the idea that genes that are more fit become prevalent in a population. .... The claim that the fittest survive becomes an array of definite results about the distribution of genes in successive populations.
>
> So the tautology objection is wrong in the first place because the principle of natural selection is not a tautology. Insofar as the principle has an heir in contemporary evolutionary theory, it is a collection of theorems in mathematical population genetics." (Kitcher, 1982, p 58)

Kitcher offers mathematical population genetics as an explicit, broad example of how survival of the fittest is not tautological. His comments show the depth of confusion surrounding this issue. The mathematical population genetic formulations of survival of the fittest are tautological without exception.[2]

We need to be careful not to be confused by his example. It is a legitimate theorem of population genetics. The theorem predicts *future survival* of alleles, based on the *present survival* of the allele *pairs*. Yes, a scientific prediction is made, but Kitcher erroneously attributes it to survival of the fittest.

In population genetics, fitness is defined in terms of survival.[3] If you define *fitness* in terms of survival[4] and invoke *survival of the fittest*, then you have given a

---

[2] I am referring specifically to the standard mathematical population genetic definitions of *fitness* and *relative fitness*. These are always defined in terms of survival. So, survival of the fittest is always tautological.

[3] *Fitness* is defined in terms of survival. Ayala defines fitness as, "The reproductive contribution of an organism or genotype to the following generations." (Ayala, 1982, p 240) Mayr does likewise, "[T]he mathematical population geneticists ... considered evolution as a change in gene frequencies and *defined fitness simply as the contribution of a gene to the gene pool of the next generation*." (Mayr, 1982, p 596, my italics) An applaudably direct definition is given by Minkoff. "The relative fitness of each genotype is *defined as its survival rate expressed as a fraction of the maximal survival rate*. The relative fitness of the optimal genotype is therefore defined as equal to 1.00, and the relative fitnesses of other genotypes are calculated as proportionate fractions or percentages." (Minkoff, 1983, p 188, my italics) Minkoff's definition is less ambiguous than Ayala's or Mayr's, but in practice they all are applied the same: fitness is survival.

173

tautology. This is precisely what Kitcher has done. It is a common mistake, and it results from evolutionary geneticists using terms — like fitness — in a confusing manner. Evolutionists are trying to take scientific results from population genetics and attribute them to natural selection. They are trying to make the Darwinian mechanism seem like science. Kitcher fell into the error caused by the terminological confusion.

*

When evolutionists force natural selection into population genetics, it frequently shows up as tautology. Gould acknowledges that the tautology is commonplace.

> [The tautology criticism] applies to much of the technical literature in evolutionary theory, especially to the abstract mathematical treatments that consider evolution only as an alteration in numbers, not as a change in quality. These studies do assess fitness only in terms of differential survival. What else can be done with abstract models that trace the relative successes of hypothetical genes A and B in populations that exist only on computer tape? (Gould, 1983b, p 143)

Gould says the tautology occurs because the data "exist only on computer tape." That rationale does not justify the tautology. A tautology is a definition masquerading as an explanation. Computer tape cannot create the masquerade. Evolutionists create it on their own, and cannot blame it on a computer.

---

4 Even Kitcher's anti-creation book has the information necessary to see the tautology. In the section where he argues against the tautology objection, he indicates that fitness is measured by measuring survival: "Scientists estimate the relative fitnesses of different alleles at the same locus by taking the fitness of an allele (or, more exactly, of an allelic pair) to be *measured by its representation in future generations.*" (Kitcher, 1982, p 57, my italics)

Neutral Evolution versus Selection

Classical selection theory argued that differential survival should eliminate diversity — leaving only the best allele in the population. Selection should eliminate all but the one allele with the highest survival. In this way, differential survival should constantly work to minimize genetic variation. Selection theory expected little genetic variation.

Nearly three decades ago, new techniques allowed measurement of genetic variation for the first time. The results were a surprise. In most populations, each gene has many versions (known as alleles). In fact, there is much more genetic variation than can be reconciled with the classical selection theory. This unanticipated result prompted various theoretical developments to accommodate it.

The selectionists modified their theory by adding several mechanisms for *actively maintaining* genetic diversity. These mechanisms are called heterozygote advantage and balancing selection. These special types of selection work to keep variation. The selectionists felt their newly modified theory could explain the data.

Nonetheless, a rival theory developed — the theory of neutral evolution. The neutralists argued that *most* (but not all) genetic change in evolution is neutral. Neutral genes drift in and out of the population. Selection cannot eliminate these neutral alleles because they have no effect on survival. Neutral evolution is merely the comings and goings of neutral genes. The neutralists argued that most genetic variation is due to neutral genes. In this way, neutralists felt their theory could explain the new data.

Thus, two opposing camps emerged: the neutralists and the selectionists. Their differences seem conspicuous and irreconcilable. Is most genetic variation due to differential survival or not? Are most gene substitutions selective, or neutral? Little in evolutionary genetics could be more basic than these questions. Yet these two clashingly different theoretical approaches were each able to accommodate the available data. This situation shows the remarkable flexibility of the theories of evolutionary genetics.

*

The neutral evolution versus selection controversy generated much heat. After many years of this dissonance, the Harvard geneticist, Richard Lewontin, lamented the inability of population genetics to decide the situation.

> For many years population genetics was an immensely rich and powerful theory with virtually no suitable facts on which to operate. It was like a complex and exquisite machine, designed to process a raw material that no one had succeeded in mining. .... Quite suddenly the situation has changed. The mother-lode has been tapped and facts in profusion have been poured into the hoppers of this theory machine. And from the other end has issued — nothing. It is not that the machinery does not work, for a great clashing of gears is clearly audible, if not deafening, but it somehow cannot transform into a finished product the great volume of raw material that has been provided. The entire relationship between the theory and the facts needs to be reconsidered. (Lewontin, 1974, p 189)

Nonetheless, the neutralist-selectionist controversy remains unresolved. Today, population genetics still struggles with its inability to come to grips with this fundamental issue.[5]

Lewontin forcefully stated the shortcomings of population genetics:

> [P]opulation genetics is not an empirically sufficient theory .... Built into [population genetic] theory are parameters and combinations of parameters that are not measurable to the degree of accuracy required. (Lewontin, 1974, p 266-267)

> If one simply cannot measure the state variables or the parameters with which the theory is constructed, or if their measurement is so laden with error that no discrimination between alternative hypotheses is possible, the theory becomes a vacuous exercise in formal logic that has no points of contact with the contingent world. *The theory explains nothing because it explains everything. It is my contention that a good deal of the structure of evolutionary genetics comes perilously close to being of this sort.* (Lewontin, 1974, p 12, my italics)

The theme of Lewontin's noted book was that population genetics has an abundance of mathematical sophistication, but little touch with the empirical world. In his wording, the theory is "not empirically sufficient." He sees that evolutionists have ignored this problem.

> It is a remarkable feature of the sociology of science that evolutionary biologists have persistently ignored the problem of empirical sufficiency.[6] (Lewontin, 1974, p 10)

Population genetics is science, but it is often closer to mathematical science than empirical science. The results you get, depend more on the assumptions you make, than on any empirical observations of the real world. In genetics there are so many 'real,' 'possible,' or 'speculated' mechanisms operating that theorists are forced to make dramatic simplifying assumptions to reduce a problem to manageable size.

Population genetics is also a field whose mathematical sophistication far outstrips its ability to make measurements of the basic parameters. For example, the most important parameter in population genetics is the *selective value* (remember to read this for the word "fitness"). Lewontin describes our limited success in measuring this central parameter:

---

[5] "[Population genetics is] a field in disarray, with contending schools of explanation, apparently no closer to agreement on outstanding issues than they were 35 years ago when I first entered the professional study of the subject. .... Population genetics as a whole seems as unable as ever to solve the problems it has set for itself." (Lewontin, 1985, p 4-5)

[6] Lewontin documented several cases in his field of population genetics.

176

Although there is no difficulty in theory in estimating fitnesses, in practice the difficulties are virtually insuperable. *To the present moment no one has succeeded in measuring with any accuracy the net fitnesses of genotypes for any locus in any species in any environment in nature.* (Lewontin, 1974, p 236, his italics)

[N]et fitness cannot be measured in nature except in special circumstances, so far not fulfilled. (Lewontin, 1974, p 239)

The reasons for the difficulty are twofold. First, there are statistical problems that place the desired accuracy of measurement beyond our reach.

[I]f we want to be 95 percent sure that we know some proportion within 2 percent of its true value, we must count 10,000 cases. In a real world with experimental error we must count more. .... We must give up the idea of directly measuring selection differences of the order of 1 percent, and 1 percent is probably large for most loci if we average over all other genes. (Lewontin, 1974, p 268)

Second, genes have many complex interactions, and our techniques often cannot isolate the genes whose survival we wish to measure. Lewontin describes these problems and acknowledges our inability to measure the essential data.[7]

Evolutionarily significant genetic variation is then, almost by definition, variation that is manifest in subtle differences between individuals, *often so subtle as to be completely overwhelmed by effects of other genes or of the environment.* (Lewontin, 1974, p 22, my italics)

Population genetics is like castles in the sky: intricately and beautifully constructed, yet often out of touch with empirical reality. Let us put it in perspective: Population genetics is respectable science, but under that hard math are soft assumptions. Are those 'airy' assumptions reasonable ones?

My point here is not to call the assumptions into serious question, but rather to acknowledge their manifold abundance. Population genetics is a remarkably flexible body of mathematical models, as amply shown by the history of the neutral evolution versus selection controversy.

---

[7] Lewontin (1985) reaffirmed his view many years later.

The Bean-bag Model

In population genetics, many assumptions are made to simplify the models and get results. The standard assumption is that genes are viewed in isolation, independently of their effects on each other. Each gene is substituted into a population based solely on its own singular selective value. This model is sometimes called bean-bag genetics because it assumes genes to be independent 'bean-bag' entities. The idea assumes away some theoretical obstacles to evolution.

Pleiotropy is when genes affect more than one trait. For example, in flies there is a gene affecting eye color that also affects the reproductive organs.

Polygeny is when a biological trait is affected by more than one gene.

Pleiotropy and polygeny are prevalent in life. This means there is typically no one-to-one correspondence between genes and traits. Each gene affects more than one trait — and each trait is affected by more than one gene. By analogy, each trait is a jig-saw puzzle, composed of *many* pieces (this is polygeny). Yet each jigsaw piece must fit *multiple* jig-saw puzzles (this is pleiotropy).

This creates a problem for evolution. How can each jig-saw piece evolve when there is all this interlocking and interdependency of the various puzzles? The standard model of population genetics assumes these problems out of existence.

*

Open any textbook on evolutionary genetics. There you will be dazzled with mathematical results derived from the standard (bean-bag) model. Even these simplified results do not readily lend themselves to empirical test (as Lewontin pointed out).

Despite the universality of the standard model as textbook orthodoxy, it has been quietly abandoned by leading evolutionary geneticists. Yet it has not been officially replaced. It is now just part of the evolutionary smorgasbord: embraced one minute, rejected the next. One minute it is offered to you as the jewel of evolutionary theory; the next minute it is overlooked in favor of drastically different models. It all depends on the question you ask. This will be seen vividly in the next chapter.

Beneficial and Neutral Mutations

In population genetics a beneficial, advantageous, or helpful trait is one that increases survival. A harmful or deleterious trait decreases survival. These concepts are usefully defined in terms of differential survival. There is nothing vague about such definitions. Nor are they tautological, as long as you do not "explain" their survival in terms of their survival.

A neutral trait is one having no effect on survival — it has neutral effect. It is neither helpful nor harmful. Neutral traits are selectively indistinguishable. Thus, beneficial traits have a positive effect on survival. Harmful traits have a negative effect. Neutral traits have no effect on survival.

Envision a spectrum ranging smoothly from harmful, to neutral, to helpful. Neutral traits are not depicted by a singular 'point' on this spectrum. Rather, neutral traits occupy a range centered on zero. The width of that range depends on the effective population size N_e. N_e determines the 'width' of the neutral range.

There is no clear-cut line of demarcation for neutral traits. Yet theorists have reached a consensus opinion.[8] Neutral traits have a selective differential s below $1/N_e$. When s falls below this, the propagation of the trait is effectively neutral in character — its survival is determined predominantly by chance. When the population size is extremely large (to infinite) this range is diminished to a singular point. As the population decreases toward zero, the range of effective neutrality expands.

Suppose a certain trait gives a selective advantage of one-percent in a very large population. In a population of 100, this same trait is *effectively neutral*. The trait has not changed, but the context has. In the small population, the trait is bantered back and forth by the whims of chance — chance dominates the process. While in the large population, the effects of chance are averaged out — so the one-percent selective advantage dominates over random chance.

Think of it this way. Nature has "noise." When differential survival is sufficiently small it disappears into the noise. Nature cannot see the differential survival through all the noise, so the noise has the dominant effect. The smaller the population, the greater is the noise. In smaller populations the noise overwhelms the effect of selection.

*

Additional genetic "noise" is caused by genetic drift. Genetic drift (also known as drift) is a random process affecting the propagation of genes without regard for their selective value. Drift can eliminate helpful genes and it can establish harmful genes, all by chance.

A main cause of drift is the sampling error inevitable in sexually reproducing organisms. A progeny cannot be a perfect copy of two different parents. A progeny is an incomplete sample of each parent. A progeny gets only half of each parent's genome. This sampling process has an inherent error that causes genetic drift.

---

[8]   Wills, 1981, p 34

In preparation for reproduction, adults produce gametes (sperm and egg) by a process of meiosis, which reduces the number of chromosomes by one half. When sperm and egg unite, the result is a progeny with a full set of chromosomes.

The gamete has half the genes of the adult. So, in an adult male, a given gene has a 50% chance of getting into a given sperm, and therefore to a given progeny. Likewise, for a female and her eggs. Thus, every gene is reproduced by the flip of a coin, independently of its value to survival. During a reproductive event, the selective value of the gene makes no difference — its chance of reproduction is 50%. Because of this chancy reproductive process, some genes do not make it into the next generation.

Now, take a wider view of the whole population. A gene can have many copies of itself within the population. Genes can get into a progeny through a male parent, or through a female parent. Viewed broadly, genes have *two* opportunities (*at 50% chance each*) of getting into a given progeny. These factors offset each other, so gene frequencies remain nearly constant from one generation to the next. Drift operates on top of this, to randomly alter gene frequencies.

Genetic drift is like flipping coins. When you flip many coins, you are likely to get nearly a fifty-fifty split between heads and tails. When you flip a few coins, the split is likely to skew one way or the other from 50 percent. This statistical skew drives genetic drift. When there are many copies of a gene in a population, its total numbers are relatively unaffected by drift. But when there are only a few copies, its numbers fluctuate rapidly.

Through drift, genes are eliminated or fixed randomly, and this effect is stronger and faster when there are fewer copies of a gene. Drift is especially forceful on new rare genes, often eliminating them altogether before they ever get a foothold in the population. For the same reason, drift is strongest in small populations, where *all* genes exist in small numbers.

*

Drift and differential survival operate at cross purposes, and the net result can be counter-intuitive. For example, most beneficial mutations never reach fixation, but are eliminated from the population by drift, despite the advantage they confer. This tends to occur within the first ten generations after the entrance of the beneficial mutation into the population.[9]

> Only a small fraction of the beneficial mutants is lucky enough to escape accidental loss in the first few generations of their existence. The fortunate few eventually attain a frequency high enough to protect them from further risk of chance extinction ... (Kimura and Ohta, 1971, p 3)

---

[9] If a mutant gene is selectively neutral, the probability is 0.79 it will be lost from the population during the first seven generations. If the mutant gene has a selective advantage of one-percent (said to be higher than typical of evolution), the corresponding probability of such loss decreases only to 0.78 — the probability of loss is less by only one chance in a hundred.

Let s be the selection coefficient of a beneficial mutation. For small values of s (said to be typical of evolution) the chance of the mutant eventually reaching fixation is $2s$. For example, a mutant with a one-percent advantage ($s = 0.01$) has only one chance in fifty that it will eventually spread to the entire population.[10] Likewise, for every mutant gene having a selective advantage of ½ percent that becomes fixed in the population, 99 equally advantageous mutants have been lost, without ever being used in evolution.[11] This result is based on the assumption that the population is extremely large (approaching infinity).

In a smaller population the outlook is less hopeful. The smaller the population, the smaller is the chance of receiving a beneficial mutation in the first place. A population one tenth as large must wait ten times longer for a beneficial mutation.

Also, the smaller the population, the more genetic drift dominates over differential survival.

> "The fact that the majority of mutants, including those having a slight advantage, are lost by chance is important in considering the problems of evolution by mutation, since the overwhelming majority of advantageous mutations are likely to have only a slightly advantageous effect. ....
>
> In our opinion, this fact has not fully been acknowledged in many discussions of evolution. It is often tacitly assumed that every advantageous mutation that appears in the population is inevitably incorporated. Also, it is not generally recognized that this fact can set an upper limit to the speed of adaptive evolution, because the frequency of occurrence of advantageous mutations must be much lower than that of deleterious mutations. (Incidentally, *this fact gives a great evolutionary advantage to a large population.*)" (Kimura and Ohta, 1971, p 11, my italics)

Kimura and Ohta correctly point out the great evolutionary advantage of large population sizes. They note that small population size can limit the speed of evolution. This conflicts with the claims of many paleontologists, who (based on fossil gaps) assert that the small population is where rapid evolution occurs.

---

[10] Kimura and Ohta, 1971, p 3; Maynard Smith, 1989, p 161-162

[11] Kimura and Ohta, 1971, p 10-11

Probability Overlooked Again

An earlier chapter showed how evolutionists frequently overlook probability science. They underestimate how rapidly probability can become a forbidding barrier. It is a casual oversight, yet a common one. McGowan provides an example from genetics.

> All the possible mutations which can occur have probably already occurred many times over, and it is likely that all the advantageous ones have been incorporated into the gene pool of the species. (McGowan, 1984, p 40)

McGowan makes two points, both false. First, there are too many possible mutations for all to have occurred at least once (much less many times over). There are 10^{130} possible proteins merely 100 amino acid units in length, far too many to have all occurred once (even over cosmic time-scales). Yet a 100 unit protein represents only a minuscule fraction of the genome.[12] Take an organism whose haploid genome size is 3.5×10^9 nucleotide sites (like mammals). There are over 10^{48} possible variations differing from that organism by merely *five* nucleotide mutations.[13] They could not all have occurred on earth — there has not been enough time.[14]

Second, McGowan makes the common mistake of assuming that all advantageous mutations are successfully incorporated into evolution. In reality, almost all advantageous mutations are eliminated by genetic drift and play no role in evolution.

---

[12] A 100 unit protein represents roughly one ten-millionth of the human genome.

[13] When the number of mutations N is not too large, the number of variations is roughly $3^N \times (3.5 \times 10^9)^N / N!$ The $(3.5 \times 10^9)^N / N!$ term is the number of combinations taken N at a time. The 3^N term is the number of variations for each combination — there are 3 alternative nucleotides for each nucleotide site (since there are 4 nucleotides in all).

[14] Actually the situation is somewhat worse. In an organism with a genome size of $N = 3.5 \times 10^9$ nucleotide sites (like mammals) there are 3N (or 10.5×10^9) possible variations that differ from the original by a *single* nucleotide mutation. In nature these occur randomly, so to get them *all* to occur will require not 3N attempts but roughly $3N \times Ln(3N+1)$ attempts. (By the time they have all occurred, some will have occurred many times, while others only once.) This is 242 billion attempts — more than many higher mammalian species produce during their entire existence. Thus, many species will not experience all possible variations that differ from the original by merely *one* nucleotide site. McGowan is wrong when he says all possible mutations have probably already occurred.

The Fundamental Theorem of Natural Selection

The Fundamental Theorem of Natural Selection was developed in 1930 by the evolutionary geneticist, Sir Ronald Fisher. It is typically presented like this:

> Fisher's (1930) fundamental theorem of natural selection states that the rate of change in the mean biological fitness of a population is equal to the additive genetic variance in fitness. Since variances are always positive, this implies that mean fitness never decreases, an elegant result which neatly captures the flavor of Darwin's assertion that natural selection leads inevitably to the improvement of the species. (Findlay, 1990, p 367)

Gould calls Fisher the "twentieth-century patron saint" of evolutionary biology, and regards Fisher's Theorem as the centerpiece of the keystone book of modern Darwinism.[15] The evolutionary geneticist, James Crow, speaks highly of the theorem:

> To me, even if Fisher's fundamental theorem is inexact and incomplete, this succinct statement captures the essence of the way selection works, and encapsulates a great deal of evolutionary insight in a simple expression. (Crow, 1990, p 270)

Such presentations suggest that natural selection is a proven fact with a precise mathematical foundation. In this way, evolutionists use Fisher's theorem to support the illusion that natural selection is science.

An illustration will help explain the real meaning of Fisher's theorem. If you placed money into a bank account where it earned 3 percent interest (compounded continuously), then you would not be surprised when you returned later and found it was still earning the same rate of interest, 3 percent.

However, if you placed half your money in a 2 percent account and the other half in a 4 percent account, then it would initially earn an *average* of 3 percent, but the average would increase with time. This is because, given time, a greater portion of your money will be in the 4 percent account. The average starts at 3 percent and slowly rises toward 4 percent. The Fundamental Theorem predicts the speed that it rises.[16]

The theorem is about growth rates. In bank accounts we refer to the growth as "interest rates." In living organisms it might be a Malthusian growth rate of populations, for example.

---

[15] Gould, 1991b, p 8 & 15

[16] First, we convert to Malthusian growth rates. Account #1 is 4 percent per year ($m_1 = 0.04$) and account #2 is 2 percent per year ($m_2 = 0.02$). The variance in m is 0.0001, so the average m is initially rising by 0.0001 per year. To interpret the results we convert back to interest rates. At the start, the average interest rate is 3 percent per year, rising by 0.01 per year. (At the end of the first year, the average interest rate is 3.01 percent per year, and the variance is reduced slightly below 0.0001.)

Let GR be the *average growth rate.*[17] The theorem says:

Rate of increase in GR = Variance of growth rates
(Variance is a statistical measure of variation.[18])

The greater the variance, the faster GR will rise.

Imagine you place money into accounts that earn different rates of interest, including *negative* interest. The Fundamental Theorem still applies. There is nothing biological about it — you simply place your money into different accounts and leave — the differential growth rates do the rest. As long as there is differential growth, the theorem indicates GR will be increasing.

The theorem does not guarantee GR will be positive. Imagine the accounts all give different rates of negative interest. GR will be negative. GR will be increasing (upward toward the least negative interest rate), as predicted by the theorem, but you will continually be losing money.

Those are actual applications of Fisher's theorem.[19] In genetics, the theorem is applied as follows. A population is comprised of distinct identifiable groups, each with its own population growth rate. So, each group is like a bank account.

*

The Fundamental Theorem is not about design, adaptation, or survival of the fittest. It is about differential growth rates. The theorem is misnamed. It is better called the *Fundamental Theorem of Differential Accrual.* The theorem is ineffectual at solving the problem of adaptation.

---

[17] Suppose there are N groups, each with its own Malthusian growth rate. Let p_i be the fraction of the total group that is in group i. Let m_i represent the growth rate of group i. Then GR is the growth rate averaged over m_i and the distribution of p_i. In statistics this is known as the *mean.* It is the sum of $m_i p_i$, as i goes from 1 to N.

[18] The variance is given by: (the sum of $m_i^2 p_i$, as i goes from 1 to N) minus GR^2.

[19] Since Fisher published his theorem it has been applied (with slight alterations) to cases of: (1) haploidy and diploidy; (2) discrete generation time (analogous to 'periodic' rather than 'continuous' compounding of interest); (3) formulations in terms of "linear fitness," rather than Fisher's original "logarithmic fitness" formulation; and (4) heterozygote advantage (where some of the variance is not "additive" and so does not contribute to incrementing the average survival). The various formulations incorporate models of heredity to different extents, but they have not altered the essence of the theorem.

In the bank accounts illustration, heterozygote advantage is like having three accounts (representing two homozygous and one heterozygous) where moneys are transferred between the accounts at fixed rates. In this situation, it is possible to have 'interest rate variance' between the accounts in such a way that the 'average interest rate' is *not* rising—the percentage of your moneys in each account remains constant. In particular, this is due to *flow* from the higher to the lower rate accounts. In heterozygote advantage this is analogous to *gene flow* from the higher surviving heterozygote to the lower surviving homozygotes due to Mendelian reproduction.

Nonetheless, Fisher gave a glowing appraisal of his idea. Of all things, he ranks it as high as the second law of thermodynamics: the universal tendency toward disorder.

> It will be noticed that the fundamental theorem proved above bears some remarkable resemblances to the second law of thermodynamics. ... each requires the constant increase of a measurable quantity, in one case the entropy of a physical system and in the other the fitness, measured by m, of a biological population. .... Professor Eddington has recently remarked that 'The law that entropy always increases — the second law of thermodynamics — holds, I think the supreme position among the laws of nature.' It is not a little instructive that so similar a law should hold the supreme position among the biological sciences. While it is possible that both may ultimately be absorbed by some more general principle, for the present we should note that the laws as they stand present profound differences — (1) The systems considered in thermodynamics are permanent; species on the contrary are liable to extinction, *although biological improvement must be expected to occur up to the end of their existence.* ... (Fisher, 1930, p 39-40, my italics)

Fisher says biological improvement of a species must be expected to occur up to the end of their existence. Thus, he builds the central illusion of naive natural selection. The illusion is aided by the use of the confusing term *fitness*. His error becomes visible when we replace *fitness* with the more appropriate term "growth rate."[20] Intuitively, we know that the growth rate cannot increase indefinitely.

Fisher did not clarify two aspects of the theorem:

- The theorem only holds true when growth rates are constant and unchanging.[21]

- The process itself diminishes the 'variance' in growth rates, so the process slows to a halt.

I have found no evolutionary texts that bring these two points to reader's attention. With those points omitted, readers got the erroneous impression that Fisher's theorem applies continually, under the widest circumstances in nature. That misperception supported evolutionary illusions: Since there is always variation in natural populations, the theorem seemed to prove that "fitness will increase indefinitely." And that is how evolutionists presented it.

Yet, the theorem cannot cope with changing growth rates. Specifically, it cannot handle: (1) the creation of new growth rates, (2) the removal of old growth rates, or (3) the alteration of existing growth rates. If such changes occur, then the

---

[20] Fisher indicates that fitness is measured by m, which is the Malthusian growth rate of the population.

[21] Also, Fisher's theorem holds true only when the growth rate of a group is identical for all group members. In the bank accounts illustration, this is automatically true. But in life it is not.

theorem does not apply. This is easiest to see in the bank accounts illustration. Imagine the various interest rates are all dropping, or that lower interest rate accounts are opened, then GR (the average interest rate) will drop.

This can happen in nature too. In life, such change can arise from many sources: mutation, recombination, migration, extinction, and from environmental changes. The theorem only applies in cases where such factors can rightly be ignored.

For example, a major source of change is mutation, yet Fisher's Theorem has no means to handle mutation. Suppose a population suddenly receives many harmful mutations (say from a dose of x-rays). Some individuals are harmed more than others, and the population growth rates thereby increase in variation. Fisher's theorem concludes only that GR suddenly rises *faster* than before. The theorem completely ignores the sudden dramatic drop in GR resulting from the deleterious mutations.

The Fundamental Theorem cannot handle change, yet change is the very thing evolutionists seek to explain. If the growth rates change, then the theorem does not apply. If the growth rates are unchanging, then the theorem says the process will slow to a halt. The theorem could hardly be less useful to evolutionists.

*

Evolutionists argue that evolutionary improvement is virtually inevitable. They build this illusion by misinterpreting the Fundamental Theorem.

> If we take the theorem literally, the mean fitness of the population should increase indefinitely as long as there is additive variance for this trait. (Crow, 1986, p 85)

Crow claims the theorem shows that fitness should increase *indefinitely* (as long as the requirements of the theorem are met). The Fundamental Theorem says nothing of the sort. Instead, it says the process will slow to a halt. The process has definite bounds it cannot go beyond.

Crow knows that, in nature, selective values do not increase indefinitely. He knows that nature is at odds with his interpretation of the Fundamental Theorem, so in his next paragraph he tries to explain the discrepancy. He argues that the environment of a species is constantly deteriorating because of diminishing resources, overcrowding, increasing waste products, and especially because of the evolution of other species. Crow claims this environmental deterioration offsets the genetic improvement predicted by the Fundamental Theorem.

Again, Crow has misinterpreted the Fundamental Theorem. The theorem cannot be applied in situations where the environment is changing. The theorem has no provisions for handling environmental change.

Crow's evolutionary genetics text (1986, p 196) shows additional errors on the matter. Crow assumed a continuous, long-term rate of gene substitution, and then used the Fundamental Theorem to calculate the variance necessary to achieve that rate. This requires a hidden assumption that some mechanism is

186

continually injecting variance into the population to replenish the process.[22] But that assumption itself voids the use of Fisher's theorem.[23]

*

The theorem lacks the meanings that evolutionists typically attribute to it. For example, Gould interprets it this way:

> [R]oughly, the rate of evolution by natural selection is directly proportional to the amount of usable genetic variation maintained in a population. Or even more roughly, genetic variation is a good thing if you want to accelerate the rate of evolution. (Gould, 1991b, p 15)

Here is an example from the college level textbook, *Evolutionary Biology:*

> In other words, evolutionary change can occur more rapidly in variable than in uniform populations. (Minkoff, 1983, p 206)

> By a corollary of Fisher's fundamental theorem, a variable population has an increased chance of continuing to evolve under changing environmental conditions. (Minkoff, 1983, p 206)

Gould and Minkoff indicate that variation allows evolution to go faster. This is a common misrepresentation that arises from forcing evolutionary imagery into the sterile theorem. The theorem does not use 'evolutionary change' and 'variation' as most people interpret those concepts.

To see the distortion, just translate to the bank accounts idea. In effect, evolutionists are saying that money increases faster in *various* fixed-rate accounts. The error then becomes visible. If you use fixed-rate accounts (as you must if you are to apply Fisher's theorem), then money increases fastest *when it is all in one account* — the one with the highest interest.

*

In summary, evolutionists use Fisher's Fundamental Theorem to enhance several illusions: (1) that natural selection is science, (2) that evolutionary improvement is virtually inevitable, and (3) that variation makes evolution go faster.

In truth, Fisher's theorem is not about natural selection, survival of the fittest, or adaptation. Rather, like population genetics, it is about differential survival. When the theorem applies, it predicts the process will slow to a halt. On the other hand, if genomes or environments are changing, then the theorem does not apply. The theorem could hardly be less useful to evolutionists. The Fundamental Theorem is completely compatible with creation theory.

---

[22] Crow made yet another error in his application of the Fundamental Theorem. He made the hidden assumption that *all* additive variance goes toward substituting beneficial mutations. In reality, much of the additive variance is due to the load of *harmful* mutations, and is used up in eliminating them.

[23] Evolutionists (such as Felsenstein, 1971, p 10, and Crow, 1968, p 165-178) have used Crow's erroneous application of Fisher's Theorem in a mistaken attempt to: increase the theoretical rate of evolution, avoid the cost of gene substitution, and solve Haldane's Dilemma.

Maynard Smith's Test of Darwinism

John Maynard Smith believes natural selection is scientific, and he tries to show it is testable. He suggests observations that he feels would refute the theory: the possibility "that evolutionary changes occur more rapidly than can be explained by neo-Darwinism."

> This would be quite easy to demonstrate if it occurred on a small scale in the laboratory. Thus suppose, for example, a population of fruit flies were kept at an unusually high temperature. By measuring the genetic variance of temperature tolerance in the population before starting, it would be possible to predict the maximum rate at which temperature tolerance would increase. If in fact it increased faster than this, then the population would have evolved by a mechanism other than neo-Darwinism. (Maynard Smith, 1972, p 86)

Accordingly to Maynard Smith, if the population actually changes *faster* than predicted, then Darwinism must be mistaken. Though not readily visible, this is an application of Fisher's Fundamental Theorem, so I will restate his argument in those terms.

- Keep fruit flies at an unusually high temperature.

- Measure the population sizes and growth rates of the various genotypes.

- The Fundamental Theorem predicts that the rate of increase of the average growth rate is equal to the variance of the growth rates.[24]

- If the actual rate of increase is faster than predicted, then the population would have evolved by a mechanism other than neo-Darwinism.

The Fundamental Theorem is mathematically proven.[25] It is always true, as long as the growth rates are unchanging. Any *empirical* discrepancies would simply mean that the growth rates changed and that the theorem did not apply to this case: The theorem itself would still stand.

In addition, Darwinism *requires* that the Fundamental Theorem does not apply much of the time. Thus, Maynard Smith's test would not even remotely threaten Darwinism.

More importantly, Maynard Smith constructed his test in a peculiar way. He suggests that to "refute" Darwinism we must provide demonstrations of evolution. Maynard Smith's test is self-contradictory. He indicates that to disprove evolutionary theory we must demonstrate *fast* evolution. This ingenious ploy tries to reverse the roles between evolutionist and adversary. According to Maynard Smith, the adversary must now try to demonstrate fast evolution.

---

[24] More precisely, the theorem says the rate of increase is given by the "additive" variance.

[25] Even if Fisher's theorem were mathematically disproven, it would not falsify natural selection. Fisher's theorem is not about natural selection.

*

Evolutionists are desperate to show that evolution is testable science. Toward this end they offer "tests" having peculiar requirements — they try to exchange positions with an adversary. Maynard Smith has provided one case, there are others. These are not tests of evolution. These are attempts to make evolution look like science.

Sickle-Cell Anemia

Sickle-Cell anemia is discussed in almost all population genetics texts because it is virtually the only well-proven natural example of a phenomenon called *overdominance, heterosis,* or *heterozygote advantage.*[26]

The normal hemoglobin gene is called the *A* allele. Sickle-cell refers to an allele (called *S*) that gives resistance to malaria when either homozygous or heterozygous. An unfortunate side effect of this allele is a disease known as sickle-cell anemia which kills most homozygotes before adulthood. Normally the sickle-cell allele is eliminated from populations due to its near-lethal effect. However, in the malarial environment of West Africa the allele is not eliminated, but is *actively maintained* in the population by differential survival. The homozygous form may be near-lethal, but the heterozygous form offers an advantage against malarial infection — thus the term heterozygote advantage. Population genetics can use the selective values of the allele pairs to predict the equilibrium frequency at which the sickle-cell allele will be maintained in the population.

That was the typical textbook account.

*

Although sickle-cell is the standard textbook example of adaptation, some aspects of it are rarely discussed. In reality, besides the *A* and *S* alleles there is a third, known as the *C* allele. When homozygous, the *C* allele offers the best resistance to malaria, and it additionally does not cause a severe anemia. The *C* allele is associated with the genotype having the highest selective value in a malarial environment, therefore it is surprising that selection acts to insure elimination of this genotype.[27]

---

[26] "Anyone who has taught genetics for a number of years is tired of sickle-cell anemia and embarrassed by the fact that it is the only authenticated case of overdominance available." (Lewontin, 1974, p 37, 199) This situation is still true: "well established examples of overdominance, ... are scarce. So far, sickle cell anemia in man is probably the best example, and this is constantly being cited." (Kimura, 1983, p 124.

[27] Templeton, 1982, p 16-22

Here are the selective values of the genotypes in a malarial environment.[28]

Genotype	Selective value	Condition
AA	0.9	Malarial susceptibility
AS	1.0	Malarial resistance
SS	0.2	Anemia
AC	0.9	Malarial susceptibility
SC	0.7	Anemia
CC	1.3	Malarial resistance

The CC genotype has a selective value of 1.3, the highest of any allele pair. Yet surprisingly, this genotype is eliminated by selection.

The mathematics of the process is complicated, so instead I will offer a descriptive explanation. If the S allele were absent, then the C allele would increase until it became fixed — it would eliminate all other alleles, including any further invasions by an S allele. However, in the case at hand, the *presence* of the S allele ultimately causes the elimination of the C allele.

When the S and C alleles are uncommon, they rarely exist in homozygous form SS or CC. The remaining genotypes AA, AS, AC, and SC then form the preponderance of the population and their selective values determine the course of events. Of these, the AS genotype has the highest selective value and therefore the S allele will increase rapidly in frequency. When it does, the SC genotype (with a selective value of only 0.7) will start to be eliminated. In this way the C alleles will be eliminated before they ever get the chance to exert their influence in homozygous form.

*

This classic field case shows that differential survival can achieve counter-intuitive results.

- The presence of a serious genetic disease can be actively maintained in a population.

- New beneficial alleles can be actively prevented from entering a population.

This contradicts the naive notion that evolution is upward, ever upward.

---

[28] As pointed out earlier, there is great difficulty in measuring selective values smaller than 1%. Note, however, that values for the sickle-cell anemia case are 20% or greater. This made the measurement more tractable.

The Shifting Balance Hypothesis

Recall that natural selection theory has difficulty with fitness barriers: peaks and valleys in the fitness terrain that prevent evolution. These barriers can keep populations stuck on a sub-maximal local fitness peak, because survival of the fittest will not allow populations to go down a fitness slope and into the canyon.[29] Evolutionary geneticists pose a solution that does not rely on warping the fitness terrain. Rather, it regards the terrain as rigid and motionless. Most vigorously promoted by Sewall Wright, it is called the Shifting Balance hypothesis. This hypothesis depends on deleterious processes (such as mutation, close inbreeding, and genetic drift) to decrease the fitness of a population and carry it down a fitness slope.

To accomplish this, theorists need to nullify differential survival and amplify the deleterious processes. Theorists do that by referring to *small population sizes* at the necessary times. The hypothesis achieves its end by shifting the balance of forces back and forth to get 'upward' and 'downward' motion as needed. Sometimes this requires large populations, and at other times small populations.

> [R]andom genetic drift is a fundamental process in the shifting balance hypothesis because random drift can shift the constellation of allele frequencies from a sub-maximal fitness peak into a nearby valley; from there, natural selection can predominate and carry the population to a higher fitness peak. (Hartl, 1980, p 336)

The hypothesis calls on a variety of randomly occurring processes, and uses them in a non-random sequence. The hypothesis 'choreographs' a sequence of specific events out of the randomly occurring events of nature. Here is the scenario and its list of requirements.

- The original species population must be large (to increase the chances of getting beneficial mutations, and for differential survival to dominate over genetic drift). The population also must have enough gene flow (through migration) to distribute the beneficial mutations throughout the population.

- After the beneficial mutations are distributed, then the population must be divided into *many isolated* sub-populations. There can be virtually no migration between these sub-populations.

- Some of these isolated sub-populations must be less than a few hundred in size (to allow genetic drift to dominate over differential survival.)

> [R]andom genetic drift increases in importance as the effective population number decreases, so a key assumption in the shifting balance hypothesis is that effective population numbers are sufficiently small that appreciable random changes in allele frequency can occur; that is to say, effective population numbers should be on the order of 100 or 200, or less, rather than 500 or more. (Hartl, 1980, p 336)

---

[29] Ecologists offered two scenarios to answer this problem: the *Stationary hypothesis* and the *Red Queen hypothesis*. Both these involve peculiar warping of the fitness terrain.

- At least one of these small isolated sub-populations must somehow succeed in randomly drifting past the fitness barrier. Close inbreeding, with its well-known harmful effects, is said to aid this process. The sub-population must go down the fitness slope, across the fitness canyon floor to the other side, (and not back again). This requires that the sub-population size remain consistently small during this period.

- Once past the fitness canyon, then (and not sooner) this sub-population must increase in size. (So differential survival can again dominate over genetic drift, and so the chance of getting beneficial mutation is increased.) Then this isolated sub-population may rise up the fitness topography on the other side of the canyon.

Thus, the shifting-balance hypothesis requires a sequence of many mechanisms in precise doses, at precise times.

*

The shifting-balance hypothesis also reveals a dilemma of modern theory. It requires the properties of both large and small populations.[30] Theorists address this dilemma by referring to migration.

Migration transforms many disunited sub-populations into one large unified population.

Lack of migration transforms one large population into many separate sub-populations.

The theorists use migration (and its absence) to arbitrarily shift back and forth between large and small populations.

Furthermore, the theory attempts to choreograph random processes to accomplish a certain end. The theorists select the effects they need and ignore the others. This is especially true of inbreeding. Inbreeding does not have an inward drive to propel a population down a specific slope of the fitness terrain. Inbreeding does not cause populations to genetically deteriorate in precisely the manner theorists would desire. Rather, it rapidly deteriorates genomes randomly, affecting all facets of the organism. It does not confine itself to those traits responsible for a given fitness barrier. The shifting-balance hypothesis has no means to account for these undesired harmful effects. It merely ignores the many harmful side-effects of the harmful processes it uses.

---

[30] Evolutionary theorists require the properties of both large and small populations. We will see another aspect of this dilemma in the next chapter.

The Many-Gene Problem

Gene, kin and group selection are used to explain altruistic traits: traits harmful to the individual yet helpful to others. Gould accepts the validity of these mechanisms, yet he holds a criticism of gene selection.

> Selection simply cannot see genes and pick among them directly. It must use bodies as an intermediary. A gene is a bit of DNA hidden within a cell. Selection views bodies. It favors some bodies because they are stronger, better insulated, earlier in their sexual maturation, fiercer in combat, or more beautiful to behold. .... *Hundreds of genes contribute to the building of most body parts* and their action is channeled through a kaleidoscopic series of environmental influences ... Parts are not translated genes, and selection doesn't even work directly on parts. It accepts or rejects entire organisms because suites of parts, interacting in complex ways, confer advantages. (Gould, 1980, p 89-90, my italics)

Gould objects to gene selection because observable traits are not due to single genes acting alone, rather they result from hundreds of genes acting together.

True enough. Yet his objection applies equally well to all evolutionary explanations. Gould put his finger on a major difficulty of evolutionary genetics — the many-gene problem. Most traits are determined by *many* genes. (This is called polygeny.) The prevalence of this makes origins difficult to explain.

Imagine a new beneficial trait has just arisen due to a rare combination of five genes. Due to sexual reproduction each gene has a fifty percent chance of being in a given offspring. Therefore, the full five-gene trait has one chance in 32 of being inherited. This is a 3 percent chance. (Not the usual 50% chance when only one gene is involved.) If females average less than 32 offspring each (as is typical of higher vertebrates), then the many-gene trait would vanish quickly. Thus, the evolutionary origin of many-gene traits is awkward to explain.

This is the primary reason that evolutionists tend to give explanations involving *only one gene.* The explanations assume that one trait equals one gene. They then explain the origin of the trait as the origin of that one gene. This type of explanation is much easier to make. That is why evolutionists employ it.

*

If evolutionists must explain a many-gene trait, then they sometimes suggest *small* populations with heavy inbreeding.

The explanation goes like this. Suppose a new trait has just arisen due to a rare combination of five genes. Sexual reproduction is likely to tear these apart. Only one in 32 of the offspring will have all five genes. Nonetheless, many offspring will have *some* of the five genes. With heavy inbreeding, these five genes may eventually be reunited in some individual. The reunited genes then have another chance to exert their combined effect, with improved survival. Accordingly, after many generations of this inbreeding, all members of the population would have all five genes. Thus, evolutionists say the origin of many-gene traits can be explained in small populations.

That scenario overlooks some objections. Inbreeding, with its well known harmful effects, has no innate desire to aid evolution. Heavy inbreeding typically harms species. Its overall outcome, after many generations, might well be worse than any benefits acquired.

In addition, genetic drift is strongest in small populations. It can easily eliminate beneficial genes and establish harmful genes. Genetic drift alone could eliminate some genes necessary for the many-gene trait.

Furthermore, the scenario conveniently began *after* all five genes were within the inbreeding group. If the scenario began before all five were together, then the closed group would prevent the genes from coming together.

Altogether, the "heavy inbreeding" scenario is unlikely.

*

Evolutionists often attempt yet another solution to the many-gene problem. If a trait requires many genes, then they use the standard (bean-bag) model of genetics. Bean-bag genetics assumes that genes are independent, non-interacting entities. It assumes that each gene is beneficial by itself and the effect of many genes is just the sum of each separate gene — the total equals the sum of the parts. Thus, if a trait requires five genes, they allot roughly 20% of the trait to each gene — then they explain the origin of each separate gene. First, one gene evolves; that is 20% of the trait. Then, the second gene evolves, and so forth till 100% of the trait is attained. The imagery builds on the central illusion of naive natural selection — evolution is upward, ever upward.

The bean-bag model pretends the many-gene problem out of existence, by assuming that the problem does not exist. That is why evolutionists tend to use it. The bean-bag model makes explanations seem more plausible.

*

In reality, the many-gene problem does exist, and seems predominant in nature.[31] Most traits are determined by many interacting genes — the total is more than the sum of the parts.

For example, the many-gene problem affects the origin of altruistic traits. There is no single gene for altruism, or for selfless self-sacrifice; no 'gene' for aiding one's fellows. Behaviors are complex, involving many genes. We cannot divide altruism into five genes, each with 20% of altruism. Altruistic traits must be determined by many interacting genes, not just one. The origin of altruistic traits rapidly becomes more implausible as the number of genes increases. When *hundreds* of genes are involved (as argued by Gould), then the evolutionary origin of altruistic traits is most untenable.

The classic evolutionary discussions of gene, kin, and group selection deal with altruistic behavior as though it were controlled by a single gene. Such explanations rapidly disintegrate, when faced with the real world many-gene situation.

---

[31] The multi-gene problem is serious, and it forces evolutionary explanations (whether gene, individual, kin, or group selective) to invoke *small* populations, *heavy inbreeding*, and *few* genes. In addition, evolutionists have had to make peculiar assumptions about the way multiple genes work together as single genes are replaced.

194

Group Selection

Survival of the fittest is not within population genetics at any level: genes, bodies, kin, groups, demes, species, or clades. We cannot tell whether a trait is "fit," at any level, with the precision required by evolutionary theory. Survival of the fittest is metaphysical. Nonetheless, differential survival is within population genetics, and the theory can predict the consequences of differential survival at various levels.

In population genetics, the term selection must be read as "differential survival." Then, the term group selection is differential survival of groups — and its consequences can be predicted.

*

By the mid 1960s, group selection developed some difficulties. John Maynard Smith provided the following argument. Suppose a mutation occurs that is harmful to the individual. The population may be rid of this mutation by a single selective death — by the death of the first individual to carry the mutation. Contrast this with the situation of group selection: Suppose a mutation occurs that is beneficial to the individual but harmful to the group. The mutation will spread throughout the group and can be removed only by elimination of the entire group.

> Thus the maintenance of a characteristic favourable only to the group requires N times as many selective deaths as the maintenance of an individually favourable characteristic, where N is the number of individuals in a reproductively isolated group. If groups are large, the selective cost of maintaining an 'altruistic' character will be prohibitive. .... (Maynard Smith, 1972, p 116)

This argument showed that group selection in a large population is prohibitively costly. Group selection has a "cost" problem. If the population size is 1,000, then the maintenance of a group selective trait requires 1,000 times more genetic deaths than an individually selective trait.

Results like these showed that group selection is a weak and inefficient force compared with individual selection. Group selection is only plausible if the 'group' is small (at most a few tens or hundreds).[32]

*

In summary, group selection has two problems[33] — the many-gene problem and the cost problem. These show that group selection is implausible except perhaps in small populations.

---

[32] As the 'group' becomes smaller, "group selection" merges with (and eventually becomes) individual selection.

[33] Note that these problems arise from the mechanics of genetics together with differential survival at various levels (gene, individual, kin, and group). These problems have nothing to do with survival of the fittest because this latter theory tries to identify the *causes* for the differential survival. These specific causes, whatever they may be, are not germane to the problems at hand. The problems can be (and have been) deliberated without referring to natural selection. There is real substance to the arguments, and that substance is not derived from natural selection.

The Origin of Sex

The origins literature uses the informal word *sex* as a shorthand term for a mixing of genetic material from two individuals. When origins theorists discuss "sex" they are not referring to the sex act, they are referring to genetic mixing. The mechanism most responsible for this mixing is known as genetic recombination.[34]

Today, the origin and maintenance of sex is one of the major problems in evolutionary theory. Marguilis and Sagan recently tried a simple solution. They suggested that Mendelian inheritance and sex are a historical accident, that these are merely an accidental holdover from the era of single-celled organisms. They claim that the maintenance of sex is therefore a "nonscientific" question that "leads to intellectual mischief and confusion."[35]

Most evolutionists disagree with Marguilis and Sagan, and feel that sex cannot be explained unless it has some useful function. If sex is useless, then what maintained its intricacy and uniformity throughout life for over a billion years?

> [S]exual reproduction seems like a lot of excess baggage to carry along if it is functionless. Evolutionary conservatism perpetuates relics, but does it do so on such a grand scale as this? .... It is difficult to see how a process as elaborate, ubiquitous, and expensive as sexual reproduction has been maintained without serving some important purpose of its own. (Crow, 1988, p 60)

Sex occurs in all major groups of life.[36] It is the leading mode of reproduction in groups as different as arthropods, echinoderms, molluscs, and vertebrates. Yet the sexual process is highly similar throughout nature. Meiosis, with its intricate movement of chromosomes, is often almost identical in these diverse groups. If sex was a rare phenomenon, then evolutionists might interpret it as neutral or non-adaptive. The observed intricacy and uniformity of sex forced evolutionists to conclude that it is a highly adaptive character, precisely shaped by selection to fulfill some function of central importance.[37] What is that function?

When a sexual organism forms gametes (sperm or egg cells) there is a meiotic division, in which half the genes are removed. Then, when sperm combines with egg, the resulting progeny contains a full complement of genes, half from each parent. In sexual reproduction only half a parent's genes are sent to each of its progeny. This is called the cost of meiosis.

---

[34] Recombination is usually associated with reproduction, but not always.

[35] As cited in Crow, 1988, p 59-60

[36] "There are grounds for doubting whether any organisms are strictly asexual ..." (Eldredge and Cracraft, 1980, p 102)

[37] Bell, 1982, p 26

Meanwhile, an asexual parent sends *all* its genes to each progeny. In the Darwinian struggle to pass on more of one's genes to future generations, asexuality is twice as efficient as sexuality. It is therefore difficult to explain how sexual reproduction might have become prevalent.

In addition, there are costs beyond the automatic genetic penalties of sex,[38] and these non-genetic costs are large. There is the cost of evolving and maintaining the sex organs. There is the cost of various kinds of incompatibility, such as blood Rh factor incompatibilities between mother and child. In a sexual organism there are problems of tissue rejection between mother and child. Also, in a male body its own sperm is like foreign tissue, due to its different genetic makeup. Special mechanisms are required to keep the body's immune defenses from destroying its own sperm. This is also true for females and their eggs. All these problems are avoided in asexual organisms.

In finding a mate, courting, and copulating, a sexual organism will face risks that further place it at a disadvantage relative to an asexual peer.[39] Loud mating calls, scents, extravagant plumage, exotic behavior, flowers and nectar all have their price. They use energy, alert predators, and frequently reduce the non-sexual functioning of the organism.

Evolutionary literature abounds with scenarios explaining how a minuscule increase in a certain trait allows a species to more optimally mate. Theorists are then satisfied they have explained the trait. For example, they offer scenarios to explain the evolution of optimal courting behaviors and even optimal copulation intervals and durations. They deliver intricate explanations of how a male can most optimally insure that his sperm is the one to fertilize a female. They give countless such scenarios, and they are quite serious about it. They seriously believe these have sufficient power to explain the evolution of optimal mating, courting, and copulation.

Yet the power of these scenarios is dwarfed by asexuality, which solves all these problems completely — in one swoop — and in the most optimal possible way. For an asexual organism these problems completely disappear. Asexual reproduction is easily the more efficient solution. Altogether these factors account for a large disadvantage to sex beyond the 50% cost of meiosis. Nonetheless, the literature focuses on the 50% figure as the major cause for concern. Again we must ask, Why is sex so extremely prevalent? Why is it here at all?

---

[38] Researchers have noted other genetic disadvantages of sex: (1) Sex (and recombination) generates a segregational load not present in an asexual population, and (2) mutational load will always be greater in sexual populations. (Williams, G. C., 1975, p 25, 151) These "loads" cause a reduction in the average survival rate of the species.

Moreover, in the neutral evolution versus selection debate the selectionists claim that heterozygote advantage is *abundant* in nature. This would imply an additional "serious disadvantage for the sexual habit in diploids, since meiotic segregation makes it impossible for heterozygotes to breed true." (Bell, 1982, p 98-99)

[39] Bell, 1982, p 67

Sex is the queen of problems in evolutionary biology. Perhaps no other natural phenomenon has aroused so much interest; certainly none has sowed as much confusion. The insights of Darwin and Mendel, which have illuminated so many mysteries, have so far failed to shed more than a dim and wavering light on the central mystery of sexuality, emphasizing its obscurity by its very isolation. (Bell, 1982, p 19)

Sexual reproduction is analogous to a roulette game in which the player throws away half his chips at each spin. .... the existence of sexual reproduction really is a huge paradox (Dawkins, 1984, p 130)

Yet puzzles remain. One problem is the existence of sex. .... Despite some ingenious suggestions by orthodox Darwinians there is no convincing Darwinian history for the emergence of sexual reproduction. (Kitcher, 1982, p 54)

[T]he prevalence of sexual reproduction in higher plants and animals is inconsistent with current evolutionary theory. ... there is a kind of crisis at hand in evolutionary biology (Williams, G. C., 1975, p v)

The origin of the sexual process remains one of the most difficult problems in biology. (Maynard Smith, 1986, p 35)

So many aspects of sex have eluded our understanding that sex is considered to be one of biology's great enigmas. (Bellig and Stevens, 1988, p ix)

A survey of evolution biologists would doubtless come up with a consensus that the elucidation of the selective pressures responsible for the origin and maintenance of sex is a "big" (maybe the "biggest") unsolved problem in evolutionary biology. .... there is no consensus about where its solution lies. .... no clear solution emerges. (Michod and Levin, 1988, p vii)

*

Some theorists suggest that sexual reproduction offers an advantage because it gives better parenting of the offspring, by providing two parents instead of one. One objection to their argument comes from evolutionary storytelling itself. Parenting need not be given by the exact genetic parents of the offspring, but may be given by a close relative.

For example, in many species of birds it is common for a young adult to delay mating and instead devote itself to helping an older pair to rear their own offspring. This is not a rare occurrence. It has been observed in 140 species of birds. It cannot be explained by the classic Darwinian theory of individual selection, so theorists used Hamilton's theory of kin selection. In many cases (perhaps 60 percent), the helper is a full-sibling and therefore shares 50 percent of its genes with the individuals it is helping. The theorists say this benefits the helper by passing its genes into the next generation through close relatives.[40]

---

[40] Gribbon and Gribbon, 1988, p 120

Taking this as it stands, an asexual organism could potentially take even greater advantage of multiple parenting. An asexual organism may parent with its own siblings. Siblings would share virtually 100 percent of their genome. This high degree of genetic relatedness is greater than that of the social insects, and twice that of most organisms. According to kin selection theory, this genetic relatedness would be more than adequate to induce an asexual species to use communal parenting. After all, where Haldane would die to save eight cousins, an asexual Haldane would die to save just one. This would pass on the entire genetic inheritance to the next generation. Accordingly, asexual reproduction would seem to have a great capacity to enroll parental support from kin. Therefore, the existence of sex cannot be explained by multiple parenting.

*

Considering the vast smorgasbord of possible evolutionary mechanisms, it is perhaps surprising that anything could pose a problem for Darwinian scenarios. They typically employ selection coefficients that are merely fractions of one-percent, which alone is usually sufficient to make them untestable. The sex problem is unique, because its terms are so fixed and unyielding. In the sex problem, the selective disadvantage will not budge. Sex has a known disadvantage of at least fifty percent.

> The primary task for anyone wishing to show favorable selection of sex is to find a previously unsuspected 50% advantage to balance the 50% cost of meiosis. Anyone familiar with accepted evolutionary thought will realize what an unlikely sort of quest this is. We know that a net selective disadvantage of 1% would cause a gene to be lost rapidly in most populations, and sex has a known disadvantage of 50%. The problem has been examined by some of the most distinguished of evolutionary theorists, but they have either failed to find any reproductive advantage in sexual reproduction, or have merely showed the formal possibility of weak advantages that would probably not be adequate to balance even modest recombinational load. *Nothing remotely approaching an advantage that could balance the cost of meiosis has been suggested. The impossibility of sex being an immediate reproductive adaptation in higher organisms would seem to be as firmly established a conclusion as can be found in current evolutionary thought.* Yet this conclusion must surely be wrong. All around us are plant and animal populations with both asexual and sexual reproduction. (Williams, G. C., 1975, p 11, my italics)

> Sex ... does not merely reduce fitness, but halves it. If a reduction in fitness of a fraction of one per cent can cripple a genotype, what will be the consequence of a reduction of 50 per cent? *There can be only one answer: sex will be powerfully selected against and rapidly eliminated wherever it appears.* And yet this has not happened. (Bell, 1982, p 77-78, my italics)

Experts on the evolution of sex are vexed by the size of the problem and the dismal history of the many attempts to solve it. They believe sex evolved, but they are not sure how. They make speculations and suggestions, but the problem is severe. A 50% disadvantage is difficult to overcome with a just-so story. This much they acknowledge.

*

So why is there sex? Why is it here? How could it ever evolve? Why is it so extremely prevalent? Why is it not lost more often? Efforts to solve these problems focused first on variation and diversity.

In an asexual organism, all progeny are mere clones of the single parent, differing from that parent only by new mutations. Sex, on the other hand, creates diversity. Sex is like a genetic shredding machine. Sex shreds every genome in every generation, and from this it rebuilds new progeny, every one different. Other than rare phenomena (such as identical twins), no two sexual progeny are the same. The value of sex then reduces to finding some value in diversity. Yet this value is not easy to find. The difficulty is acknowledged by evolutionary experts:

> The real difficulties begin to appear only when one attempts to discover where this value resides. It is not, of course, difficult to imagine benefits that might be gained by having diverse rather than uniform progeny, but it turns out to be very difficult indeed to conceive of any benefit in diversity, when uniformity appears to permit one to reproduce twice as rapidly. (Bell, 1982, p 78)

> [T]he costs of sex to the individual are usually high and these costs are unlikely to be compensated for by benefits to the species. ... the costs of sex are explicit and borne by individual organisms, while *the postulated benefits of sex have been vague and not readily modeled.* The crises involving the question of sex can be seen clearly in this contrast between the costs and benefits of sex. (Michod and Levin, 1988, p 2, my italics)

Again, the problem centers on that immovable 50% disadvantage to the individual.

*

Traditionally the theorists tried to explain sex by emphasizing the group rather than the individual. The explanation involved group selection rather than individual selection. Though sex is a disadvantage to the individual (at a whooping 50% rate), sex was claimed to convey some evolutionary advantage to the species as a whole. Sex would then be classed as an "altruistic" trait because it operates at expense to the individual, to the benefit of a group.

The group selection explanation claimed that sex helps a species evolve *faster*. The advantage of faster evolution seemed self-evident. This explanation was most vigorously expounded by the geneticists Weismann, Fisher and Muller, early this century. One form of the explanation went like this:

> Sex increases diversity, enabling a species to more rapidly adapt to changing environments and thereby avoid extinction.

They said sex creates diversity, and diversity allows evolution to go faster.[41]

---

[41] On occasion, Fisher's Fundamental Theorem was used to support the idea that sex allows evolution to go faster. Sex creates diversity, and Fisher's theorem was said to

Another form of explanation used group selection as follows:

> Sex provides a means to combine the advantageous mutations from separate individuals, thereby enabling a species to evolve faster.

These explanations seemed intuitively reasonable and were taught unchallenged until virtually the present day.[42]

*

By the mid 1960s these explanations had developed difficulties. One was a difficulty with group selection, a difficulty hitting with special force on the problem of sex. Several independent lines of reasoning (as discussed in previous sections) showed that group selection is a weak and inefficient force. Group selection is only plausible where the group is numbered in the few tens or hundreds. This result collides with the sex problem, particularly because sex is so widespread. Since group selection is a weak force how can it override individual selection operating at a stiff 50% rate? How could it maintain this situation, not just once or twice, but for the vast preponderance of species in nature? Moreover, group selection is only efficient in small populations, and nature does not comply with this mandate. How could group selection be responsible for the prevalence of sex in nature?

> It turns out to be so difficult to conceive situations in which group selection is a more powerful influence on gene frequencies than individual selection that since 1966 there have been few explicit defenses of the position that group selection is primarily responsible for any *widespread* features of biological organization ... (Bell, 1982, p 46-47, my italics)

*

---

prove that diversity makes for faster evolution. Such support is mistaken, because Fisher's Theorem uses *variation* in a manner unlike that delivered by sex. Moreover, Fisher's Theorem cannot be applied to 'changing genomes' (as produced by sex). It can only be applied when genomes are unchanging.

[42] Evolutionists avoid overthrowing an evolutionary theory unless they have another one to replace it with. For this reason, evolutionary theories often persist many decades after evolutionary specialists know them to be false. This happened, for example, with the explanation of sex. "Weismann explicitly stated that sex exists for the good of the species, and even though Lloyd Morgan pointed out the fallacy [as early as 1890], this view remained the dominant one *for nearly 80 years. Why this should have happened is something of a puzzle.* The view does have a certain intuitive appeal, but *that does not explain why it was not subjected to more critical scrutiny.*" (Ghiselin, 1988, p 11, my italics)

The evolutionary sex problem was in for another surprise setback. Remember that sex was said to speed evolution in the following way: If a population contains beneficial mutations in separate individuals then sex can bring these benefits together in future progeny. An asexual population cannot do this, so theorists reasoned that evolution would be faster in sexual species. Theorists soon realized, however, that though sex brings beneficial mutations together, it also tears them apart with equal facility.

Thus began, in the 1970s, the modern debate on the evolutionary significance of sex. With Crow and Kimura on one side and John Maynard Smith on the other, the debate continued for several rounds. The dust finally settled and a surprising result of population genetics was established. Sex could not speed evolution unless the population is very large. :

> [P]opulations would have to be in the millions for recombination to be important in increasing the spread of favorable mutations. (Williams, G. C., 1975, p 145)

As pointed out by Bell, the theory had now developed an internal contradiction: The theory simultaneously requires properties of both small and large populations.

> Its motive force is group selection, and for very general reasons group selection requires a particular population structure in order to be effective: the population must be broken up into a great many small, semi-isolated groups. But we have learnt that sex will accelerate evolution only in large populations. These two features ... are not easy to reconcile, and indicate that the whole basis of the theory may be seriously flawed. (Bell, 1982, p 98)

For group selection to be plausible the group must be quite small, but the group will not see a selective advantage for sex unless it is extremely large. Therein lies the contradiction.

*

The theory received yet another setback. The above results assumed that genes exert independent effects and do not interact. That is, individual genes are neither aided nor hampered by the selective effect of other genes. Each gene exerts its effect independently of others. This seemed to provide a good starting point, since it is the common "bean bag" model used in population genetics textbooks.

Nonetheless, genes frequently interact with a combined effect greater than the sum of each gene taken separately. (If the interacting genes are at the same loci it is called *heterosis*, and if at different loci it is called *epistasis*.) Many examples can be cited and these phenomena are believed to be quite common, perhaps even predominant in nature.[43] When this is true, then sex actually slows evolution. This is because sex breaks up gene combinations with no regard for their

---

[43] Selectionists assert that heterozygote advantage occurs frequently (perhaps predominantly) in nature.

selective value. Sex does this constantly. Generation after generation it shreds genomes to build new progeny. It dramatically slows the spread of favorable gene combinations since these can only fleetingly exert their united influence before they are broken up again.

Meanwhile, in an asexual organism, gene combinations are inherited together and are not split apart. Therefore, a favorable gene combination would exert its influence in every descendant, rapidly propelling it to predominance in the population.

These results showed that in most plausible situations, sex is expected to hold back evolution, not accelerate it.

> [I]t has proven difficult to produce explicit models that show that mixis [i.e., the genetic mixing caused by sexual reproduction] accelerates adaptive evolution. (Michod and Levin, 1988, p 2)

*

This realization provoked a boldfaced, 180-degree turn-around in the explanation of sex. Now, it was claimed, sex is an advantage not because it hastens evolution, but because it *slows* evolution. Evolutionary experts have seriously made such claims. This situation was observed and lamented by Bell.

> To save the situation, then, we must perform a complete *volte-face*: just as it was self-evident to Weismann, Fisher and Muller that a faster rate of evolution would benefit a population, so we must now contrive to believe in the self-evident desirability of evolving slowly. (Bell, 1982, p 100)

The theorists, led by Williams and Thompson, plainly acknowledged the situation:

> [T]he occasional production of extremely fit genotypes in the sexual population will have no permanent significance, as long as fitness depends at all on heterosis and epistasis. Given any plausible level of heterosis and complex interactions among loci [ie. epistasis], almost all of a sexual population will have suboptimal genotypes, no matter how long selection continues. All that this means is what everybody knows, that sexual reproduction generates recombinational load, *but I suggest that this mundane fact may be the primary significance of sexuality in evolution.* It *greatly retards* the final stages of multilocus adaptive change and *severely limits the attainable precision of adaptation.* (Williams, G. C., 1975, p 150, my italics)

They accomplished the 180 degree turn-around by proposing a new theory of extinction, as follows. An asexual species rapidly adapts to its environment. Then when the environment changes, the species is too specialized and too dependent on its particular niche. As the niche vanishes, the species goes extinct. So, asexual species frequently adapt themselves out of existence by refining a mode of life that eventually disappears. Meanwhile, sexual species lag behind. Sex blunts the precision that a species can adapt to a particular niche. Therefore, when the environment changes, the sexual species is less likely to be dependent on its niche. Sex slows evolution, indirectly allowing the species to avoid extinction.[44] ... At least, that was what some evolutionary experts seriously claimed.

Evolutionary theory is so plastic it can accommodate virtually anything. Nothing demonstrates that flexible story-telling like the evolutionists' attempts to explain sex.

*

Perhaps the benefit of sex lay not in accelerating the spread of beneficial mutation, but in more rapidly eliminating harmful mutations. Sex would then act like a more efficient dust mop, each generation clearing away harmful mutations. In this way, sex could benefit populations by keeping them from genetically deteriorating.

One such hypothesis is called Muller's ratchet. Though proposed in 1964 it underwent little development[45] until recently. According to this idea, an asexual population can never get to contain, in any line of inheritance, a number of harmful mutations smaller than the present least-loaded individual. When all the organisms contain at least N harmful mutations, then an asexual population cannot produce an individual with fewer than N mutations.[46] The mechanism operates like a ratchet: asexual lineages can collect more harmful mutations, but never less. As more mutations are accumulated in the population the 'ratchet' clicks irreversibly downward.

On the other hand, in a sexual population there is the chance of getting progeny with fewer harmful mutations than in either parent. So, sexual populations are freed from the ratchet mechanism. When the mutation rate is sufficiently low, sex can help selection to rid populations of harmful mutation. Muller said this is the advantage of sex. His hypothesis suggests that sex has a long-term benefit for the group.

Muller's hypothesis has a difficulty for evolutionists. Darwinism emphasizes immediate *short-term* benefits for the individual. Evolution cannot look ahead to the future. It can only select traits based on their current, immediate utility. Because Muller's hypothesis would require a far-sighted process of group selection to prevail over short-term individual selection, it is not plausible at explaining the origin and prevalence of sex. For this reason, evolutionists originally disregarded Muller's hypothesis in favor of other scenarios.

Recently, evolutionists have shifted away from the idea that sex helps evolution. They are now re-embracing Muller's idea that sex maintains the long-

---

[44] Williams' book is on the evolution of sex. He concluded his book on a doleful note: "I am sure that many readers have already concluded that I really do not understand the role of sex in either organic or biotic evolution. At least I can claim, on the basis of the conflicting views in the recent literature, the consolation of abundant company." (Williams, G. C., 1975, p 169)

[45] Bell, 1982, p 101

[46] A mutation could be corrected by a back-mutation, but these are so incredibly rare that we may ignore them here. The ratchet will click downward much faster than can be compensated by back-mutation.

term genetic well-being of species.[47] This shift — away from evolution and toward maintenance — is compatible with creationist views. The shift shows the desperation of evolutionists and that the traditional methods of evolutionary theorizing have failed to produce an adequate solution.

Most evolutionists now recognize that no single evolutionary scenario is powerful enough to plausibly explain the origin of sex. So they now combine multiple scenarios together in an effort to provide greater plausibility.[48] They note that a "pluralistic" view of the sex problem is emerging.[49] This trend toward pluralistic explanations is typical of evolutionary theory today.

*

The evolutionary origin and maintenance of sex (and genetic systems in general[50]) remains an acknowledged mystery. The 50% disadvantage is too steep, and the phenomenon too universal to be justified by stories. It is fair to say that the firmest and most plausible evolutionary theories predict that sex should be non-existent.

> I think it clear that if the world were otherwise — if meiosis and fertilization were rare or unknown … — there would be no mystery. No one would wonder why these elaborate processes have not been evolved … (Williams, G. C., 1988, p 293)

---

[47]   Bell, 1988, p 138

[48]   For example see Bell, 1988, p 138

[49]   Michod and Levin, 1988, p vii

[50]   Sex is not the only mystery surrounding the origin of genetic systems. There are other, lesser known, paradoxes. For example, every biology student learns Mendel's Rules and yet their existence runs counter to evolutionary expectations. "The more rigorous and general arguments … strongly suggest that random Mendelian segregation should seldom be evolutionarily stable. And yet it is certainly the general case; so we must recognize another major paradox in the evolution of genetic systems." (Bell, 1982, p 439)

The prevalence of recombination is also a mystery: "[S]election will always favour a reduction in the rate of recombination, provided that there is any degree of epistatic interaction between loci. .... there is remarkable unanimity among theorists that the ineluctable suppression of recombination is not only a very general but also a very robust result. This conclusion is [by observation] manifestly false; that is the paradox of recombination." (Bell, 1982, p 407)

"We have the anomalous situation that a detailed population genetic analysis reveals not only that the standard explanation for the evolution of recombination will not work, but also that there is a good evolutionary reason for believing that modifiers will be selected to eliminate recombination." (Felsenstein, 1988, p 79)

The "alternation of generations" back and forth between diploid (human adults) and haploid (their sperm and eggs) poses a problem (Bell, 1982, 443) as does the evolutionary role of haploidy and diploidy: "[T]he casualness of the few attempts to provide a functional account of haploidy and diploidy constitutes a major scandal." (Bell, 1982, p 443)

205

*

Creationists expect that the genetic mechanisms of sex serve some useful biological function. They intuitively viewed that function as the long-term *maintenance* of healthy populations. Most likely, sex serves such a function, as suggested by hypotheses like Muller's ratchet. Such functions come naturally to the creationist's worldview. And unlike evolution, a designer can be "far-sighted," can see the long-term benefit of sex, and can build it into life.

Moreover, message theory claims that biological traits serve a dual role: as instruments of survival and as conveyors of a biotic message. This suggests that sex is part of the biotic message. In fact, sex has the two features necessary for the biotic message:

- Sex has a substantial uniformity throughout life. This unifies the many diverse organisms on earth, often in a quite visible way. (This sends the unifying message.)

- The origin and prevalence of sex resists naturalistic explanation. (This sends the non-naturalistic message.)

These two features together make sex quite useful in the biotic message.

Summary

Population genetics cannot explain adaptation, since it does not try. Population genetics explains genetic change, not adaptation.[51]

Natural selection and population genetics are separate theories. Population genetics can perform all its science, without ever mentioning natural selection. Natural selection can be shown as non-science, without ever mentioning genetics.

Evolutionists try to give natural selection legitimacy by forcing it into population genetics. This is accomplished through misusing the terms *survival of the fittest, natural selection, selection,* and *fitness.*

Evolutionists have misnamed and misrepresented Fisher's "Fundamental Theorem of Natural Selection." In truth, it could hardly be less supportive to them. The theorem is completely compatible with creation theory.

Population genetics is scientific, but it is more like mathematical sciences than the empirical sciences. Population genetics has numerous mathematical models. The models are flexible and have little contact with the empirical world. Basic parameters (such as selective values) usually cannot be measured with the accuracy necessary for testing.

The flexibility of evolutionary genetics is shown by the neutralist-selectionist controversy. These two clashingly different theories have each been able to accommodate the data. This controversy—still raging after several decades—is a tribute to the inability of evolutionary genetics to come to grips with empirical reality.

Biological traits and genes typically have a many-to-many relationship, not a one-to-one relationship. This fact causes theoretical problems for evolution. The standard models of population genetics assume these problems out of existence, by presuming that genes are independent, non-interacting "bean-bag" entities.

Most beneficial mutations are eliminated before getting a foothold in the population. A selective advantage of one-percent is said to be large for evolution. Yet such mutations will be eliminated 49 times out of 50, without ever being used in evolution. In small populations the outlook is even less hopeful.

The most famous field case of "evolutionary genetics in action" is sickle-cell anemia. Yet it refutes the naive notion that evolution is ever upward, and it offers no support for large-scale evolution.

The evolutionary origin of sex and genetic systems remains a penetrating mystery with no agreed solution. The problem is that the most plausible evolutionary theories indicate that sex should not exist.

Message theory explains sex in a direct way. Sex has the two necessary features of the biotic message.

---

[51] "We must agree with Waddington who said: The whole real guts of evolution — which is, how do you come to have horses, and tigers, and things — is outside the mathematical [population genetic] theory." (Eldredge and Cracraft, 1980, p 272)

8

Haldane's Dilemma

[O]ur brains tripled in size within a million years or so.[1] (Gould, 1980, p 131)

In the 1950s the evolutionary geneticist, J. B. S. Haldane, calculated the maximum rate of genetic change due to differential survival. He reluctantly concluded there is a serious problem here, now known as Haldane's Dilemma.[2] His calculations show that many species of higher vertebrate could not plausibly evolve in the available time. We begin our study with a simplified account of the calculations.

Evolution requires the substitution of old prevalent traits with new rare traits. There are limits to the rate these substitutions can occur, limits that depend primarily on the reproductive capacity of the species. Haldane's Dilemma examines these limits.

Imagine a breeding population of 100,000 individuals. Imagine 99,998 have the old trait O, and two (a male and female) have the new trait N. Imagine trait N has just arisen from O by beneficial mutation. The evolutionary goal is to substitute trait N for trait O in the population. To accomplish this goal, differential survival must eliminate the 99,998 type O individuals and all their heirs.

This can be accomplished in a single generation if there is perfect selection. (That is, if the survival values of O and N are 0 and 1 respectively.) Yet, there is an enormous cost involved. For every surviving type N individual there are 49,999 individuals (type O) that must perish without heirs. The population size must be regenerated from the two survivors.

Now allot the maximum speed to evolution. Let us assume evolution can happen like this continuously, generation after generation, for millions of years. Take a species like man with a nominal 20 year generation time.[3] Extrapolate backward from this known species to a time 10 million years ago. This is three times earlier than the said occurrence of the four foot high australopithecine "Lucy." This is twice as old as the alleged split between gorilla, chimpanzee, and man. In that much time, how many traits could be substituted at this crashing pace? One per generation, maximum — approximately 500,000.

---

[1] Gould says the evolution of upright posture occurred around the same time, and is even more remarkable than the rapid tripling of brain size. (Gould, 1980, p 132)

[2] Haldane, 1957

[3] The present generation time of man is roughly 30 years (Kimura and Ohta, 1971, p 28). Ayala (1985, p 72) uses a 25 year generation time for primitive man. Dawkins (1986, p 228) uses 25 years as the average generation time for man from three million years ago to the present. Stebbins (1982, p 357-358) uses 20 years as the average for the ancestral line of hominids from at least 4 millions years ago and perhaps much earlier.

These substituted traits are simple changes having arisen by mutation. These can be of many types. The new trait might be a DNA inversion, gene duplication, or deletion, for example. Also, organisms are not merely the possession of the right genes. The position and sequence of genes on a chromosome are important to their action, expression, and propagation. So, a substituted trait can be something as simple as a new location of a gene on a chromosome. The substituted traits can be many different things. Yet, every time you wish to move a gene to a new position, or delete a gene, or duplicate a gene, or substitute any trait,[4] no matter how trivial, then there is a cost to be paid.

According to the neo-Darwinian synthesis, these substituted traits are typically a new version of a gene — an allele. The new substituted gene typically differs from the old gene by one newly mutated nucleotide. So, the substituted trait is nominally a nucleotide. The following discussion deals with substituted traits as though they are all nucleotides. This focuses the problem and makes it more comprehensible, while remaining true to the essence of modern evolutionary thought.

With these clarifications, let us return to the example. Take an ape-like creature from 10 million years ago, substitute a maximum of 500,000 selectively significant nucleotides and you would have a poet philosopher? What does that sound like to you? How much information can be packed into 500,000 nucleotides? It is roughly one-hundredth of one percent of the nucleotide sites in each human ovum.

Is this enough to account for the significantly improved skulls, jaws, teeth, feet, speech, upright posture, abstract thought, and appreciation of music, to name just a few? If you find it doubtful, then you are beginning to understand why this is important. It sets a limit on the number of traits that can be substituted by differential survival in the available time.

*

In many respects the above example paints a very optimistic picture of evolution. First, selection in nature is not perfect. It is rarely as intense as this example. When selection is weaker, the substitution requires more time.

Second, beneficial mutations are not easily produced. They are rare. A population of 100,000 is not likely to receive a major one every generation.

Third, the effect of harmful mutations has not been counted. These must be eliminated by differential survival, and this raises the cost of the process.

Fourth, time was not deducted for periods when the population is stuck on a local fitness peak, undergoing little if any change. This phenomenon — known as stasis — is recognized by punctuationists as a major feature of the fossil record. They say species spend most of their time in stasis. Based on the fossil record, Gould estimates[5] that the typical species spends at least 90 percent of its time in

---

[4] The evolution and maintenance of *anything* — including "evolutionary stable strategies" — incurs costs of substitution and maintenance.

[5] Gould, 1982c, p 84, and 1982e, p 137. Gould also feels that the punctuated equilibria model applies to the hominid fossil record (see for example Gould, 1987c and 1987d) and to human evolution (Gould, 1980, p 125-133).

stasis where little or no morphological change occurs. Such morphological stasis probably indicates genetic stasis.

> [Punctuated equilibria] exerts some constraint upon genetic modes. Gradual and sequential substitution of genes will not be a good model for the origin of higher taxa if stasis be prevalent. (Gould, 1982e, p 138)

That fact alone would substantially reduce the time available for making substitutions. The number of substitutions could be less than 50,000 (one tenth its previous value).[6]

Fifth, to get past fitness barriers, evolutionists have proposed the shifting balance hypothesis. This hypothesis requires various deleterious mechanisms, of which inbreeding is the most notable. Even if these mechanisms eventually succeeded, the population would likely lose many beneficial traits in the process. It is a poor exchange if the population loses one beneficial trait in getting around a fitness barrier caused by the beneficial effects of another trait. The cost of the trait would have already been paid but the population would no longer have anything to show for it. The trait might then have to be replaced or re-evolved, adding extra cost to the process.

Sixth, often the initial traits are not directly replaced by the final traits. There would be many intermediate steps along the way, so traits would typically be substituted many times to achieve the final result. There would be fitness canyons to be skirted by long circuitous paths. For example, many selective substitutions are required to get several genes into the right sequence and linkage on the chromosomes. This is not accomplished in one substitution.[7]

Seventh, and not least, a human-like population would not have the reproductive capacity required for this process. There is no possible way for females to produce an average of 100,000 offspring each.

---

[6] A few years later, punctuationists made a subtle attempt to 'decouple' genetic evolution from morphological evolution, as though the two are not closely related. (e.g., Gould, 1985a, p 7) Possibly a geneticist had made them aware of Haldane's Dilemma, and the decoupling was suggested as a way to avoid amplifying the problem. If that is true, punctuationists have not actually said so. Haldane's Dilemma has remained the trade secret of evolutionary geneticists.

[7] Changing a nucleotide can be substantially more difficult than described above, because a given nucleotide can take part in more than one gene. For example, each nucleotide determines its complimentary nucleotide on the other side of the DNA double helix, and each side of the double helix can code for a different gene, thus each nucleotide can participate (indirectly) in more than one gene. Also, DNA is read in groups of three nucleotides (known as a codon), so the same strand of DNA can be read three different ways depending on the reading frame. In this way two genes can overlap completely or partially. Because a nucleotide can participate in different genes it can be difficult to change, like changing a puzzle piece that must fit into more than one jig-saw puzzle.

210

This general problem is called the **Cost of Substitution**.[8] Theorists often say the population must bear the cost of substitution. That is true, but it does not reveal the real problem. If the population cannot plausibly bear the cost, then the given evolutionary explanation is not credible.

Terminology

To understand Haldane's Dilemma further we need some terminology. Define a genetic death as an individual who fails to contribute genetically to a birth in the next generation. A genetic death is the termination of a genetic line of inheritance. This can happen because the individual dies before reproductive maturity, or fails to mate, or is sterile, for example.

Define a survivor as an individual who does not end in genetic death, but succeeds in leaving an heir.

All births end as either survivors or genetic deaths.

$$\text{Births} \quad = \quad \text{Survivors} + \text{Genetic Deaths}$$

We will categorize genetic deaths into five types, depending on the cause of death. The five causes are: mutation, segregation, balancing, substitution, or random. We will define these later, for now we can develop our equation.

$$
\begin{aligned}
\text{Births} \quad &= \quad \text{Survivors} \\
&+ \quad \text{Mutation Deaths} \\
&+ \quad \text{Segregation Deaths} \\
&+ \quad \text{Balancing Deaths} \\
&+ \quad \text{Substitution Deaths} \\
&+ \quad \text{Random Deaths}
\end{aligned}
$$

In principle, we can count these values over a population for many generations. We do not need to learn the specific cause of death for each individual, as that would be more information than we need. We only need reasonable estimates of these values over the long term. These estimates must be taken over those circumstances a species meets in its evolution: large population sizes and small, good times and bad, as they occur. Ideally, these estimates should recognize that the population spends most of its time in stasis.[9]

We are interested in relative numbers, rather than absolute numbers. So we will normalize by dividing both sides of the equation by the number of survivors.

---

[8]   This line of argument was often called "The Cost of Natural Selection." The term is a misnomer because the argument is not about survival of the fittest, nor with the design, function, or adaptation of traits that are substituted. The argument is concerned only with the substitution of traits, so the term *Cost of Substitution* is appropriate.

[9]   During such times the substitutions are slowed if not stopped altogether.

By rearranging we obtain:

$$B - 1 = P_M + P_X + P_B + P_S + P_R$$

B is the births per survivor. It is the measure of the specie's long term realized reproduction rate. The P's are 'payments' made each generation. The subscripts M, X, B, S, and R stand for mutation, segregation, balancing, substitution, and random, respectively. These payments begin as births. These births are doomed, in the Darwinian sense at least. They are born, but they will die without heir. When their life is out, they become genetic deaths. Since that is their destiny these payments have units of 'genetic deaths per survivor.'

This equation is valid if the species is not extinct. The '1' symbolizes that, over the long term, every survivor must be replaced by one birth to keep the species from going extinct. The quantity B-1 is called the total reproductive excess. It is the relative number of births remaining after the need for continuity is quenched. It is the relative number of births available to pay the various costs of doing evolutionary business.

In the literature on Haldane's Dilemma, the term **reproductive excess** is used in a narrower sense, here equivalent to P_S.

$$P_S = B - 1 - P_M - P_X - P_B - P_R$$

The quantity P_S is the relative number of births available to pay the cost of substitution. P_S is what remains of the birth rate after subtracting all other payments.

The quantities P_M, P_X, P_B, and P_R symbolize the average payments made each generation toward the costs of mutation, segregation, balancing, and random death, respectively. The next section will explain the meaning of these terms and give a feeling for their size.

Payments and Costs

Population genetics can calculate the genetic deaths caused by a given type of evolutionary process. This gives the cost of that process. There are five types of costs: C_M, C_X, C_B, C_S, C_R. These correspond to the costs of mutation, segregation, balancing, substitution, and random death, respectively.

Assuming the species does not go extinct, then over the long term the average per-generation payments must equal the average per-generation costs.

$$P_M=C_M, \quad P_X=C_X, \quad P_B=C_B, \quad P_S=C_S, \quad P_R=C_R$$

The cost C_S and payment P_S are of special interest to us. C_S is the cost of substitution: the cost of substituting genes. Unlike other costs, C_S is typically expressed as a cost 'per substitution,' rather than a cost 'per generation.' (The conversion is a simple one and need not concern us here. When the time comes to apply this value we will do so correctly.) P_S is special, because it is the only payment counting toward gene substitution.

*

In the 1960s, it became possible to study amino-acid sequences of proteins and nucleotide sequences of DNA and RNA. These studies revealed large amounts of genetic variation. For any species, most genes exist in many different versions (alleles). This posed a problem for theorists. The classical theory of selection predicted that differential survival should have eliminated all except the best one or two variants. Yet real populations contain much more variation than could be accommodated by that explanation.

Selectionists eventually answered the problem as follows. They argued that genetic variation is actively maintained in populations by peculiar types of differential survival. They said heterozygote advantage, for example, actively prevents genetic variation from being removed from the population. Heterozygote advantage occurs due to the mixing of genes from two parents by sexual reproduction. This mixing (known as Mendelian segregation) creates homozygotes and heterozygotes each generation. Heterozygote advantage is when the heterozygote genotype has a survival advantage over the homozygotes. The classic case of heterozygote advantage is sickle-cell anemia.

Heterozygote advantage incurs a special cost. The inferior homozygotes meet a higher incidence of genetic death, and these homozygotes are constantly being produced anew by Mendelian segregation in each generation. Thus, new homozygotes are produced, and go marching off to their genetic deaths. The population must supply the births, but cannot count them toward gene substitution. In this way, Mendelian segregation creates a cost, known as the cost of segregation C_X.

The neutralists pointed out that selectionists were employing this explanation too much. It was single-handedly incurring a cost too high for any mammalian species to pay.

> [I]f 2000 overdominant loci are segregating, each with 1% heterozygote advantage, and if the selection is carried out by premature death of less fit homozygotes, each individual must produce on the average roughly 22,000 young in order to maintain the population number constant from generation to generation. It is evident that no mammalian species can afford such reproductive waste. (Kimura, 1983, p28)

In short, the cost of segregation C_X can be large, if not overwhelming. This realization forced selectionists to shift their emphasis away from heterozygote advantage.

*

Soon the selectionists had developed an alternate mechanism for maintaining high levels of genetic variation. The new mechanism, generally called balancing selection, relies on four types of selection. It involves traits whose survival values change depending on environmental conditions of time, space, population density, or gene frequency. These are called temporal-dependent, spatial-dependent, density-dependent, or frequency-dependent selection.

Suppose a particular gene is advantageous only when uncommon — this type of balancing selection is frequency-dependent. Differential survival will then actively maintain the gene in the population at a low frequency. This is how balancing selection could maintain genetic variation in the population.

These mechanisms cause genetic death and incur a cost of balancing selection C_B.[10]

*

The vast majority of mutations are harmful. These occur randomly, despite the fitness of the individual. Harmful mutations must be removed from the population by differential survival, and therein lies a cost. The population must produce many individuals who go marching off to a genetic death because they have harmful mutation. A cost must be paid but no beneficial gene substitution is achieved. The cost of mutation C_M is caused by harmful mutation. (A later section will show that the cost of mutation can be large.)

*

Chance events also impose a cost on a species. Often an organism dies not because of its adaptations (or lack thereof) but because it is simply standing in the wrong place at the wrong time. This random death penalizes the fit and the unfit alike, in equal portion. Random death continually eliminates a portion of the population without regard to adaptation.

Random death happens in countless ways. For example, a disease may sweep through a population, killing all but a few. These few might not have any particular trait enabling them to survive. They might have avoided the disease simply by chance. Flood, fire, famine, landslides, accidents of nature, disease and predation can all inflict a heavy cost randomly. When a whale swoops up a mouthful of plankton by the thousands it is not because those individuals are unfit. For the most part, it is because they just happened to be in the whale's path. This process incurs a cost of random death C_R.[11]

Some people believe there is no such thing as truly random death. They see that no two organisms are completely identical, therefore selection is always acting, in every death, no matter how small the effect. Selection, they say, is always scrutinizing every organism, making its effect felt no matter how infinitesimal, accumulating its consequence over many generations. This is how Darwin tended to present it. Yet population genetics shows this view is false. All real populations are finite in size and therefore when selection coefficients get sufficiently small the effect of differential survival disappears into the 'background noise' of random events. Neutrality is not a singular 'point' on a continuum of selection values. It is a range of selection values centered on zero. There is such a thing as random death and it increases as population sizes decrease.

I am not saying that natural events (such as flood and fire) cause only random death. Things are rarely that tidy in nature. The effect here is not all or nothing. Rather, random death is a substantial part of natural events. Random death takes its toll along side differential survival.

---

[10] Some types of balancing selection have lower cost than heterozygote advantage.

[11] Population genetics commonly deals only with *relative* frequencies of genes, and so ignores random death as irrelevant.

In addition, differential survival itself causes some genetic deaths that must be counted as random. Not all advantageous traits are heritable. For example, a genetically inferior organism may be larger, faster, or stronger, simply because it happened to have better nourishment when it was young. This genetically inferior organism may then out-compete genetically superior opponents, thereby causing genetic deaths. Yet the advantage is not heritable, so the genetic deaths do not count toward gene substitution.

In addition, differential survival does not necessarily operate in a consistent direction. Environmental conditions sometimes change so differential survival operates in the opposite direction. Differential survival may tug one way, then another, back and forth. Many of its genetic deaths are effectively random and must be counted as random genetic deaths.

*

If a species is to survive, then its genetic deaths must be replaced. These costs $(C_M, C_X, C_B, C_S, C_R)$ must be paid by the total reproductive excess of the species.

Haldane's Model

Differential survival is required for selective gene substitution, and this causes genetic death. There is no way around it. Some individuals must live, and others must die without heirs. The substitution of a gene incurs some number of genetic deaths. We divide this by the number of survivors who reproductively 'pay' for the genetic deaths, and the ratio is called the cost of substitution. In the introductory example for this chapter the cost was enormous: 49,999.

Haldane found the cost of gene substitution is reduced if the replacement is slower, over more generations. Thus, the cost is lower if the selection coefficients are smaller. He found the cost is minimized and becomes nearly constant for all selection coefficients less than ten percent ($s < 0.1$), which is said to cover most evolution. The selection coefficients need not remain constant during gene substitution, but may vary. As long as s is less than 0.1 then the cost is kept constant and at a minimum.

Haldane also found that the cost of substitution depends on the dominance of the substituted gene and on its frequency at the start of the selection process. For example, suppose a new recessive gene begins at one copy per 50,000 individuals. The following table shows that the cost of substitution is 100,011. The equivalent of 100,011 entire populations must be selectively eliminated during the process of one gene replacement. If the mutation was fully dominant, then the cost would only be 12. This shows that dominant genes are much less costly than recessives.[12]

---

[12] Recessive substitutions are costly because (when expressed in homozygous form) they select *against themselves* (in heterozygous form).

Starting occurrence of gene	Cost of dominant gene	Cost of recessive gene
500,000	14	1000013
50,000	12	100011
5,000	9	10008
500	7	1006

This table shows the cost of substitution versus starting occurrence and dominance of the gene — for genes having a selective advantage less than 10 percent. The left column gives the starting occurrence —the number of diploid individuals per copy of the gene when substitution begins.

After examining tables like this, Haldane estimated that over a variety of circumstances the substitution of a gene incurs an average cost of thirty ($C_S = 30$).

*

These tables were derived for populations of constant size, so some critics argue that Haldane's estimated cost does not apply to natural populations that vary in size. That criticism is mistaken. The tables are used only as an aid to making the estimate of 30. That estimate is not obtained by assuming any particular population size, nor even a constant population size. Rather, it expresses only that averaged over the expected range of circumstances the cost is 30. Haldane's model is quite general. It is concerned with costs and payments, both averaged over the range of expected circumstances.

*

Haldane then surveyed the capacity of higher vertebrate species to pay the various costs. He estimated that averaged over the long term these species have a reproductive excess of one tenth ($P_S = 0.1$). This means the typical higher vertebrate can reproduce an additional one tenth its population size each generation and devote this excess specifically (and with perfect efficiency) to paying the cost of substitution.

*

In summary, the cost of substitution C_S is 30 and it is paid off in installments (P_S) of 0.1 each generation. At that rate it takes ($C_S \div P_S$) 300 generations to pay the cost of substituting one gene. Haldane's conclusion was clear: over the long term, the average rate of gene substitution is no better than one gene every 300 generations.[13]

This does not mean these substitutions occur sequentially, one by one. Several genes can undergo substitution simultaneously at various speeds. If you average all these speeds, then the total rate can be one per 300 generations. Over the long term, a faster rate than this is not plausible — the species cannot plausibly pay the cost.

---

[13] See also Brues, 1969; Crow and Kimura, 1970, p 244-252; Crow, 1968, p 168-173; Ewens, 1979, p 252-256; Johnson, C., 1976, p 184-188; Kimura and Ohta, 1971, p 16-32 & 44-88; Kimura, 1968; Maynard Smith, 1968; Milkman, 1983, p328-376; O'Donald, 1968 & 1969; Van Valen, 1963; Wills, 1981, p 22-67; Merrell, 1981, p 187-193; Grant, 1985, p 162-170.

The implications are dramatic. Take our example of a human-like population with a nominal generation time of 20 years. Given 10 million years, the population could selectively replace a maximum of 1,667 nucleotides. This would have the information content of less than 10 lines of text in this book. It amounts to one three-hundredths of one one-hundredth of one-percent of the human genome. This is before making the previously mentioned deductions that Haldane did not account:

- Stasis — those long periods where the species does not change. (Gould estimates this is at least 90 percent of the time.)

- Long detours around fitness canyons that require multiple substitutions at the same nucleotide sites. (This is also obligated by the genetic code.)

- Deleterious processes (such as inbreeding and genetic drift, which remove beneficial genes).

- The increased difficulty posed by pleiotropy and polygeny (which includes most genes in nature).

These factors would substantially reduce the number of substitutions available to explain evolution.

Think about it again. Is 1,667 selectively significant nucleotides enough to make a sapien out of a simian?

> Haldane's dilemma lay in the fact that the cost of evolution appeared to be so extremely high that to bring the cost within reasonable bounds, it appeared that the rate of evolution had to be inordinately low. (Merrell, 1981, p 189)

Survivors Pay the Cost

David Merrell argues that if population sizes fluctuate, then Haldane's assumptions are not valid and therefore rapid evolution can occur. He provides the following example.

> Perhaps the easiest way to visualize the implications of the concept of the cost of evolution or the substitutional load is to consider a population of bacteria exposed for the first time to an antibiotic. If, among several million bacteria, there is only one resistant to the antibiotic, it will survive and become the progenitor of subsequent generations of that population. The cost, in this case, is measured in the millions of individuals, and is paid in a single generation. The population size certainly did not remain constant during the period of substitution, which lasted, not 300 generations, but only one. The cost certainly was great, but in light of the alternative, the cost of not evolving was greater. (Merrell, 1981, p 192)

In his example, Merrell is correct that the cost is high. The error in his reasoning is his claim that the cost is paid in a single generation.

Informally we may say the millions of individuals 'pay' for evolution by selectively dying, but this is not how the term is used in Haldane's model. The cost is 'incurred' by differential survival while replacing a gene. The 'currency of exchange' is the millions of individuals. Yet, the cost is 'paid' by the reproductive excess of the survivors.

In Merrell's example the cost is not paid in a single generation. The survivors will need many generations to build up their numbers again to the level where they were before. (Or to the level where they are likely to receive another beneficial mutation.) This, as always, is limited by the reproductive excess of the species. Merrell's error is the attempt to represent all evolution by a single generation.

This example also shows how the appeal to 'fluctuations in population size' does not provide an escape from Haldane's Dilemma.

*

There is also confusion about the term "cost." Haldane showed that the faster the evolution, the greater the cost. Nonetheless, some evolutionists want to argue the opposite.

> How can there be a cost of substituting a beneficial new allele, when the population is steadily improved thereby? One might better ask what is the cost of not evolving? It has been difficult to use this principle in the actual study of evolution. (Crow, 1992, p 136)

> As a whole, the fitness of the population would be enhanced by the appearance of the beneficial mutation. Rather than paying a *cost*, the population would receive a benefit. However, even if the environment does change, the cost of not evolving is greater than the cost of evolving.[14] (Merrell, 1981, p 192)

Contrary to Haldane's model, evolutionists argue that "the cost of not evolving is greater than the cost of evolving." They reason that if the population does not evolve, then the entire population will die rather than just a part of it — that therefore the cost becomes large, if not infinite.

Their error is partly one of elementary mathematics. In Haldane's model, "cost" is the number of genetic deaths divided by some number of survivors. If the number of survivors is zero, then the cost is *undefined* — not large or infinite. This is because division by zero is undefined.[15]

---

[14] This error is also seen in the last sentence of the previous quote from Merrell.

[15] This confirms our physical interpretation: the cost must be paid by the *survivors*. If there are no survivors, then there really is no saying what the "cost per survivor" is — it is undefined.

Haldane's model places no limitations whatever on the minimum rate of substitution. According to Haldane's model, the cost of not evolving is precisely zero. If there are no substitutions, then there is no cost of substitution. Evolutionists have erred in two ways:

- They assumed that if a population is not evolving, then it will go extinct.

- Then they tried to evaluate extinction with Haldane's model. Haldane's model places limitations on evolutionary explanations, but for cases involving extinction no further limitation is possible or necessary.

Evolutionists also make arguments based on another confusion over the term "cost." They argue[16] that with the appearance of a beneficial mutation "rather than paying a cost the population would receive a benefit" — erroneously implying there is no real cost. They are using the term *cost* with another meaning: a loss or disadvantage. Such a usage does not alter the cost as defined in Haldane's argument. Haldane showed there is a real reproductive cost to substitution.

*

Some evolutionists try to cast doubt on Haldane's Dilemma by presenting it in an unlikely, if not bizarre, manner. They render it like this: If a population receives beneficial mutations too rapidly, then it will be unable to bear the cost and will go extinct.[17] That notion misrepresents the problem. Haldane's argument is not a theory of extinction, it is a criterion of plausibility. If a population cannot bear the cost of an evolutionary explanation, then that evolutionary explanation is not plausible.[18]

---

[16] See Merrell's statement quoted earlier. For other examples see Van Valen (1963), Brues (1969), and Felsenstein (1971, p 11).

[17] For example, see Felsenstein, 1971, p 5; Berry, 1980, p 148; or Hartl, 1980, p 377-378

[18] Van Valen wrote, "I like to think of it [Haldane's Dilemma] as a dilemma for the population". He confused the issues further by arguing that "a dilemma for a population exists only when the environment changes in such a way that the initial population genome is inferior to one that could ultimately be evolved by the population." He then relied on those errors to deflect Haldane's Dilemma from human evolution. He argued that much of human evolution "has been such as to present no dilemma to the populations" because the increase in human brain size was not necessarily disadvantageous to the initial population of *homo erectus*. (Van Valen, 1963, p 185-186) His erroneous argument hinges on: (1) shifting the "dilemma" onto populations; and (2) interjecting irrelevant issues, such as 'environmental changes' and 'genomes that could ultimately be evolved.'

Small Populations

Mayr feels there is a way around Haldane's Dilemma. He says most crucial evolutionary events take place in small populations (numbered in the tens or hundreds) where things can happen rapidly.

> [Haldane pointed out] that large, widespread populations — in fact all more populous species — are evolutionarily inert, because new alleles, even favorable ones, require very long periods of time to spread through the entire species range. Genetic homeostasis strongly resists any changes in a large, undivided gene pool. (Mayr, 1982, p 602)

> ... Haldane's calculations pertain to large populations, while rapid evolutionary changes happen most frequently in small populations. Haldane may indeed be right for large, populous species. This is indicated by the evolutionary inertia of such species as revealed by the fossil record, but his calculations are not valid for small [sic], particularly for founder populations, the very populations in which most of the crucial evolutionary events seem to take place. (Mayr, 1982, p 594)

The fossil record does not show large-scale evolution, it shows prolonged stasis and large gaps. In response to that setback, evolutionists claim that evolution occurs predominantly in *small* populations that leave few, if any, fossils. Mayr employs this same scenario — small populations — in an effort to solve Haldane's Dilemma.

In essence, Mayr seeks to increase the speed of differential survival by decreasing its effectiveness. In small populations, differential survival is less effective, and random processes operate with greater strength. 'Change' can occur faster in small populations, but the change is more often harmful, not beneficial. In small populations, harmful genes can rapidly replace beneficial genes, simply by chance. This is a common result of genetic drift and inbreeding in small populations. In small populations, scarce beneficial mutations are almost always eliminated. Mayr seeks to speed up differential survival by amplifying mechanisms (such as genetic drift and inbreeding) that are fundamentally at odds with it.

*

Small populations have another disadvantage. When theorists claim that evolution happens faster in small populations, they are implying that the rate of beneficial mutation is extremely high. Kimura says the implied rate is unrealistically high. I will here follow his discussion.[19]

The rate of lethal mutations per gamete per generation is 1.5% in fruit flies. This seems typical of most organisms. We know that beneficial mutations are extremely rare. How rare? Let us take an optimistic view of evolution and assume that the rate of beneficial mutation is as high as 1/1,000 that of lethal mutations. This would make the rate of beneficial mutation v equal to 1.5 out of 10^5 gametes ($v = 1.5 \times 10^{-5}$). Let us assume these mutations have, on average, a selective advantage of one percent. ($s = 0.01$) According to theorists this would be higher than typical of evolution. Finally, let us take an effective population size N_e of 10,000. With these assumptions we can calculate the rate of substitution as follows. The rate of beneficial mutation per organism is (for diploids) twice the rate per gamete: $2v$. This multiplied by the population size gives the expected number of beneficial mutations appearing in the population each generation: $2N_e v$. Genetic drift eliminates most of these. The chance that a beneficial mutation can successfully substitute into the population is $2s$. Therefore, K, the number of substitutions per generation, is given by the product of these last two quantities:

$$K = 4N_e sv$$

For the above values, K is one substitution every 167 generations. For a smaller population the substitution rate is reduced further still. A population of 1,000 could average at best one substitution every 1,670 generations.[20]

This does not take into account the ability of the population to actually pay the cost of substitution. It assumes that cost is not a limiting factor and ignores it altogether. Instead, the argument focuses on the rate of beneficial mutations, combined with the chance that they can escape elimination by genetic drift. The results show that the maximum credible rate of substitution is still quite low.

When theorists suggest that evolution occurs rapidly in a small population, they are implying that beneficial mutations must occur roughly as often as lethal mutations. That proposition is seriously doubtful.

---

[19] Kimura, 1983, p 27. (See also Kimura and Ohta, 1971, p 12)

[20] Kimura and Ohta conclude that if the average selective value of beneficial mutations is one tenth percent ($s = 0.001$) or less, then it is unlikely that K = 1 is attained unless the population size is a million or more.

Migration or No Migration

Evolutionists simultaneously want the advantages of both large and small populations, without the disadvantages. That is a problem because populations cannot be both large and small. Theorists try to solve this by transforming the problem. To do this they use the presence (or lack) of migration.

The theorists assume that *one large* population is segmented into *many small* semi-isolated sub-populations. The magic ingredient transforming 'one large' into 'many small' (and vice versa) is the presence (or lack) of gene migration. Migration occurs when an individual from one sub-population immigrates into another group and mates. Theoretical studies show that very slight amounts of migration are sufficient to unify and genetically 'homogenize' a collection of sub-populations.

These results have transformed the problem — now evolutionists (led by Sewall Wright) desire to embrace both 'migration' and 'lack of migration' simultaneously. This led them to a position that is vague or even self-contradictory.[21]

> There must be situations, and a great many of them, where *the population is neither one large unit nor is it completely divided into subgroups.* The population may be highly structured with *subgroups that are isolated enough to prevent random exchange of genes, but between which there are some migrants.*[22] (Crow and Kimura, 1970, p 244, my italics)

From such a position the theorists are poised to answer your objections.

What can speed up the rate that a population receives beneficial mutations? The answer: migration.

How does rapid biological change occur? The answer comes back immediately: Lack of migration.

What prevents inbreeding from rapidly deteriorating the vitality of the sub-populations? Again the answer: migration.

What reduces the cost of substitution? Answer: Lack of migration.

What can increase the power of differential survival over genetic drift? Answer: migration.

In short, their explanation lacks structure.

*

An alternative view of their model is as follows. In genetics the idea of migration only has meaning when we are discussing a sexually reproducing species. (An asexual species has no gene migration.) Evolutionists try to explain how gene substitution can occur rapidly, and toward this end they refer to small sub-populations and migration — terms that have meaning only for sexual species.

---

[21] For example, see Grant, 1985, p 168-169

[22] Crow and Kimura are referring to Wright's theory of evolution. For another example of the migration/no-migration, unified/subdivided population see Stanley, 1981, p 69.

So, these theorists are implying that somehow sex hastens the spread of beneficial genes: that sex makes evolution happen faster. The last chapter showed this notion is in error. Sex will not significantly hasten the spread of beneficial genes unless the effective breeding size of the population is numbered in the several millions.[23] That result was obtained for a randomly mating population, where organisms breed with mates randomly chosen throughout the population. Therefore, it is hard to envision how the sporadic lack of migration between sub-populations can speed-up the spread of beneficial genes.

Sex is no help in speeding up evolution. Therefore, sex, with a sporadic lack of migration, does not solve Haldane's Dilemma.

Empirical Arguments

Evolutionists make many empirical arguments against Haldane's calculations.

> [Haldane's] conclusion was in apparent conflict with well-established rapid rates of evolutionary change, as for instance in freshwater fishes, as well as with the high level of heterozygosity in most natural populations. Obviously Haldane had made some unrealistic assumptions. (Mayr, 1982, p 594)

> The conclusion of these calculations — that evolutionary rates must be slow — is clearly contradicted by the rapid evolutionary changes that have occurred in the past 10,000 years in numerous species of domesticated plants and animals, by the rapidity with which industrial melanism has been established in many moth species over the past two centuries, and by the numerous examples of pesticide resistance that have developed in the present century. These biological facts seem to require some revision in the assumptions of the model. (Merrell, 1981, p 189)

Evolutionists cite cases of 'rapid change' as empirical counter-examples to Haldane's calculations. Their examples are: rapid change in freshwater fish; high levels of heterozygosity; rapid change in domesticated plants and animals; industrial melanism; and pesticide resistance. These examples suffer from several faults, as follows.

First, Haldane's model is not about just any kind of change. It focuses on change due to a specific cause: gene substitution by differential survival. Many genetic processes cause "rapid change," but the change is usually harmful because it is random. Differential survival is the key motive force in evolution, and Haldane's model places limitations on the speed at which it can substitute traits. Therefore, merely citing examples of "rapid change" is too unspecific to be relevant to Haldane's Dilemma.

---

[23] "[P]opulations would have to be in the millions for recombination to be important in increasing the spread of favorable mutations." (Williams, G. C., 1975, p 145)

Second, the observed high levels of genetic heterozygosity do not pose the slightest difficulty for Haldane's model. On the contrary, these observations only deepened the problem. Selectionists tried to explain this data by reference to heterozygote advantage. In response, the neutralists used a Haldane-style cost analysis to show that the associated cost of segregation C_X, all by itself, would be too high for most higher vertebrates to pay.

Third, Haldane's two key parameters (cost $C_S=30$, reproductive excess $P_S=0.1$) were intended as estimates for higher vertebrates in the wild. These values were never intended to represent artificial selection such as the domestication of plants and animals. Artificial selection uses artificially severe selection, combined with artificially elevated reproductive excess of the survivors.[24] Clearly, artificial selection is not representative of higher vertebrates in nature.[25] Moreover, much of the 'change' occurring in artificial selection is due to heavy inbreeding. Such change is random, so it is almost always harmful to the species. As already noted, random or harmful change cannot solve Haldane's Dilemma.

*

The two remaining cases are: industrial melanism and pesticide resistance. They are not sufficient counter-examples because they are selected cases.[26] Evolutionists chose cases with the fastest evolution, and then argued that these are typical of *all* evolution. They erred by selecting. Haldane's model identifies the rate of evolution averaged over the expected range of circumstances that species meet in nature.

Evolutionists (unknowingly) selected these cases because the gene substituted into the population is typically dominant, and therefore incurs a low cost of substitution.[27] Studies of industrial melanism and pesticide resistance show that, in most cases, the new substitutions are genetically dominant.[28] Whereas

---

[24] With the proper re-evaluation of costs and payments, Haldane's model can successfully apply to cases of artificial selection. However, this does not solve Haldane's Dilemma: a problem especially poignant for real cases of *low* reproductive excess. Artificial selection is not representative of this and therefore it is not a counter-example to Haldane's Dilemma.

[25] Reproductive excess is a limiting factor in the evolution of any species, including those that are artificially selected. Haldane began his classic paper on this subject with an example of the artificial selection of cows, in which he noted the above fact. However, when he estimated a typical reproductive excess P_S of 0.1 it was not intended to represent artificial selection. (Haldane, 1957, p 511-524)

[26] Cases of insect pesticide resistance also involve *severe* selection, which evolutionists acknowledge is not typical of evolution.

[27] Evolutionists point to microorganisms as another favorite example of "rapid gene substitution." Ordinarily, microorganisms are effectively haploid and therefore have no recessive or semi-dominant genes. All their genes are 'dominant,' and so incur the lowest cost of substitution.

[28] "It is most interesting that in over 90% of the species of moths in which the genetics of industrial melanism has been studied, the melanistic phase is controlled by a single gene that is dominant to the allele for the lighter form that it has replaced." (Merrell,

mutations in nature are usually recessive, and Haldane's cost estimate allowed for a *blend* of dominant and recessive substitutions, as expected for the higher vertebrates.

In addition, Haldane's Dilemma has greatest impact for species having long generation times and low reproduction (such as elephants). Yet evolutionists give 'counter-examples' involving species (such as insects and bacteria) with short generation times and high reproduction.[29]

Thus, evolutionists have selected examples that are unrepresentative of the problematic cases.

The Environmental-Change Scenario

Classical population genetics viewed the effects of a mutation as constant and unchanging. Mutations were either harmful, neutral, or beneficial. Classical theory expected that a beneficial mutation is created directly in a mutational event. Yet, that theory had difficulties plausibly supplying the abundance of beneficial mutations required by evolution. The theorists needed more beneficial mutation, so they tried to supply these with a scenario: the environmental-change scenario.

They suggested that many beneficial mutations are created through an *indirect* process. The process begins when nature creates mutations directly. Most of these are harmful and are eliminated by differential survival. Nonetheless, some mutations are neutral, or only slightly harmful. These are not eliminated, but may linger in the population at low frequencies for quite some time. When the environment changes, then some of these nearly-neutral mutations become beneficial.[30] Theorists say this process creates beneficial mutation indirectly, adding to those directly created by nature.

Theorists use this environmental-change scenario to wring more beneficial mutations from nature.

- The scenario is used to increase the initial starting frequency of a beneficial mutation, thereby lowering the cost of substitution.

- The scenario is used to increase the creation rate of beneficial mutations, thereby supplying them faster.

1981, p 91) "In a high proportion of such cases, the basis for [insecticide] resistance could be traced to a single dominant, or semi-dominant gene" (Merrell, 1981, p 99)

[29] Haldane's estimates can be amended for cases of increased reproductive excess. For example, a species with a reproductive excess of 2 could substitute genes at a rate of 15 generations per substitution. This is not unreasonable for many species of insects and would account for observed cases of melanism and mimicry.

[30] Kimura (1990, p 157) uses the environmental-change scenario (which he calls the Dykhuizen-Hartl effect) in his "four-stage scenario" theory of macroevolution.

Yet the environmental-change scenario ignores half the story. The theorists only counted those cases where nearly-neutral mutations become beneficial. They did not count those cases where beneficial mutations become neutral or harmful. When the entire scenario is tallied, the outcome is quite different. In fact, evolution is worse off with the scenario than without it. Let us take these two cases in turn.

As a beneficial mutation is substituted into a population, it incurs a cost. Most of the cost is incurred before the mutation has risen to moderate frequencies. The theorists seek to eliminate this major portion of the cost, so they suggested the environmental-change scenario. Accordingly, many mutations drift into the population in neutral or near-neutral genes. Some of these rise to a substantial frequency, perhaps even to fixation, without incurring any cost. When the environment changes then some of these may become beneficial. These are then at a high enough frequency, perhaps even at fixation, that the cost is greatly reduced. In this way, the theorists suggest the cost can be reduced, or perhaps eliminated, for many beneficial substitutions.[31]

> Most of the cost is in the early generations when the favored gene is still rare. This means that genes that are initially common, either because of a high mutation rate, or because they were only mildly disadvantageous previously, are the easiest to substitute. (Crow and Kimura, 1970, p 248)[32]

The theorists are ignoring half the story. When the environment changes, it does not have a predisposition to favor the organism. Environmental change (like mutational change) is *random* in its concern for organisms — and random change is largely harmful. When the environment changes, some beneficial mutations will become detrimental. This will happen vastly more often than the converse. On average, for every gene that becomes beneficial, there will be many that become injurious. This effect raises the cost of the evolutionary process.

For example, a new neutral gene can drift into a population, and replace the original gene. Neutralists believe this occurrence is predominant in nature. Then the environment changes and the new gene becomes harmful. It must then be replaced, perhaps by a gene like the original, thereby incurring the complete cost of substitution. This shows how a cost of substitution can be incurred without the population any time having a benefit. When the entire environmental-change scenario is tallied, it cannot solve Haldane's Dilemma.

---

[31] The environmental-change scenario was used in this way by Haldane, (1961, p 351 & 359-360). In fact, he used it to argue that substitutions typically begin at a frequency of 10^{-4} or greater, and from this he estimated that the average cost is 30. Since the scenario is erroneous, his justification for such a low cost has lost its foundation.

[32] Crow and Kimura's scenario has another weakness. Even if entirely successful it could reduce the cost only slightly. Haldane's cost estimate of 30 is already heavily weighted towards dominant genes at relatively high initial gene frequencies. Therefore, their scenario cannot plausibly solve Haldane's Dilemma.

Theorists use the environmental-change scenario for a second purpose. As you recall, rapid evolution in a small population requires an unrealistically high creation rate of beneficial mutation. Some theorists[33] try to solve this problem · with the environmental-change scenario. They suggest that nearly-neutral genes are maintained at low, yet not insignificant, frequencies. Then, when the environment changes, these can become beneficial. These indirectly elevate the creation rate of beneficial genes, beyond that produced directly by mutation alone.

Again, their argument ignores half the story. Random environmental change is usually detrimental. For every gene that becomes beneficial there are many that become unfavorable. Many beneficial genes, on their way to fixation, will suddenly become harmful, and must then be replaced. Thus, when the entire scenario is tallied, it does not solve the evolutionary problems.

In summary, theorists are trying to squeeze more beneficial mutations out of nature. They desire to increase the initial starting frequency and creation rate of these rare commodities. Toward this end they use the environmental-change scenario. They invoke random change, but they invoke it selectively. They select those consequences that help their scenario, and they ignore the predominantly harmful consequences.

The Cost of Mutation

Many evolutionists assume that differential survival removes harmful mutations with no further issue. Yet, there is a problem here that should not be ignored. Mutations have harmful effects, and their elimination places a burden on the reproductive capacity of a species. This creates a cost of mutation. It can be substantial, perhaps overwhelming.

Let us focus on a species with a human-like genome and reproductive capacity. The following argument will use two parameters of the human genome, both taken from Kimura's book (1983). Kimura is the founder and leading proponent of the neutral theory of evolution, and his figures form the basis of my discussion. Kimura gives the size of the haploid human chromosome set (inside the sperm or egg) as 3.5×10^9 nucleotide sites.[34] This number is typical of mammals.[35]

The second parameter we need is the rate that mutations occur at these nucleotide sites. The rate is not accurately known, but we can get an estimate. Kimura notes that when DNA is replicated, copying errors occur at the rate of one per 10^8 to 10^9 nucleotide sites.[36] These errors accumulate by a factor of 50 each generation for a mutation rate of 50×10^{-8}.

---

[33] See for example, Ewens, 1979, p 256

[34] Kimura, 1983, p 46, 238

[35] Kimura, 1983, p 143

[36] Maynard Smith (1989, p 61) makes a similar estimate.

> Because in man the number of cell divisions along the germ line from the fertilized egg to a gamete is roughly 50, the rate of mutation resulting from base replacement according to these figures may be 50×10^{-8} to 50×10^{-9} per nucleotide pair per generation. (Kimura, 1968, p 626)

In 1988, Kondrashov sited several sources of data that show the mutation rate in humans is higher, somewhere between 2×10^{-8} and 1×10^{-7} per nucleotide per generation.[37]

Kimura uses the mutation rate in many of his calculations. For the human gamete (the haploid chromosome set), he uses a neutral mutation rate of 1×10^{-8} per nucleotide site per generation.[38] This same figure — 1×10^{-8} — is what I will use for the total mutation rate. Thus, my figure is roughly 50 times lower than Kimura's early estimate, 10 times lower than Kondrashov's data, and the same one that Kimura uses for his calculations.

Additionally, I will adopt an additional assumption that works against me. I will assume that a full 97% of the human genome is totally inert. By totally inert I mean that mutations, either alone or in any combination, have no detrimental effect whatever, either in this generation or in any future generation.

This is a questionable assumption — that a full 97% of the genome is totally inert. Nonetheless, it works against the point I am making. The assumption means that only 3% of the genome is available to suffer harmful mutations — thus, each offspring suffers only 3% of the harmful mutations it otherwise would. Nonetheless, this reduced incidence of harmful mutation is already sufficiently high to cause serious difficulty for evolution.

Let p be the probability that a given nucleotide site will suffer a harmful mutation. Then $(1-p)$ is the probability it will not happen. Thus, the probability p_0 that n nucleotides will *all* avoid harmful mutation is just $(1-p)$ times itself n times.

$$p_0 = (1-p)^n$$

The value p_0 is the probability that an offspring is free of new defects. Then $1/p_0$ is the number of offspring needed to get one without new defects. Suppose p_0 is 0.8, then each parent, on average, must produce 1.25 offspring to obtain 1 free of new defects.

In a sexual species these offspring must be generated by the females. The females must produce enough offspring to replace themselves and their mates. This requires that the average female produce $2/p_0$ offspring to replace herself and a mate with progeny that are defect-free.

$$B_T = \frac{2}{p_0}$$

---

[37] Kondrashov , 1988, p 439

[38] Kimura, 1983, p 238-239.

The number B_T represents a reproductive threshold necessary to avoid error catastrophe. When reproduction falls below this threshold then genetic deterioration is inevitable.[39]

We now apply the two parameters taken from Kimura's book. Let $p=1\times10^{-8}$ (the mutation rate). Let $n=2.1\times10^8$ (3% of the nucleotide sites in the human diploid genome $= 3\% \times 2 \times 3.5\times10^9$). Then B_T is 16.3.

On average, human females do not each conceive as many as 16.3 children. Therefore, under the conditions assumed above, a human-like species is unable to keep up with the rate of deleterious mutation. The mutation rate is too high, and incurs a cost the species is unable to pay through its reproductive capacity. The cost is great, and we have not tallied the other costs (such as substitution, segregation, and random death) that place additional demands on reproductive capacity. The species could not maintain its well-being, no matter how severely differential survival weeds out the unfit.

The standard model of genetic evolution predicts that this deterioration will proceed unrestrained, so each generation will see fewer organisms free of defect. Multiple defects accumulate through the generations and a progressive genetic deterioration is guaranteed. Sex, by itself, cannot alter this outcome by 'mixing' the gene pool. No matter how the gene pool is mixed it would rapidly accumulate harmful defects and dwindle in defect-free genes.

*

The public has been led to expect that a species will maintain its well-being while waiting for beneficial mutation to raise it to new evolutionary heights. (This is the central error of naive natural selection.) Yet the details of evolutionary genetics actually suggest something different. It suggests that organisms can be subject to a continual, irreversible downward slip. This is the metaphor of the battalion of soldiers slipping backwards down the evolutionary hill. A human-like species could be precariously close to this.[40]

Though this type of analysis is not widely known to the public, it has had an impact on specialists. Some theorists[41] say a high percentage — 95 to 99 percent — of the human genome is inert junk having no bearing on survival. Other evolutionists see that argument as logical, but find its conclusion difficult to accept.

---

[39] B_T is a severe threshold. Let f equal the actual rate of reproduction divided by B_T. When f is less than 1, then the defect-free organisms are reduced to a fraction f of their previous numbers in *each* generation. After 300 generations the fraction remaining is f^{300}. If f is less than 1, then the deterioration is rapid and compelling.

[40] "[W]e know very little about the evolution of mutation rates. .... However, one species whose mutation rate is clearly too high (at least in my opinion) is *Homo sapiens*. It is possible that as our life cycle became longer in the recent evolutionary past, the mutation rate adjustment, which is very slow at best, has not kept pace." (Crow, 1986, p 207)

[41] For example Lowenstein and Zihlman, 1988, p 57

> I believe it is unlikely that mutations at 99% of the genome are neutral, which would be necessary to make the rate of deleterious mutations in mammals acceptable from the traditional point of view. (Kondrashov, 1988, p 439)

The 'cost of mutation' argument does not yet prove human de-evolution. The available data is too premature for that conclusion, and I leave the matter unresolved. Rather, I argue that the cost of mutation is an important concern and ought to be common in evolutionary discussion. It has a clear relationship to Haldane's Dilemma: the cost of mutation can be a major factor that organisms face.

Truncation Selection

The cost-of-mutation analysis is a substantial problem. Some theorists try to resolve it by rejecting the standard model of population genetics. They propose other theories of genetics and selection.[42] The major class of these ideas is called truncation selection. It has been proposed in various ways. To ease understanding, I will describe it in its strict form.

The standard model of population genetics holds that the propagation of genes can be viewed in isolation of each other. It holds that, on average, genes are selected independently of each other, depending on the magnitude of their individual survival effect.[43]

The theory of truncation selection is in sharp contrast to this. It suggests a radically different view of the relationship between genes and environment. It suggests that genes cannot be viewed independently, but interact in a highly peculiar way.

Genes have effects ranging broadly from lethal, to harmful, to neutral, and sometimes to beneficial. The theory of truncation selection de-emphasizes this range of effects and regards all genes as defects, except for the one least harmful or most beneficial. The theory supposes that nature somehow counts the number of defects in each individual, then uses this count to rank all organisms on a scale ranging from fewest to most defects. Truncation selection then removes those organisms at the lowest end of the ranking. Those organisms having more than a threshold number of defects are eliminated.

In this way, each genetic death removes the optimally greatest number of defect mutations from the population. Truncation selection is therefore more efficient at paying the costs of mutation and substitution. This is the reason evolutionists propose it. It is used as a potential theoretical solution to cost problems. The idea seems to have been first suggested in the 1960s in response to Haldane's Dilemma.

---

[42] For example, see Kondrashov, 1988

[43] The standard genetic model acknowledges that, for diploids, different alleles of the same gene can have complex effects on survival. These matters are handled with the concepts of homozygousity, and heterozygousity.

Truncation selection shows up rarely in evolutionary discussions. It is never emphasized in articles on evolution. Try looking in an evolution book. You will not find it. Better still, look in an evolutionary genetics textbook. You will be lucky to find more than a few pages on truncation selection.[44] Virtually the only time you see it is in response to a cost problem.

For thirty years, evolutionists suggested truncation selection as one solution to Haldane's Dilemma. Yet they failed to pursue it further.[45] It is a special solution to a problem. It is part of the evolutionary smorgasbord: accepted one minute, overlooked the next. It all depends on the question you ask.

Many evolutionary geneticists feel that truncation selection is unrealistic and unsubstantiated as a mechanism of broad importance. Yet, if it is to solve Haldane's Dilemma, then it must be a predominant mechanism in nature. Since evolutionists have not seriously pursued the matter, this book will discuss it no further.

Methinks It Is Like A Weasel

Evolutionists often use computers to simulate evolution. These demonstrations sought to convince the public that evolution by natural selection is a scientifically proven fact. A famous simulation is by Richard Dawkins in his 1986 book, *The Blind Watchmaker*. He programmed a computer to simulate the evolution of a phrase from Shakespeare's *Hamlet*:

METHINKS IT IS LIKE A WEASEL

The phrase is 28 characters long and made of 27 possible characters (26 upper-case letters and a space character). So, there are 27^{28} possible phrases of that length. From 28 randomly chosen letters, the chance of originating the target phrase is one chance in 10^{40}.

Dawkins programmed the computer to mimic the cumulative selection process of Darwinism. It starts out with 28 random characters. The computer uses this as a 'parent' and makes many copies with a certain chance of random error, to simulate mutations. From these N mutant copies, the computer selects the one closest to the target phrase and uses it as the 'parent' of the next generation. This process of cumulative selection continues generation after generation until it reaches the target phrase.

---

[44] John Maynard Smith's 1989 textbook, *Evolutionary Genetics*, for advanced college undergraduates, offers virtually no discussion of truncation selection. This is noteworthy because he suggested truncation selection in 1968 as a possible solution to Haldane's Dilemma. Moreover, his text does not mention Haldane's Dilemma, the cost of substitution, or substitutional load — even though he was involved in that debate. It is as if the problem (and its suggested solutions) no longer exists.

[45] "Not much attempt, however, has been made to confirm that [truncation] selection occurs and is really responsible for gene substitution and maintenance of genetic variability in nature." (Kimura, 1983, p 32)

The first time Dawkins ran the program, the computer started with:

```
WDLMNLT DTJBKWIRZREZLMQCO P
```

After 20 generations of cumulative selection the phrase was:

```
MELDINLS IT ISWPRKE Z WECSEL
```

After 30 generation the phrase was:

```
METHINGS IT ISWLIKE B WECSEL
```

By generation 40 the phrase was within one letter of the target:

```
METHINKS IT IS LIKE I WEASEL
```

The target phrase was finally reached in generation 43.

Dawkins ran the simulation again, starting with a new random sequence of letters. This time the computer reached the target in 64 generations. On a third run, the computer reached the target in 41 generations. This is an average rate of 1.8 generations per substitution.

Evolutionists advertised the rapid simulated evolution as evidence for Darwinism.[46]

> How is it that creationists invariably produce mathematical calculations that purport to show that evolution is impossible while the mathematical models of population geneticists, modern micro-computer simulation programs ... all show the opposite "that evolution works!" Why the difference? (Sonleitner, 1991, p 19)

> Yet [the simulation] not only succeeds in accomplishing its task, but it does so very rapidly and consistently. It never fails — NEVER. (Wise, D., 1989)[47]

The computer simulations use many unrealistic assumptions that favor evolution. First, the simulations assume away everything that could prevent evolution.

- They do not allow extinction, which normally would terminate all further evolution.

- They do not allow error catastrophe, which normally would cause a degeneration away from any target sequence — no matter how severe the selection.

- They do not allow canyons and hills in the fitness terrain, which normally would prevent evolution.

- In short, they assume naive natural selection — that evolution is upward, ever upward.

Having artificially disallowed all possible failure modes, it is not surprising that the evolution simulations work.

---

[46] For example, Max, 1991, p 23-24

[47] David Wise wrote a program that recreates Dawkins' simulation. The quote is from his documentation that accompanies the software.

The only question remaining is: How fast will the evolution happen? Here the simulations use additional assumptions to artificially increase the speed. Dawkins' simulation gives many unrealistic advantages to evolution:

- The simulation disallows recessive mutations, ordinary epistasis, poly-genic and pleiotropic effects — which would normally increase the cost of substitution and slow down evolution.

- The simulation assumes perfect selection (s=1), which is not typical of nature. Evolutionists ordinarily acknowledge that the typical beneficial mutation has less than a one percent advantage (s<0.01).

- The simulation assumes extreme truncation selection, which is not like nature.[48] Nature has no means to count mutations, rank the population by the count, and keep only the highest ranking individual. Truncation selection gives an unrealistic advantage to evolution by substantially lowering the cost of mutation.

- The simulation disallows any costs due to random death, balancing selection, heterosis, or segregation.

- The simulation assumes a high probability of beneficial mutation. It assumes that a mutation has one chance in 27 of being so beneficial that the rest of the population is completely wiped out. This high rate of beneficial mutation reduces the cost of harmful mutation and increases the speed of evolution.

- Dawkins did not say in his book, but his simulation must have assumed a high reproduction rate (N=100 or higher). This is higher than real species can produce. For a sexual species to accomplish this, the females must give at least 200 progeny each.

- Dawkins did not say, but he must have chosen the mutation rate to optimize the speed of evolution. If he had chosen a low mutation rate, (such as 10^{-8} as in humans) then the simulation would require roughly 50 million generations. On the other hand, if he had chosen too high a mutation rate, then it would cause error catastrophe and the target phrase would never be reached. Dawkins picked the mutation rate that produced the fastest evolution.

Dawkins' readers got the impression he casually threw the computer simulation together and speedy evolution just happened automatically. In reality, Dawkins carefully designed his simulation to favor rapid evolution. One could hardly design a simple, easily understood simulation that is faster. His computer simulation aids the illusion that evolution is simple in concept, inevitable, and fast.

---

[48] The simulation assumes a deterministic version of extreme truncation selection, by selecting *exactly* one organism each generation. The species goes exactly to the brink of extinction each generation, but never into extinction. There is no margin of safety.

The context of Dawkins' argument confuses many of his readers. He carefully describes the hemoglobin molecule as a string of amino acids, and acknowledges that it is effectively impossible to originate by random chance. He then offers his simulation as a solution to the problem. Readers get the impression his string of letters represents a gene or protein, such as hemoglobin.

So, readers felt that his simulated speed of evolution can occur for the hemoglobin gene, and by extension for other genes too. This created the impression that many genes can evolve at that rate simultaneously within an organism — altogether perhaps many thousands of substitutions per generation.

In reality, the string of letters represented the entire genome of an organism, not just one gene. Evolution of other genes cannot occur simultaneously, since there are no other genes.[49] The simulated speed — 1.8 generations per substitution — is the total rate of evolution for his organism.

*

The many unrealistic assumptions in Dawkins' simulation have not been clarified by evolutionists. For example, John Maynard Smith asks and answers the key question:

> What ... is the least realistic feature of [Dawkin's] model, regarded as a model of evolution by natural selection? [Answer:] Perhaps it is the fact that the program has a representation of the optimum message, and determines the 'fitness' of actual messages by comparing them to the optimum. No analogous process occurs during natural selection. (Maynard Smith, 1989, p 13 & 305)

Maynard Smith points out only one unrealistic feature of Dawkin's model: fitness was determined by comparing with a distant ideal target.[50] That is only a token gesture to the unreality of the model. Readers readily brush aside his reservations about the target phrase, since they intuitively recognize it is merely a simple, visual way to keep score.

Maynard Smith gave little clarification to the matter. This is worrisome since it is from his evolutionary genetics textbook, and he is a world authority most familiar with Haldane's Dilemma. His textbook is intended for advanced college

---

[49] There can be no other genes. In fact, if the phrase is increased in length (without changing the reproductive capacity or probability of mutation), then error catastrophe soon occurs.

[50] The 'distant ideal target' is the aspect of the simulation that evolutionists most readily acknowledge as unrealistic. Dawkins offered his "biomorphs" simulation program as a way around that criticism. (Dawkins, 1986, p 50-74) A distant ideal target is not formalized into the program itself, nonetheless it can easily still exist in the mind of the user, since the user does the selecting. The major difference is that the user selects simulated 'phenotypes' which are complicated mappings of underlying 'genotypes' — so the result of selection is less direct. Thus, a distant ideal target still exists, its effect is just more difficult to assess.

A major attraction of the program is that the biomorphs often develop interesting, even "life-like" shapes. This is largely because Dawkins *designed* the program to employ types of symmetry (e.g., segmentation, radial, bilateral or offset bilateral symmetry) that are interesting and life-like.

undergraduates. Yet the text omits discussion of the problem or of a would-be solution. This regrettable circumstance reflects the approach of most evolutionary geneticists today.

*

The computer simulation that Dawkins used for his book is lost,[51] and the evolutionist, David Wise, offers a simulation[52] that functions identically to Dawkins' original. Users can specify their own target phrase of various lengths, set the reproduction rate, and watch the simulated evolution on their own computer — which all seemed to make the simulation especially convincing. With a high reproduction rate (N=100), it corroborates Dawkins' result: on average his target phrase is reached in 48 generations.

Yet the simulation uses mutation in a peculiar way. Each progeny is identical with the parent except that a single letter position is selected at random and a randomly selected character is inserted in that position.[53]

That method of mutation favors evolution: (1) It automatically prevents error catastrophe (except at low reproduction rates). (2) It automatically places the mutation rate in the optimum range for producing fast evolution. (3) It automatically distributes mutations into progeny in a way that optimally produces the fastest evolution. (4) It does these things automatically for any length of target phrase.[54] Thus, whatever the user does, the user sees optimally fast evolution and gets a false sense that evolution is easy.

That method of mutation is not true to nature. In nature, nothing counts mutations and assures exactly one in each progeny. A more realistic type of mutation should be used in the simulation, so that each letter has a *probability* of mutation.[55] Suppose we use this correct method of mutation while leaving the 'average rate' unchanged (at 1 chance in 28). This subtle correction to the simulation nearly doubles the time needed to evolve the target phrase: to 86 generations.

---

[51] Dawkins, 1991, personal letter

[52] David Wise's simulation, for the IBM compatible PC under DOS, is circulated by the National Center for Science Education — a major anti-creation organization.

[53] The simulation Dawkins reported in his book probably used this method of mutation, called deterministic mutation. This is consistent with the fact that he used this same method in his biomorphs program. (Dawkins, 1986, p 55) It is also consistent with his results. To duplicate Dawkins' results with non-deterministic mutation would require a reproduction rate of N=200 or higher. In a sexual species, this would require females to produce 400 progeny each.

[54] Since that method of mutation is simple, possible, and favors evolution under wide circumstances, we can ask: Why didn't life evolve to use it?

Or, the first time an organism replicates it could use perfect replication, and thereafter use one mutation in each progeny. (This can be simulated by Wise's program.) This method of mutation is exceedingly good at preventing error catastrophe and ensuring rapid evolution under the widest circumstances. Why didn't life evolve it?

[55] Wise's program allows users to employ this type of mutation (called non-deterministic mutation).

Then we reduce the reproduction rate to that of the higher vertebrates, say to N=6. In a sexual species, this would require females to produce 12 offspring each. This is overly optimistic for many species. The simulation then goes into error catastrophe and does not reach the target phrase. We can eliminate the error catastrophe by lowering the mutation rate.

Then, by exploration we can find the mutation rate that produces the fastest evolution.[56] With this optimal mutation rate, on average the target phrase is reached in 1663 generations — that is 62 generations per substitution.

Thus, the simulation — with its numerous unrealistic assumptions that favor evolution — is less than five times faster than Haldane's estimate of 300 generations per substitution. Ironically, this suggests that Haldane was too optimistic about the speed of evolution.

Summary

If a particular Darwinian scenario is to be plausible, then species must be capable of paying all the costs of doing evolutionary business. The costs must be paid through the reproduction of survivors. If the survivors cannot pay the cost, then the given evolutionary scenario is not plausible.

Haldane's Dilemma does not test natural selection. Instead it tests whether differential survival can supply a superabundance of selective traits within the available time. The results show that many higher vertebrates could not have evolved in the time alleged by evolutionists. In ten million years, a human-like population could substitute no more than 1,667 beneficial mutations.

Since evolutionists have failed to find error in Haldane's analysis, there are only two other possibilities: (1) Something is wrong with the present version of the evolutionary story. Or, (2) The standard model of evolutionary genetics — the one prominently displayed in all evolutionary textbooks—is wrong.[57] Population genetics, so far, has failed to coherently support our evolutionary origins.

Evolutionists often use computers to simulate evolution. The simulations favor evolution by using many unrealistic assumptions. These created the illusion that evolution is simple, virtually inevitable, and fast.

---

[56] In this case the optimum mutation rate is one in 56.

[57] Perhaps evolutionists will move to openly adopt a different model of population genetics (such as some form of truncation selection) as a potential theoretical solution to cost problems. They would be embracing a model whose significance and extent is presently questionable on empirical and theoretical grounds. Most significantly, they would have to give up the illusion — now universal in evolutionary textbooks — that evolutionary processes are simple and virtually inevitable.

9

The Neutral Theory of Evolution

Evolutionists often make explanations the following way: Eyes are advantageous; therefore, given enough time, an organism was sure to evolve eyes. One could replace "eyes" with other terms — like optimum mutation rates, genetic variation, linkage between genes A and B, or dominance of allele C — and find many examples from the literature. These explanations merely cite some 'selective advantage' together with the immensity of time.

Neutralists favor less reliance on mechanisms that employ selective advantage. They understand that such explanations incur a cost of substitution that heaps up quickly, making evolution implausible. They are working to keep the heap from becoming too great.

In fact, a Haldane-style cost argument was the main argument used by Motoo Kimura when he introduced the theory of neutral evolution. His second most potent argument was his recognition (also discussed in the previous chapter) that rapid selective evolution requires an unrealistically high rate of beneficial mutation.[1] These arguments were never 'for' the neutral theory. They are arguments *against* selective evolution, severely limiting its speed. The neutral theory was proposed as a way to make evolution faster.

According to the neutral theory, most evolutionary change at the genetic and molecular levels is from the substitution of neutral mutations — mutations that have no selective value. The rate of neutral substitution is determined by the rate of neutral mutation. In natural populations, neutral evolution is not cost-limited and is much faster than selective evolution.

This chapter will illuminate several aspects of the theory that evolutionists have confused or avoided.

---

[1] Kimura, 1983, p 26-27. As an evolutionist, Kimura reached these conclusions reluctantly. (Kimura, from a 1982 personal communication in Milkman, 1983, p 330)

Substitutional Load

Haldane's Dilemma asks, Given typical reproductive capacity and selection coefficients, what is the maximum number of nucleotides that can be substituted in the available time? For higher vertebrates the answer is, "Too few to plausibly explain origins." Haldane's Dilemma is based on an explicit analysis of costs and payments.

There is another argument — substitutional load — which approaches the data from a different direction. First, it assumes that evolution occurs within the available time, and then it calculates the differences in survival rates that would be required. The argument proceeds as follows.[2] Given typical selection coefficients of $s=0.01$ and an average of 6 substitutions per generation what amount of differential survival would be required. The answer is called the substitutional load, and in the case of mammals it is too large to be plausible.[3]

These two approaches — cost and load — share the same theoretical foundation.[4] Both approaches examine the ability of species to make substitutions within the available time. They just state the result differently. The load argument is less explicit and more obscure.

Haldane's Dilemma is formulated in terms of cost. It is still unresolved after almost four decades, yet few evolutionary genetics books mention it. If they mention the problem at all, it is through the mechanics of load. Why? Haldane's Dilemma puts the problem more forcefully. A number like 1,667 nucleotide substitutions cannot be ignored, even by casual readers. It says too clearly that evolutionists have serious explaining to do.

In the substitutional load argument no such number is visible. For the evolutionist, it is a sanitized version of Haldane's Dilemma. You can read discussions of load without getting the impression that evolutionary assumptions are threatened. Load is therefore the instrument of choice that neutralists and selectionists used in their debate.[5]

---

[2] See Lewontin, 1974, p 218-226 for examples and discussion.

[3] The average individual in the population would have a survival value 3×10^{-30} times smaller than the optimal individual. We do not see such enormous differences of overall survival in nature.

[4] Cost and load also share the same terminology. There are costs of mutation, segregation, and substitution. These costs have parallels in mutational load, segregational load, and substitutional load. (The term "genetic load" is often used interchangeably with these three last terms.)

[5] In those few cases where neutralists refer to Haldane's model, they typically mention the 300 generations per substitution. Yet they do not explicitly state the number of substitutions available for human evolution — it is just too embarrassingly low.

The neutralists correctly pointed out that selectionists require substitutional loads higher than natural populations can possibly bear.

> An important argument in support of the [neutral] theory is that the rate of evolution of amino acid sequences has been too rapid for selective explanation. It may seem strange to claim that evolution has been *too fast* for natural selection which is, after all, a kind of motive force, but the claim rests again on the genetic load argument. (Lewontin, 1974, p 218)

> [U]nder the assumption that the majority of mutant substitutions at the molecular level are carried out by positive natural selection, *I found that the substitutional load in each generation is so large that no mammalian species could tolerate it. .... This was the main argument* used when I presented the neutral mutation-drift hypothesis of molecular evolution. (Kimura, 1983, p 26, my italics)[6]

*

Substitutional load is technically defined as follows. During the coarse of substituting a new mutation, there is an average selective value for the population. Also, there is a selective value of the optimum genotype in the population. The substitutional load is the fraction by which the average selective value is reduced in comparison to the optimum. Substitutional load predicts the amount of differential survival necessary to accomplish a given substitution rate.

By the above definition, neutral substitutions cause zero load.[7] Neutralists argued that because neutral evolution causes no load, it can go at virtually unlimited speed.[8] In short, neutralists confused the concepts of load and cost. The confusion was thorough because neutralists loosely equated the concepts of load and cost, and often used the terminology interchangeably. The neutralists' argument created the erroneous impression that neutral mutations have no cost of substitution.

If selectionists doubted the matter, they did not heatedly challenge the neutralists on it. Selectionists, after all, were themselves already quite assailable on the issue of cost. Instead selectionists allowed the neutralists' error to circulate, and then rode along on its coattails.

---

[6] It was Kimura who, in 1960, first rephrased Haldane's cost argument in terms of substitutional load. (Kimura, 1983, p 25)

[7] Neutral substitutions do not require differential survival (instead they require genetic drift) so the load is zero by definition. More precisely, according to Kimura (1968, p 625), the substitutional load $L = 4N_e \cdot s \cdot \log_e(1/p)$, where N_e is the effective population size, s is the selective value, and p is the starting frequency. For neutral mutations, s goes to zero, so the load goes to zero.

[8] "[F]or a nearly neutral mutation the substitutional load can be very low and there will be no limit to the rate of gene substitution in evolution." (Kimura, 1968, p 625)

Selectionists amplified the illusion by misusing the concept of load.[9] They did this by interpreting the word "load" in a non-technical, informal way. (Just as they had done with the concept of "cost.") They claimed that the substitution of a more advantageous allele for a less advantageous one cannot be considered a "load," since the fitness of the species is thereby increased. The selectionists' erroneous load argument created the illusion that beneficial mutations have no load and no cost of substitution.[10]

*

Haldane's Dilemma surprises most people. The issue is central to the debate between neutralists and selectionists. Yet it was not visible because it was stated in terms of load—which concealed the problem from view. Evolutionists conducted the neutrality versus selection debate as though an arcane internal discussion of interest only to their specialists. They gave no hint that evolutionary genetics itself has a serious problem here. Even close observers were unaware of the severity of the problem.

Historically, the concept of load has deeply obscured, rather than revealed, the critical issues.[11] The issues can be communicated easily without the concept of load.

---

[9] Evolutionists misrepresented the load concept in various ways to create the false idea that it is not a problem. For example, Crow writes, "From the population standpoint, a load is not necessarily bad; it may provide the genetic variability needed to keep up with environmental changes and to allow for future evolution." (Crow, 1992, p 132)

[10] Though neutralists doubted the selectionists' argument, they did not challenge it as forcefully as they might have. For example, Kimura (1983, p 135) notes that, "One popular criticism [of Haldane's Dilemma] is that the substitution of a more advantageous allele for a less advantageous one cannot be considered a load, since the fitness of the species is thereby increased." He then objects to that argument, but for the wrong reason. He says the argument "overlooks the important biological fact that for each species the environment, both physical and biotic, is constantly deteriorating ..." The correct objection is that substitutions incur a cost — always. Neutralists, however, are evolutionists and they rely on selection to create all real adaptation. So they were reluctant to press the matter further.

[11] Neutralists and selectionists debate each other using various arguments about substitutional load. Lewontin (1974) discussed those arguments at length. The concept of load is so obscure that he concluded in frustration, "If the reader has the feeling by now that there is nothing in the arguments but arbitrary number-juggling that can be made to support any preconceptions, he has rightly understood my message." (1974, p 221-222)

The Cost of Neutral Substitution

The appendix to Haldane's Dilemma contains a derivation for the minimum possible cost of substitution. The cost is given by p_0, the frequency of the trait at the start of the substitution:

$$Cost = \log_e\left(\frac{1}{p_0}\right)$$

The derivation shows that the substituted trait need not be selective to have a cost. Thus, even neutral traits have a cost of substitution. The rule is: Nothing can go from rare to predominant without paying a reproductive cost.

The above formula gives a lower limit of the cost. Neutral mutations have a much larger cost. They increase and decrease, randomly back and forth, incurring costs in both directions. Moreover, they may randomly move toward fixation, only to be ultimately eliminated. It takes many such attempts to achieve one successful neutral substitution. The process is extremely inefficient, slow,[12] and incurs a high reproductive cost. The cost of a neutral substitution is much larger than a selective substitution.

Sexual reproduction mixes genes from two organisms into one new progeny. The mixing does not change the cost of substitution. Neutral genes ideally fit the standard model of population genetics. They are independent of one another. They do not interact with other genes in a selective way. Therefore, a reproductive excess that pays for a given neutral substitution cannot, on average, aid or inhibit the substitution of other genes. In effect, each substitution must be paid by separate reproductive excess. In this mode, neutral genes fit Haldane's model precisely. They are like selective genes — except they are more costly — and genetic mixing does not change this fact.

---

[12] Let N_e be the effective population size. According to Kimura (1983, p 35), on average, a neutral substitution requires $4N_e$ generations to reach fixation, if we exclude the cases in which it is lost. A population of 50,000 would require 200,000 generations to complete a given substitution, and this does not include the time required for unsuccessful attempts.

Stochastic Reproductive Excess

Next we identify what pays the cost of substituting neutral mutations. Remember, costs are paid by the reproductive excess of survivors. The chapter on Haldane's Dilemma subdivided reproductive excess into several portions. None of those portions can pay for neutral substitution because, on average, none of them favors a neutral mutation. Over the long term, each of them cancels itself out concerning any neutral substitution.

Yet, there is something that can make the reproductive payments. We may call it a stochastic reproductive excess, and it is caused by short-term random fluctuations from the long-term average. The stochastic reproductive excess has an average value of zero. Its amplitude is a small fraction of the total reproductive excess, and decreases as population size increases[13] because in larger populations the random fluctuations tend to average out faster. This random fluctuation causes genetic drift and pays the cost of its substitutions.

To illustrate this, take an asexual species with a constant population size. Suppose each parent has many offspring, but exactly one offspring that survives to parenthood. There is no reproductive excess available for any trait. Because of this, nothing can ever be substituted into the population.

Now suppose the offspring *randomly* survive to parenthood at the same average rate as before. Some parents will randomly have many surviving progeny, while other parents will randomly have none. This creates a source of stochastic reproductive excess that can pay for substitutions.

*

Next, take a population of sexually reproducing organisms. Imagine the organisms mate for life and give exactly two offspring that survive to parenthood. There seems to be no reproductive excess for any trait. Without reproductive excess, the rule would indicate that substitutions cannot occur. Nonetheless, traits can still increase from rare to predominant.

How is this possible?

Despite first appearances, the example does not contradict the rule. There is no reproductive excess at the level of individuals, but there is at the level of genes. This is due to the alternation of generations between haploid and diploid. In the life cycle of sexual organisms, the chromosomes are alternately halved and then doubled. The diploid father randomly puts half his genes into a given haploid sperm. Likewise, the mother randomly puts half her genes into a given haploid egg. This part of the life cycle halves the number of genes. When the sperm and egg unite, then the genes are back to their normal 'doubled' number. From the point of view of a gene inside an egg, this doubling is like a reproductive event: first there is one gene and then there are two. This creates a source of reproductive excess.

Through the complete life cycle, the genes are halved and then doubled. So, on a long term average, the reproductive excess is precisely zero. Over the short term, however, it can fluctuate slightly above and below zero. The fluctuation is

---

[13] The amplitude of the stochastic reproductive excess is inversely proportional to the square root of population size.

quite small in magnitude, and goes smaller for larger population sizes. We may refer to this as a stochastic reproductive excess at the level of genes. It causes genetic drift and pays the cost of substitutions.

Let us now compare neutral and selective substitutions. A neutral substitution has a greater cost and the cost increases more rapidly as population size increases. At large population sizes, a neutral substitution is especially inefficient and costly.

In addition, for all but the smallest populations, a neutral substitution is paid by a smaller reproductive excess.

Therefore, in populations that are not small, neutral evolution would seem more cost-limited and slower than selective evolution. Yet it is not. Neutral evolution actually is faster.

What makes neutral evolution fast? Why can't beneficial mutations simply use the same thing to go fast? These matters have always been mysterious about the neutral theory. Next we will resolve them.

Many for the Cost of One

Neutral evolution takes advantage of a special cost reducing mechanism. The mechanism can remove cost limitations and allow for a high rate of neutral substitution. The mechanism requires a large genome and a high mutation rate.

For an illustration, start with a population of asexual organisms that have large, identical genomes. (Such low diversity would represent a situation shortly after a population bottleneck.) Imagine the mutation rate is so high that each individual receives 100 new neutral mutations each generation. Thus, many new neutral mutations all ride along together in the same line of inheritance. After perhaps many thousands of generations of genetic drift, only one of the original lines of inheritance will remain. At that point, 100 substitutions will be completed, not just one. Thus, many substitutions are made at the cost of one. This cost reduction effect is what reduces the average cost of neutral substitutions.

At the beginning, new segregating sites are created by neutral mutation faster than they are eliminated by genetic drift or fixation. So they accumulate in the population until an equilibrium is reached. As they accumulate, the average cost per substitution goes down and the neutral substitution rate slowly increases toward the point predicted by the neutral theory: 100 per generation. Costs are still incurred and paid. At equilibrium, the substitution rate predicted by a cost/payment analysis exactly equals the rate predicted by the neutral theory.[14]

---

[14] The cost reduction required by the neutral theory cannot be achieved if the genome is too small. This requirement is implicit in the "infinite sites model" of the neutral theory.

The Payment Multiplier Effect

Asexual organisms have stochastic reproductive excess only at the level of individual bodies. Sexual organisms have an additional source at the level of genes.[15]

Sexual organisms, however, cannot take much advantage of the cost reduction effect. The genome is not just one long strand of DNA. Rather, the genome is broken into many chromosomes that segregate separately. (In humans there are 23 pairs of chromosomes.) Crossing-over and recombination, in effect, further subdivide the chromosomes into many smaller segments of DNA that segregate separately. This is typical of sexual reproduction. It minces the genome into many small pieces and mixes the pieces throughout the population.

For the sake of easy discussion, suppose the genome of a sexual organism is subdivided into N equal segments that segregate separately. This decreases the cost reduction effect by a factor of N. So, the average cost of a neutral substitution increases N-fold. At the same time, however, the stochastic reproductive excess has increased N-fold. Each of the N segments is segregating separately and independently generating its own random fluctuations of stochastic reproductive excess. The substitutions are N-fold more costly, but they are paid by an N-fold increase in stochastic reproductive excess. This cost/payment analysis shows that N does not affect the substitution rate.

In conclusion, sexual organisms take insignificant advantage of the cost reduction effect. Nonetheless, neutral evolution in sexual organisms is not cost limited. This is because a payment multiplier effect vastly increases their stochastic reproductive excess.[16]

---

[15] In sexual organisms there is stochastic reproductive excess at the level of the individual and at the level of the gene. These combine together for greater amplitude, but they do not combine by simple addition. They are random with respect to each other, so they sometimes aid and sometimes oppose. If two such stochastic sources are the same size and are added together, then their combined amplitude is not double, it increases only 41 percent.

[16] The cost reduction required by the neutral theory cannot be achieved if the genome is too small. Whether in sexual or asexual organisms, the neutral theory requires a large genome in order for the cost reducing mechanisms to remove cost limitations. This requirement is implicit in the "infinite sites model" of the neutral theory. The model assumes the genome is sufficiently large that each new neutral mutation occurs at a site that is not already segregating neutral mutations. That assumption is only approximately true in natural organisms. For example, Kimura (1983, p 239) estimates that, in a small human population, 6 percent of the nucleotide sites are segregating for neutral mutations. This means that new neutral mutations have a 6 percent chance of violating the infinite sites model. This effect will slightly reduce the neutral substitution rate.

Selective Evolution

Neutral evolution gets around cost limitations by using two mechanisms: the cost reduction effect and the payment multiplier effect. We now identify why selective evolution cannot use these same mechanisms.

The cost reduction effect cannot reduce the cost of selective evolution in sexual organisms. It would require that at least two beneficial mutations occur near each other on the DNA (to prevent them from getting split apart by sexual reproduction) and that they occur near each other in time (so that they share the same cost of substitution). This would occur so rarely that it could not significantly help selective evolution.

There is another reason why the cost reduction effect cannot help. The reason is easiest to see in an asexual organism, but it applies to any tightly linked segment of DNA, including those inside sexual organisms. To operate, the mechanism requires a high rate of beneficial mutation. Yet the beneficial mutation rate is always dwarfed by the harmful mutation rate. Error catastrophe will occur long before the mechanism can achieve a cost reduction. Error catastrophe occurs when the harmful mutation rate is too high. At that point, harmful mutations accumulate faster then they can be eliminated, and genetic deterioration is inevitable.

For the above reasons, the cost reduction effect cannot remove the cost limitations from selective evolution.

*

The payment multiplier effect can generate high levels of stochastic reproductive excess. A stochastic reproductive excess, however, is random and cannot pay for selective evolution. Moreover, the payment multiplier effect does not multiply the non-stochastic reproductive excess. The payment multiplier effect is therefore completely useless to selective evolution.

*

Genetic drift cannot tell whether a mutation is beneficial or neutral, so some theorists suggest that genetic drift can substitute beneficial mutations "as though neutral" and thereby achieve a high substitution rate. That scenario fails because beneficial mutations do not wait for the exhaustingly slow, inefficient process of drift. Instead, they race on ahead, rapidly impelling themselves into the population. As they go, they cause genetic deaths and incur costs. Quite simply, beneficial mutations do not behave as though neutral.

*

Some theorists suggest that *very slightly* beneficial mutations can be 'effectively' neutral and so be substituted as a neutral mutation would be. That scenario overlooks its own bad side-effects. By the same scenario, very slightly *harmful* mutations will be substituted as though neutral. According to the neutral theory, these substitutions occur at a rate given by their mutation rates. Since slightly harmful mutations greatly outnumber slightly beneficial mutations, the net result of the substitutions will be harmful. Kimura acknowledges that this is a problem.[17]

---

[17] Kimura, 1983, p 248. Using a mutational load argument, Kimura attempted to show that the genetic harm is not large. However, his argument allows that merely 10,000

The Neutral Substitution Rate

Neutral mutations can be subdivided into two types: expressed neutral mutations and inert mutations. **Expressed neutral mutations** have an effect beyond the level of DNA. They change the organism in some tangible way, with a neutral effect on selective value. They can be expressed in proteins, enzymes, or in the development, function, and morphology of the organism. This is classically what was meant by "neutral" mutation.

Inert mutations, on the other hand, have no effect beyond the genetic level. They are not expressed in any way. They have a neutral effect on selective value simply because they do nothing.

We now estimate the maximum number of expressed neutral substitutions that could occur in a human-like species in ten million years.

Error catastrophe is when harmful mutations accumulate too fast and genetic deterioration becomes unavoidable. The standard genetic model — the one model taught in every evolutionary textbook — predicts that error catastrophe occurs when the mutation rate gets much above one harmful mutation per progeny. (That is 0.5 harmful mutations per gamete per generation.) At that rate, each progeny typically has one more harmful mutation than its parents. Above this threshold, the species would rapidly accumulate harmful mutations from generation to generation. The standard genetic model has no special provisions that would allow selection to halt this degenerative process.

Kimura estimates that amino-acid altering mutations are roughly ten times more likely to be definitely harmful than neutral.[18] That would indicate that expressed neutral mutations cannot be more common than about 0.05 per gamete per generation.

The neutral theory predicts that the neutral substitution rate is equal to the neutral mutation rate per gamete.[19] Therefore, expressed neutral mutations are substituted no faster than 0.05 per generation.[20] In ten million years, a human-like population could substitute no more than 25,000 expressed neutral mutations. That amounts to 0.0007 percent of the genome. That is not enough to explain

---

gene loci are available to suffer harmful mutation. In short, he assumed that 99.7 percent of the genome is inert. Because of this he substantially underestimated the genetic harm that results from the process.

[18] Kimura (1983, p 199, 210, 212, 296, 321) estimates that amino-acid altering mutations are roughly 10 times more likely to be harmful than neutral. King and Jukes (1969, p 795) cite references to estimate that 90 to 95 percent of mutations are harmful, and only 5 to 10 percent are neutral.

[19] Kimura, 1983, p 46-48

[20] Evolutionists now employ two theoretical mechanisms — unequal crossing-over and gene conversion — to explain peculiar patterns in the genetic data. These have an effect that was not accounted in our discussion: They prevent or slow the divergence of duplicate genes. Because of these mechanisms the "divergence of duplicate genes may proceed much more slowly than traditionally thought." (Wen-Hsiung and Graur, 1991, p 168)

human evolution. Moreover, those substitutions have a neutral effect on survival, so they do nothing to explain new improvements in biological design.

This issue is direct and important. Yet evolutionary genetics textbooks do not mention it. A student can study those books without ever seeing the issue, without ever getting a hint that evolution has a problem. The textbooks accomplish this by approaching the data in a peculiar way. We will see this next.

*

Evolutionists acknowledge that there are usually considerable uncertainties about divergence times founded on fossil evidence.[21] They see, however, that the separation between the lines leading to humans and chimpanzees could not have occurred much farther back than about 7 million years ago. Comparing the DNA of humans and chimpanzees shows that, on average, the differences would require over 1.3×10^{-9} substitutions per nucleotide site per year.[22]

That unit of measurement — substitutions per site per year — is how evolutionary geneticists publish their results. Its significance is then invisible to readers. No one looking at it sees a key peculiarity. I will next explain the significance.

We will allot the maximum possible speed to evolution by assuming that all the substitutions are neutral. According to the neutral theory, the neutral substitution rate equals the neutral mutation rate per gamete. Mammalian gametes (the sperm or egg) have 3.5×10^9 nucleotide sites, so the above substitution rate would require them to experience 4.55 neutral mutations per year. A progeny receives all the mutations from the sperm and egg, so it would experience 9.1 neutral mutations per year. Therefore, in a human-like species with a 20 year generation time, each progeny would receive over 182 new mutations.

If these 182 new mutations were expressed, they would almost all be harmful, not neutral. Each progeny would receive nearly 182 new harmful mutations (plus those of its parents). This is well over the rate that would cause error catastrophe.

*

---

[21] Wen-Hsiung and Graur, 1991, p 68

[22] Wen-Hsiung and Graur, 1991, p 84. (Actually their figure is for *synonymous* substitutions only, therefore the *total* substitution rate would have to be higher.) Moreover, they and other evolutionists have commonly used the formula k=P/2T to estimate the substitution rate. (Where T is the time, and P is the portion of sites that differ between the two species.) Maynard Smith (1989, p 149-150) notes that the formula results in an underestimation because it would miss cases where two or more substitutions have occurred at the same site. He shows that the correct formula is $k = -\log_e(1-P)/2T$.

Our above calculation substantially underestimates the mutation rate inherent in the evolutionary process. First, it did not tally many types of mutation — such as insertions, deletions, frame-shift mutations, inversions, and chromosomal mutations. It only tallied mutations that exchange one nucleotide type for another.

Second, our calculation did not tally any mutations to organelles outside the nucleus, such as the DNA in mitochondria. According to evolutionists, the mitochondrial DNA of mammals requires a substitution rate ten times higher than the DNA in the nucleus. Evolutionists interpret this to mean that the mutation rate must be roughly ten times higher in mitochondria.[23] These mutations would add to the total mutation rate for the organism.

Third, our calculation was based on a published substitution rate that evolutionists obtained by *averaging* together the substitution rates of many separate genes. The averaging causes an underestimate of the mutation rate necessary to drive evolution.

Let me explain this in detail. The substitution rates for various genes differ widely, by many orders of magnitude. This is significantly greater than can be explained on the basis of statistical fluctuations alone.[24] Also, the mutation rate per nucleotide is roughly constant for various genes, within a factor of two or three. Evolutionists explain this situation as follows. They say high substitution rates are due to the mutation rate, but lower substitution rates are due to a slowing caused by "functional constraint." Therefore, the mutation rate should be estimated based on the high substitution rates, not the average substitution rate.

To see this clearer, take the case of the protein histone. Histone is virtually identical in mammals, so its substitution rate is effectively zero. Yet the histone gene receives essentially the same mutation rate as other genes. Evolutionists say that histone remained unchanged because it is "highly constrained" functionally, in other words, because virtually all its mutations are harmful. So, according to evolutionists, histone sustains numerous harmful mutations, yet it contributes zero to the average substitution rate, thereby lowering the average. The average therefore does not reflect the true mutation rate.

In summary, 182 new mutations per progeny substantially underestimates the mutation rate implied by the current evolutionary scenario.

---

[23] Wen-Hsiung and Graur, 1991, p 86-88

[24] Wen-Hsiung and Graur, 1991, p 69-70

The Inert Genome

Evolutionists imply that human-like progeny each receive at least 182 new mutations.[25] If these are expressed, and we assume (as suggested by Kimura[26]) that 90% of expressed mutations are definitely harmful, then each progeny would receive 164 new definitely harmful mutations. This is 164 times higher than the rate that would cause error catastrophe.

Evolutionists handled this problem by assuming that most of the genome is not expressed, that it is mostly inert junk that does not suffer harmful mutation. Two decades ago, they suggested that over 99 percent of the mammalian genome is inert.[27]

> [W]e believe the conclusion is inevitable that in the human genome, nucleotide substitution has an appreciable effect on fitness in only a small fraction of DNA sites, possibly less than 1% of the total. (Kimura and Ohta, 1971, p 28)

In essence, evolutionists were trying to rationalize "rapid" evolution by requiring very little of it.

The evolutionary scenario, as presently told, requires that the expressed portion of the human genome must be less than one part in 164. That is only 0.6 percent. Since the typical gene is 1000 nucleotides, that could encode about 22,000 genes.[28] That is not enough to encode all the things that make humans.

*

Neutralists sought to take more than 99 percent of the genome and lock it safely away so it could not suffer harmful mutation. Yet they were vague and cryptic in their statements about it. As a consequence, most evolutionists were unaware of the implications.

For example, many evolutionists claim that the acquisition of new adaptations can occur only after gene duplication.

> It is widely acknowledged by evolutionists that if genes, many genes, did not occur in multiple copies, there would be no opportunity for the evolution of complexity. .... You cannot transform [a gene] fundamentally into something else because you will lose the essential function performed by that gene. But if you have more than one copy, then one copy can continue to perform an essential function and the other is free to vary. So that *redundancy of multiple copies is absolutely necessary to the evolution of complexity.* (Gould, 1990a, p 30, my italics)

---

[25] Satta and Chigusa (1991, p 127) cite a figure for primates of 8×10^{-9} substitutions per site per year and a generation time of 20 years. They seem unaware that it would require each progeny to receive 1,120 new mutations. If expressed, these would result in a mutation rate a thousand times higher than would cause error catastrophe.

[26] Kimura, 1983, p 199, 210, 212, 296, 321

[27] For example see King and Jukes, 1969, p 794.

[28] Using the same argument, and an estimate that the genome (then said to be 4×10^9 nucleotide sites) is 99% inert, King and Jukes (1969, p 794) calculated that "there cannot be many more than 40,000 genes."

249

There is a simple reason why that mechanism cannot operate much. There is not enough space: 22,000 genes is not enough to make a human, even without gene duplicates in the picture. If the expressed fraction of the genome is small, there would be little room for duplicates of genes.

Lots of space would be available for duplicate genes, if they were inert. But inert genes are not expressed and do not function. They cannot suffer harmful mutation, so by the same constraint they cannot get beneficial mutation. Thus, they would have no realistic chance of evolving new functions.

As another example, evolutionists still occasionally claim that genetic throwbacks occur from as long ago as 40 million years. That idea requires that a significant portion of the genome is devoted to old genetic information from ancient ancestors. The expressed portion of the genome is not large enough to hold old useless information. (According to the model it is not even large enough for the information necessary for the modern organism.) The *inert* genome, on the other hand, might hold old information, but it would rapidly deteriorate from mutation. If a significant portion of it were suddenly expressed (as in a genetic throwback), then it would contain numerous harmful mutations. It would probably be lethal or not even recognizable as a specific throwback.

Though gene duplicates and genetic throwbacks conflicted with the concept of a highly inert genome, few people realized it because evolutionary geneticists were cryptic about why a highly inert genome was necessary.

*

The discussions of the last two chapters reveal a trend that we now review. Evolutionary geneticists suggested peculiar new theoretical mechanisms in an effort to wring more beneficial mutations from nature. Then they tried to reduce their theoretical dependence on beneficial mutation. Then they shifted away from selective mechanisms, and they developed the neutral theory in an effort to make evolution faster. Then they attempted to reduce the expressed portion of the genome, so as to avoid error catastrophe.

The trend is unmistakable. As data slowly made the easiest evolutionary explanations untenable, evolutionary geneticists used more of their available theoretical flexibility. At every turn, they reached ever farther into their theoretical smorgasbord, and their explanations progressively got more stretched and unlikely. This trend from genetics has occurred in all branches of evolutionary theory. As science advances, the infinitely flexible evolutionary theory merely retreats and adapts.

The data now indicates that a highly inert human genome is difficult to accept. Maynard Smith, for example, acknowledges that 9 to 27 percent of the human genome codes for protein.[29] This dilemma was invisible because evolutionary textbooks did not discuss it. Evolutionists have not said how they intend to accommodate the situation.[30]

---

[29] Maynard Smith, 1989, p 204

[30] Evolutionists will probably now move to openly adopt some form of truncation selection as their official model of evolutionary genetics.

Mutational Load

Error catastrophe places a limitation on the maximum plausible rate of evolution. That creates a serious central problem for evolutionists. Yet their textbooks do not mention it, so students get no hint that a problem exists. Let me give a few key examples. Kimura's 1983 definitive treatise on the neutral theory does not discuss the problem. Nor does Maynard Smith's 1989 selectionist treatise.[31] Nor does Wen-Hsiung and Graur's 1991 text, *The Fundamentals of Molecular Evolution.* Their silence is remarkable.[32]

Moreover, one can study evolutionary genetics textbooks without finding a coherent evolutionary model that solves the problem. Instead, they universally display their standard model — which erroneously makes evolutionary processes seem simple and unavoidable.[33]

*

All evolutionary genetics textbooks discuss harmful mutation in terms of mutational load. Mutational load is a concept for estimating how harmful mutation rates affect differential survival. The concept assumes that mutation and selection are in equilibrium, that is, the rate that new harmful mutations occur in the population equals the rate they are eliminated by selection.[34] In other words, the concept makes the hidden assumption that error catastrophe does not occur. Evolutionary textbooks do not draw attention to this detail.

---

[31] Maynard Smith's 1989 textbook does not discuss the conflict between error catastrophe and the presumed evolutionary rates in higher vertebrates. The absence is noteworthy since he an expert on error catastrophe and he intends for students to be "confronted by the problems of contemporary science." (p *v*) He offers merely three sentences of discussion on what he calls the "synergistic" action of harmful mutations (p 57). The discussion is cryptic. If we read into it, it vaguely leaves room for some unspecified special-purpose mechanism of truncation selection to eliminate harmful mutations. His discussion offered no documentation on this key issue and entirely failed to illuminate its relationship to evolutionary theory. This situation is unfortunate, especially for a textbook intended for advanced undergraduates and graduates (p *v*). Yet it is typical of evolutionary genetics textbooks to date: They fail to coherently address the central issues.

[32] Here are other examples of evolutionary genetics textbooks that do not discuss the problem or offer a coherent solution: Ayala, 1982; Crow, 1986; Hartl, 1980; Merrell, 1981; Kimura and Takahata, 1991.

[33] A few evolutionary genetics textbooks mention an alternative model (such as truncation selection), however, they do so in a smorgasbord fashion, without defending it and without connecting it to evolutionary theory in a unified, coherent, and testable manner. It is just another mechanism among many. Evolutionists merely call it out when discussing problems (such as the cost of substitution or mutation) that it would seem to resolve. Other than that, they completely ignore it, in preference for evolutionary models that are easier to sell. This is another example of how evolutionary theory is a smorgasbord, not science.

[34] Maynard Smith, 1989, p 55-57

Also, the concept compares the selective value of an average mutated individual with that of a theoretically optimal 'flawless' individual who has no harmful mutations. For organisms with many genes and high mutation rates, a flawless individual is an insignificantly rare occurrence. In the real world, we cannot compare the average individual with one that does not exist. So, in real world situations, the physical meaning of the concept becomes obscure. (Evolutionists sometimes use this very point in an attempt to explain away loads that are implausibly high.)

In addition, the evolutionists' discussions of mutational load focus on one gene or perhaps up to 10,000 genes. Because they deal with such a small number of genes (rather than the whole genome) the calculated mutational load is artificially low. Students come away from those discussions with the false impression that harmful mutation is not a problem for evolution.

In summary, the real world meaning of mutational load can be obscure and confusing to students. Textbooks do not point out that it inherently assumes the absence of error catastrophe. Moreover, textbooks calculate it for only a small number of genes, and thereby created the illusion that the total mutational load is small. Mutational load allowed evolutionary textbooks to discuss harmful mutation at length — without ever revealing the existence of a serious problem.

Summary

Nothing can go from rare to predominant without paying a reproductive cost. Even neutral substitutions have a cost. These facts and Haldane's Dilemma were obscured for decades by the concept of substitutional load.

Several mechanisms remove cost limitations from neutral evolution, so it is limited instead by mutation rate. These same mechanisms do not help selective evolution.

Evolutionary geneticists have known for decades about error catastrophe. It was the unstated reason why they claimed that a high percentage — 99 percent or more — of the human genome must be inert junk.[35] They needed that assumption in order to make their model of rapid evolution even remotely compatible with observed rates of harmful mutation. Their assumption now conflicts with evidence that 9 to 27 percent of the genome codes for protein.

A high rate of neutral biological evolution requires a high rate of expressed neutral mutation — which brings with it a high rate of harmful mutation — which brings on error catastrophe — which makes an evolutionary scenario implausible. This argument limits the maximum plausible rate of neutral evolution. In particular, it refutes the accounts of evolution currently exhibited in evolutionary genetics textbooks. In ten million years, a human-like species could maintain its genetic well-being and substitute no more than 25,000 expressed neutral mutations. That is merely 0.0007 percent of the genome. That is not enough to account for human evolution.

The above argument is direct and important. Yet it is the trade secret of evolutionary geneticists. They drew no attention to it, except for a few cryptic references in specialized journals. Evolutionary genetics textbooks simply do not mention the problem or offer a coherent solution. Instead, they focus exclusively on "substitutions per site per year" and mutational load — which obscures the problem from view.

Neutralists and selectionists assured us that evolution is a "fact" and that they are just working out the genetic details. They did not admit the existence of deep problems. Despite decades of debate behind the scenes, they continued to present the illusion that the essential evolutionary processes are simple, fast, and virtually inevitable.

---

[35] The United States is now beginning the human genome project — a decade long enterprise to sequence the entire human genome. Some evolutionary geneticists have argued that, to save money, we only need to sequence the small fraction of the genome that is expressed.

10

Gradual Intergradations and Phylogeny

So far, we have seen the failure of the theoretical mechanisms of evolution: (1) Natural selection does not scientifically explain life's designs. (2) Population genetics fails to offer coherent support for evolutionary origins. Nonetheless, to establish evolution as a fact, we would not need to understand its mechanism. After all, we can demonstrate the fact of gravity without understanding its mechanism. Can we also demonstrate evolution?

Conceivably this could be done in two ways — if life had a pattern of gradual intergradations or phylogeny. This chapter examines how these two patterns are measured, thereby clarifying the battleground between evolution and message theory. This prepares us for later chapters that examine life's pattern in detail.

The Measuring Stick

Scientists try to mimic evolution by conducting biological experiments in laboratories, in breeding pens, and in the wild. The experiments often produce marked biological change in organisms. These experimental demonstrations are valuable evidence in the origins debate.

Yet, experimental demonstrations cannot be evaluated by themselves, independent of the rest of the world. They must be compared with the record of life, both fossil and living. The comparison tells the relative merit of the experiments.

Experimental demonstrations are the measuring stick of morphological gaps in the record of life. And vice versa. Gaps are the measuring stick of experimental demonstrations. Demonstrations and gaps cannot be assessed independently. We use one to assess the other.

*

Our visualization is helped with the concept of morphology space, which is an abstract multi-dimensional space, where each dimension represents one characteristic of life. A given dimension can represent body temperature, or length of fur, or thickness of tooth enamel, and so forth. Think of an organism as a point in morphology space. Its location depends on the many characters of the organism.

The morphological difference between two organisms is represented by the distance between them. When two organisms are similar, they are close together. Groups of similar organisms form clusters in morphology space.

For the purpose of illustration, morphology space is often depicted in two dimensions. Experimental demonstration is represented by an ellipse around a data point. The data point represents the original organism, and the ellipse represents its demonstrated variation. The size of the ellipse indicates the magnitude of the demonstration. The larger the ellipse, the larger the effect it depicts.

254

When organisms are close together (relative to experimental demonstration) then the ellipses are linked together. These can be linked together, one to another, so that large groups are inter-linked. The organisms have been 'linked' by the measuring stick. This would be strong evidence that the linked group credibly shares a common ancestry. This method is general and powerful. In principle, the measuring stick could unite any collection of organisms, without requiring any further pattern of any kind.

Frequently, organisms are linked by their ability to interbreed. If two organisms can successfully interbreed, then their common ancestry is reasonably established.[1]

Though individual cases are not always easy to assess, the methodology is reasonably clear and quite general. Organisms are linked by spanning the gaps with experimental demonstration.

Evolutionists need not complain about inadequacies of the fossil record, because, in principle, any fossil gaps may be bridged by experimental demonstrations. Likewise, evolutionists need not complain about insubstantial experimental demonstrations, because, in principle, these may be made quite substantial by discovery of suitable specimens (fossil or living).

On earth the measuring stick method fails to span substantial portions of life. The method fails miserably and in a surprisingly uniform way. Today no evolutionist seriously argues that experiments have proven large-scale evolution. The major evidence for evolution comes from other sources.

*

There is a pressing need for this measuring stick because evolutionists often overstate their case. Douglas Futuyma gives a typical example:

> "There is no gap between thrushes and wrens, between lizards and snakes, or between sharks and skates. A complete gamut of intermediate species runs from the great white shark to the butterfly ray, and *each step in the series is a small one,* corresponding to the slight differences that separate species. ....
>
> The steps from eagle to vulture, from vulture to turkey, and from turkey to the first birdlike fossil Archaeopteryx are *not all that great*; and the step from Archaeopteryx to small dinosaurs is *quite slight.* ....
>
> If you ask, 'What would I have to do to transform a primitive mammal into a bat or a whale?' the answer is, '*Nothing very drastic.*' ....
>
> One of the most amazing aspects of evolution is *how easy it is to account for major transformations through rather simple changes* in developmental processes." (Futuyma, 1983, p 58, 61, 62, and 62 respectively, my italics)

---

[1] Common ancestry is most convincing when interbreeding produces fertile, viable offspring. Impaired fertility or viability is less convincing, and more difficult to assess. These criteria are discussed more in the chapter, Discontinuity Systematics.

He also makes the following statement later in the same book:

> The changes that mutation and natural selection can bring about in any one species within the short span of human observation are limited in degree; we can see one species of fly give rise to another, but we do not expect to see flies transformed into fleas in laboratory experiments. *That would be asking too much.* Such great alterations can only be formed by successive transformations of intermediate steps. (Futuyma, 1983, p 204, my italics)

Futuyma described the gaps as: "no gap," "small," "slight differences," "not all that great," "quite slight," "nothing very drastic," and "easy … simple changes," but when it comes to experimentally demonstrating these he says, *"That would be asking too much!"*

To resolve his incongruous statements, we need a standard that is free of opinion. The standard we can all endorse is the standard that science always turns to: experimental demonstration. This is the measuring stick by which scientists measure each other's claims. A phenomenon qualifies as a natural process if we can substantially demonstrate it in a reasonably repeatable fashion.

*

Evolutionists acknowledge that evolution is difficult to demonstrate.

> It is almost as hard for scientists to demonstrate evolution to the lay public as it would be for churchmen to prove transubstantiation or the virginity of Mary. The process of evolution, though it pervades our lives, is subtle and hard to detect. (Wills, 1989, p 9)

In recent years, evolutionists increasingly acknowledge that the fossil record fails to show the gradual evolution of substantial new traits.

> It is interesting that all the cases of gradual evolution that we know about from the fossil record seem to involve smooth changes without the appearance of novel structures and functions. (Wills, 1989, p 94-96)

Also, evolutionists have increasingly acknowledged the large morphological gaps in the record. Directly from this comes their bald assertion that the gaps were traversed by *small* populations that evolved *too rapidly* to leave fossil evidence.

> But it is the pattern that interests us most here. And if the fossil record tells us anything about evolutionary pattern, it is that some episodes of diversification can happen so rapidly that no detailed, stratified record showing the gradual development from primitive to advanced is ever formed. (Eldredge, 1982, p 47)

> [E]volution is not quite what nearly all of us thought it to be a decade or two ago. This evidence comes largely from the record of fossils … We seem forced to conclude that most evolution takes place rapidly, when species come into being by the evolutionary divergence of small populations from parent species. (Stanley, 1981, p xv)

> [W]e seem to have no choice but to invoke the rapid divergence of populations too small to leave legible fossil records. (Stanley, 1981, p 99)

Even worse is the phenomenon of convergence, also alleged to occur rapidly in small populations and leave no fossil record. Here there is the additional difficulty of achieving convergence between two unrelated forms. Yet this undemonstrated idea is widely used by evolutionary theorists.

To these cases we respond with renewed emphasis: Show us experimental demonstrations corresponding to the magnitude of the claims.

Yet such demonstrations have not been forthcoming. Experimental demonstrations have never been major evidence for evolution. Instead, the so-called evidence has been extensively extrapolated, far beyond anything mankind has actually seen.

> Today it is still commonly claimed that Darwin's natural selection is the evolutionary mechanism *par excellence.* However, this assertion is not based on any factual evidence, for nobody has ever demonstrated that natural selection can bring about anything but events that are trivial from an evolutionary perspective. (Lovtrup, 1987, p 4)

*

In summary, life's gaps and experimental demonstrations cannot be assessed separately: They must be compared. When experimental demonstrations can span the gaps in the record, then two groups of organisms are linked together. The common ancestry of the two groups then seems assured. In principle, this method is strong enough to unite any collection of life, without requiring any further pattern. Nonetheless, this method has failed to show that life has an evolutionary origin.

Extrapolation

Evolutionists commonly try to extrapolate small-scale experimental demonstrations into evidence for large-scale evolution. They try to legitimize this practice in various ways. For example, Mark Ridley uses the philosophical principle of uniformitarianism.

> All that is needed to prove evolution is observed microevolution added to the philosophical doctrine of uniformitarianism, which (in the form that is needed here) underlies all science. (Ridley, 1986, p 119)

> We only have direct observation, in nature and the laboratory, of evolution on the small scale. We can see the species barrier being broken. But to extend the principle to greater degrees of difference we need the philosophical principle of uniformitarianism. Uniformitarianism (in the required form) simply states that a process that we have seen in operation for a short period of time could have operated for longer, to produce proportionally larger effects. Although it can be tested, it is not really an empirical principle: it should be trusted more for its logical force. It is needed in all science. It is the principle by which we extend theories that have been tested on the small scale to explain observations on a much larger scale. .... If uniformitarianism is denied, all of science becomes impossible. There is nothing scientifically special or peculiar in the dependence of the theory of evolution on uniformitarianism. (Ridley, 1985, p 7)

257

Ridley's application of uniformitarianism is faulty. He is attempting the same rhetorical tactic that Charle's Lyell used over 150 years ago in the field of geology.[2] He is shifting the term uniformitarianism between two distinctly different meanings. Ridley's argument (like Lyell's) gets its power from equivocation.

In one usage, Ridley represents uniformitarianism as an accepted methodology of all science. The other usage represents a concealed way of assuming that the fitness terrain is a uniform incline: a slope rising ever upward. Ridley's argument falsely shifts uniformitarianism between these two unrelated ideas.

There is a second error in Ridley's argument. He implicitly models evolution as a march up a uniform fitness incline. This is the central error of naive natural selection. That model is without foundation. The fitness terrain is not an incline. It has contour, with hills and valleys. The biological change demonstrable in a microscopic region does not necessarily extend over a larger macroscopic portion of the same terrain. The terrain can only be mapped out by actual experimental demonstrations. In fact, evolutionary mechanisms are so tangled that any extrapolation of experimental results is suspect.

*

Over-extrapolation is a common error for evolutionists. It is so common, they routinely attempt it under circumstances where it is plainly senseless.

For example, Loftin discusses the reduced or lost eyes of various blind cave animals,[3] and by the time he is done he has extrapolated it into a "main line of evidence for macroevolution."

> Blind cave animals provide some of the most clear and convincing examples of vestigial organs one can find anywhere. Vestigial organs are one of the main lines of evidence for evolution .... The argument for evolution is essentially based upon projecting microevolution over vast reaches of times. The blind cave salamanders, as a group, show a logical sequence of steps from species that closely resemble surface species to forms that are more and more unlike anything now existing on the surface. This gives us some insight into what microevolution can do, given time. Left to itself, *micro* becomes *macro*. (Loftin, 1988, p 26)

Lost or reduced organs are poor evidence for the evolution of adaptations, but Loftin's attempt to extrapolate it into major evidence for evolution is shear folly.

*

In summary, evolutionists often present their case by extrapolating. They do this with the help of naive natural selection. Evolutionists imply that a microscopic view of the fitness slope looks the same as a macroscopic view. Therefore, they say small biologic change can be extrapolated to prove evolution. Their error is naive natural selection. Evolutionary theory is so tangled that any extrapolation of results is questionable.

---

[2] For detailed discussion of Lyell's equivocation, see Gould, 1987, p 117-126

[3] Loss of eyes in a species of cave fish has been demonstrated by breeding experiments to involve several genes. (Lande, 1982, p 149)

Message Theory versus Evolution

An ordinary designer could get carried away and create too many designs. A designer could be too egocentric or too busy showing-off. Or a designer might continue creating for the shear fun of it all! Or a designer might get caught-up in overdoing, like a cosmic workaholic. One can imagine many types of motivations for an ordinary designer. But life was not created by an ordinary designer.

Life's designer had specific and unusual intentions. Message theory is explicit. It says life was fashioned to look unlike evolution. To successfully accomplish this, the designer had to avoid creating life forms too densely packed within morphology space. A densely packed system of life — without gaps — would look like evolution.

Message theory says the gaps in life are intentional, because they look *unlike* evolution. If life forms could be significantly spanned by linking them together with experimental demonstrations, then message theory would be wrong. If gradual intergradations of small steps linked life on a large scale, then message theory would be refuted. Message theory is testable science. The biotic message cannot peacefully coexist with evolution. They cannot both be correct. It is one or the other, and clear-cut evidence of large-scale evolution would be clear-cut evidence against the biotic message.

*

There is another method that might establish evolution as a fact. This method requires that the data have a special type of pattern, a pattern not attributable to anything but evolution, a pattern due to descent with modification: a pattern of lineage and phylogeny.

From an observer's point of view, a lineage is a recognizable line of ancestry with identifiable ancestors and descendants. A **phylogeny** is merely discrete segments of lineage connected into an identifiable tree-structure of ancestry.

We attempt to identify lineages within morphology space. This requires a strategically located void, or absence of data points. To have a lineage, the data must not occur in certain places, but must form a trail narrow and long. Data must be absent from the regions at right angles to the trail—there must be a void orthogonal to the trail. If the data cooperates, then this method is sufficiently powerful to bridge large gaps in the record. The size of gaps is unimportant, instead pattern is important. If a phylogeny were sufficiently clear-cut, then it could span large gaps in the record and establish evolution as a fact.

Yet life was designed as a biotic message. Life was designed to resist all naturalistic interpretations. Therefore, the biomessage sender had to defeat the appearance of lineage. This was done with diversity. Diversity is the antithesis of lineage. Diversity destroys the semblance of lineage. Diversity places data points into those "void" regions. In my wording: Diversity thwarts phylogeny.

Life's organisms were designed in a special way.[4] Organisms are distributed in morphology space to defeat the observer's attempt to construct lineage toward any of them. The organism is like a sentry, guarding against phylogeny construc-

---

[4] When I speak here of the created "organism," I am referring to life that was originally created as a highly integrated or inter-reproductive group. This is called a baramin.

tion toward the others. These sentries stand in the void regions, orthogonal to any would-be lineages. This placement invalidates the lineages an observer tries to construct.

Each life form guards other life forms, and is guarded by others in return. They are all guarding each other, in a mutually interlocking fashion. This occurs at a higher level too, among larger groups of taxa. Groups of organisms guard other groups. Altogether, the observer's attempt to construct phylogeny is defeated.

Message theory claims that life was constructed to resist the appearance of phylogeny. Diversity is a major tool for accomplishing this. Life's diversity is not a *tour de force* by a designer, rather diversity has a purpose. The purpose is to confound naturalism and send the biotic message. Even Darwin could not avoid this observation.

> Nature may almost be said to have guarded against the frequent discovery of her transitional or linking forms. (Darwin, 1859, p 301-302)

The issue before us is this: Is phylogeny spoken by the data, or imposed onto the data by evolutionists? Is phylogeny unambiguous and clear-cut? Message theory predicts there should be no large-scale phylogeny. Any would-be phylogenies should be confounded by the presence of organisms within the void region.

*

Evolutionists often claim they have identified a lineage, yet they universally fail to discuss essential details. They fail to show the lineage is truly recognizable: that it is long and narrow. They especially fail to show there is an appropriate void in the vicinity surrounding the alleged lineage. They fail to show the lineage is clear, rather than merely a best guess or hunch.

In fact, their claims can typically be refuted by pointing out that evolutionary experts give quite different ancestries for the same species.

*

As more fossils have been found, the gaps and the lack of phylogeny have become more distinct. The discovery of new fossils has tended to obscure lineages previously felt reliable. This matter gives a new twist to an old issue. Creationists could now appeal to the same explanation that evolutionists have used so heavily. Creationists could argue that occasionally an indecisive appearance of phylogeny is actually an artifact of an incomplete record.

As an analogy, take a page full of random dots and begin randomly erasing. Once in a while this might result in a region looking vaguely like a lineage of dots, and this can happen simply by chance. As the missing dots are "discovered" and re-inked, they look less like lineage. It is the same with fossils. As we discover more fossils, the data looks less like lineage.

Though a few alleged lineages might be artifacts of our incomplete fossil record, that argument cannot be a major shelter for message theory. Message theory would be refuted if the record contained clear-cut phylogeny of sufficient strength to span life on a large scale. Message theory is testable science.

*

In summary, there are two separate ways to potentially refute message theory and establish evolution as a fact: gradual intergradations (i.e., a correspondence between life's morphological gaps and experimental demonstration) and phylogeny. If these exist with sufficient strength to span the pattern of life, then message theory would be wrong and evolution would be right.

Convergence

The term convergence has two meanings. In one meaning it is an observation; in the other, an explanation.

In the first meaning, convergence is a convenient term for summarizing observations. It says two organisms share a similar trait that cannot be explained by common descent. In this sense, convergence is effectively an anti-evolutionary term. I will use the term this way, to denote observations. This allows me to draw from field literature in which the term is embedded.

In the second meaning, convergence is a label for the associated evolutionary explanation. Evolutionists claim that similar traits can independently evolve from quite different ancestors, and converge toward the same design solution. Let us refer to this as the "convergence explanation."

*

Message theory says life was designed as a biotic message. Life was designed to look like the product of a single designer (the unifying message). Yet life was also designed to resist evolutionary interpretation (the non-naturalistic message).

Since phylogeny looks like evolution, the biomessage sender was out to destroy phylogeny. This was usually accomplished by using diversity. When appropriately used, diversity destroys the appearance of phylogeny. In my wording, diversity thwarts phylogeny.

The exception is convergence. Convergence is a way that *similarities* can destroy phylogeny. Convergence confounds observers when they try to construct phylogeny. Every evolutionary systematist acknowledges this fact.

> Perhaps the biggest single problem facing the evolutionist in the determination of phylogenies ... is to distinguish resemblances due to homologous characters from those due to convergent ones. (Cain, 1982, p 1)

> The major stumbling block ... is convergent evolution: if a similar characteristic evolved independently in two groups, they may be mistakenly classified as relatives. Usually, however, convergent evolution can be spotted because it gives rise to contradictory evolutionary trees. (Futuyma, 1983, p 54-55)

> [T]he fossil record shows that resemblance alone is not an accurate measure of closeness of relationship. (Ayala and Valentine, 1978, p 232)

In short, convergence thwarts phylogeny. By destroying phylogeny, convergence sends the non-naturalistic message.

261

Moreover, convergences are difficult to explain by evolutionary processes. The evolution of new adaptation is difficult enough. The *separate* evolution of *similar* adaptations is even more implausible. Thus, convergences again send a non-naturalistic message.

In addition, convergences are similarities between disparate groups of organisms. Convergences unite far flung groups together. By knitting life together into one unified whole, convergences send the unifying message.

Convergences are valuable. They send both the unifying and non-naturalistic messages. They meet the objectives of the biotic message, so a biomessage sender should use them often. This expectation is fulfilled in nature.

> Separate development of similar features is *very common* in evolution; we refer to it as parallelism, or convergence. (Gould, 1980, p 271, my italics)

Convergence will be discussed more in later chapters.

Reshaping Old Arguments

A scientific theory can shed new light onto old mysteries. It reshapes our vision of the world, giving fresh insights and solutions. A theory is especially viable if it transforms critical objections into corroborating evidence. Consider the following examples:

> The fact that we cannot draw a firm line between plants and animals, or between unicellular organisms and multicellular ones, is difficult to reconcile with the creation model. (McGowan, 1984, p 78)

> Some scholars think that *Archaeopteryx* comes from the Pseudosuchian thecodonts. Perhaps down the same line as the crocodiles. Others go back to the position of T. H. Huxley, and think that the birds are the modern-day representatives of the dinosaurs, having evolved through the Coelurosaurs. Neither position gives any comfort to the Creationist. (Ruse, 1982, p 313)

Ruse and McGowan have made specific challenges against the creation model. Yet their statements are evidence for message theory. They show that the data is unified together (the unifying message), in a manner devoid of clear-cut phylogeny (the non-naturalistic message). Ruse and McGowan have unknowingly made fine arguments for creation.

*

Here is another example. Molecular/genetic research from Carl Woese recently transformed our view of single-celled organisms. Single-celled life actually falls into three different kingdoms of life: eukaryotes, eubacteria, and archaebacteria. Nevertheless, the data shows these three cannot be placed into an ancestor-descendant relationship. Edey and Johanson comment on this:

> They are basically too different for any one to have evolved directly from any of the others. And yet they go about their business in a sufficiently similar fashion, as to suggest beyond doubt that all three learned it from one teacher. (Edey and Johanson, 1989, p 321)

Microscopic life is precisely as message theory predicts. All life is clearly related because there was one 'teacher' (this is the unifying message). Yet life forms resist interpretation as ancestors and descendants (the non-naturalistic message).

*

Glenn E. King complains that creationists misuse minority viewpoints. He complains that creationists improperly quote a minority of evolutionists as evidence against the majority opinion. He argues that the opinion of a minority of evolutionary scientists does not have the authority to "banish" the majority.

As a specific example, he offers the case of the australopithecenes. Here is the case recounted simply. Some evolutionists feel these organisms are candidates as mankind's ancestor, while others disagree. Oxnard, for example, specifically argued that australopithecenes are not man's ancestor. Creationists quote Oxnard's opinion as supportive of their position. King complains that such quotation is misleading since it only represents a minority viewpoint. He continues:

> It remains to be seen whether or not Oxnard's thesis will be sustained by the scientific process. It is possible that Oxnard will prevail .... *If this happens, the result will still be consistent with evolutionary theory.* (King, G. E., 1982, p 63-64, my italics)

King argues that: (1) If the majority prevails, then evolution wins; and (2) If Oxnard prevails, then the outcome is still consistent with evolutionary theory. Either way evolution cannot lose. It seems evolution is so plastic it can adjust to either situation.

Nonetheless, King has missed the point. A lack of clear-cut phylogeny is positive evidence for the biotic message, and the quotation of evolutionary experts (such as Oxnard) is appropriate to establish this fact.

Summary

Morphological gaps and experimental demonstrations cannot be assessed separately: They must be compared. When experimental demonstrations can span the gaps, then the common descent of the spanned organisms is reasonably assured. This method is strong enough to unite any collection of organisms, without requiring any further pattern. In principle, this method could prove evolution.

Nonetheless, the gaps in life are much larger than the experimental demonstrations.

In response, evolutionists claim that small-scale experimental demonstrations can be *extrapolated* to prove large-scale evolution. Their illusion thus builds on the idea of naive natural selection. Extrapolation of experimental results is suspect, because the fitness terrain has a convoluted contour and evolutionary theory itself is too tangled.

*

There is a second, completely independent method that could potentially prove evolution — the identification of a clear, large-scale phylogeny. So long as the phylogeny is clear-cut, it can span large gaps in the pattern of life. In principle, this method could prove evolution.

The absence of clear phylogeny can be shown merely be citing evolutionary experts. Their wide disagreements about ancestry is sufficient evidence.

*

Message theory predicts that gradual intergradations and phylogeny are systematically absent on a large scale.

The theory also expects that "convergences" should be common because they serve the goals of the biotic message: (1) They unify life; (2) They thwart phylogeny; and (3) They resist naturalistic explanation.

The predictions of message theory could hardly be more contrary to Darwinism. Later chapters will document that message theory correctly predicts and explains fine details in the pattern of life.

Modern Systematic Methods

Systematics is the study of patterns in systems. Given an arbitrary collection of objects, systematics tries to identify the pattern of the objects. Systematics employs taxonomy and classification, with which it often seems synonymous. Biosystematics is the study of biological patterns.

Classification is the task of organizing objects into groups and naming them, thereby providing structure to our perception. Classification is useful, especially for large systems of objects, because it provides a convenient means of information storage, retrieval, and communication.

Practical classification systems are typically hierarchical and tree-structured, such as those used by libraries to catalog their books. Hierarchical classification schemes are the most general in purpose. Modern computers, for example, provide the means to store information in a hierarchically organized form.

> Hierarchical classifications are extremely efficient ways to organize large bodies of data or large numbers of units; governments, armies, and even colleges are organized on such a plan. Hierarchies may represent the only logical architecture for organizing great complexity.[1] (Ayala and Valentine, 1978, p 229)

The modern system of classifying life is based on Linnaean taxonomy. This system was founded by the creationist, Carl Linnaeus, preceding Darwin by over a hundred years. Linnaeus developed the hierarchical method of biological classification and its nomenclature, which are still used today, and the fact that it was not developed by evolutionists demonstrates that evolutionary theory is unnecessary to biological classification.

Modern methods have refined the Linnaean method in several directions. They have become tools for studying nature, each with specific goals. Presently there are four major schools of biosystematics: phenetics; Hennigian cladistics; Darwinian taxonomy; and transformed cladistics. Though each of these schools has its own distinct philosophy, they are based on only two great methodologies: phenetics and cladistics.[2]

Phenetics and cladistics try to classify objects like genes, organs, individual specimens, or species, but all the objects must be at the same level. Most biological classification is at the level of species.

---

[1] A hierarchy (though not strictly the only logical architecture for organizing great complexity) is widely applicable, and is readily observed and grasped by the mind. It is therefore suitable for the biotic message.

[2] The book by Wen-Hsiung and Graur (1991) has a good review of the details of phenetics and cladistics that are not covered here. It appears in a chapter with the misleading title, "Molecular Phylogeny."

Objects are composed of numerous *characters*. Characters are complex traits, such as vertebra, hair, molars, or hemoglobin. Systematics analyzes this character data.

Phenetics and cladistics produce dendrograms: a tree-structured branching diagram with the objects located only at the tips of branches. Typically the dendrogram is dichotomous: each branching point splits into two sub-branches.

A dendrogram is not a phylogeny, though they both have a tree-structure. A dendrogram fails to specify ancestors. By contrast, a phylogeny must specify ancestors. A phylogeny is composed almost entirely of ancestors.

The dendrogram produced by phenetics is called a **phenogram**. The dendrogram produced by cladistics is called a **cladogram**.

Phenograms and cladograms look the same, but they mean different things because they are constructed with different objectives in mind. Both can be constructed for any collection of objects, no matter how diverse, no matter how randomly related.

Phenetics

Phenetics focuses on phenetic similarity: the overall similarity between whole bodies. If genes are the objects being classified, then the phenetic method focuses on the overall similarity between whole genes.

A phenetic classification is achieved in two steps. The first step is the measurement of similarity or dis-similarity between a pair of objects.

This measurement can be done in many ways. Typically, a pair of objects is compared *character by character* to assess the overall degree of difference between the objects. If the pair of objects both possess the character (or neither possess the character), then it is tallied as a similarity. If one object has the character while the other does not, then it is tallied as a dis-similarity. This comparison process continues until all the characters have been compared and tallied.

This yields a number representing the morphological distance between the two objects. The more different the objects, the greater the number, and the farther apart they are in morphology space. This measurement focuses on a pairwise comparison between objects where each object is ultimately taken as a whole body (the totality of the comparisons between their many characters).

This measurement is made for every pair of objects.

All these measurements result in a matrix of numbers. The matrix has rows and columns like a checkerboard, with one number in each cell. Each cell contains the number resulting from the comparison between two objects. The comparison between objects X and Y, is contained in row X of column Y. The number in that cell is the measurement of the dis-similarity between these two objects.

In the second step, phenetics takes the matrix of dis-similarity measurements and builds a phenogram. In a phenogram, phenetically similar objects should be located near each other on adjacent branches of the phenogram, while less similar objects are placed on branches farther apart.

Phenograms can be understood through a rough analogy. Imagine you are told only the distances between many pairs of cities. Imagine you must use only this information to draw an abstract map of a special highway linking the cities. The highway is to be tree-structured (as a dendrogram), where the cities are located only at the tips of the branches of the highway. There are many such highways possible, but you must draw the best one: the one with the shortest total pavement. Thus, from the pairwise distance measurements, you must link the cities together with an abstract tree-structured highway having the shortest total spanning distance. This task is like constructing a phenogram. Phenetics accomplishes this task for objects from a multi-dimensional morphology space.

The process is mathematically complex and heavily dependent upon numerical methods, so phenetics is also known as numerical taxonomy.

On a phenogram, objects that are separated from each other by fewer branch points should tend to be more similar overall than to objects that are farther away. This is the very nature of a phenogram, and it is true no matter what the nature of the objects. Phenograms do not identify phylogeny, and are not based on a knowledge of phylogeny.

Most pheneticists acknowledge that phenograms have no inherent evolutionary implications. Phenetic systematists can go about their business without thinking of evolution.

To sum up: phenetic classification involves the *pairwise measurement of overall similarity*, and then the construction of the best phenogram, the phenogram having the shortest total spanning distance.

Cladistics

Cladistics bases classification on an analysis of character distribution. It focuses on the way *single* characters are *distributed* throughout the system of objects. Cladistics places objects into a nested hierarchy, i.e., one that optimally nests the characters of the objects.

Imagine placing all the objects onto the endpoints of a dendrogram. Imagine labeling each branchlet of the dendrogram with a unique set of characters. This can loosely be called a cladogram.

Hopefully, the labels on the branchlets will correspond with the characters of the objects on those branches. Frequently they will not correspond, because some characters will fail to be nested — they will be non-nested. We may count these non-nested characters. This indicates how well the cladogram nests the objects: The smaller this count, the better the cladogram.

In principle the method is simple. First, place all the objects into a cladogram. Then count the instances where characters are non-nested with regard to that cladogram. Do this process again for a different cladogram. These two cladograms are then compared: The one with the smaller count is the better cladogram. This process of generating and comparing cladograms continues, and at any given moment there always exists a best cladogram. The best cladogram is the one that minimizes the number of non-nested characters (or maximizes the nested characters). Cladistics tries to find the optimal nested pattern of the objects.[3]

Thus, phenetics is analog and cladistics is digital. Phenetics measures (in some way) the overall similarity between objects, while cladistics counts the non-nested (or nested) characters of cladograms.

Lack of a Character

Phenetics and cladistics have different views on the lack of a character. Phenetics sees the lack of a character because it makes a pairwise comparison between two whole objects. This allows it to see the lack of a character (or more precisely, the difference in character between the two objects).

Cladistics cannot directly see the lack of a character, because it does not make pairwise comparisons between objects. Instead it compares data structures, called cladograms. The cladograms are compared by determining how well they nest the characters of the objects. This determination is made by counting the presence of identifiable characters. The cladist can look at a cladogram and count the nested characters. Or the cladist can count the non-nested characters. But the cladist cannot count the lack of a character, because there is no reference point for making this comparison. Lacking? Compared to what? Does a given object lack one character? Or fifty million? Are the lacking characters nested or non-nested? That is the difficulty.

We can see the absence of a given character (such as the absence of hemoglobin), and we do this by arbitrarily supplying a reference point (the hemoglobin). We cannot see the absence of an unknown character because there are an infinite number of them, and therefore we cannot count them. Cladists argue that supplying an arbitrary reference point (such as hemoglobin) gives that reference point undue weight in our perception of nature, thereby distorting our perception. They say cladistics gives an unbiased view of nature, and that cladistic methodology unarbitrarily classifies objects by using characters we can actually see.

There are countless characters that some organisms possess, but others lack. This information, by itself, would be an incoherent muddle. The lack of a character takes on a coherent, systematic importance only *after* the best phenogram or cladogram is identified. Then these provide a favored structural reference frame for identifying the lack of a character. For example, the common snakes are classified as a sub-group of the tetrapods — tetrapods are based on a four-legged body plan — yet snakes do not have four legs. The snakes' lack of four legs took on importance only after they were classified as tetrapods.

---

[3] In practice the task of finding the best cladogram becomes impossibly difficult if the number of objects is more than fifteen or so. Therefore, cladists rely on various computational methods that (hopefully) *construct* the best cladogram, rather than 'find' it by exhaustive searching and comparing.

Incongruity

Phenetics and cladistics organize objects into dendrograms, and an incongruity occurs when the objects do not fit smoothly. Both methodologies seek to minimize incongruity, yet incongruities are not uncommon in nature. Incongruity can be phenetic, cladistic, or absence.

Phenetic incongruity is an *overall similarity* between two objects located on *distant* branches of a phenogram. A classic example is the overall similarity between porpoises, sharks, and ichthyosaurs.

Cladistic incongruity is a similarity between *characters* that are *non-nested* within a cladogram. The similarity between human eyes and octopus eyes is a good example.

Absence incongruity is when a species lacks characters that a cladogram (or phenogram) says it should possess. For example, the common snakes are based on a tetrapod body plan, but they do not have four legs. Their lack of four legs is an absence incongruity.

The Convergence Explanation

Phenetic and cladistic incongruities cannot be explained by common descent. Evolutionists account for these by the *convergence explanation*: the independent evolution of similarities.

The public is misled when evolutionists cite examples of "convergence." The public presumes the evolutionist has identified the convergence by identifying two separate lineages that evolved a similarity. This creates the illusion that lineages have been positively identified. In reality, the evolutionist infers convergence from an incongruity in a phenogram or cladogram, without ever identifying an ancestor, lineage, or phylogeny.

The convergence explanation is implausible since it requires the separate evolution of a highly similar biological trait. For that reason, evolutionists avoid the convergence explanation when they can.

The Loss Explanation

In principle a loss explanation explains the loss of a character in a lineage. In practice, however, it is used to explain absence incongruity. Quite simply, the absence is explained through loss.

The loss explanation is used in another way too. Absence incongruity and cladistic incongruity are two different views of the same data. A character can seem non-nested in a cladogram — like a cladistic incongruity — because the character is *absent* from places that would make it nested. Because absence and cladistic incongruities are valid views of the same data, their explanations can be somewhat interchangeable. Loss and convergence can be different explanations for the same data.

Loss is a very simple process compared to convergence. For that reason, theorists prefer to use loss rather than convergence explanations.

*

Many evolutionary explanations require the independent loss of the same character by several different lineages.

> The independent loss of a character in separate lineages is a particularly frequent form of convergence. (Mayr, 1982, p 228)

The public is misled when evolutionists speak (as Mayr has above) of lineages that have lost a character. It sounds as if lineages have been identified. The loss explanation subtly conveys the illusion of ancestry. The evolutionist says "lost characters," but the observation is "incongruity in a dendrogram." There is a substantial difference.

*

The convergence explanation is least plausible when characters are highly similar or identical. This is because the separate origin of identical characters is so improbable. Yet in precisely this situation the loss explanation is most effective.

The loss explanation works best when characters are identical. Accordingly, many species inherit a common character, some lose it, and the rest retain it as a shared identical character.

The loss explanation requires that the nearest common ancestor (whoever it was) must have plausibly possessed the character. If the nearest common ancestor could not have plausibly possessed the character, then the loss explanation is not plausible. This means the loss explanation is most effective when the species involved are taxonomically close together.

The loss explanation can seem to explain away many cladistic incongruities, thereby making a given cladogram seem better than it actually is. In this way, the loss explanation can elevate an inferior cladogram to favored status.

Darwinian Taxonomy

Darwinian taxonomy is the earliest school of biosystematics still in use today. It gets its name from Darwin's major influence on it. It rose in stature along with Darwin, and until a few decades ago it was the only school of taxonomy used by evolutionists. It is also called classical taxonomy and evolutionary taxonomy.

In the era following Darwin, evolutionists fully expected to find phylogeny in the record of life. Darwin's theory indicated that phylogeny should exist, so Darwinian taxonomists actively sought to identify ancestors and lines of descent. They sought to identify phylogeny and base their classification on it.

That task was not easy. The record of life has no clear-cut phylogeny, so the Darwinians sought extra help to identify it. Darwinian taxonomists soon believed that evolutionary theory (and natural selection in particular) can provide helpful hints pointing to the "true" phylogeny in the data. Toward this end, they construct Darwinian scenarios to explain the evolution of a given species. Then the various scenarios are compared to assess which are the most believable. They regard these best scenarios as useful evidence that differentiates the unreasonable phylogenies from the true one.

At least that was the rationale, and other than this goal, the Darwinian taxonomists have suffered for lack of a clearly defined method. At one instant they use phenetics, and the next they use cladistics. They appeal to both methods in what would seem a haphazard fashion. For that reason, it is sometimes also called eclectic taxonomy.

*

Darwinian taxonomy seeks to base its classification on phylogeny, but this has shown to be a difficult enterprise.

> Classification has proven to be exceptionally difficult. Since the true phylogenies of most groups are not known for certain, taxonomists tend to rely upon their own opinions as to the most plausible phylogeny. Since opinions differ, there are frequently a number of different classifications in use, each implying a different phylogenetic history. As old phylogenies are modified by new evidence, old classifications must be modified as well. Therefore classifications are not at all immutable and stable but are altered frequently. (Ayala and Valentine, 1978, p 246)

> After the 1880s there was a gradual but noticeable decline of interest in macrotaxonomy and in phylogenetic studies. This had numerous reasons, some internal to the field and some external. Most important perhaps was a feeling of disappointment over the difficulty of getting clear-cut results. .... The futile attempts to establish the relationship of the major phyla of animals induced at least one competent zoologist at the turn of the century to deny common descent. Fleischmann (1901) called the theory a beautiful myth not substantiated by any factual foundation. Kerkut, fifty years later, does not draw such an extreme conclusion but he is almost equally pessimistic about ever achieving an understanding of the relationship of the higher animal taxa. Honesty compels us to admit that our ignorance concerning these relationships is still great, not to say overwhelming. This is a depressing state of affairs considering that more than one hundred years

271

have passed since the great post-*Origin* period of phylogeny construction. The morphological and embryological clues are simply not sufficient for the task. (Mayr, 1982, p 217-218)

The difficulty with the use of a phylogenetic approach in systematics emerged after the first wave of enthusiasm for it had subsided and has remained apparent to perceptive observers ever since. *We cannot make use of phylogeny for classification, since in the vast majority of cases phylogenies are unknown.* (Sokal and Sneath, 1963, p 21, *their italics*)

Phylogeny could not be seen in the fossil record, so Darwinian taxonomists placed ever greater emphasis on scenarios to help identify the "true" phylogeny. They readily grabbed onto new principles in hopes that these would lead them to the phylogeny and from there to a stable classification. They tried each new fashion in scenario invention. They tried the now defunct "embryological recapitulation argument." Yet the changing fashions of evolutionary thought have failed to reach the goal. All that remains is a long history of conflicting attempts at phylogeny construction and classification.

This being a history of ideas, *it is impossible even to begin giving a history of the sequence of classifications for the various higher taxa of animals and plants that have been proposed in the last two hundred years.* Yet it is a fascinating story. In each generation new hopes were raised by new principles (such as recapitulation) or newly discovered characters, but progress has been slow. (Mayr, 1982, p 217-218, my italics)

Modern systematists have become frustrated with their attempts to find phylogeny. Many argue that the narrative scenarios have proven to be fruitless, conflicting, and untestable.

We reject outright any predilection for narrative-type scenarios of phylogenetic history if they are not expressed in a rigorously testable form. The literature is replete with these narratives, many of which may sound very reasonable, but all too frequently there is little or no way to subject them to critical analysis. In such cases, the descriptions of historical events essentially lie outside the realm of scientific inquiry. (Eldredge and Cracraft, 1980, p 19-20)

Because of the frustration, modern systematists have sought a means to accomplish classification directly, without the intermediate step of identifying phylogeny. This factor prompted a modern exodus of systematists away from Darwinian taxonomy. Since the 1960s, phenetics and cladistics have risen as schools of their own. Both have well-defined methods for directly obtaining a classification. Unlike Darwinian taxonomy, the phenetic and cladistic schools have fruitfully applied their rigorous methods with computers.

*

Darwinian taxonomists claim that their classification has greater information content because it incorporates *both* phenetic and cladistic information. The phenetic and cladistic schools counterargue that point. They say that including both types of information causes most of the information to be lost. This is because we cannot determine, by examination, whether a given portion of a Darwinian classification was constructed using phenetic or cladistic techniques. A classification does not provide earmarks for identifying one type of information from the other. In the resulting confusion, both types of information are lost.

However, if the classification has been constructed from a well-defined method, then the classification contains information that can be usefully extracted by anyone who knows that method. Phenetics and cladistics provide such a method, while Darwinian taxonomy does not.

Hennigian Cladistics

The cladistic method was founded by Willi Hennig. Hennig emphasized a particular justification for his method. Cladistics, he claimed, aims to represent (within a cladogram) the pattern of **cladogenesis**: the splitting of lineages during evolutionary descent. The nested pattern of a cladogram is said to depict that newly evolved characters are passed only to descendants. This school is known as Hennigian systematics, after its founder.

The school is sometimes called phylogenetic systematics, which is a misnomer[4] because cladistics does not provide phylogeny, nor is it based on such knowledge. A cladogram is not a phylogeny, and cladistics does not and cannot identify ancestors.

> [M]ost cladists recognize that ancestors cannot be differentiated using cladistic method. .... a cladistic diagram is to be regarded as a rather abstract hypothesis of relationships and therefore not a [phylogeny] tree, even though it looks like one. Ancestors are conceived by most cladists as solely hypothetical constructs. (Hill and Crane, 1982, p 295)

> Hennigians refuse to accept that ancestral species can be recognized; they must have existed, they may be hypothesized, but they cannot be recognized. (Charig, 1982b, p 415)

Though cladistics does not identify ancestors, evolutionists commonly use cladograms and related imagery to create the illusion of ancestry. Usually these illusions are subtle, though occasionally they are far fetched.

> It is, in fact, possible to draw a diagram separating life forms into finer and finer subdivisions, ending with the individual species, rather like the individual leaves of a tree. Imagine that through some magic, all we could

---

4 Darwinian taxonomy is more deserving of the term *phylogenetic* systematics since it at least attempts to identify phylogeny directly.

273

see of a real tree were its individual leaves distributed in space. Would we suppose that somehow those leaves had just sprung into existence where they were? Surely not! We would suppose that they were supported by an unseen trunk, branches and stems, dividing and subdividing, and that the leaves hung at the end of the finest, final stems. (Asimov, 1981, p 85)

*

Hennigian cladists often squabble with each other over "Whose cladogram is the best cladogram?" In these squabbles, Hennigian cladists sometimes tinker with their cladogram to make it better. They try to explain away the incongruities by using a loss explanation. They say their opponent's cladogram is mistaken, and the loss explanation promotes their own (inferior?) cladogram as the best one. The loss explanation is used to make a cladogram seem better than it actually is.

This raises an interesting issue. Cladistics cannot directly see the lack of a character without arbitrarily giving special weight to that character. If cladistics cannot see the lack of a character, then what justifies the loss explanation?

Once a best cladogram is obtained, then the incongruities become visible. Suddenly these take on great importance because they need special explanation, and "loss" is sometimes a convenient explanation. When Hennigian cladists use the loss explanation, they do not feel they are being arbitrary. Rather, they feel the additional weight they give these specific characters is justified by the cladogram.

This practice can lead dangerously to circular arguments. The Hennigian cladist uses "loss of character X" to argue for a favored (though inferior) cladogram, and then uses that same cladogram as justification that character X deserved special recognition. The lost character justifies the cladogram, and the cladogram justifies the lost character.

Transformed Cladistics

In recent years, a group of cladists has developed into its own school: transformed or modern cladistics. These systematists argue that evolutionary theory is not required to do taxonomy. They reject just-so stories, and they reject the idea that evolutionary theories have proved helpful for identifying the pattern of life. They argue that cladistics does not have any necessary evolutionary implications. They have worked to eliminate from their methods any terminology or reasoning that implies evolution.

Transformed cladists have especially objected to the loss explanation, arguing that its inherent circularity degrades the objectivity of the cladistic method. They say loss explanations (and associated circular arguments) should be avoided, because an injudicious over-use would seriously threaten the cladists' claim to a non-arbitrary method. Transformed cladists plead with their Hennigian comrades to refrain from using the loss explanation so frequently.

Transformed cladists recognize that the cladistic method can be applied to any system of objects, no matter how unrelated.[5] Transformed cladists argue that their transformed, clarified methodology is unspoiled and undistorted by evolutionary theory. With real justification they claim their method provides an unbiased means for studying the natural order or pattern of life. Because of this, the method is also known as natural order systematics or pattern cladistics. Since the method provides an unbiased means of studying nature it appeals to creationists.

Many scientists have erroneously viewed transformed cladistics as a form of neo-creationism. This misinterpretation has even been encouraged by some ill-intentioned evolutionary systematists.[6] Presently, most transformed cladists are self-stated evolutionists who express notable dissatisfaction with evolutionary theory and methods.

> A systematist need attach no particular meaning to the term 'Darwinism' ... in order to proceed with his everyday work of discovering what species exist, what their biological characteristics are, where they occur, how they are interrelated, how they are to be named, and so on. A systematist may pursue all of these activities, and achieve unlimited success in their objectives, while giving no thought to notions of struggle for existence, natural selection, gene recombination, punctuated equilibria, or for that matter evolution. (Nelson and Platnick, 1984, p 143)

---

[5] The cladistic method can be applied to *any* system of objects, yet this fact does not stop Hennigians from making impassioned claims that evolutionary theory is an essential justification for the cladistic method. (For example see Ridley, 1986)

[6] As noted by Janvier, 1984, p 58-59

Summary

Phenetics and cladistics focus on different aspects of system pattern. Phenetics focuses on overall similarity, and de-emphasizes the distribution of single characters. Cladistics does the opposite. Both methods study nature and obtain useful classifications.

Incongruities in phenograms and cladograms are common, and evolutionists 'explain' these as convergence or loss. Because the convergence explanation is improbable, evolutionists prefer to use the loss explanation when they can.

Illusion is created when evolutionists cite examples of "convergence" and "lost characters." The public presumes that evolutionists identified these by first identifying phylogeny. In reality, evolutionists infer convergence and lost characters from phenograms or cladograms, without ever identifying phylogeny.

Illusion is created when evolutionists refer to phenograms and cladograms as "phylogenies." Phenograms and cladograms identify no ancestors and are not phylogenies.

Darwinian taxonomy is a patchwork of cladistic and phenetic methodologies, together with an emphasis on Darwinian stories. The method tries to identify phylogeny and maximally represent it within a classification. The method failed because phylogeny could not be identified. Its collapse in the 1960s prompted the rapid rise of other methods.

Hennigian cladistics is cladistic methodology plus Darwinian stories. It is sometimes mistakenly called, "phylogenetic systematics" — which is misleading because the method does not identify phylogeny. Hennigians often use the loss explanation to promote inferior cladograms to favored status. That practice can lead to circular reasoning and destroy objectivity. Hennigians naively believe that evolutionary theory provides a firm justification for their methodology. They also insist that transformed cladistics has no legitimate justification.

Transformed cladistics rejects evolutionary theories and just-so stories. Its proponents legitimately argue that it is a well-defined neutral method for studying nature — and that no other justification is necessary.

A new methodology, called Discontinuity Systematics, has been developed to study biosystematic issues central to the origins controversy. That method is explained in a later chapter.

12

Evolutionary Illusions

The origins debate is beclouded with many illusions that use words and imagery to distort our perception in favor of evolution. Those illusions must be identified and removed, so we can see clearly. The present chapter focuses on the illusion that large-scale phylogeny actually exists. Three devices have been used to create this illusion of ancestry:

- Illusion is created by deleting diversity. By artificially concealing or obscuring diversity, evolutionists create the impression that they have identified a lineage. This effective technique is virtually undetectable to the non-specialist.

- Illusion is created with tree-structured imagery, such as cladograms and phenograms. These are said to be evidence for evolution, but they do not identify a single ancestor-descendant relationship.

- Illusion is created with misleading terminology. The terminology is loaded with evolutionary imagery that the public interprets as stating direct ancestry. Evolutionists have given the terminology new technical definitions that mean something else entirely. There is disparity between the evolutionists' technical definitions and public perception, and that disparity is ideal for creating illusion.

Supraspecific Ancestors

Supraspecific groups are groups containing more than one species. They are known from the classification system as taxa of rank higher than species. Birds, mammals, and reptiles are supraspecific groups. Normally, these are useful labels that help us conveniently discuss diverse collections of organisms.

The illusion of ancestry is created by using supraspecific groups as ancestors and descendants in evolutionary lineages.

> [T]he literature on macroevolution is fraught with references to the derivation of one higher taxon from another, as when, for example, mammals and birds are conventionally said to be separately derived from "reptiles." (Eldredge, 1989, p 158)

That practice is objectionable for several reasons. One objection is based on reproduction. There is no reproductive mechanism above the species level. A supraspecific group cannot be an ancestor because it is not a reproductive entity. Species can reproduce and leave descendants, but supraspecific groups cannot. For example, reptiles, as a group, cannot have a descendant.

> We have already concluded that, logically, only species can serve as evolutionary units. Taxa of higher rank are merely monophyletic aggregates of one or more species, and thus do not exist in the same sense as do species and cannot serve as ancestral or descendant units. *Nonetheless, the literature is replete with phylogenetic trees depicting ancestor-descendant relationships among genera and taxa of even higher rank.* (Eldredge and Cracraft, 1980, p 114, my italics)

> Evolutionary theory does not allow for supraspecific ancestors: a genus does not evolve from a genus, a family from a family and so on. (Forey, 1982, p 133)

Another objection is that supraspecific groups distort our perception of the data, and the more diverse the group, the greater the distortion. The distortion makes it easier to create the illusion of lineage.

The distortion occurs in two ways. First, it creates imaginary data that do not actually exist. Suppose someone lists the mammal in an evolutionary lineage. There is no such data point as a mammal.[1] The word "mammal" artificially

---

[1] Supraspecific groups are not real data points, they are abstract creations of the process of classification.

"[S]upraspecific ancestors of evolutionary taxonomy, although often designated, are taxonomic artifacts. They are not groups and, in fact, they bar any attempt to discover a natural group. They are a convention and do not represent an evolutionary phenomenon. They have no part to play in phylogeny reconstruction — recognizing pattern." (Forey, 1982, p 135)

"[O]nly trees involving species as ancestors and descendants have any meaning beyond the cladogram level of analysis. There is no formal difference — just semantic confusion and the retention of non-monophyletic groups — between cladograms and trees involving taxa of rank higher than species." (Eldredge and Cracraft, 1980, p 128)

creates a data point somewhere near or within the vast morphological region spanned by mammals. The greater the diversity of the supraspecific group, the greater is the flexibility in placing this imaginary data point.

Second, a supraspecific group deletes data points that do exist. It strips the data of diversity. When someone lists the mammal in an evolutionary lineage, the word effectively conceals the enormous variety contained within mammals: the seals, bats, whales, bears, moles, beavers, etc. The greater the diversity of the supraspecific group, the more diversity is concealed.

The ability to artificially create and conceal data is precisely what is needed for the illusion of lineage, and this ability is provided by supraspecific groups. The illusion is aided when the supraspecific groups are large and diverse. This accounts for the frequent use of supraspecific groups as ancestors and descendants in evolutionary literature.

Laurie Godfrey gives a typical use of supraspecific groups as she rebuffs the creationists.

> [Creationists have charged] that the fossil world has revealed no intermediates between 'basic kinds' such as 'sharks and whales'. What nonsense! There are multitudes of intermediates between such 'kinds' … Between sharks and whales, for example, we find bony fishes, amphibians, reptiles, mammal-like reptiles, and some mammals. (Godfrey, 1983b, p 203)

Godfrey's intermediates are all supraspecific groups. One of her intermediates — the reptiles — is a group that includes snakes, turtles, lizards, dinosaurs, ichthyosaurs (extinct dolphin-like reptiles) and flying pterosaurs. Her other listed groups are diverse too. The diversity in these groups thwarts her attempt to construct lineages and identify intermediates.

Evolutionists create the illusion of lineage by using groups above the level of species. They also reach below the level of organisms, to body parts.

The Evolving Body-Parts Scenario

> A technical course in the evolution of mammals is largely an exercise in the identification of teeth, and an old professional quip holds that mammalian evolution is the interbreeding of two sets of teeth to produce some descendant choppers. (Gould, 1987b, p 23-24)

Evolutionists frequently display selected body parts as though these were a lineage. They arrange a series of teeth in a row to show the evolution of teeth. Or they arrange selected jaw bones, brain lobes, or eyes, etc. These are frequently offered in textbooks with the allusion that these represent lineages. Often, an author knows the body parts are from organisms that could not reasonably have formed a lineage, but this fact is not clearly conveyed to readers.

The use of selected body parts alters our perception of the data in two ways. First, it deletes the diversity that would ordinarily confound the construction of lineages. By selecting body parts from some organisms and ignoring others, a sequence with a lineage-like appearance can more easily be obtained.

Second, when body parts are separated from organisms, then important data is missing. Lineages become easier to construct and harder to refute. Body parts, taken in isolation, are harder to identify as "convergent" or unrelated by direct ancestry. They are easily selected by evolutionists for incorporation into "lineages."

This took place in a public debate between the anti-creationist Philip Kitcher and a leading creationist.[2] Kitcher displayed a diagram from the *Journal of Morphology*, showing a sequence of jawbones. He asserted that the diagram shows a complete transition of intermediate forms in the evolution of the mammalian middle ear. He then challenged his creationist opponent to point out any gaps in the transition. Kitcher strongly implied that this represented a lineage. As presented, it seemed stunning evidence for evolution.

Kitcher's presentation was misleading in several ways: the selective presentation of data (which artificially deletes diversity), the isolated evolving body parts, and the misleading terminology.

In addition, the original article has essential details that Kitcher failed to relate to his audience. Two of the eight depicted specimens are entirely hypothetical — in all but one specimen, unknown or undescribed structures and details are reconstructed. The hypothetical reconstructed structures include the organ at issue here, the middle ear and alleged precursors. The actual specimens vary in size — yet the drawings were scaled so the fossils all seem the same length. Most importantly, the article specifically denies that the diagram depicts true ancestor-descendant relationships.[3] The original article contains sufficient evidence to rebut Kitcher's presentation.

---

[2] The debate was February 1985 with the creationist Duane Gish at the University of Minnesota.

[3] Allin, 1975, p 430

280

This is a common occurrence. The technical literature typically promotes the evolutionary view by using misleading terminology and hypothetical reconstructions. Yet many papers contain subtle disclaimers and notes of caution. The problem occurs when other evolutionists convey the technical literature to the public. Things get simplified or left out, and it ends up like unassailable evidence of evolution. The remedy is to re-examine the original technical paper.

> Frequently, secondary references portray evolutionary lineages much more vividly than does the original paper reporting them. (Cuffey, 1984, p 264)

Nested Supraspecific Groups

Commonly, evolutionary lineages are offered like this:

> The vertebrates evolved into the tetrapods, who gave rise to the amniotes, who descended into the mammals, and from these there finally arose the rabbits.

The statement sounds like it specifically names an evolutionary lineage: vertebrate, to tetrapod, to amniote, to mammal, to rabbit.

In reality, the statement says nothing about origins. It speaks of lineage and descent only in the trivial sense of sameness. The rabbit's own great-great-grandparents were vertebrates; its great-grandparents were tetrapods; its grandparents were amniotes; and its parents were mammals. The statement cannot possibly be refuted because it is trivially true by definition. Yet, the statement is misleading. It masquerades as though it says something about origins.

This approach is commonly used to create the illusion of ancestry. The named ancestors — vertebrate, tetrapod, amniote, mammal — are actually **nested supraspecific groups**, where each "descendant group" is inside the "ancestor group." Evolutionists use this approach to sound like they have specifically named a lineage, when they have not.

The public is vulnerable to this illusion. Nested supraspecific groups often have names. The public typically does not know the names or the nested relationship. So, the public cannot tell whether a given lineage is actually just nested supraspecific groups. In this way, the illusion is usually undetectable to the nonspecialist.

To make a significant statement about rabbit ancestry, you must name an ancestor that has non-rabbit characteristics. Paraphyletic groups are used for this purpose.

Paraphyletic Groups

Evolutionists define a paraphyletic group as a group that does not contain all its descendants. That definition is misleading, because it implies that ancestors and descendants are identified, when they are not.

In reality, the term has a different meaning. A **paraphyletic group** is a supra-specific group identified by its *lack* of certain characters.[4] For example, reptiles are a paraphyletic group because they contain those amniotes (organisms with an amniote egg) that remain after you remove the birds and mammals. Reptiles are the amniotes who lack hair and feathers.

Invertebrates are also a paraphyletic group, since they are multicellular animals that lack a backbone. Fish are paraphyletic, since they are vertebrates that are not based on the tetrapod body plan. Amphibians are paraphyletic: roughly, they are the tetrapods who lack an amniote egg. There are numerous other examples with technical latinized names.

Paraphyletic groups are used to create the illusion of ancestry, because they have an important property. Theorists want to name the ancestor that originated a given descendant. To be significant, the ancestor and descendant cannot be identical. At the very least, the ancestor must have non-descendant characteristics. Paraphyletic groups fill this basic requirement because they are defined by their lack of certain characters (characters that exist in presumed descendants).

Paraphyletic groups aid the illusion of ancestry in another way — they tend to be large and diverse. As supraspecific groups, they provide the means to create and delete data. The greater the diversity of the group, the greater the flexibility in creating and deleting data. Since paraphyletic groups tend to be very diverse, they are especially potent for the illusion of lineage.

*

Most classic evolutionary lineages are paraphyletic groups. This example is heard often:

> The invertebrates originated the fish, who gave rise to amphibians, who descended into reptiles, and from these there finally arose the mammals.

The statement sounds like it specifically names an evolutionary lineage: invertebrate, to fish, to amphibian, to reptile, to mammal. In addition, the statement meets the basic requirement that ancestor and descendant are not identical. Yet each of the alleged ancestors is a paraphyletic group.

The named groups are supraspecific and could not possibly be ancestors. Moreover, these groups are breathtakingly diverse, and the diversity defeats our attempt to identify a narrow lineage. In short, the above statement sounds like it identifies a lineage, when it does not. The statement has the sound of evolution, without actually supplying the evidence. Evolutionists commonly use this approach to seem like they have specifically named a lineage.

---

[4] Cladists justifiably argue that paraphyletic groups are uncharacterizable artificial associations of species.

The public is especially vulnerable to this illusion. Paraphyletic groups are often given names. Yet the public typically does not know the names, and cannot tell if a named ancestor is really a paraphyletic group. So, the illusion is virtually undetectable to the non-specialist.

The illusion from paraphyletic groups repackages the illusion from nested supraspecific groups. Both illusions use names generated by classification methods. Both illusions use diverse supraspecific groups to distort our perception. Both illusions artificially create and delete data.

*

Paraphyletic groups tend to be especially diverse when they are largely extinct and their member species are poorly preserved or fragmentary. There is a reason for this. When a fragment of a little known fossil species is discovered, taxonomists often have difficulty determining whether the fossil actually lacks the diagnostic characters whose presence would remove the specimen from a paraphyletic group. Typically, taxonomists assume the fossil actually lacks the missing characters. Such specimens end up being classified into a paraphyletic group, for lack of a better place. Paraphyletic groups then become repositories for the scraps, fragments, and leftovers from the process of classification.[5]

Extinct paraphyletic groups are especially helpful in creating the illusion of ancestry. They are made of incomplete and fragmentary specimens. They perform a task which theorists might otherwise perform themselves — the elimination of specialized characters. As specimens become increasingly fragmentary, it becomes easier to arrange selected body parts into sequences and refer to them as lineages. Simultaneously, it becomes increasingly harder to refute these alleged lineages by showing that the whole organisms contain specialized characters that conflict with the alleged lineage. The practice of arranging various teeth and jawbones into a lineage is aided when teeth and jawbones are all that remains.

*

Darwinian systematists are especially fond of paraphyletic groups. They seek to promote these groups. They seek to give them distinct names, and they want these names accepted by the technical community.[6] Then they can say, "The *ABCs* were the ancestors of the *XYZs*." It sounds specific. It sounds like lineage. Yet it puts an illusion on the public. The average citizen (lacking knowledge of these names) is powerless before such an illusion.

---

[5] "In short, extinct paraphyletic groups are phenetic associations of scraps, whose limits are arcane, agreed or disputed among a few palaeontologists. The reader who doubts that statement — that the limits of extinct paraphyletic groups are not common knowledge — may put it to the test by trying to determine, from the literature or any other source, what character of a newly discovered fossil would place it in the Rhipidistia, Anthracosauria, Coelurosauria, Palaeoniscoidei, Pholidophoridae, Eosuchia, or any other such [paraphyletic] group, but not in an included subgroup. To save wasted effort, recall that to place a fossil in one of these groups, but not in an included subgroup, would mean knowing the homology that linked those groups. And since paraphyletic groups have no homologies of their own, the task is impossible. If it is possible, the group is not paraphyletic." (Patterson, C., 1982b, p 63-64)

[6] "Many, perhaps most, higher taxa established by traditional methods of evolutionary taxonomy are paraphyletic ..." (Raup, 1988, p 305)

Darwinian systematists seek to create ancestors by creating paraphyletic groups. They seek to create these artificial groupings, to name them, and protect them from being dismantled by other systematists. Paraphyletic groups, especially those that are extinct, are a key factor in the illusion of ancestry.[7]

> I suggest that claims that phylogeny is more than mere systematics, and that in many cases it is known, rest entirely on paraphyletic groups. .... The mysterious additional element, the extra information that transforms systematics into phylogeny, is extinct paraphyletic groups. (Patterson, C., 1982b, p 63-64)

Degree of Divergence

A debate is occurring in systematics. Though the debate is heated, it is exclusively between evolutionists. They have presented it to the world as a disagreement over mere technical minutiae of taxonomy. The issues seem to be these:

1) Can a group of organisms be appropriately classified based on the *lack* of a character?

2) Should classifications reflect *only* cladogenesis (branching of a lineage)?

3) Can classifications also reflect the *degree of divergence* of descendants from an ancestral stock?

On one side, the Hennigian cladists reject the first and third points. Their opponents, the Darwinian taxonomists, are the opposite.

At first, the debate seems concerned with whether degree of divergence should be included into classifications. If a group of organisms has diverged a great morphological (phenetic) distance from its ancestors, then it has the appearance of a group isolated all by itself in morphology space. The group then displays a large phenetic degree of divergence from its ancestors. Should classification acknowledge this distinctive group by giving it a separate category of elevated rank? The Darwinian taxonomists say yes. Cladists say no, and argue that classifications should be based *only* on nested hierarchies of similarities.[8] .

---

[7] For example, the various alleged ancestors of the mammals — i.e., the cynodonts, eucynodonts, advanced cynodonts, therapsids, quasi-mammals, and the mammal-like reptiles — are all paraphyletic groups. (see McKenna, 1987, p 76)

[8] The Hennigian cladists are sometimes called "phylogenetic taxonomists," which is misleading. Cladists give neither phylogenies nor ancestors. They acquired the name "phylogenetic" because they reject 'degree of divergence' as a criterion for making classifications, and they view degree of divergence (erroneously) as *non*-phylogenetic data. Hennigian cladists therefore felt they were promoting "phylo-genetic" systematics.

It sounds like a debate over subtle technicalities. One can read the technical literature and get the impression the debate has no real importance, except to a few systematists. It would seem a debate for stuffy taxonomists perhaps, but not of importance to pedestrians.

Yet the debate has been widely underestimated. The debate is about how evolutionists are going to present 'ancestors' to the public. The opposing evolutionists have incompatible solutions to the problem.

*

On a technical level, the debate is whether to recognize paraphyletic groups. Cladists do not recognize these as natural taxonomic groupings. Cladists view these as artificial associations of organisms, groupings created arbitrarily by man, groupings possessing no objective reality in nature. Paraphyletic groups are not created by the cladistic method. Yet a paraphyletic group is created whenever Darwinian taxonomists take a cladistic classification (such as a cladogram) and move a nested sub-group due to degree of divergence.

The Darwinian taxonomists argue that when a group of descendants has diverged a great morphological distance from its ancestors, then this should be recognized in the classification by allotting the group its own category separate from (and perhaps of co-equal rank with) its ancestors. Their strategy is beguiling. They say they want to recognize degree of divergence, when their real impetus is to recognize ancestors. Darwinian taxonomists need ancestors, and they are attempting to create them.

*

Take an example from the literature of the debate. The classic example involves birds, crocodiles, and lizards. On the basis of overall similarity, the phenetic method classifies lizards near the crocodiles, and birds are placed in a group somewhat distant.

The cladistic method approaches the matter differently. On the basis of shared characters, it classifies the birds near the crocodiles, and places lizards in a separate more distant category. The phenetic and cladistic classifications are in conflict here, which is not uncommon.

Darwinian taxonomists switch between phenetic and cladistic methods, depending on the circumstance. They acknowledge that the cladistic method is better at representing branching (cladogenesis). So why do they want to use the phenetic method for the case of birds?

The answer is illuminating. The cladistic method does not provide ancestors. If you ask, "Who was the ancestor of the birds?" a true cladist will not give you a direct answer, but will answer with a sister group or a nebulous hypothetical common ancestor. A cladist will say, "The crocodiles are a sister group of the birds" or, "The crocodiles share a common ancestor with the birds." Such statements are unsatisfying. They do not specifically state the ancestor, yet they are specific enough to make the absence of an ancestor painfully obvious.

The Darwinian taxonomists are more deserving of the term "phylogenetic," since phylogeny (and its representation within a classification) is their foremost concern. The problem is that Darwinian taxonomists could not identify phylogeny, so their claim to the term eventually withered. The term was then adopted by the Hennigians.

The Darwinian taxonomists want to approach the problem directly, by naming the ancestor. This is not easy. First, there is a large phenetic gap between crocodiles and birds. Second, there is large diversity near both the crocodiles and the birds. These facts thwart the attempt to construct a lineage and identify ancestors.

So Darwinian taxonomists seek to artificially create a lineage. To make the data conform, they conceal diversity by creating supraspecific groups. They seek to create an ancestor of the birds, so they need a supraspecific group with non-bird characteristics: a paraphyletic group. A great deal of diversity must be hidden, so they emphasize a large paraphyletic group (reptiles) and a large supraspecific group (birds). The emphasis is achieved by making these groups co-equal rank in the classification. With this in place, the Darwinians say, "The birds evolved from the reptiles" and the illusion appears. It sounds as if they have clearly identified a lineage, when they have not.

This example involved commonly understood words: birds and reptiles. Precisely because those words are commonly understood, they form this standard case for discussion. Yet those words are used to create illusion. The illusion is even more effective when the words are not commonly known, because then all you hear is, "The *XYZs* evolved from the *ABCs*." It sounds specific and it sounds like evolution, and the subterfuge is virtually undetectable by the non-specialist.

*

Darwinian taxonomists create the illusion of ancestry in two ways.

- Darwinian taxonomists seek to artificially supply direct ancestors by creating paraphyletic groups.

- On the other hand, Darwinian taxonomists seek to emphasize the nested pattern of life (as displayed in cladograms) as implied evidence of common descent.

Darwinian taxonomists cannot emphasize both aspects of pattern at the same instant. They are forced to choose the instances when they embellish one pattern at the expensive of the other. Darwinian taxonomists, by their own rationale, seek to create paraphyletic groups predominantly when there is a large phenetic distance between a given group and the cluster of its presumed ancestors. This rationale supports the means to artificially create ancestors — especially where these are most desperately needed — where large morphological gaps and diversity of the clusters conspire most visibly against lineage. This is the unifying factor in the apparently unmethodical Darwinian taxonomy. Darwinian taxonomy uses phenetics and cladistics, as necessary, to create the best overall illusion of ancestry, with specified 'ancestors' and branching points.

Other schools of taxonomy rarely if ever employed paraphyletic groups. Only Darwinian taxonomists have strongly emphasized these groups and have a special strategy behind their use. The vigor in which Darwinian taxonomists defend paraphyletic groups is unmatched by any other school of taxonomy.

This explains the historical parallel between the rise of Darwinism and the rise of paraphyletic groups within systematics. The new-founded evolutionary movement needed ancestors, and the new Darwinian systematists attempted to provide them.

> Is it not strange that the justification of phylogeny, as something beyond systematics, resides in extinct paraphyletic groups? For those groups are the inventions of evolutionists, those who appeal to them as demonstrating the path of descent. So far as I know, such groups did not exist in pre-Darwinian taxonomy, for palaeontologists were then preoccupied with the real problem of allocating fossils to Recent groups. Nor do I find any extinct paraphyletic groups in Haeckel's (1866) trees. Such groups are therefore a later invention, imagined by evolutionists, those most committed to the confirmation of Darwin's views. (Patterson, C., 1982b, p 63-64)

*

The debate within systematics is not as minuscule as evolutionists led us to believe. The opposing evolutionists have contrary solutions to the problem of ancestors. The Darwinian systematists seek (by taxonomic legerdemain) to directly specify ancestors, while the cladists claim that ancestors cannot, should not, or need not be specified.

The modern shift from Darwinian systematics to phenetics, and then to cladistics, was caused by the breakdown of the illusion of ancestry. This shift in methodology has been precisely paralleled by a strategic shift away from phylogeny and toward the nested hierarchy (cladograms) as the major evidence of evolution. The seemingly benign debate over degree of divergence has been the anvil on which evolutionists hammer out their shifting strategy.

Linearizing with a Steamroller

Many classic textbook lineages are illusions created by selecting a few organisms and connecting them with arbitrary lines. This practice deletes much of life's diversity.

> The apparent 'straight-line evolution' (orthogenesis) that was described in many textbooks written forty to a hundred years ago [is inaccurate] .... the 'straight lines' that these textbooks present are *produced by selecting a very few out of many different kinds of organisms* that have evolved *and then drawing arbitrary lines between them.* (Stebbins, 1982, p 91, my italics)

Lineage is like a ladder: long, narrow, and readily discernible. Gould says the fossil record shows a labyrinthine bush, not ladders. He acknowledges that

287

lineages have been artificially constructed by linearizing the data with a steam-roller.

> Bushes represent the proper topology of evolution. Ladders are false abstractions, *made by running a steamroller over a labyrinthine pathway* that hops from branch to branch through a phylogenetic bush. We cannot force the successful bushes of evolution into a ladder because we may follow a thousand pathways through them, and *we cannot find a criterion for preferring one over another.* Who ever heard of the evolutionary trend of rodents or of bats or of antelopes? Yet these are the greatest success stories in the history of mammals. Our proudest cases do not become our classic illustrations because *we can draw no ladder of progress* through a vigorous bush with hundreds of surviving twigs. (Gould, 1987b, p 24, my italics)

> [W]e can draw no rising ladder for the evolution of antelopes, rodents, or bats — although these are the three great success stories of mammalian evolution. But if only one twig survives, *we apply a conceptual steamroller and linearize its labyrinthine path* of lateral branching back to the main stem of its depleted bush. (Gould, 1987c, p22, my italics)

The illusion of lineage is created by concealing life's diversity. This is done by selecting some organisms and arbitrarily connecting them as a "lineage." With this technique, the ancestors and descendants may even be real species, not merely supraspecific groups.

This technique is easily accomplished in evolutionary literature, because there is generally no discussion whether an appropriate void exists orthogonal to an alleged lineage. All you read is, "The *ABCs* were ancestors to the *XYZs*" so it sounds like a lineage has been identified. The public is powerless to see through the illusion because they are unaware that diversity has been arbitrarily concealed.

Often, sister groups are reasonably distinct, separate, and a large morphological distance from their alleged ancestor. To overcome this difficulty, phylogenetic charts are often fudged by drawing clear connections where they have merely been assumed.

> The beginnings of new limbs [on the tree of life] are seldom even close to the part of the tree from which they supposedly sprang, and a number of branches usually appear close together without any connection. Charts depicting ancestries through the ages are sometimes fudged by drawing connections where they are assumed; the more honest ones have dotted lines. (Wesson, 1991, p 39)

Mosaic Evolution

In the 19th century, scientists saw that organisms are highly integrated systems, and body organs are finely tuned to work together. Scientists felt that if evolution was to be plausible, then organisms must evolve with optimal inter-coordination between the body organs. The organs must harmoniously evolve with each other. This expectation was called the harmonious development of the type.

That concept influenced how theorists viewed lineages. Most of a species' organs should be comparably intermediate between the preceding ancestor and the succeeding descendant. Body organs should be in transition altogether, in harmony. Theorists expected to find this pattern displayed in the fossil record.

Eventually, theorists admitted difficulty in identifying such lineages, and they needed to explain the difficulty. They soon felt that harmonious development lacked sufficient flexibility to account for the data. So, they threw it out, replacing it with the concept of mosaic evolution.

Mosaic evolution is the idea that as a species evolves, its organs do not necessarily evolve in harmonious synchrony, rather some organs might evolve quickly, while other organs linger behind and evolve later. Mosaic evolution was invented because theorists needed greater theoretical flexibility. The older view placed constraints on evolutionary expectations. Mosaic evolution merely rejected the older view, thereby providing maximal flexibility for adjusting evolutionary theory to fit the data.

> The concept of "mosaic evolution," developed by Louis Dollo and others, refuted the notion of harmonious development by affirming that *individual organs could have independent phyletic histories, despite the evident correlation of parts within any organism.* (Gould, 1977, p 234, my italics)

Mosaic evolution is a wide open concept. It does not shape our vision. It places no constraints on our expectations of nature. Since it allows anything, mosaic evolution is not a scientific theory.

*

Some evolutionists try to make mosaic evolution seem testable, by giving it a narrower interpretation. They say mosaic evolution predicts that harmonious development does not occur, or is unlikely.[9] So it seems to make a testable prediction.

That idea could be contradicted only by finding lineages that show harmonious evolution of body organs. The narrow version of mosaic evolution could be "refuted" only by proving evolution. This subterfuge is commonly used to make evolutionary theories seem like testable science.

*

---

[9] Evolutionists try to make mosaic evolution seem like predictive, testable science. For example, Minkoff writes, "The principle of mosaicism predicts that transitions between major taxonomic groups should not take place all at once, nor even in all characters at the same rate." (Minkoff, 1983, p 297) For other examples see Stebbins, 1982, p 283; or Strahler, 1987, p 410.

Mosaic evolution was not motivated by a theoretical mechanism that demanded it. Rather, it was motivated by adverse data. Evolutionists saw that the data failed to confirm reasonable expectations, so they retreated to a position of lower expectations.

Yet mosaic evolution had an importance. It gave theorists the maximum elasticity in selecting organisms for lineages. Theorists were no longer constrained by any theoretical expectations. Theorists were free to see lineage in the data in whatever way it might occur.

Despite this freedom, theorists still had difficulty identifying lineages. Eventually, they became frustrated with the search, and began to de-emphasize the significance of lineage. Mosaic evolution attained its greatest impact as theorists moved away from lineage and increasingly emphasized a copiously branching pattern of descent. Mosaic evolution was combined with highly branching evolution to give the greatest flexibility for adapting to data. Each body organ could have its own quirky rate of evolution. Each organ could rapidly evolve, halt altogether, or anything in-between. The quirky evolution of individual body organs could be interspersed with innumerable branching events. Thus, body organs could show up among the evolutionary branches in countless ways without causing any difficulty for theorists to explain.

*

Mosaic evolution confuses many people. Formally, it describes how body organs evolve within a single lineage, so people presume it is identified by first identifying lineage. That view is reasonable, however, evolutionists use the concept differently.

Evolutionists do not identify mosaic evolution by identifying lineage. Rather, they use the terms *mosaic evolution* and *mosaic form*[10] to describe an organism that has characteristics from two separate groups (usually supraspecific groups) presumed to be ancestor and descendant groups. Mosaic forms have characteristics from two groups, where at least one of the groups is paraphyletic. Thus, the term feeds into the illusion created by paraphyletic groups.

*

In summary, mosaic evolution is not a scientific explanation. It merely rejected the constraints of an older theory. When evolutionists cite examples of mosaic evolution, they have not identified evolution or a phylogeny.

---

[10] The term *mosaic form* is often used interchangeably with intermediate form or transitional form.

Misuse of Terminology

Many illusions are created simply by misusing words. Here are the words used to create the illusion of ancestry:

- Primitive / Ancestral (These are used interchangeably.)

- Advanced / Derived (These are used interchangeably.)

- Intermediate form/Transitional form (These are used interchangeably.)

- Lineage / Phylogeny (These are often used interchangeably.)

The public interprets these words in a straightforward way, based on the concept of lineage. If you have identified a lineage, then:

> The ancestral organisms and characters are from the ancestors of the lineage.

> The derived organisms and characters are from the descendants of the lineage.

> The intermediate forms are identified as the intermediate members of the lineage.

All these words have a simple meaning, understood by the public. The public reads them as signifying direct ancestry and identifiable phylogeny.

Modern evolutionists, however, have redefined these words with "technical" definitions, grossly at odds with public perception. In each case, the words are redefined so that no ancestor, lineage, or phylogeny ever need be identified. Typically, the words now refer to phenograms, or especially to cladograms.

The evolutionist says, "Trait X is ancestral to trait Y." Or, "Organism C is an intermediate form between A and B." Or, "We have identified the phylogeny of the mammals." That sounds like evolution. Yet despite the sound, the evolutionist is technically only saying something about phenograms or cladograms, not ancestry. This disparity between technical definition and public perception is unacceptable. Evolutionists use these words in a manner that misleads the public.

Primitive and Ancestral

The terms *primitive, ancestral, advanced* and *derived* are filled with evolutionary imagery that subtly conveys the illusion of ancestry. The illusion is difficult to penetrate because of confusion.[11] These words are used so many ways that one often cannot tell what they mean.

For instance, the terminology is applied at different levels: body-parts, species, and supraspecific groups. Here are examples.

- The four chambered heart is advanced. (Body-parts).

- The first bats were primitive. (Species).

- The reptiles have ancestral characteristics. (Supraspecific groups).

All three statements convey the illusion of lineage. Lineage involves organisms and species (reproductive entities), not body parts or supraspecific groups. By using the terminology at these other levels, evolutionists convey the imagery of lineage, without actually identifying it.

Further ambiguity arises because the terminology has multiple meanings. Suppose we are comparing organisms (or characters) X and Y. X is primitive and ancestral[12] if it is:

1) An ancestor of Y.

2) Simpler than Y.

3) Older in geochronological age than Y.

4) A paraphyletic group that lacks some characters of Y.

5) More generalized than Y. (Generalized characters are from a higher, broader level of the Linnaean hierarchy.)

In short, there are five disparate interpretations for the terminology. The first one is the meaning presumed by the public. It is the most direct. The other four are the ones evolutionists use in practice.

Because there are so many interpretations, there is ample room for unobvious (and therefore especially harmful) tautologies. For example, take the statement, "The first bats were primitive." That statement is a tautology when using interpretation #3, since the first of anything would be primitive by definition. The first bat is always the "first" bat, and we are not enlightened by defining it to be "primitive." Thus, the statement masquerades as if it says something interesting about lineage.

---

[11] "The terms 'primitive' and 'advanced' have unfortunate connotations." (Futuyma, 1983, p 59)

[12] Note: The terms *advanced* and *derived* have meanings opposite from primitive and ancestral.

That illusion-making stratagem is used for such classic cases as the mammal-like reptiles.

> The geological age of appearance of the character may also indicate whether it is derived or primitive .... this remains an important criterion for certain groups, including the mammal-like reptiles.[13] (Kemp, 1982, p 12)

For another example take the statement, "Bacteria are an ancestral form to the multicelled organisms." By interpretation #2, this statement merely says that bacteria are simple and multicelled organisms are complex. Such a statement may be true, but it says nothing about ancestry, unlike the sound of the original statement.

Evolutionists often use interpretations #4 and #5, which involve classification, phenograms and cladograms. Such use has grown in recent years. The lack of recognizable phylogeny has progressively become more undeniable. Evolutionists have therefore shifted their emphasis away from phylogeny, and toward classification as their major source of evidence. This shift in strategy has worked its way into their terminology.[14]

*

We encounter this terminology frequently in evolutionary literature. There are sweeping panoramas like, "The primitive X's then gave rise to the advanced Y's." "The presence of ancestral fossil specimens confirms our evolutionary predictions." The terminology is so ambiguous it is useless, except for creating the illusion of ancestry. It has the sound of evolution, but even experts cannot see through the confusion to decipher the terms.

---

[13] "To most comparative biologists, the concept of primitive and derived characters has evolutionary connotations, but it need not be interpreted in this way only." (Cracraft, 1983a, p 172)

[14] Technical words already exist for the evolutionists' intended purpose. Words like *plesiomorphy*, and *apomorphy* convey the desired technical meanings without misleading the public.

Intermediate and Transitional Forms

The terms *transitional form* and *intermediate form* convey the imagery of evolution. Yet there is much confusion surrounding them.

For example, Joel Cracraft uses a peculiar definition:

> Evolutionists know that characters do not transform simultaneously, but evolve instead at very uneven rates. This variability in rate produces organisms who possess some characteristics (primitive ones) similar to those of their ancestors and others (derived) shared with closely related forms, including possibly their descendants. *Each species, then is an intermediate in some sense of the word;* all species possess primitive and derived characters. .... *Most evolutionists would not claim, of course, that these intermediate forms are necessarily the direct ancestors of a later group.* (Cracraft, 1983b, p 146, my italics)

Cracraft specifically rejects intermediate as an indicator of actual ancestry. Rather, he defines it so every species is an intermediate. By using a peculiar definition, Cracraft found an abundance of intermediate forms.[15]

Halstead uses the opposite approach.

> What we have to do, because the transition is so gradual, is draw an arbitrary line; if it [the organism] has character X we will call it A, if not we will call it B. Hence, by definition there can never be an intermediate, because we have drawn arbitrary lines in such a way that an animal is forced to be either one thing or the other.[16] (Halstead, 1984, p 253)

Halstead says the classification system does not allow for intermediates, since it forces us to place organisms in one category or the other.[17] He says this explains why there are no intermediate forms.

In short, one evolutionist (Cracraft) says that every species is an intermediate form, while another (Halstead) says that not one species is intermediate. Both authors try to get around this pointed issue by redefining the terminology to make it effectively useless.

*

More commonly, evolutionists define intermediate form as a species that has characteristics from two separate [supraspecific] groups. One objection to that definition is that it intertwines intermediate forms with supraspecific groups. Intermediate forms are used as evidence for ancestor-descendant relationships, but supraspecific groups are unacceptable as ancestors and descendants.

---

[15] If you want to believe in something, the easiest solution is to assert its existence, and, when that fails, to define it such that it cannot help but exist. (see Cracraft, 1983b, p 146) Cracraft has done just that with the idea of transitional forms.

[16] For a similar approach to the problem of intermediate forms see Raup, 1983, p 156-158; and Strahler, 1987, p 396-397

[17] Raup (1983, p 157) similarly argues that the classification system prevents us from recognizing intermediate forms. He claims this as a reason why so few intermediate forms have been identified. Strahler also uses this argument. (Strahler, 1987, p 396-397)

Another objection to that definition is that "intermediate form" would have essentially the same definition as convergent form. Convergences and intermediates would be observed the same way, the only difference would be how they are explained. If the situation can be explained by common descent, then it is an intermediate form. If not, then it is convergence. These are two different ways of looking at the same data. Thus, intermediates reflect the whims of phylogenetic speculation.[18] As phylogenetic fads and fashions change, so do the alleged intermediate forms. Many of today's convergent forms were once thought to be intermediates.

*

Cracraft makes another attempt at the issue.

> Part of the confusion apparent in the scientific literature ... I suggest, stems from the definition of 'transitional form.' Is a taxon a transitional form only if it can be assumed to be directly ancestral to another taxon? Or is it transitional if it is 'intermediate' in morphology but not necessarily directly ancestral? (Cracraft, 1984, p 202)

Cracraft correctly notes that the term transitional form has been a source of confusion, but he again specifically rejects it as an indicator of direct ancestry. He then shifts the definition of the terminology. He shifts it to cladograms, as many evolutionists are doing.[19] In his usage, a species is intermediate to other species if they all have a pattern of nested similarities, as displayed on a cladogram.

Cracraft's definition is invalid. Cladograms are tree-structured diagrams with organisms only at the tips of the branches. The cladogram structure is highly symmetrical, and the symmetry prevents us from placing an organism into any privileged position. So the status of "intermediate" cannot be granted uniquely. Suppose someone says:

The cladogram shows that Y is intermediate between X and Z.[20]

The symmetry of the cladogram allows us to turn that statement around:

The cladogram shows that Z is intermediate between X and Y.

These two statements are equally valid uses of Cracraft's definition, yet they are contradictory.

---

[18] Message theory predicts that "convergence" should be common and large-scale phylogeny should be non-existent. By evolutionists own observations, convergence is common and intermediates are rare. This is especially noteworthy because evolutionists see these in much the same way: as sharing the characteristics from two separate groups.

[19] See Cracraft, 1984; also see Strahler, 1987, p 420-421

[20] This example is from Strahler, 1987, p 420-421

The public reads the terminology directly, with common sense. An **intermediate** or **transitional form** is determined by lineage. Once a clear lineage is identified between organisms X and Y, then the intermediate forms are self-evident. Intermediates and lineage are bound-up together; you cannot have one without the other. In principle, an intermediate can be entirely different from the endpoints X and Y. It only requires a significant pattern of lineage. This uses the terminology in a self-apparent manner, consistent with common understanding.

Creationists reasonably argue that there are no intermediate forms, and evolutionists responded with their time-worn counter-attack: They claim that creationists misunderstand science.

> Creationists typically seem to misunderstand the meaning of *transitional* in taxonomic science. I was taught that a transitional form is one that shows morphological genetic traits connecting two distinct groups. To my knowledge, biologists never insist that the "intermediate form" must fall on a direct line of ancestry. Typical transitions are *chimeras* or mosaics, combining significant characteristics (and patterns of characteristics) from the two groups. (Nahigian, 1991, p 46)

For the evolutionists' intended meaning, they could use other terminology — like *chimera, chimeric form, mosaic,* or *mosaic form* — but these fail to carry persuasive power for evolution. Evolutionists prefer the words intermediate and transitional form because these convey the illusions of evolution.

Lineage and Phylogeny

In recent years, evolutionists have redefined lineage and phylogeny to mean cladogram (or sometimes phenogram). The motive is twofold.

- Darwinism predicts that lineage and phylogeny exist, yet identifying these has proven frustrating. Evolutionists want to continue using the words, so they redefine the words away from the frustrating meanings.

- Evolutionists want to amplify the evidence for evolution. They believe the major evidence for evolution is life's pattern of nested hierarchy — as displayed in cladograms. Therefore, they seek to equate phylogeny with cladograms, so the two are viewed as synonymous.

Evolutionists meet both these goals by redefining lineage and phylogeny in terms of cladograms. This shift in meaning is a major change in strategy.

> If phylogenies of one sort are to pass away, is the notion of phylogeny doomed also? We judge not, for there is an alternative notion, here simply termed classification. Notions of this kind can be looked upon as phylogenies — as historical statements of ancestry and descent. But they are different in character. They include no ancestral taxa. They deny the postulates of darwinian systematics: that ancestral taxa have an objective identity independent of their descendants; that ancestral taxa can be discovered and identified as such; that ancestral taxa are under the constraints of empirical investigation. This shift in meaning of the term *phylogeny* from a Darwinian to a cladistic sense marks a revolution in biological systematics. (Nelson and Platnick, 1984, p 153-154)

The shift in meaning is virtually undetectable by the public. Here is an example.

> It is possible, then, to deduce phylogeny, that is, genealogical history, by a careful, logical analysis of which organisms share which characteristics. A genealogy derived in this way may be considered a hypothesis, always subject to possible revision. If the hypothesis makes predictions that are borne out, we gain more confidence that it is correct. (Futuyma, 1983, p 55)

Futuyma explains how we can identify phylogeny and genealogy in a testable scientific manner. His discussion is misleading, since he is referring to cladistic analysis, where no ancestors are ever identified.

Other evolutionists subtly build the new meanings into their definitions. For example, Berra defines lineage like this:

> Lineage — The line of descent from a particular ancestor; a *major group* of plants or animals across a span of time, *all members of which derive from a common ancestor.* (Berra, 1990, p 171, my italics)

His definition would allow evolutionists to use a cladogram or phenogram as a "lineage."

Evolution

Evolutionists commonly define evolution as biological change or a change in gene frequencies. Such definitions allow illusion to thrive by equivocation. Evolutionists argue that if you accept change in gene frequencies, then you must also accept evolution since these are the same thing. Mayr provides an example:

> [E]volutionary change is also simply a fact owing to the changes in the content of gene pools from generation to generation. It is as much a fact as the observation that the earth revolves around the sun rather than the reverse. (Mayr, 1991, p 162-163)

In a similar way, Fox argues that the difference between human offspring and their parents proves evolution:

> The fact of evolution … can no more be denied than one can deny his own senses. Each of us need only examine human offspring and their parents to attain this inference. (Fox, 1984, p 209)

In a similar way, Saladin misused the word evolution for rhetorical force during an oral debate:

> Now, maybe the funniest thing about tonight's debate is … that the evidence for evolution is so convincing even Dr. Gish [a creationist] accepts almost all evolution! He's a closet evolutionist! (Saladin, 1984, p 17)

Along the same lines, Kitcher mistakenly claims:

> The main thesis of evolution is that species are not fixed and immutable. (Kitcher, 1982, p 7)

The disparity between public interpretation and the evolutionists' technical definition is ideal for creating illusion.[21] As long as people are fooled by that illusion, we must protest its source. We cannot allow the origins debate to be decided based on confusing language.

Evolution refers to large-scale biological change, effectively from atoms to accountants. Anything failing to make that ultimate claim is not evolution (and is open to acceptance by creationists). Evolution is either all the way — or it is creation. This is already its *de facto* meaning within the origins debate, at least among the thoughtful public.

*

Macroevolution is the evolutionists' term for large-scale biological change. Microevolution is their term for the biological change that we can confidently demonstrate, usually this is change within a species.

---

[21] Here is an example of the illusion. Saladin writes, "Gish [a creationist] distorts the meaning of evolution as a ploy to make it more assailable (the straw man tactic). .... Correctly stated, evolution simply says this: Populations of organisms exhibit genetic change over a period of time, and this enables them to adapt to changes in their environment. If Gish had defined evolution correctly, he would have found it difficult or impossible to refute in this debate. It is clear from [Gish's book] *Evolution? The Fossils Say No!* that even he accepts evolution on these terms." (Saladin, 1988, p 36)

Evolutionists needed the terminology for an internal debate they are having. The Darwinians argue that large-scale evolution is just the long-term accrual of small-scale biological change.[22] Their opponents, the punctuationists, refute that notion. They point out that the small-scale changes visible in the living and fossil world cannot account for the overall evolution of life. The punctuationists are making a potent anti-evolutionary argument. Evolutionists needed to debate each other, but they wanted to reassure the world that they are not questioning the "fact" of evolution. The words macro- and micro-evolution served that purpose.[23] When the debate is conveyed in that language, its real significance is imperceptible to the public. Evolutionists said they were merely debating the detailed relationship between macro- and microevolution, not doubting the fact of evolution.

Yet in the origins debate we are doubting evolution, it is the very issue under discussion. The evolutionists' terminology serves to obscure evolutionary difficulties and create illusion in the public mind.

Evolutionists often use the term microevolution as a weapon in the origins debate. According to their argument, if you believe in microevolution, then you are an evolutionist.[24] Such arguments fool the ear, but have no logical basis.

Some creationists tried to clarify the debate by saying, "Microevolution is not real evolution." Though the argument is legitimate, it sounds nonsensical on its face. Again, the sound of the words placed creationists in an awkward position.

So, we must clarify terminology for the origins debate. The term macroevolution is self-redundant and unnecessary. Macroevolution *is* evolution. The term is needlessly repetitive. The term microevolution is an oxymoron — it is self-contradictory. There can be no "micro" evolution. Evolution is either thorough-going and complete — or it is creation. The term microevolution lends itself to misleading arguments and ought to be abandoned. There are other words (such as biological change, genetic change, or variation) that convey the needed meaning without confusion or illusion.

In summary, evolutionists often misuse the word evolution and create illusion by equivocating this simple word. The origins debate must clarify the matter. Evolution refers to large-scale transformation, from molecules to man.

---

[22] "Most of modern evolutionary theory (as judged, for example, from the issues of the bimonthly journal *Evolution*) lies squarely within the realm of microevolution. .... Little work is geared to bridging the conceptual gap between microevolution and macroevolution, the latter taken simply as large-scale, long-term accrual of adaptive change." (Eldredge, 1989, p 58, 59)

[23] "We understand very little about evolution, particularly the type of evolution involved in the creation of the major taxa, the kingdoms, the phyla and so on. We call this 'macroevolution', to distinguish it from a seemingly different process, 'microevolution', which is characteristic of evolution in the lower taxa. However, *the term 'macroevolution' serves more to hide our ignorance than symbolize our understanding.*" (Woese, 1987, p 177, my italics)

[24] Evolutionists often argue that if you accept microevolution then you must accept evolution, and conversely, that if you reject evolution then you are also forced to reject microevolution. (For example see Wills, 1989, p 110-111)

Strategic Motives

There are strategic motives for evolutionists to redefine terminology in peculiar ways. By redefining the key terms, evolutionists effectively silence opponents. Opponents are placed in an awkward position where they cannot communicate effectively.

Let me describe how this happened to me. I claimed that, "Large-scale phylogeny is systematically missing from the record of life." That is a serious statement about the empirical world. It deserves to be said. An evolutionist responded, "That is not true, we have identified many large-scale phylogenies" and he offered a cladogram as an example. Our debate soon degenerated into an argument over the definition of phylogeny. An important point about the empirical world was sidetracked into a seemingly dry debate about the definition of words. After further discussion the evolutionist dug in his heels. "I do not accept your definition of phylogeny," he declared. That move would leave me without the key term necessary to communicate my claim about nature.

The evolutionists' redefinition of the term phylogeny is a strategic move that turns their opponent into a mute: unable to communicate serious objections to evolution. This applies to all the terminology of the origins debate. By redefining the key words, evolutionists effectively silence or sidetrack opponents.[25] The opponent can no longer communicate effectively, because all the key words have been taken away.

Summary

The origins debate is not just about facts, cold and hard. It is also about illusions, soft and evanescent. It is about how illusions are created and maintained. Terminology is key to grand illusions. Terminology, so often dry, dull, and disregarded, can sometimes be the lifeblood of a controversy. This is the case in the origins debate.

Names are used to create the illusion of lineage. Names do not reveal the diversity around and within the named group. Thus, names can artificially conceal diversity. The public is especially vulnerable to these illusions.

For example, illusion is achieved by concealing life's diversity within the compact names of supraspecific groups. Supraspecific groups have names, and evolutionists list these as ancestors and descendants in lineages. It then sounds as if lineages have been specifically identified, when they have not.

There are five taxonomic methods for creating the illusion of lineage.

- Nested supraspecific groups — These are used in "lineages" that masquerade as though they say something about origins. They are trivially true by definition, because the "ancestors" and "descendants" are effectively identical.

---

[25] When creationists use the terminology in legitimate commonsense ways, then evolutionists have typically argued that the creationist misunderstands or misrepresents science.

- Paraphyletic groups — These supraspecific groups are defined by the *lack* of certain characters. When used in lineages, they provide the formal requirement that ancestor and descendant are not identical. Darwinian systematists are especially fond of this approach, so they frequently create paraphyletic groups and give them names.

- Linearizing the data with a steamroller — Some organisms are arbitrarily selected and connected together into a "lineage." This technique artificially deletes the diversity that normally confounds the construction of lineages.

- Cladograms and phenograms — These tree-structured diagrams have the superficial appearance of a phylogeny, and evolutionists encourage this interpretation by calling it a "phylogeny." These are not phylogenies because no ancestors are identified.

- Convergent characters and lost characters — Evolutionists cite examples of "convergent" and "lost" characters, and this creates the illusion that phylogeny has been identified. In reality, evolutionists infer these from phenograms or cladograms. (For details see the chapter, Modern Systematic Methods.)

These illusions are not always compatible. For example, the "degree of divergence" controversy in systematics seems like a dull debate. Even close observers are unaware that the debate is about how evolutionists are going to present 'ancestors' to the public. Darwinian systematists want to use paraphyletic groups as ancestors. Their opponents, the Hennigian cladists, say that paraphyletic groups are artificial, and that ancestors cannot (or need not) be identified. Hennigians prefer the approach of calling a cladogram a "lineage" or "phylogeny," and they misleadingly call their method "phylogenetic systematics." Their real debate is about how to put the best evolutionary face on the data.

Illusion is created by misusing the key words of the origins debate: ancestral, primitive, advanced, derived, intermediate, transitional, lineage, and phylogeny. Evolutionists have redefined all these terms so that no ancestors ever need be identified. These words are used to convey the sound and imagery of direct ancestry, without supplying the evidence.

The evolutionists' peculiar definitions of terminology also served a strategic purpose. The definitions made it awkward for an anti-evolutionist to communicate. By taking away all the key words, evolutionists effectively silenced opponents.

The evolutionary definitions are illegitimate because: (1) They function to create illusion. (2) They protect the illusion by inhibiting an opponent's ability to communicate. (3) Other terminology exists that conveys, without illusion, the evolutionists' intended meaning.

13

The Fossil Record

Darwinian theory expected that the fossil record should contain: (1) gradual intergradations of life forms; and (2) a comprehensive phylogeny of recognizable ancestors and descendants.

Message theory says exactly the opposite. Life is a biotic message, designed to look *unlike* evolution. Life was designed so that gradual intergradations and phylogeny are systematically absent. There is no middle ground between message theory and evolution. They cannot both be true.

Fossils are the strongest evidence bearing on the origins debate, and the only direct evidence we have of past events.[1] This chapter examines the fossil record, documenting facts that will surprise most people. The predictions of message theory are fulfilled in detail.

For documentation, I quote only evolutionists. Each of them firmly believes that large-scale phylogeny exists, and their statements to that effect are ubiquitous, if not unavoidable. Yet there can be (and is) a difference between what they believe and what they observe. For the sake of clarity, I try to separate the two and cite the observations. I also avoid citing their illusory statements. That is the context of these quotations.

Within evolutionary literature there is substantial support for message theory. The data systematically shows: (1) large morphological gaps; (2) sudden fully-formed appearances followed by little if any change; (3) "convergence" (which is awkward for evolution to explain); and (4) lack of identifiable phylogeny. The fossil record is not Darwinian.

---

[1] Some evolutionists believe the fossil record contains their *most favorable* evidence, without which they would have no case. "It is doubtful whether, in the absence of fossils, the idea of evolution would represent anything more than an outrageous hypothesis." (Stanley, 1981, p 72)

Gaps in the System of Life

Closely compare these two quotations.

> For over a hundred years paleontologists have recognized the large number of gaps in the fossil record. Creationists make it seem like gaps are a deep, dark secret of paleontology … (Cracraft, 1984, p 204)

> [F]or more than a century biologists have portrayed the evolution of life as a gradual unfolding … Today the fossil record … is forcing us to revise this conventional view (Stanley, 1981, p 3)

Evolutionists are finally (and with the greatest reluctance) publicly acknowledging the large morphological gaps in the system of life. The gaps are so distinct and systematically consistent that evolutionists now recognize them as real, rather than as an artifact of poor fossil preservation.

> [T]he absence of fossil evidence for intermediary stages between major transitions in organic design, indeed our inability, even in our imagination, to construct functional intermediates in many cases, has been a persistent and nagging problem for gradualistic accounts of evolution. (Gould, 1982a, p 140)

> The known fossil record is not, and never has been, in accord with gradualism. What is remarkable is that, through a variety of historical circumstances, even the history of opposition has been obscured. … 'The majority of paleontologists felt their evidence simply contradicted Darwin's stress on minute, slow, and cumulative changes leading to species transformation.' … *their story has been suppressed.* (Stanley, 1981, p 71, my italics)

> [O]ne must acknowledge that there are many, many gaps in the fossil record. … there is no reason to think that all or most of these gaps will be bridged. (Ruse, 1984, p 101)

> We are faced more with a great leap of faith — that gradual, progressive adaptive change underlies the general pattern of evolutionary change we see in the rocks — than any hard evidence. (Eldredge and Tattersall, 1982, p 57)

> The record jumps, and all the evidence shows that the record is real: the gaps we see reflect real events in life's history — not the artifact of a poor fossil record. (Eldredge and Tattersall, 1982, p 59)

> [T]he fossil record flatly fails to substantiate this expectation of finely graded change. (Eldredge and Tattersall, 1982, p 163)

> [T]he fossil record itself provided no documentation of continuity — of gradual transitions from one kind of animal or plant to another of quite different form. (Stanley, 1981, p 40)

303

[G]aps in the fossil record — particularly those parts of it that are most needed for interpreting the course of evolution — are not surprising. (Stebbins, 1982, p 107)

[W]e have so many gaps in the evolutionary history of life, gaps in such key areas as the origin of the multicellular organisms, the origin of the vertebrates, not to mention the origins of most invertebrate groups. (McGowan, 1984, p 95)

Undeniably, the fossil record has provided disappointingly few gradual series. The origins of many groups are still not documented at all. (Futuyma, 1983, p 190-191)

The lack of ancestral or intermediate forms between fossil species is not a bizarre peculiarity of early metazoan history. Gaps are general and prevalent throughout the fossil record. (Raff and Kaufman, 1991, p 34)

Paleontologists had long been aware of a seeming contradiction between Darwin's postulate of gradualism ... and the actual findings of paleontology. Following phyletic lines through time seemed to reveal only minimal gradual changes but no clear evidence for any change of a species into a different genus or for the gradual origin of an evolutionary novelty. Anything truly novel always seemed to appear quite abruptly in the fossil record. (Mayr, 1991, p 138)

Curiously, the gaps become *larger,* the higher the taxonomic level. The major transitions of body plan are consistently the least supported by the record.

[G]aps between higher taxonomic levels are general and large. (Raff and Kaufman, 1991, p 35)

Most families, orders, classes, and phyla appear rather suddenly in the fossil record, often without anatomically intermediate forms smoothly interlinking evolutionarily derived descendant taxa with their presumed ancestors. (Eldredge, 1989, p 22)

[T]here are all sorts of gaps: absence of gradationally intermediate 'transitional' forms between species, but also between larger groups — between, say, families of carnivores, or the orders of mammals. In fact, the higher up the Linnaean hierarchy you look, the fewer transitional forms there seem to be. For example, *Peripatus*,[2] a lobe-legged, wormlike creature that haunts rotting logs in the Southern Hemisphere, appears intermediate in many

---

[2] Evolutionists often claimed *Peripatus* as a major intermediate form. However, Gould (1992c) now argues that this is due to the evolutionists' tradition of misleadingly using a "straightening rod" to push an odd organism into a linear array as an intermediary between two large conventional categories of organisms. Gould removes *Peripatus* from its status as an intermediate. He argues that *Peripatus* (and its group, the Onychophora) represents, not an intermediate, but a separate unique group whose closest relatives appeared far earlier, in the Cambrian explosion.

respects between two of the major phyla on earth today — the segmented worms and the arthropods. But few other phyla have such intermediates with other phyla, and when we scan the fossil record for them we find some, but basically little, help. Extinction has surely weeded out many of the intermediate species, but on the other hand, the fossil record is not exactly teeming with their remains. (Eldredge, 1982, p 65-66)

[T]ransitional sequences between higher taxa are not as frequent as we would like (Cuffey, 1984, p 266)

Transitions between major groups of organisms ... are difficult to establish in the fossil record. (Padian, 1991, p 18)

What one actually found was nothing but discontinuities: All species are separated from each other by bridgeless gaps; intermediates between species are not observed. .... The problem was even more serious at the level of the higher categories. (Mayr, 1982, p 524)

Gould acknowledges that the small gradual changes observed in the fossil record are so minuscule that they cannot reasonably be extrapolated into large-scale evolution.

[W]ell-represented species are usually stable throughout their temporal range, or alter so little and in such superficial ways (usually in size alone), that an extrapolation of observed change into longer periods of geological time could not possibly yield the extensive modifications that mark general pathways of evolution in larger groups. Most of the time, when the evidence is best, nothing much happens to most species. (Gould, 1988b, p 14)

Completeness of the Fossil Record

Darwinians have perpetually complained about the fragmentary and incomplete fossil record. They had hoped that as fossils were found, the gaps would be filled and phylogeny would become clear. Yet history has shown the opposite.

> [O]ne of the most pervasive myths in all of paleontology ... is the myth that the evolutionary histories of living beings are essentially a matter of discovery. Uncertainties in our interpretations of the fossil record are ascribed to the incompleteness of that record. Find enough fossils, it is believed, and the course of evolution will somehow be revealed. But if this were really so, one could confidently expect that as more hominid fossils were found the story of human evolution would become clearer. Whereas if anything, the opposite has occurred. (Eldredge and Tattersall, 1982, p 127)

> One thing which has struck me very forcibly through the years is that most of the classic evolutionary lineages of my student days, such as *Ostrea-Gryphaea* and *Zaphrentis delanouei,* have long since lost their scientific respectability, and in spite of the plethora of palaeontological information we now have available, there seems to be very little to put in their place. In twenty years' work on the Mesozoic Brachiopoda, I have found plenty of relationships, but few if any evolving lineages. (Ager, 1981, p 20)

> [S]ome of the classic cases of darwinian change in the fossil record, such as the evolution of the horse in North America, have had to be discarded or modified as a result of more detailed information — what appeared to be a nice simple progression when relatively few data were available now appears to be much more complex and much less gradualistic. (Raup as cited in Godfrey, 1984, p 177)

> Many fossils have been collected since 1859, tons of them, yet the impact they have had on our understanding of the relationships between living organisms is barely perceptible. .... In fact, I do not think it unfair to say that fossils, or at least the traditional interpretation of fossils, have clouded rather than clarified our attempts to reconstruct phylogeny. (Forey, 1982, p 120-121)

> With the benefit of hindsight, it is amazing that palaeontologists could have accepted gradual evolution as a universal pattern on the basis of a handful of supposedly well-documented lineages (e.g. *Gryphaea, Micraster, Zaphrentis*) none of which actually withstands close scrutiny. (Paul, 1989, p 105)

As more fossils have been found, the gaps and the lack of phylogeny have become more distinct.[3] The discovery of new fossils has tended to obscure lineages previously felt reliable.

---

[3] Berra makes a common mistake about the fossil record: "Still more fossils are discovered every year, and each one further weakens the creationist position." (Berra, 1990, p 128)

Stasis

Stasis is a lack of biological change. It is effectively an anti-evolutionary term because it means non-evolution.

Paleontologists now acknowledge that the fossil record documents stasis. Fossil species tend to remain unchanged throughout their fossil history. This observation refutes Darwin's predictions.

> "Paleontologists just were not seeing the expected changes in their fossils as they pursued them up through the rock record. .... That individual kinds of fossils remain recognizably the same throughout the length of their occurrence in the fossil record had been known to paleontologists long before Darwin published his *Origin*. Darwin himself, ... prophesied that future generations of paleontologists would fill in these gaps by diligent search .... One hundred and twenty years of paleontological research later, it has become abundantly clear that the fossil record will not confirm this part of Darwin's predictions. Nor is the problem a miserably poor record. The fossil record simply shows that this prediction is wrong.
>
> *The observation that species are amazingly conservative and static entities throughout long periods of time has all the qualities of the emperor's new clothes: everyone knew it but preferred to ignore it. Paleontologists, faced with a recalcitrant record obstinately refusing to yield Darwin's predicted pattern, simply looked the other way.*" (Eldredge and Tattersall, 1982, p 45-46, my italics)

> Darwin's prediction of rampant, albeit gradual, change affecting all lineages through time is refuted. The record is there, and the record speaks for tremendous anatomical conservatism. Change in the manner Darwin expected is just not found in the fossil record. (Eldredge and Tattersall, 1982, p 48)

> [S]tasis, or nonchange, of most fossil species during their lengthy geological lifespans was tacitly acknowledged by all paleontologists, but almost never studied explicitly because prevailing theory treated stasis as uninteresting nonevidence for nonevolution. ... {T]he overwhelming prevalence of stasis became an embarrassing feature of the fossil record, best left ignored as a manifestation of nothing (that is, nonevolution). (Gould, 1993, p 15)

Intermediate Forms

Intermediate and transitional forms should be determined by phylogeny. Once a clear phylogeny is identified, then the intermediate forms become self-evident. Intermediates and phylogeny are bound-up together — you cannot have one without the other.

Life does not show large-scale phylogeny, so evolutionists rely on other definitions of intermediate. In the following quotations, the authors may define intermediate in peculiar ways, but they are unified in their observation that the data is scarce of clear-cut phylogeny.

> [T]here are so many intermediates for many well-preserved taxa that it is notoriously difficult to identify true ancestors even when the fossil record is very complete (Godfrey, 1984, p 177)

> [I]ntermediate taxa exist for many groups. This does not necessarily mean, of course, that we have highly corroborated hypotheses about direct ancestral-descendant relationships of these taxa. Such a hypothesis is methodologically difficult to study. (Cracraft, 1983a, p 182)

> In many cases, the problem is not a lack of intermediates but the existence of so many closely related intermediate forms that it is notoriously difficult to decipher true ancestral-descendant relationships. (Godfrey, 1983b, p 199)

> I agree ... that ancestor-descendant relationships cannot be objectively recognized in the fossil record. (Schoch, 1983)

> We now have so many intermediate forms that arguments are occurring among modern fossil hunters as to how many forms there are and how they are related. (Root-Bernstein, 1984a, p 11)

> Intermediates are rare, but they do exist. (Eldredge, 1982, p 125)

> *A persistent problem in evolutionary biology has been the absence of intermediate forms in the fossil record.* Long-term gradual transformations of single lineages are rare and generally involve simple size increase or trivial phenotypic effects. Typically, the record consists of successive ancestor-descendant lineages, morphologically invariant through time and unconnected by intermediates. (Williamson, 1982, p 163, my italics)

> Transitions exist at two levels in the fossil record. First, there are species-level transitions. These are the transitions the young Darwin expected to see in the fossil record. They are rare, but they are known. Second, there are intermediates between groups at higher levels of the taxonomic hierarchy: families, orders, classes, phyla. These exist in abundance in the fossil record — fishes with limblike fins and lungs, mammal-like therapsid reptiles, birdlike theropod dinosaurs, hominids combining primitive apelike and derived humanlike traits, and so on. *Even when intermediates exist in abundance, some modern paleontologists are loathe to arrange them into ancestral-descendant sequences.* (Godfrey, 1983b, p 202, my italics)

The Evolutionary Bush

> [E]volution is a copiously branching bush (Gould, 1987c, p 20)

Darwinism expected that evolution should produce an evolutionary tree of descent. Yet evolutionists cannot recognize the tree, so they now call it a copiously branching evolutionary "bush." The bush metaphor describes a pattern where phylogeny is not discernible — lineage is unclear — the phylogenetic tree cannot be resolved.

> [M]ost groups of organisms are best visualized as highly complex phylogenetic bushes .... In large parts of the natural system it is impossible to demonstrate that one particular taxonomic sequence is superior to other alternatives. (Mayr, 1982, p 242)

The bush metaphor is promoted most vigorously by punctuationists, such as Stephen Jay Gould. A clear lineage is like a ladder or a continuous chain: long, narrow, and readily discernible. Gould says the fossil record shows a bush, not ladders.

> The common phrase the 'evolutionary tree' of a familiar animal or plant conveys the impression that evolutionary ancestry resembles the growth of a tree, in which the trunk, already recognizable at an early age, leads directly to the modern form of the animal or plant. This impression is unrealistic. The evolutionary 'tree' of most common animals and plants begins in the form of a 'shrub,' of which several branches are about equally prominent. (Stebbins, 1982, p 118)

> There is no central direction, no preferred exit to this maze — just a series of indirect pathways to every twig that ever graced the periphery of the bush. (Gould, 1987b, p21)

> The proper metaphor of the bush also helps us to understand why the search for a 'missing link' between advanced ape and incipient human — that musty but persistent hope and chimera of popular writing — is so meaningless. A continuous chain may lack a crucial connection, but a branching bush bears no single link at a crucial threshold between no and yes. .... No branch point can have special status as the missing link — and all represent lateral relationships of diversification, not vertical sequences of transformation. (Gould, 1987c, p 20)

Even when viewed broadly the microscopic bushes show little directionality. Step back and look at them from afar and they are bushy even on a macroscopic scale. They do not add up to identifiable "trends."

> *[N]o matter how high we tune the power of our microscope, we cannot escape an evolutionary topology of branching and bushiness. .... The metaphor of the bush (and the falsity of the ladder) permeates evolution at all genealogical scales, from the history of a species to the unfolding of life's entire tree. Bushiness is a pattern*

of self-similarity that emerges whenever we magnify successively smaller segments of life's tree. .... life's tree is a fractal, and tiny parts, when magnified, look much like the whole. (Gould, 1987d, p 19, my italics)

But the vast majority of bushes display no persistent trends through time. All paleontologists know this, ... (Gould, 1993, p 15)

And so it goes for most groups in most long segments of geological time— lots of evolutionary change, but no story of clear and persistent direction. (Gould, 1993, p 18)

Evolutionary paleontologists expected to find directionality, so they typically failed to report its absence. They are now only beginning to study it.

[W]e expect life's bushes ... to tell some story of direction change. If they do not, we do not feature them in our studies — if we even manage to see them at all. .... [P]aleontologists are now beginning to study this higher order stasis, or nondirectional history of entire bushes. (Gould, 1993, p 15, 16)

The Record of Phylogeny

The fossil record lacks clear phylogeny.

I conclude, therefore, that some (many/most?) phylogenies will never be known, certainly not in full detail. (Ruse, 1984, his parenthesis)

Even when all evidence is used, there are often several alternate phylogenies that are equally plausible. This is especially true for taxa in higher categories, such as phyla or classes. (Ayala and Valentine, 1978, p 244-245)

It is, however, very difficult to establish the precise lines of descent, termed *phylogenies,* for most organisms. (Ayala and Valentine, 1978, p 230)

It is often difficult to judge where any given fossil type falls among the many branches of a phylogenetic tree. (Ayala and Valentine, 1978, p 235)

[P]hylogeny ... is "in the vast majority of cases ... unknown and possibly unknowable" (Sneath and Sokal 1973, p 53). On the latter point, I have come to the same conclusion (Patterson, C., 1982b, p 61, Patterson is quoting Sneath and Sokal, and adding his own comment.)

Indeed, there is often much debate within the systematic community over which phylogenetic hypothesis best explains the available comparative data. (Cracraft, 1983a, p 177)

Species, or taxa generally, which can be placed in a higher taxon, but whose relationships are otherwise obscure, are commonplace. (Nelson and Platnick, 1981, p 263)

Indeed, it is the chief frustration of the fossil record that we do not have empirical evidence for sustained trends in the evolution of most complex morphological adaptations (Gould and Eldredge, 1988b, p 19)

Similarity is usually a reasonably accurate indicator of relationship where the classification of taxa below the rank of orders is involved. In the classification of the higher taxa (orders, classes, and phyla) similarity is no longer a reliable guide and disappointingly little progress was therefore made. *It comes as rather a surprise to most nontaxonomists how uncertain our understanding of degrees of relationship among organisms still is today.* For instance, it is still unknown for most orders of birds which other order is a given order's nearest relative. The same is true for many mammalian families and genera, for instance the Lagomorpha, Tubulidentata, Xenarthra, and Tupaia. Yet these uncertainties in the classification of higher vertebrates are very minor compared to those of the invertebrates, the lower plants, and most of all, the prokaryotes and viruses. When one reads recent discussions on the classification of the lower invertebrates one is struck by the fact that some of the same questions are still controversial that were argued about in the 1870s, 80s, and 90s. There are usually majority opinions, but *the mere fact that unorthodox alternatives have vigorous proponents indicates the degree of still-prevailing uncertainty.* .... Many problems concerning the relationship of the taxa of arthropods are also still unsolved, and likewise the derivation of the arthropods from the annelids. Kerkut (1960) quite rightly has called attention to these uncertainties, of which of course no one is better aware than the specialists in the field. (Mayr, 1982, p 217-218, my italics)

The gaps in the record are real, however. *The absence of a record of any important branching is quite phenomenal.* Species are usually static, or nearly so, for long periods, species seldom and genera never show evolution into new species or genera but replacement of one by another, and change is more or less abrupt. (Wesson, 1991, p 45, my italics)

[T]he origin of no innovation of large evolutionary significance is known. (Wesson, 1991, p 45)

[L]arge evolutionary innovations are not well understood. None has ever been observed, and we have no idea whether any may be in progress. There is no good fossil record of any. (Wesson, 1991, p 206)

Convergence

Convergence (i.e., similarities that cannot be explained by common descent) furthers the goals of the biotic message. Message theory predicts that life should have substantial convergence. This expectation is true of the fossil record.

> Teeth are particularly prone to parallel evolution .... Hypsodonty evolved independently in many [mammalian] families (Butler, 1982, p 236, Hypsodonty is when the tooth crown continues to grow throughout life.)

> [In mammals] parallel evolution in the dentition is the rule, rather than the exception: comparatively few characters are unique to a single taxon. (Butler, 1982, p 240)

> The transition from single-celled plants to many-celled plants ... took place independently in many different evolutionary lines. (Stebbins, 1982, p 247)

> This shift from filter feeding to dependence on nutrition from the mother and egg occurred independently many times in various lines of animal evolution. (Stebbins, 1982, p 272)

> [I]t is likely that multicellular organisms evolved more than once (McGowan, 1984, p 78)

> [The pattern of the data] suggests that muscle has evolved independently a number of times, from more primitive myoepithelial cells. (Gans and Northcutt, 1983, p 269)

> Indeed, it has become very evident in the last 50 years that many previously accepted bird families like nuthatches, creepers, titmice, Old World flycatchers, thrushes, and several other avian families or subfamilies are *converging assemblages of unrelated birds.* (Mayr, 1984, p 252, my italics)

> [H]aplodiploidy is said to have originated independently, and often many times, within each group. .... sociality is said to have evolved several times within the Hymenoptera. (Gould, 1983a, p 58, 59)

> Photoreceptors originated at least forty times independently in the animal kingdom, and in another twenty cases it cannot be determined whether the eyes found in related taxa were patristic or convergent developments. This and many other cases illustrate how difficult it often is to partition synapomorphies into those that are homologous and those that are not. (Mayr, 1982, p 228)

"There are many mammals from the Palaeocene and Eocene that show intermediate stages in the development of a fourth cusp ... These mammals belong to many different families in several orders — Insectivora, Primates, Condylarthra, Artiodactyla, Rodentia and so on. We have here an example of widespread parallel evolution ..." [This determination has been made] "without the necessity of tracing individual phyletic lines." (Hill, and Crane, 1982, p 281)

[I]n fact, the little that we do know of the phylogeny is known only with varying degrees of uncertainty, for we are often unable to recognize which characters are true synapomorphies and which are merely parallel or convergent. (Charig, 1982b, p 420-421)

No matter what sort of phylogenetic scheme one proposes for whatever group, there are generally some resemblances or shared characters that can only be explained by postulating parallelism or convergence. Evolutionary parallelism is a way of life for the angiosperms. (Cronquist, 1980, p 13)

Evolutionary parallelism is so rampant in the angiosperms that taxonomists have learned to be suspicious of individual similarities or even syndromes of similarities as inevitable proof of relationships. No matter how we arrange things, there are generally some pieces of evidence that do not fit. We constantly face choices in which if the similarities between A and B are accepted as indicating a relationship, then other similarities between B and C must be dismissed as reflecting parallelism or convergence. (Cronquist, 1980, p 4-5)

Various Organisms

The remainder of this chapter is largely documentary. It establishes the lack of evolutionary evidence for several taxa of interest. Massive documentation could be provided.

... I suggested that ichthyosaurs had just dropped out of the sky. The embarrassing fact is that we have not yet found the ancestor of the ichthyosaurs. This has not prevented paleontologists from speculating, though, and most reptilian groups, at one time or another, have been proposed as possible ichthyosaur ancestors. (McGowan, 1984, p 158-159)

Plesiosaurs appear in the fossil record at the beginning of the Jurassic Period, and, like their distant relatives the ichthyosaurs, they were already highly specialized from the very beginning. (McGowan, 1984, p 159)

Highly complex animals — echinoderms, trilobites, and other arthropods; articulate and inarticulate brachiopods; and several classes of mollusks, including cephalopods — *all appear in the Cambrian Period in considerable diversity and without recognized ancestors.* (Raff and Kaufman, 1991, p 31, my italics)

Three major evolutionary problems emerge from echinoderm history as we know it. The first is the lack of any identifiable ancestors for the phylum. Echinoderms appear in the record with all of the basic echinoderm patterns fully recognizable. Second, there are no transitional forms between classes. .... but beyond that even the earliest echinoderm classes are quite distinct morphologically from one another. .... we have before us classes with radically different body plans appearing in the first radiation of echinoderms. (Raff and Kaufman, 1991, p 31-33)

[T]he late Triassic brachiopod *Halorella*, ... has no apparent direct ancestors or descendants, yet it turns up simultaneously in places as far apart as Indonesia, northern Siberia, Turkey and Nevada. (Ager, 1981, p 15)

Peregrinella, ... is one of the most distinctive brachiopods in the whole record and it has internal structures which make it clear that none of the abundant brachiopods in the strata above or below could possibly be classified as even distant relations. .... In other words, we have fossils that just suddenly appear around the world at one moment in geological history and 'whence, and whither flown again, who knows'? ... the Mesozoic brachiopods are now very thoroughly documented in every stage and the relations of these large and distinctive forms can hardly have been missed. (Ager, 1981, p 16-17)

To be sure, there are still major groups whose origins remain enigmatic. Bats, for example, have the poorest fossil record of all major vertebrate groups despite their numerical abundance in the world today. .... There are some remarkably well preserved early Tertiary fossil bats, such as *Icaronycteris index*, but *Icaronycteris* tells us nothing about the evolution of flight in bats because it was a perfectly good flying bat. (Godfrey, 1983b, 199)

The history of snakes, particularly in earlier forms, is fragmentary (Stebbins, 1982, p 120)

[T]he fossil record of plant evolution is incomplete and hard to interpret (Stebbins, 1982, p 214)

The origin of the molluscan body plan is obscure and somewhat controversial. (Stebbins, 1982, p 261)

[N]o fossil amphibian seems clearly ancestral to the lineage of fully terrestrial vertebrates (reptiles, birds, and mammals) (Gould, 1991, p 25)

The body plan found in vertebrates, including ourselves, is shared by some marine phyla, including the Echinoderms (starfishes, sea urchins, and sea cucumbers). The wormlike ancestor of this group of phyla *is unknown, either living or as a fossil* (Stebbins, 1982, p 264-265, my italics)

The evolutionary pathway from the burrowing, tentacled worm that was the most likely intermediate stage between jellyfishes and the chordate-vertebrate line is not known (Stebbins, 1982, p 271)

The modern egg-laying monotremes found in Australia have no known fossil record but may be descended from one of the orders that flourished during the Lower Cretaceous — probably a different one from the ancestors of the marsupials and placentals. (Stebbins, 1982, p 294)

Opinions among specialists are divided as to whether the marsupial pouch preceded the placenta or whether these two ways of caring for the young evolved separately in different lines. (Stebbins, 1982, p 298)

[M]odern mosses, liverworts, and ferns are separated from each other by wide gaps, the early differentiation of spore-bearing plants may never be known. Their common ancestor may have resembled some very simply constructed liverworts ... but we cannot be sure of this. (Stebbins, 1982, p 224)

The extinct ancestors of pterobranchs are unknown as fossils.[4] (Stebbins, 1982, p 272, his italics)

The course of evolution from sessile colonial animals to free-swimming fishes is not documented by the fossil record.[5] (Stebbins, 1982, p 272-274)

---

[4] After acknowledging the lack of fossil ancestors for the pterobranchs, Stebbins continues onward to give an "embryological" argument for the relatedness of pterobranchs with the vertebrates.

[5] From this point, Stebbins continues onward to make "educated guesses" of ancestry based on embryology.

Dinosaur genera were periodically replaced throughout the long reign of that order, but no genus is clearly ancestral to any other. (Wesson, 1991, p 41)

The origin of reptiles is obscure ... (Wesson, 1991, p 41)

[T]here are no fossils leading to primitive chordates or linking them with the vertebrates to which they must have given rise. .... The earliest known members of major vertebrate groups are very different from each other. A major step was the development of a jaw, but no known jawless fish seems to qualify as ancestor. (Wesson, 1991, p 41)

The first known insect looked much like a modern bug, and the interrelationships of different orders of insects (dragonflies, cockroaches, beetles, flies, and so forth) are unknown. (Wesson, 1991, p 41)

[N]o one knows for sure just what group of aquatic Paleozoic arthropods gave rise to the insects. What is known is that millipedes, centipedes, and insects share a number of peculiarities that combine to convince entomologists of their shared evolutionary origins; wherever they came from, they appear very definitely to have descended from the same common ancestor. Beyond that, *the range of theories on insect affinities is almost bewildering.* (Eldredge, 1987a, p 129, my italics)

The record of plants is even more discontinuous than that of animals. When fossils of land plants appeared, without recorded ancestry, about 450 million years ago, major lines had already been formed, with no evident linkage among them. (Wesson, 1991, p 44)

The stages by which a fish gave rise to an amphibian are unknown. There are resemblances between the first amphibians and certain (rhipidistian) fish with bony fins, but the earliest land animals appear with four good limbs, shoulder and pelvic girdles, ribs, and distinct heads. .... In a few million years, over 320 million years ago, a dozen orders of amphibians suddenly appear in the record, none apparently ancestral to any other. (Wesson, 1991, p 50)

The Flowering Plants

Angiosperms are the flowering plants. The fossil record has failed to yield a phylogeny for these distinctive life forms.

Unfortunately, the pathways along which [the angiosperms] evolved are very poorly known. Charles Darwin called their origin 'an abominable mystery.' More recent discoveries have shed as yet little light upon it. Even compared to other plants, the earliest flowering plants and their immediate ancestors have a particularly spotty fossil record. .... Hopefully, future fossil discoveries will eventually clear up at least in part this annoying mystery. (Stebbins, 1982, p 243)

[M]ost theories of origin [of the angiosperms] previously proposed have accepted one or other particular gymnosperm group as ancestral, the theories have conflicted. (Hill and Crane, 1982, p 270)

In the last 20 years many fossils once thought to be ancestral to angiosperms have been discounted as such, or, ... they have proved doubtfully attributable owing to limited preservation of diagnostic characters. (Hill and Crane, 1982, p 270)

[In the angiosperms] The number of higher taxa of unknown or at least uncertain relationship is, however, still very large ... (Mayr, 1982, p 244)

For the time being one should treat the various major groups of Angiosperms as more or less independent units, i.e. as of separate phylogenetic origin. (Meeuse, 1982, p 266)

Although there has thus been much recent progress in knowledge of early angiosperms, the main theoretical outlook on the problem of their origin has altered surprisingly little in the past twenty years. Like the question of the relationships of angiosperms to one another, this problem is phylogenetic, and it concerns the broad question of their relationships to other seed plants. Exactly which group or groups may have given rise to angiosperms, and how to define an angiosperm, are distinctly relevant questions that have propagated a variety of conjectures. Faced with such a diversity of speculations many botanists and palaeobotanists in recent years have tended to avoid proposing wider phylogenetic judgements; and phylogenetics in general is no longer held in the great esteem that it once was. Where phylogenetic diagrams have occasionally been offered they have sometimes been developed too intuitively or tentatively to facilitate full understanding of how they were arrived at. As Harris *et al* succinctly point out, it has appeared distinctly possible in many such cases to reach other equally plausible conclusions from the same published evidence. (Hill and Crane, 1982, p 270-271)

Without an adequate fossil record one cannot be mathematically certain that any particular group of angiosperms could not possibly be ancestral to another, but surely the Apiales must rank very far down on the list of logically possible ancestors for the Asterales. (Cronquist, 1980, p 14-15)

A similar difficulty exists when botanists try to arrange the orders and families of flowering plants into a system that reflects evolutionary history. .... This is because of ... the presence of numerous examples of parallel and convergent evolution. .... At present, however, the arrangement of different kinds of flowering plants on a hypothetical evolutionary tree is so complex and uncertain that it is omitted from this general volume (Stebbins, 1982, p 243-244)

The fossil record has failed to yield a phylogeny for the flowering plants. They fit the pattern predicted by message theory.

Birds

Eldredge implies that creationists lack sufficient human imagination to see the truth of bird evolution.

> Anatomists were among the last holdouts against accepting the idea of evolution ... Imagining intermediate stages between, say, the front leg of a running reptile and the perfected wing of a bird seemed to them impossible, as it still does to today's creationists. That the problem perhaps reflects more the poverty of human imagination than any real constraint on nature is an answer not congenial to the creationist line of thought. (Eldredge, 1982, p 132)

The evolution debate is not about a poverty of imagination. It is about poverty of demonstration. The birds are a good example of this.

Gould illuminates the current disagreement among evolutionists over the ancestry of birds. He shows that evolutionists have dramatically different suggestions for the ancestry of birds. This is solid evidence that there is no clear phylogeny.

> All paleontologists advocate a close affinity between dinosaurs and birds. The current debate centers about a small shift in phyletic branching points: birds either branched from pseudosuchians or from the descendants of pseudosuchians — the coelurosaurian dinosaurs. If birds branched at the pseudosuchian level, they cannot be labeled as descendants of dinosaurs (since dinosaurs had not yet arisen); if they evolved from coelurosaurs, they are the only surviving branch from a dinosaur stem. (Gould, 1980, p 270)

Even the famous fossil bird, *Archaeopteryx*, fails to provide a clear phylogeny.

> [*Archaeopteryx*] is a true transitional form between some reptiles and birds, although *most paleontologists would not necessarily declare it to be the direct ancestor of birds*. (Cracraft, 1984, p 203, my italics)

Also, there is no gradual intergradation of species linking birds gradually with other life forms. There is a substantial gap between birds and other life.

> [*Archaeopteryx*] pointed toward descent, but what still failed to materialize were the *gradational* changes predicted by gradualism — slow, continuous, species-to-species transitions connecting genera or families. (Stanley, 1981, p 75)

Finally, birds are united by design with all other life. Birds cannot have been made by a separate designer. Life had one designer, and the birds display this fact. Thus, the birds fulfill the predictions of message theory. Birds are part of the biotic message.

Horses

[T]he lineage of modern horses is a twisted and tortuous excursion from one branch to another, a path more devious than the road marked by Ariadne's thread from the Minotaur at the center to the edge of our culture's most famous labyrinth. Most importantly, the path proceeds not by continuous transformation but by lateral stepping (with geological suddenness when punctuated equilibrium applies, as in this lineage ...) (Gould, 1987b, p 20)

Evolutionary genealogies are copiously branching bushes — and the history of horses is more lush and labyrinthine than most. (Gould, 1987b, p 20)

Bushiness now pervades the entire phylogeny of horses. (Gould, 1987b, p 24)

It is impossible to find an absolutely continuous gradation from an ancestral species to a new family or order — eohippus to the modern horse, for instance — because this requires millions of years (Futuyma, 1983, p 83)

[T]he [horse] skeletons usually displayed in a museum exhibit represent only the main stages, and the story which is told is therefore an oversimplification of the true situation. There are all manner of side branches and interrelationships that are not depicted, and any particular stage in the series is not necessarily considered to be the direct ancestor of the next. (McGowan, 1984, p 143, my italics)

Mammals

The gradual transition from therapsid reptiles to mammals is so abundantly documented by scores of species in every stage of transition that *it is impossible to tell which therapsid species were the actual ancestors of modern mammals.* (Futuyma, 1983, p 85, my italics)

[T]he transition to mammal-ness *seems* to have been made by several different lineages, leading some authors to propose (even quite recently) a 'directedness' to mammalian evolution as the only rational explanation of this apparently wide-spread parallelism. (Kirsch, 1983, p 197)

Homology of the ear ossicles of mammals with bones involved in the jaw articulation of other tetrapods is usually cited as the chief triumph of comparative morphology. De Beer (1971) regards this homology as proved 'beyond possibility of error'. However, it is not beyond doubt, for Bjerring writes of the theory as 'ready for cancellation' (1977), and Jarvik (1980) argues that the incus and malleus of mammals are homologous not with the quadrate and articular, but with the stylohyal and ceratohyal. (Patterson, C., 1982b, p 36)

[E]xperts on Mesozoic mammals (Crompton, Hopson, Jenkins, Kermack, Parrington) believe that the ear ossicles of monotremes and therians evolved in parallel. (Patterson, C., 1982b, p 47, his parenthesis)

Why the Ape?

[W]hy should God have made such grotesque parodies of humankind as orang-utans and gorillas? (Ruse, 1982, p 5)

We have come at last to the relationship between humans and their alter ego, the apes. Message theory applies uniformly throughout, without special exception. It applies to man, and clams, as well as apes. The predictions of message theory are uniformly fulfilled.

Evolutionists acknowledge that the data on human evolution is not easy to interpret. The fossil data is fragmentary and difficult to restore. There is an overabundance of species names devoted to fossils of dubious significance. Professional rivalries and jealousies, and the desire for fame and reputation have had significant effect. Myths are plentiful, and hypotheses frequently arise unprompted by the data. Dating of pre-human fossils is often complex and ambiguous, and there are serious gaps in the record. Many conflicting phylogenetic interpretations are possible.

> The literature on human paleontology can be very difficult to read. Until recently, most paleontologists concerned with human evolution knew little about the genetic theory of evolution. Partly for this reason and partly because of their desire for fame and reputation, anthropologists have had a history of giving each new fossil a separate name, as if it were an unprecedented discovery of such importance that it merited advertising. (Futuyma, 1983, p 106)

> Caveats aside, it seems true to say that the quest for human origins is something that has had a very checkered history. Until recently, there were a few, important, brilliant discoveries, but progress was spasmodic and marred by long barren periods, misunderstandings, failures in interpretation, professional rivalries and jealousies, and, on more than one occasion, outright dishonesty. .... Somewhat naturally, whenever anyone discovers a possible human ancestor, there is a tendency to magnify its importance. Therefore, it is made as unique as possible and given its own fancy name. (Ruse, 1982, p 237)

> Many books about fossil men present the reader with a staggering number of 'scientific' names to keep track of, suggesting that practically every one of our ancestors was a species of his own. Early finds of fossil men were indeed so rare that the proud discoverer was prone to emphasize their distinctness and importance by giving them a new species or genus name. Unfortunately, the tradition has continued and is still practiced even now although the number of known fossils has grown rapidly. For instance, recently an almost indeterminable skull fragment was dubbed a new genus and species although the fossil probably belonged to a species already known and there was no morphological detail that could be used to distinguish it. (Kurten, 1984, p 5-6)

It is true that the data are fraught with numerous problems, ... Many fossils are fragmentary, and the bones are sometimes difficult to restore to their original condition. An added problem is that the dating of human fossils [is] often complex and ambiguous. Finally, there are serious gaps in the fossil record. (Bower, 1983, p 123)

Most hominid fossils, even though they serve as a basis for endless speculation and elaborate storytelling, are fragments of jaws and scraps of skulls. (Gould, 1980, p 126)

Compared to other sciences, the mythic element is greatest in paleoanthropology. Hypotheses and stories of human evolution frequently arise unprompted by data and contain a large measure of general preconceptions, and the data which do exist are often insufficient to falsify or even substantiate them. Many interpretations are possible. (Hill, A., 1984, p 189)

The problem with most analyses of the hominid fossil record is that they are conducted on this speculative level, where time is often allowed to dictate ideas of ancestry and descent without relationships at the more fundamental level having been first determined. (Eldredge and Tattersall, 1982, p 128)

There are serious gaps in the ape-human record.

It appears that our own species, in particular, is the product of a remarkable event of quantum speciation. (Stanley, 1981, p 139)

The pattern of primate evolution is still imperfectly known because of gaps in the fossil record. (Stebbins, 1982, p 310)

Imaginations run riot in conjuring up an image of our most ancient ancestor — the creature that gave rise to both apes and humans. This ancestor is not apparent in ape or human anatomy nor in the fossil record ... (Lowenstein and Zihlman, 1988, p 56)

There is no clear-cut phylogeny linking man and apes.

Today, we have almost the opposite problem in interpreting new hominid fossils; often, there are too many places into which they might potentially fit. (Eldredge and Tattersall, 1982, p 71)

[I]f we look at the morphology of the various stages in the sequence we find that the simple linear model will not hold up. .... Nevertheless, the underlying desire to see human evolution in terms of the simplest progression possible still lingers, albeit in modified form the linear model is still cherished by a few. (Eldredge and Tattersall, 1982, p 121-122)

Within the past few years five different trees have been offered for the branching order among hominids, chimps, gorillas, orangutans, and gibbons. (Willis, 1989, p 284)

With the spotty evidence at our disposal we can construct an almost unlimited number of scenarios to account for the final arrival on earth of modern man, and at this point we are unable to make clear choices between any of them. The general pattern, if you will, *is* chaos. (Eldredge and Tattersall, 1982, p 155, their italics)

[T]he human family does not consist of a solitary line of descent leading from an apelike form to our species (Stanley, 1981, p 5)

Exactly which ramapithecid is most closely related to hominids is not known, and it is highly unlikely that an actual hominid ancestor is represented among the forms discovered so far. (Eldredge and Tattersall, 1982, p 129-130)

Looking back over the various members of the human family ... we see that the old connect-the-dot approach to human evolution simply will no longer work. (Stanley, 1981, p 155)

The details of our ancestry remain uncertain, ... our family tree has taken on an increasingly punctuational shape. (Stanley, 1981, p 164)

[T]he precise identity of the common ancestor for apes and humans is in doubt. (Bower, 1983, p 119)

[T]he account of our own origins on earth remains largely unknown. (Willis, 1989, p 34)

[W]e cannot confidently determine which, if any, of the known Miocene forms was the common ancestor for apes and humans (Bower, 1983, p 119)

With respect to human origins, the discoveries made during the past fifteen years present a complex picture. The facts do not support the hypothesis of a simple progression *Ramapithecus* — Australopithecus — Homo habilis — H. erectus — H. sapiens. (Stebbins, 1982, p 352)

Both Dryopithecines and *Ramapithecus* and its relatives were involved ... but their relationships to each other and to modern apes and humans are not yet clear. (Stebbins, 1982, p 351-352)

I depict human evolution as a bush rather than a ladder, ... (Gould, 1980, p 127)

And then where is the ancestral hominid species? The best answer we can give right now is that we no longer have a very clear idea of who gave rise to whom; we only know who didn't. This uncomfortable state of affairs can be summarized in three simple statements: (1) *Robustus* didn't evolve into boisei. (2) Africanus didn't evolve into boisei. (3) Boisei didn't evolve into either africanus or robustus. (Shipman, 1986, p 92)

I want to argue that *Australopithecus*, as we know it, may not be the ancestor of *Homo*; and that, in any case, ladders do not represent the path of evolution. (By 'ladders' I refer to the popular picture of evolution as a continuous sequence of ancestors and descendants.) (Gould, 1973, p 57, his parenthesis)

Moreover, we still have no firm evidence for any progressive change within any hominid species. (Gould, 1973, p 57)

What has become of our ladder if we must recognize three coexisting lineages of hominids (*A. africanus*, the robust australopithecines, and *H. habilis*), none clearly derived from another? Moreover, none of the three display any evolutionary trends during their tenure on earth: none become brainier or more erect as they approach the present day. (Gould, 1973, p 60)

The exact relationship between the chimp, gorilla, and human branches is not quite clear; some results place the chimp closer to man than the gorilla, while others, for instance a recent study of mitochondrial DNA, suggest that the ape line branched from the human line before splitting itself into proto-chimp and proto-gorilla. (Kurten, 1984, p xii)

So the pattern emerges. We do not see constant progressive brain enlargement through time, or a climb to a more completely human posture. We see instead new 'ideas,' like upright posture, developed fully from the outset. We see the persistence, through millions of years, of species which continue on unchanged ... (Eldredge and Tattersall, 1982, p 8)

The hominid fossil record is far from complete. (Futuyma, 1983, p110)

The primates confirm the predictions of message theory. There are large gaps, and there is no clear-cut phylogeny.

So why the Ape? The apes have no special significance in the over-all pattern — unless you happen to be interested in *our* origins. Natural historians tend to separate man from nature. Aristotle, Descartes, and Kant, for example, felt that man was a creature apart from the rest of life.[6] Gould laments this common inclination for stopping short of unified and comprehensive theories.

> ... an all too common tendency among natural historians — the erection of a picket fence around their own species. The fence sports a sign: 'so far, but no farther.' Again and again, we encounter sweeping visions, encompassing everything from the primordial dust cloud to the chimpanzee. Then, at the very threshold of a comprehensive system, traditional pride and prejudice intervene to secure an exceptional status for one peculiar primate. .... *The specific form of the argument varies, but its intent is ever the same — to separate man from nature.* (Gould, 1980, p 136, my italics)

---

[6]   Mayr, 1991, p 24

Gould sees the tendency of natural historians to separate man from nature. Gould is correct, and this is precisely the importance of apes for the biotic message. The apes thwart any attempt to separate man from nature: they unify man with nature. The apes possess innumerable similarities to us. The apes show that we are a part of this unified collection of objects. We are a part of the biotic message, so we must draw the same conclusions about our origins. The apes make it abundantly clear — The designer of earth's diverse life forms and the designer of man are the same. Our designer authored the biotic message.

Kenneth Miller writes:

> The big emotional issue among creationists is human evolution. It might be safe to say that all their previous arguments exist only to support the notion that humans are *in no way linked* to the other animals. (Miller, K., 1982, p 9-10, my italics)

Miller is mistaken. Creationists are not saying that humans are "in no way linked" to other animals. On the contrary. All organisms are linked by design, not descent. This has been part of creationist thinking from the beginning. Because of this, the discovery of the apes in the fifteenth and sixteenth centuries did not frighten them.

> Now you would have thought that the discovery of these half-animal, half-men [apes] would have most profoundly scared and upset people — this evidence of a link between animals and man. And yet the literature of that period contains no evidence of any such frightened references. (Medawar, 1983, p 106)

Summary

Darwinians perpetually complained about the "incomplete" fossil record. They believed that as more fossils were found, the gaps would be filled and phylogeny would become clear. History has shown the opposite. As more fossils have been found, the morphological gaps and the lack of phylogeny have become more distinct. The discovery of new fossils has generally obscured lineages previously felt reliable.

Darwinism predicted an identifiable tree of evolutionary descent, yet the record does not display it. Phylogeny is not discernible, lineage is unclear, the phylogenetic tree cannot be resolved. So, evolutionists now call it a copiously branching evolutionary "bush." The bush metaphor is promoted strongest by punctuationists.

Intermediate and transitional forms ought to be determined by lineage. Once a clear lineage is identified, then the intermediate forms would be self-evident. Since the record does not show large-scale lineage, it does not show significant intermediate forms.

Within evolutionary literature there is substantial support for message theory.

- Gradual intergradations and identifiable large-scale phylogeny are systematically absent from the record of life.

- The record shows large gaps between new biological designs. The gaps tend to become larger, the higher the taxonomic level. The major evolutionary transitions of life are the least supported by the record.

- The record shows that new biological designs typically make abrupt appearances, followed by non-evolution, called stasis. They tend to remain virtually unchanged throughout their fossil history.

- Convergence is effectively anti-Darwinian, since it means that two organisms share similar traits that cannot be explained by common descent. The record shows that convergence is common.

These observations support message theory and contradict Darwinism. Yet evolutionists now recognize these are real, rather than an artifact of poor fossil preservation.

Finally, the apes visibly unify mankind with the system of life, thereby thwarting any attempt to separate mankind from nature. This shows that our designer and the author of the biotic message are the same.

14

Punctuated Equilibria

For Darwin, the alternative mechanism to be displaced was Divine Creation. If he had argued instead for something akin to the modern punctuational model, he would have been offering something that was no more cogent in a scientific sense. ... his arguments would have lost credibility. (Stanley, 1981, p 48)

There is no doubt that the new punctuational movement will bring joy to the hearts of creationists ... (Stanley, 1981, p 165)

Punctuated equilibria is an evolutionary theory proposed in 1972 by paleontologists Stephen Jay Gould and Niles Eldredge (and soon joined by Stephen Stanley). The theory says species are typically not evolving.[1] Rather, species are in stasis most of their existence, a state of unchanging equilibrium. The equilibrium is punctuated occasionally by short events of rapid evolution. Most evolution is said to occur speedily during these brief punctuation events. Punctuationists say this explains three major observations from the fossil record: the dramatic fossil gaps between species, the sudden appearance of new fossil species, and the lack of evolution thereafter (called stasis).

That is how punctuated equilibria was often explained. Deeper aspects of the theory remained mysterious, particularly its peculiar emphasis on speciation. This chapter exposes the theory and the motives for it.

---

[1] "If ever there was a myth, it is that evolution is a process of constant change." (Eldredge and Tattersall, 1982, p 3)

Lineage versus Branching

Phylogeny can be divided into two components:

- **Anagenesis** — evolutionary transformation within a single lineage. This is also called phyletic evolution.

- **Cladogenesis** — evolutionary branching events. This is also called speciation, since a new species splits off an older species and the two coexist.

In a phylogenetic tree, anagenesis is represented by all the visible limbs; cladogenesis is represented by the point where limbs meet. Phylogeny can exist with little or no cladogenesis, but it cannot exist without anagenesis. There cannot be a phylogeny without anagenesis.

Darwin correctly understood that cladogenesis can lead to diversity, but anagenesis is essential for real evolution. Darwin expected to find anagenesis in nature. His book *The Origin of Species* focused entirely on origin through anagenesis. He did not even discuss the origin of species by speciation.

Early Darwinians fully expected to see anagenesis in the fossils, and that era devoted much effort to find it. Darwinian systematists set out to identify ancestors and lineages, and trace the evolutionary tree. The effort led to frustration and disappointment. Gould admits to the absence of significant anagenesis in the fossil record.

> Conventional anagenetic change [i.e., anagenesis] may occur within populations, but most reported cases are dubious, and I do not believe that this mode accounts for much in the total pattern of evolution. Valid cases tend to add a rib, a bump, or a millimeter over millions of years — and such changes simply do not extrapolate to the evolutionary patterns that historians of life are charged to explain. (Gould, 1988a, p 328)

Because of frustration, modern evolutionists have shifted away from anagenesis. This shift in emphasis is at the heart of punctuated equilibria. The theory dramatically de-emphasizes anagenesis and lineage, while emphasizing cladogenesis and speciation.

The Species Concept

> There is probably no other concept in biology that has remained so consistently controversial as the species concept. (Mayr, 1982, p 251)

The neo-Darwinians, like Darwin, emphasized phyletic evolution and anagenesis. They expected to find lineage in the fossil record. This theoretical view influenced how they defined the term species.

The neo-Darwinians saw species as abstract, ephemeral, transient entities, which transformed (typically in a gradual way) along an identifiable course, like the flow of a river. That view made the definition of species somewhat arbitrary. It was like trying to define some meaningful, non-arbitrary place in the flow of a river. It could not be done. Suppose a species is unlike its distant phyletic descendants. Are they all one species? Or many? And where should we draw the dividing line? These questions cannot be decided in a non-arbitrary way.

Neo-Darwinian theorists opposed any definition of species that was too rigid. They had long battled against the early creationist view that species are fixed and immutable. Neo-Darwinians saw species as transforming entities. After all, transformation is the essence of evolution.

Punctuationists are changing the species definition. They have almost completely de-emphasized phyletic lineage. Instead, they emphasize a splitting, branching evolution, where species are separated by large magnitude punctuation events, remaining unchanged thereafter. This has influenced the view of species. Punctuationists argue that species are discrete "individuals," with identifiable births (at speciation) and deaths (at extinction). This concept of species as individuals is a substantial shift in evolutionary thought.

Thus, punctuationists have returned to a species definition remarkably like that of early creationists. This aggravates the neo-Darwinians, and the two groups of evolutionists argue over it. Their debate is driven by their opposing theoretical views.

Speciation

Punctuated equilibria places a special emphasis on speciation. The emphasis has two parts: dominance, and non-directionality.

Punctuated equilibria says that speciation dominates as the plexus of evolutionary change. That is, speciation events are where most evolution occurs.[2]

> [M]ost major change is related to speciation events. Certainly no one has ever shown much real evolutionary change to occur in lineages where there has been little or no speciation. (Eldredge and Tattersall, 1982, p 186)

---

[2] "Speciation ... allows change to happen. The myth that change itself produces new species is gone. Instead it is new species that produce change." (Eldredge and Tattersall, 1982, p 61)

> [A]natomical change seems in general to be concentrated in speciation 'events.' (Eldredge, 1985b, p 129)

So, speciation events are closely tied to punctuation events. During these speciation/punctuation events, a new species experiences a large magnitude of evolutionary change.

The theory claims that at speciation/punctuation events the direction of evolutionary change has a large component of randomness. The change is often not adaptive.[3]

> There simply is no hard and fast relationship between the origin of new species and the sorts of anatomical and behavioral changes which are the stuff of adaptive evolution. (Eldredge and Tattersall, 1982, p 50)

> [T]he direction of speciation is highly unpredictable (or, we might say, highly random) (Stanley, 1981, p 184)

> There is *nothing inherently directional* about these [speciation events] .... [T]he initial variations would be *stochastic with respect to [directional] change.* (Eldredge and Gould, 1972, p 220-221, my italics)

In short, punctuated equilibria has three central postulates:

Postulate 1: Most evolution occurs in short, rapid bursts (called punctuation events) followed by stasis. This produces a large morphological gap.

Postulate 2: Most evolution occurs at speciation. (In other words, punctuation events are closely tied to speciation.)

Postulate 3: Speciation has no inherent directionality. A daughter species tends to originate in a random, non-adaptive direction from the parent species.

These postulates made it difficult to explain adaptation. How can adaptation arise if change is concentrated in events that are random concerning adaptation? To explain adaptation, punctuationists had to emphasize a special mechanism.

---

[3] Punctuationists indicate that the direction of a speciation event is random with respect to preceding and succeeding events. (See Eldredge, 1985b, p 131, 138)

Species Selection

Punctuationists elaborated a mechanism called species selection: selection at the species level. According to this idea, entire species are selected, rather than individual organisms. Entire species survive or perish, according to their adaptations. Thus, while species may arise in random directions, their survival as a whole is not random.

Speciation is to species selection as mutation is to individual selection.[4] Speciation provides the new raw material for species selection to operate on, just as mutation provides new variation for individual selection to act on.

Species selection gives adaptive direction within the punctuationists' theory. Many scientists have reasonably interpreted species selection as the punctuationists' major mechanism for the creation of adaptation.

*

Punctuationists made species selection more appealing by altering the concepts of species and selection.

- Punctuationists promoted the concept of species as individuals.

- Punctuationists broadened the concept of selection.[5] They said selection operates on individuals — where "individuals" can be genes, bodies, kin, groups, demes, species, or clades. This rhetorical device conceals the convoluted nature of evolutionary theory and makes it seem simple.

Thus, the punctuationists' concepts — of species, selection, and species selection — all blended together smoothly with their theory, and created the illusion that evolutionary theory has structure.

*

Species selection requires that species are driven extinct because they are less adapted. That idea, however, remains speculative and is not clearly supported by the fossil record.

> The disturbing reality is that for none of the thousands of well-documented extinctions in the geologic past do we have a solid explanation of why the extinction occurred. .... Equally plausible alternative scenarios can be invented with ease, ... Sadly, the only evidence we have for the inferiority of victims of extinction is the fact of their extinction — a circular argument. (Raup, 1991, p 17)

*

Species selection also has theoretical problems. The anti-punctuationist, John Maynard Smith (1987 & 1988), used population genetics to show that species selection is quantitatively inadequate to account for the degree of adaptation observed in the record.

---

4   Eldredge and Gould, 1972, p 220

5   Gould, 1990a, p 28-32

The argument goes like this.[6] Group selection incurs a high reproductive cost. This high cost makes group selection implausible in most real world situations. The larger the group, the greater the cost. Since species are large groups, species selection would be extremely costly and implausible. So, species selection cannot be the mechanism of widespread general importance that punctuationists claim.

The punctuationists responded to Maynard Smith's argument by retreating while making vague statements. They claim they never elevated species selection to the role of predominant adaptation creating mechanism, yet they disagree among themselves concerning its role. For example, the punctuationist, Stanley (1988) says species selection "simply looms larger" in the punctuational model than in a gradualistic framework, but he does allot it a significant role in creating adaptations. On the other hand, Gould and Eldredge (1988a & 1988b) now acknowledge that species selection "cannot explain complex morphological adaptations," but they are vague about what does explain these.[7] They cite only hierarchy theory with its multi-leveled processes and complex interaction between levels. Presently, punctuationists remain unclear about species selection and adaptation.

The Labyrinthine Evolutionary Bush

Most evolutionary students know that punctuated equilibria tries to explain: (1) the large gaps between species; (2) the sudden appearance of new fossil species; and (3) the non-evolution (stasis) of species thereafter.

Punctuated equilibria has a fourth purpose, not yet generally acknowledged. The theory attempts to explain the systematic lack of recognizable phylogeny. Though the attempt is not explicit, it is a major thrust of the theory. Evolutionists have not been thoroughly frank about the absence of identifiable phylogeny. Yet the problem grows embarrassing. Punctuationists, with their more literal reading of the fossil record, are grappling with the problem directly. Punctuationists are trying to solve the problem with a theory.

The three postulates of punctuated equilibria would obliterate the semblance of lineage and phylogeny. The resulting pattern would be too bushy, too un-resolvable to identify specific lineages that branch off from each other. The limbs of anagenesis would get lost in all the branching, bushy cladogenesis. Thus, punctuationists declare that evolution is a labyrinthine bush, not an identifiable tree.

---

[6] Maynard Smith does not say the exact source of his argument. I assume it is a Haldane-style cost argument since he is known to use these adroitly. For example, see the section on Group Selection, in the chapter, Population Genetics.

[7] "[Species] persist as large and stable populations ... usually changing little (if at all) and *in an aimless fashion* about an unaltered average — the equilibrium." (Gould, 1991a, p 16, my italics) His statement seems to disallow individual selection as the usual cause of adaptation.

> Repeated episodes of speciation produce a bush. Evolutionary 'sequences' are not rungs on a ladder, but our retrospective reconstruction of a circuitous path running like a labyrinth, branch to branch, from the base of the bush to a lineage now surviving at its top. (Gould, 1973, p 61)

Gould admits that a clear phylogeny cannot be seen on any scale — no matter how we tune our vision.

> [N]o matter how high we tune the power of our microscope, we cannot escape an evolutionary topology of branching and bushiness. .... The metaphor of the bush (and the falsity of the ladder) permeates evolution at all genealogical scales, from the history of a species to the unfolding of life's entire tree. Bushiness is a pattern of self-similarity that emerges whenever we magnify successively smaller segments of life's tree. .... life's tree is a fractal, and tiny parts, when magnified, look much like the whole. (Gould, 1987d, p 19)

In short, punctuated equilibria tries to rationalize the observed absence of clear phylogeny. Here are examples of the concept in action.

> [T]o the extent that speciation produces numerous closely allied forms, it is going to be difficult to identify direct ancestors precisely. Thus, speciation, because it is often 'hidden' in the fossil record and because it increases the diversity of living organisms at any point in time, contributes to the difficulty of precisely identifying ancestral-descendant relationships at whatever scale. (Godfrey, 1983b, p 207)

> The multiplication of lineages through splitting ('speciation'), when coupled with the high improbability of preservation of members of *single* lineages, contributes to the reluctance of many paleontologists to assign ancestral (rather than close cousin) status to particular fossil forms. Only under exceptional conditions of preservation will direct ancestors of successive adaptive radiations be preserved. (Godfrey, 1983b, p 202)

> This myth is the belief that each population along the alleged continuum from ape to man must be intermediate in character between the population preceding and the one following. The punctuational scheme complicates things, but in a useful way. It allows for deviation. When one species sprouts from another, it may evolve in an altogether new direction — a direction not characteristic of earlier speciation events. (Stanley, 1981, p 151)

> We can expose what we might call 'the fallacy of the missing link,' or the mistaken idea that two species that existed at different times and did not interbreed can be connected only by species of intermediate form. (Stanley, 1981, p 155)

> [I]f this diversification has taken place through the multiplication of species through speciation, then the fossil history of life is something that cannot be directly discovered. ... Our lives would be greatly simplified if we could just draw lines on a time chart to join up earlier fossils with later ones in a progressive sequence. Unfortunately, we can't. .... Descendants there are, and ancestors there must have been. The problem is, how do we recognize them? (Eldredge and Tattersall, 1982, p 127, my italics)

332

Given numerous speciation events subsequently separating the pair, most members of intermediate taxa will not be in the direct line of ancestry of *either* modern form. (Godfrey, 1983b, p 204)

The main problem with such phyletic gradualism is that the fossil record provides so little evidence for it. Very rarely can we trace the gradual transformation of one entire species into another through a finely graded sequence of intermediary forms. (Gould, Luria, and Singer, 1981, p 641)

Driven by Observation

Historically, as more fossils have been found, the gaps and the lack of phylogeny have become more distinct. The discovery of new fossils has tended to obscure lineages previously felt reliable. This trend is directly opposite from what Darwinians had expected. Punctuationists saw this trend, and correctly concluded that the fossil record must be more complete than previously thought.

This point — that the fossil record is not seriously incomplete — is profound. It is what ultimately motivated the punctuationists. They saw that the fossil record cannot be brushed aside as incomplete, rather it must be explained as it stands. They therefore sought to read the record more literally and explain it directly.

Punctuationists eventually produced their theory, with its special emphasis on speciation. Yet, the theory did not arise by observing speciation events in living organisms or from an understanding of genetics.

Although some species have undoubtedly originated during our recorded history, no human has ever seen a new species form in nature. (Stanley, 1981, p 73)

Punctuated equilibrium ... is not a theory of any genetic process. (Gould, 1982e, p 138)

Instead, punctuationists say they read their theory from the fossil record. This is the basis for their strongest arguments. This is consistent with their avowed posture of taking the fossil record more literally. This explains why they stress that their theory is an empirical "fact" based on observation.[8] This also explains why the punctuationist movement is led by paleontologists, rather than field biologists or geneticists.

Nonetheless, they cannot have gotten their notions of speciation from the fossil record, because speciation cannot be seen in the fossils. Instead, fossils show organisms, and we interpret the pattern interrelating them. If the pattern formed a clear phylogeny, then we could identify and study the branch points: speciation. Yet, by punctuationists' own observations, the pattern is too bushy to identify phylogeny. Therefore, punctuationists cannot have identified (much less studied) speciation in the fossil record.

---

[8] The tendency of punctuationists to emphasize their theory as an observational fact has been noticed by others, for example Gayon, 1989, p 9-11.

I suggest that punctuationists based their theory on observations that the fossil record has a systematic pattern of morphological gaps, sudden appearance, stasis, and absence of phylogeny. These are the only things that could have elicited their theory. Their peculiar theoretical notions were driven by their need to explain those observations.

- Their first postulate was necessary to explain morphological gaps, sudden appearance, and stasis.[9] (Speciation never was necessary to explain these.[10])

- Their second and third postulates were necessary to explain the absence of identifiable phylogeny. This was the purpose for the special emphasis on speciation.

One of their notions of speciation seems mysterious at first — their third postulate — the idea that speciation typically occurs in a random direction. They do not emphasize this postulate much, yet it is an essential part of their theory. Without this postulate, speciation would occur in some preferred direction, and this would ultimately create an identifiable phylogeny. I suggest that punctuationists specifically constructed their theory to *destroy* phylogeny, and the third postulate was necessary to accomplish the job. The third postulate allowed punctuationists to "predict" that evolution is an undecipherable labyrinthine bush, rather than an identifiable tree.

The third postulate is what ultimately drove punctuationists to promote species selection as their special explanation of adaptation. If punctuationists had refrained from the third postulate, then they would not have been forced to embrace species selection.

In turn, the punctuationists' view of speciation/punctuation events influenced their definition of species, so they championed the idea of "species as individuals."

In short, the whole towering theoretical enterprise was driven by problematic observations of the fossil record. Punctuated equilibria is not a prediction of genetics or any other well-understood biological processes. Rather, it is specially constructed to adapt evolutionary theory to explain the observed fossil record. We can legitimately accept the observations and reject the explanation.

---

[9] According to punctuationists, species arise *suddenly* compared to geological timescales observed in the fossil record, but *slowly* compared to human or historical timescales. (Gould, 1991a, p 14-16) That is not a prediction of any evolutionary theory. It is merely a claim, conveniently chosen to advocate evolution while minimizing conflict with available observations. Why should virtually all species (with long and short generation times, in all environments) evolve at speeds that are unobservable in both the fossil and living worlds?

[10] Moreover, speciation (i.e., branching) allowed punctuated equilibria to accommodate the fossil sequence. For example, alleged ancestors could coexist with (or even outlast) descendants without causing any difficulty for the theory.

Misdirection

With punctuated equilibria, evolutionists try to steal the creationists' prediction.

> So the creationist prediction of systematic gaps in the fossil record has no value in validating the creationist model, since evolution theory makes precisely the same prediction. (Weinberg, 1984a, p 8)

Punctuationists explain a pattern that looks, for all the world, like creation. This left them wide open for criticism. So they followed the old maxim: The best defense is a good offense. They have been outspoken opponents of creation. All their major arguments are against a designer, not for punctuated equilibria.

For example, Gould's favorite argument — the argument from imperfection, the panda principle — is an explicit attack on a designer. (His argument was refuted early in this book.)

Gould continually stresses that imperfection is the sign of evolutionary history. His approach is a classic example of misdirection. The real issue is phylogeny. Phylogeny is the sign of evolutionary history. By continually emphasizing imperfection, Gould had a weapon to use against creation, while simultaneously directing attention away from phylogeny.

Punctuated Equilibria versus Neo-Darwinism

Some scientists think punctuated equilibria and neo-Darwinism are nearly the same. That view is mistaken. The two theories are substantially different, sharing only their commitment to common descent.

Neo-Darwinists believed in gradual evolution through phyletic lineages. They expected to see gradual intergradations and identifiable phylogeny. The fossil record did not display either, so they dutifully claimed the fossil record is incomplete.

By contrast, punctuationists are convinced the fossil record is not so incomplete and must be taken more literally. So, they invented a theory that expects neither gradual-intergradations nor identifiable phylogeny. They claim evolution occurs in short, rapid, nearly directionless bursts, concentrated at speciation.

These two theories could hardly be more different and still be common descent. The differences cut straight to the center of the origins controversy.

The two groups of evolutionists debate each other heatedly. Yet they unite to reassure the world that they are not debating the fact of evolution. This tactic is not new.

> The evolutionists presented a rather solid front as long as they still had to convince the world of the fact of evolution. This was largely true until about 1882, the year of Darwin's death. In the next twenty years, however, more and more events took place which sowed seeds of dissension among them.[11] (Mayr, 1982, p 540, my italics)

---

[11] Mayr (1982, p 542) says of that era, "The issue, however, which separated the two camps most decisively was whether evolution was gradual or saltational." This is largely the same issue debated between today's punctuationists and neo-Darwinians.

Evolutionists say they are merely debating the mechanisms of evolution, specifi-cally its "tempo and mode." Those terms are opaque to the public. The public gets the mistaken impression the debate is about dry academic details.[12]

In reality, the debate between neo-Darwinists and punctuationists is spectac-ular and profoundly relevant. They are debating how to explain the absences of gradual-intergradation and phylogeny. Neo-Darwinists want to explain this by the "incompleteness" of the fossil record. Punctuationists say the incompleteness argument does not hold up, so they offer a special theory to explain the situation.

Punctuated Equilibria is Not Science

Punctuated equilibria explains that ancestry should not be discernible in the fossil record. That idea makes evolutionary theory untestable. So punctuationists launch a bold cover-up. They claim that statements about ancestry are inherently unscientific and not susceptible to disproof.

> The problem with statements about ancestry is that they are not susceptible to disproof, and are thus essentially nonscientific. The only way we can make scientific (i.e., testable) statements about fossil species is to restrict ourselves to discussing relationship without specifying whether the rela-tionship concerned is that between an ancestor and its descendant, or that between two species descended from a common ancestor. We are able to make testable statements of this more general kind because, after all, evolution does involve change, and relationship is reflected in the common possession of evolutionary novelties. (Eldredge and Tattersall, 1982, p 128)

They are mistaken. Take the example, "Organism A was an ancestor to organism B." That statement could be falsified by identifying a clear-cut phylogeny where A is not an ancestor to B. Eldredge and Tattersall overlooked this because it would require them to identify a phylogenetic tree, a task they are apparently trying to avoid.

*

---

[12] When evolutionists talk about "tempo" they are discussing whether evolution is gradual or abrupt. When they talk about "mode" they are discussing whether evolution is phyletic (with an identifiable tree of descent) or highly branching and speciating (as a labyrinthine bush).

Punctuated equilibria is a large step toward the truth, for it is motivated by an honest appraisal of the fossil record. Yet it is a large step backward for evolution — into unfalsifiability.[13] It removes the last traces of testability. The theory tolerates large gaps between species, sudden appearance of new species with non-evolution thereafter, and systematic absence of recognizable phylogeny. Punctuationists somehow believe these are predictions of evolution.

> Niles Eldredge and I .... argued that two outstanding facts of the fossil record — geologically 'sudden' origin of new species and failure to change thereafter (stasis) — reflect the predictions of evolutionary theory, not the imperfections of the fossil record. (Gould, 1984a, p 123)

> Stasis has become interesting as a central prediction of our theory.[14] (Gould, 1991a, p 16)

Punctuationists say their idea is testable.[15] They feel that gradual fossil series would refute their theory.

> If morphological adaptations usually accumulate (in geological perspective) with no tendency to any rapid initial setting and stabilization, then punctuated equilibrium is wrong (Gould, 1982c, p 87 footnote)

It is a clever artifice. One can "refute" punctuated equilibria only by providing convincing evidence that evolution has occurred.[16] Evolutionary descent with modification has at last descended, modified, and adapted itself right out of science.

---

[13] "Punctuated equilibrium is unscaled, and by nature untestable. It hardly deserves recognition as a conjecture of major importance for palaeontological theory and practice." (Gingerich, 1984, p 116) "[Punctuated equilibrium is] a hypothesis that is virtually impossible to test (at least in the fossil record) and highly questionable on biological grounds ..." (Schopf and Hoffman, 1983, p 438)

[14] Stasis is not a prediction of evolution. "Stasis is now generally recognized as an intriguing puzzle by evolutionists. No definitive resolution is in sight ..." (Gould, 1991a, p 16)

[15] Gayon documents this point, and adds that a majority of evolutionary biologists conclude that punctuated equilibria is not testable. (Gayon, 1989, p 10)

[16] Punctuated equilibria is scientifically acceptable only if it can be positively demonstrated (by experimental demonstrations for example), and then only insofar as it is demonstrated. The science then comes from the demonstration, not the theory. The theory assumes (or requires) that the evolution it seeks to explain is a fact. The theory is specially constructed to match the fossil record, and it "predicts" a pattern that could hardly look less like evolution. The theory is unfalsifiable and therefore unscientific.

Summary

Punctuated equilibria claims to explain three facts of the fossil record: (1) the large morphological gaps between fossil species; (2) the sudden appearance of new fossil species; and (3) the lack of evolution after a species first appears.

There is another goal of the theory, though punctuationists have not been candid about it. Even most evolutionists are unaware it is a major thrust of the theory:

(4)   Punctuated equilibria tries to explain the absence of identifiable phylogeny.

This fourth goal gives the theory its distinctive character. The fourth goal is responsible for:

- The claim that speciation is where most evolution occurs.

- The claim that speciation tends to occur in a random, non-adaptive direction.

- The redefinition of the species concept to "species as individuals."

- The emphasis on species selection as a key adaptive mechanism.

These visible parts of punctuated equilibria are the direct result of the fourth goal.

Punctuationists did not get their notions of speciation by observing it in the living or fossil world. Instead, their notions were invented to destroy phylogeny. They needed to explain the observed absence of phylogeny, and speciation was the key. They claim that evolution occurs in short, rapid, nearly directionless bursts, concentrated at speciation, and this creates an indecipherable bush, not an identifiable tree of descent.

Punctuationists stress imperfection (rather than phylogeny) as the sign of evolutionary history. By emphasizing imperfection, they had a weapon to use against classical creation theory, while misdirecting attention away from the embarrassing absence of phylogeny.

Punctuated equilibria and Darwinism could hardly be more different and still be common descent. Yet, the true nature of the debate was concealed by opaque discussions of "tempo and mode." Their debate is about how to explain the absence of gradual intergradations and phylogeny. Darwinians say the absence is caused by incompleteness of the fossil record. Punctuationists say the incompleteness argument will not hold up, so they explain the absence with a theory.

Punctuated equilibria boldly claims to predict a pattern that looks for all the world like creation. It is evolutionary theory at its most illusionary. One can refute punctuated equilibria only by providing convincing evidence that evolution has occurred.

Hierarchy Theory

Darwinism's two major predictions — gradual intergradations and phylogeny —are refuted by the fossil record. As this became progressively clearer, evolutionists shifted their emphasis. They now concentrate your attention intensely on life's hierarchical pattern of nested similarities. They claim this pattern is evolution's major prediction and evidence.

> Evolution is descent with modification, and this implies a prediction: similarities will be hierarchically distributed among organisms. (Cracraft, 1984, p 196)

> Those nested patterns of similarity have always been the strongest evidence that life must have had an evolutionary history (Eldredge, 1987b, p 32)

Evolutionists emphasize that life's nested hierarchy is neatly represented in cladograms, now prominently displayed in evolutionary texts. Many evolutionists endorse cladistics as the preferred means to study nature.[1] To encourage this shift in focus, they redefined the key words of the origins debate in terms of cladograms.[2]

Thus, evolutionists have shifted their emphasis away from phylogeny and toward nested hierarchy. That word — hierarchy — has recently become fashionable in evolutionary theory.[3] There is even a movement, called hierarchy theory, specially designed to strengthen this emphasis.

Evolutionary Pluralism

Hierarchy theory is promoted most by the punctuationists.[4] There are reasons for this association. Punctuationists have been most active in anti-creation tactics, yet they are the evolutionists most aware of the dismal setbacks of the fossil record. They are faced with the acute problem of presenting evolution in the best light.

---

[1] Punctuationists have sensed a match between their view of process (cladogenesis) and a method best to reveal that process: cladistics. So they have tended to strongly endorse cladistics as the preferred method to study nature. Punctuationists are desperate for evidence of evolution, so they are reaching out to cladistics since they believe (mistakenly) that it supplies evidence in their favor.

[2] For details see the chapter, Evolutionary Illusions.

[3] Gayon, 1989, p 33

[4] Hierarchy theory is most vigorously promoted by Gould, Vrba, Salthe, Damuth, Stanley, and especially Niles Eldredge in his book (1985b).

At every opportunity, punctuationists opt to give their theory the greatest explanatory flexibility. They tend to embrace all evolutionary mechanisms to the maximum extent the data will permit. They actively promote evolutionary **pluralism**: a multitude of conflicting evolutionary mechanisms acting at various levels with feedback between levels.

> [H]ierarchy theory is a formal embodiment of the principle that evolution is probably a more complex affair than the [neo-Darwinian] synthesis would have us believe. (Eldredge, 1985b, p 214)

> [P]robably the most interesting revision now occurring within evolutionary theory is the attempt by many to construct a hierarchical theory of natural selection in which natural selection is still the agency of change, but it does not only work on bodies, as in Darwin's theory, but works on a whole hierarchy of increasing levels in genealogy. It works on genes below and it can work on species above. (Gould, 1990a, p 28)

Hierarchy theory attempts to give structure to the pluralism.

Stephen Jay Gould is a leading hierarchy theorist. He endorses a genealogical hierarchy where selection can occur at five levels: gene, organism, deme, species, and clade.[5] He also endorses complex ties of feedback,[6] with positive and negative interaction between levels.

Gould further suggests that evolutionary processes should be placed into a hierarchy of time.[7] He suggests three tiers for the hierarchy. The first tier incorporates evolutionary events of the ecological moment. The second tier covers a longer interval and is the level where punctuated equilibria alters and undoes the pattern of the first tier. The third tier covers a still longer interval and is the level where mass extinctions drastically alter the patterns produced at the first and second tiers.

Hierarchy theorists classify evolutionary mechanisms into a multi-leveled tree, where levels interact, control, and influence each other in complex ways. In this manner, hierarchy theorists try to give structure to evolutionary theory.

All the talk of "levels influencing and controlling one another" is empty. It is like all the medieval attempts to delineate the hierarchy of the archangels, to determine their pecking order, who controls who. No matter how much structure you try to give it, it is not science unless it is testable, and hierarchy theory does not make evolution testable. It merely creates the illusion that evolutionary theory has firm structure.

---

5   Gould, 1985a, p 2; and 1982e, p 140

6   Gould, 1983a, p 175; and 1982e, p 140

7   Gould, 1985a

Hierarchy Theory and Anti-Reductionism

The emphasis on pluralism and hierarchy led evolutionists to endorse anti-reductionism. The public, however, is not acquainted with anti-reductionism. It is an abstract concept, unfamiliar even to most scientists.

Hierarchy is an excellent metaphor for teaching the anti-reductionist point of view. The upper levels of a theoretical hierarchy cannot be reduced to the lower levels. The upper levels have "emergent properties" that cannot be reduced. It is eminently reasonable, and the hierarchy metaphor is ideal for showing the validity of the anti-reductionist perspective. By tying the hierarchy metaphor closely to their theory, the hierarchists had a ready means to illustrate and validate the irreducible nature of evolutionary theory.

> The hierarchy of levels is a contingent fact of the empirical world, not a mere issue of semantics or methodological styles. Punctuated equilibrium ... requires hierarchy, and questions reductionism. (Gould, 1982e, p 140)

That had a strategic importance. Hierarchy theory provided the means to covertly circumvent falsificationism. Their argument goes like this:

> Evolutionary theory is not easy to test because it is hard to totally comprehend. It is hard to totally comprehend because its pluralism is *not reducible* to a single level of theory. Yet irreducibility is not a fault, rather irreducibility is a *justifiable* and expected result when science attempts to deal with a complex, hierarchically oriented reality.

In case you had not noticed, the issue of testability simply gets left by the wayside. In this way, evolutionists use hierarchy theory to deflect the thrust of falsificationism.

Evolutionists are trying to have it both ways: They claim creation theory is untestable and unscientific. However, when defending evolution against the same charge, they become anti-reductionistic hierarchy theorists. Their theory, with its accent on hierarchy, provides cover for this shift in focus.

Amplifying the Nested Pattern

Hierarchy theorists emphasize two types of hierarchies.

- Hierarchy theorists try to give structure to evolutionary theory by organizing its mechanisms into a hierarchy. (As I did with the hierarchy of fitness bags.) This is called a control hierarchy because one level (such individual or gene selection) controls or influences another level.

- Hierarchy theorists try to amplify nature's nested pattern as evidence for evolution. This pattern is called a systematic hierarchy because the various levels of the hierarchy (such as orders, classes, phyla) do not control each other, rather they are levels of a systematic classification.

341

Much of the hierarchists' discussion is nebulous and confusing.[8] They suggestively place diagrams of the two hierarchies next to each other. They say the two hierarchies are connected[9] and they show diagrams to that effect.[10] They claim the data forces them to adopt this approach.

> It is not the demonstration, or any concomitant necessity, of hierarchically arrayed processes that forces us to consider a hierarchically structured evolutionary theory. Such matters of process remain contentious and highly debatable. .... Rather, it is the existence, seemingly undeniable, of hierarchical arrays of genealogical and ecological entities, all generally conceded to be somehow the product of and thereby relevant to the evolutionary process, that forces us to adopt a hierarchical approach. (Eldredge, 1985b, p 120)

Hierarchy theory draws illusory connections between the systematic hierarchy of life and the control hierarchy of evolutionary theory. In this way, hierarchy theory tries to amplify the evidence for evolution.

Hierarchy Theory as Illusion

Hierarchy theory is profoundly mistaken, and built on the longest lasting illusion of modern science. Evolutionary theory does not predict a nested hierarchy. Evolutionary theory is a smorgasbord, and it makes no predictions. Here is an example.

> According to evolutionary biology, this pattern of nested resemblances is the straightforward, expected result of ancestry and descent: new characters arising from time to time are inherited by subsequent descendants. A hierarchical arrangement of similarities is the inevitable consequence. Since all organism [sic] are held to be related by this process, the major prediction of evolutionary theory is that *there is one single nested pattern of resemblance linking all organisms in nature.* (Eldredge, 1981a, p 17-18, his italics)

> We would predict that there must be one (not several or many) single, coherent pattern of similarity linking all forms of life together. (Eldredge, 1981b, p 37)

Eldredge claims that evolution predicts "one single nested pattern." This can be broken into two predictions: single and nested.

---

[8]   Other workers have noted the vague and confusing anti-reductionist rhetoric. "My own view is that they [the anti-reduction arguments of the hierarchy theorists] rest upon a conceptual foundation that is at best vague and poorly articulated and at worst consists of nothing more than argument by vehement repetition and the invocation of authority." (Caplan, 1988, p 199) "It would be difficult to imagine a more confusing debate than this [hierarchy] one." (Gayon, 1989, p 33)

[9]   Grene, 1987, p 507-508

[10]   Eldredge, 1985b, p 187-188

Evolution does not predict that life should be a single unified pattern. If we found a living marine invertebrate, having no similarity whatsoever to any known life, then evolution would not be falsified. Rather it would immediately accommodate this new situation. If life comprised two or more separate patterns, then evolutionary theory would immediately adjust. Evolution does not predict a single, unified pattern. Evolution can accommodate multiple, dis-united patterns.

In addition, common descent does not predict a nested pattern. Common descent has two components: anagenesis (transformation within a lineage) and cladogenesis (evolutionary branching events).

Anagenesis is an essential component of evolution, yet it does not predict a nested pattern. A long transforming lineage of descent does not create a nested pattern.

Even cladogenesis does not ensure a nested pattern. The pattern of descent depends on the extent that evolved characters are later lost. Suppose losses are significant, and characters are replaced at a high rate. Then there is no reason to expect a nested pattern. Descendants could be totally different from their distant ancestors and sister groups, with little or no semblance of nested similarities linking them.

Descent with modification does not predict a single pattern nor a nested pattern. It can accommodate vastly different patterns, depending on the blend of biogenesis, anagenesis, cladogenesis, loss, and replacement that theorists *choose* to invoke. Descent with modification does not predict nature: theorists adapt it to nature.

Summary

Evolutionists now emphasize life's nested hierarchy as the major prediction and evidence of evolution. Hierarchy theory was invented to enhance this evidence and display evolution in its best light. It is actually a three-pronged illusion.

1) Hierarchy theory tries to give hierarchical structure to evolutionary theory. Thereby creating the illusion that evolutionary theory has a firm, clear, testable structure.

2) Hierarchy theory lends an excellent metaphor for teaching anti-reductionism. The emphasis on anti-reductionism is then used to covertly deflect the thrust of falsificationism and conceal the untestability of evolutionary theory.

3) Hierarchy theory tries to amplify life's hierarchical pattern as a major evidence of evolution. In reality, evolution never did predict a hierarchical pattern. Evolutionary theory can easily accommodate multiple, dis-united, non-nested patterns.

16

Nested Hierarchy and Convergence

Any system of objects can be forcibly classified into a nested hierarchy. Some systems do not have to be forced, rather they display a nested pattern with clarity without having to be coerced. Life has such a pattern. There are no tetrapods that are not based on the vertebrate body plan. There are no amniotes that are not based on the tetrapod body plan. There are no mammals that are not also amniotes. These are the familiar examples, and many more can be given. They are powerful generalizations. Life is like nested Chinese boxes of subsets within subsets within subsets. Life is comprised of nested similarities. This significant pattern must be explained.

This chapter explains life's nested pattern, together with the subsidiary pattern of convergence.

Convergence

Convergence is a convenient term for summarizing observations. It means that two organisms share a similarity that cannot be explained by common descent. In this sense, convergence is effectively an _anti_-evolutionary term.

The _convergence explanation_ is how evolutionists explain convergence. They claim that similar traits independently evolved in two separate lineages and converged on the same design solution.

In nature, the convergence of similar structures is common, yet the convergence of _identical_ structures is essentially unknown.

> [I]t is emphatically not true that highly convergent forms are effectively identical. (Gould, 1980, p 38)

> [C]onvergence never renders two complex organisms completely identical (_a circumstance that would strain Darwinian processes beyond their reasonable power_) (Gould, 1980, p 41, my italics)

344

This situation, evolutionists say, is due to probability. They say the separate evolution of identical traits is highly improbable.

> Complex structures, ... do not reappear in the same form. This statement invokes no mysterious directional force in evolution, but merely asserts a claim based upon mathematical probability. (Gould, 1980, p 269)

> [O]rganisms contain so many complex and independent parts that the chance of all evolving twice toward exactly the same result is effectively nil. Evolution is irreversible; signs of ancestry are always preserved; convergence, however impressive, is always superficial. (Gould, 1980, p 39)

In short, evolutionists claim that 'identical' is extremely improbable, but 'similar' is very probable. Their claims span the range of probability based on the subtle difference between identical and similar. Evolutionary theory does not have the precision required by their claims. It is all too convenient for evolutionists to loosely adapt to the data after the fact. The evolutionists' probability argument created the illusion that evolutionary theory has something firm to say about nature.

Yet there is a deeper issue here. The evolutionists' probability argument misdirected our attention and allowed them to create another illusion. Completely identical convergence would not strain evolutionary processes in the slightest. On the contrary, such a circumstance would be an enormous relief to evolutionists. To understand why, we need additional insight about how 'Natural' selection works.

> The abandonment of useless specializations presents evolutionary challenges to populations and the necessity for a steady flow of beneficial mutation. Improved fertility and viability, for example, implies the importance of unrealized environmental factors and the need for the maintenance of genotypic variation. Given sufficient time, the minor increment of a useful trait necessitates that selection pressure be contingent upon an advancement in complex design. On the other hand, increased inclusive fitness requires considerable physiological interaction to acquire increased survival and reproduction. Thus, a diversified gene pool adds overriding selective value in connection with increased species diversity. A primary interrelationship between organism and environment, as predicted by evolutionary theory, substantiates natural selection as the main cause of the appearance of higher taxa. In association with genetic 'hitchhiking,' the removal of deleterious mutations implies the importance of unrealized environmental factors and the need for descent with modification.

The previous paragraph was written by a computer running a simple artificial intelligence program. The program randomly selects phrases from a list, and combines them into sentences.[1] Despite its seemingly complicated structure, the text is complete nonsense. Several of these nonsense sentences are concatenated to form paragraphs. The program is called a Report Writer. To generate a report, you provide a list of relevant phrases. The computer then asks one question: How many paragraphs would you like?

The Report Writer illustrates something about 'Natural' selection — evolutionary theory in action. 'Natural' selection is the inclination of evolutionists to *select* the simplest *natural* process to explain the observed data. One of the simplest and most powerful processes is transposition. The Report Writer demonstrates transposition nicely.

The Report Writer uses a simple transposition process. Every repetition of a given phrase is identical. The program merely transposes the phrases together in different combinations to form sentences. From an observer's point of view, the identically repeated phrases make the overall text easy to explain. Given enough text, the observer recognizes the identical repetition, and then realizes that the writer was not intelligent, but was rather dumb (in this case a very dumb computer program).

Identical repetition is not a sign of intelligence (even in our everyday language), rather it is *repetition with variation* that has always been the mark of intellect. Think of our classic examples of music, art, poetry, or literature. This mark of intelligence is often called "theme and variation." Life on earth has this pattern.

Identical repetition of biological design would be easy to explain with a transposition process. Transposition would move a character trait from one species into a different species. Do not be too concerned whether biological mechanisms can actually provide for this transfer of organic information. If nature had a suitable pattern of identical character traits, then theorists would claim *the pattern itself* as evidence that a transposition process exists.

Evolutionists insist that convergence could never be identical, and they claim this is a prediction of evolutionary theory. That is mistaken. To put the issue succinctly: If convergent character traits were identical, then they would no longer be "convergent" — they would be transpositions.

---

[1] The phrases are in four different categories: A,B,C, or D. To create a sentence, the computer randomly selects one phrase from each of the four categories. It then constructs a sentence randomly in one of six different configurations: "BCD." "DCB." "A,BCD." "A,DCB." "B,A,CD." or "D,A,CB." The computer easily makes these random selections, capitalizes the first letter, adds the punctuation, and concatenates sentences together into paragraphs. The idea has been around for many years. An INTERLISP version of the program was given to me in 1981 by Dr. George Hadden.

346

Empedocles

A lack of experimentally demonstrated mechanisms has never been a serious obstacle to evolutionists. An undemonstrated transposition process is a key factor in one of the oldest of evolutionary theories. Empedocles (492-432 BC) proposed a theory for the origin of living beings. As love began to amalgamate the elements, scattered parts of bodies formed. At first, there were only heads or limbs without bodies, heads without eyes or mouths, and so on. While floating, these parts attracted each other and joined in a variety of combinations. A sort of natural selection then preserved the favorable combinations, and imperfect ones perished.[2]

In short, there are many body parts, each with many copies. The copies are transposed and combined in various ways. Many are eliminated by a process of survival of the fittest (acting in a non-inventive way as executioner of the unfit). Life then ends up with a striking pattern of similarity and diversity.

Empedocles' theory has been viewed as preposterous[3] by our standards, yet in its time it was a serious attempt to cope with life's pattern of similarity and diversity. His theory fell not because of a lack of mechanisms (genetic or otherwise), for his theory never pretended to supply these. Rather, it failed because a closer examination shows that life resists being interpreted as the result of transposition.

*

Transposition processes are still relevant today. We will next discuss several examples, showing that theorists are perfectly willing to embrace transposition simply because they *perceive* its pattern.

Some theorists use transposition to explain the origin of the eukaryotes from simpler one-celled prokaryotes. Prokaryotes (such as bacteria) lack a cell nucleus, while eukaryote cells have chromosomes bounded within membranes of the cell nucleus.

The theory proposed by Lynn Margulis suggests the first eukaryotes originated when one bacterium swallowed another, and the two cells formed a mutually beneficial symbiotic relationship. Allegedly, the two organisms became intertwined so they were one reproductive organism. This process, called endosymbiosis, has never been experimentally demonstrated. Instead it was suggested based on the mere pattern of similarities between prokaryotes and eukaryotes.

> [T]he primary force of [the endosymbiosis] argument rested not on its direct verifiability (or falsifiability) but on its power to explain: it offered a solution to a number of major taxonomic and evolutionary puzzles, and provided at least a logically plausible account of the origin of eukaryotic cells (Keller, 1986, p 48)

Presently, the hypothesis of endosymbiosis remains poorly supported.

*

---

[2]   Mayr, 1982, p 302; and Gould, 1977, p 413

[3]   Mayr, 1982, p 302

Transposition (also known as lateral transfer) has also been invoked at the level of molecules. It is used to explain the transposition of genes that code for specific proteins. The most famous example is in plants called legumes, some of which contain a hemoglobin-like molecule.

> These legume-hemoglobins (called leghemoglobins for short) seem so peculiar in function, and so restricted in taxonomic distribution among plants, that several biologists have proposed an origin as interlopers from the animal kingdom by lateral transfer. (Gould, 1986, p 21)

Again, lateral transfer was suspected because of the _perceived_ pattern.

> [L]ateral transfer [originally] seemed attractive for two major reasons: the apparent restriction of globins to a small group of closely related plants (indicating transfer to them directly rather than deep homology in all plants) and supposed similarity in structure for a complex molecule across a wide taxonomic gap. (Gould, 1986, p 22)

In the above article, Gould calls into question this best known case of lateral transfer, because new data has arisen which alters our perception of the pattern. By altering the pattern, it alters the processes that must be used to 'explain' the pattern.

The new pattern, described by Gould, does not seem to demand lateral transfer. The new data shows that the leghemoglobin molecule is not highly similar to vertebrate hemoglobin after all, and additionally it is not limited to legumes but may have a much broader distribution within the plant kingdom.

Thus, transposition (or lateral transfer) is embraced and renounced wholly on the basis of pattern.

Octopus Eyes

Dawkins says it would be "worrying" if convergence were totally identical. He seems confident that evolutionary theory could not accommodate such a situation:

> When we look in detail we find — *it would be worrying if we didn't* — that the convergence is not total. The different lines of evolution betray their independent origins in numerous points of detail. For instance, octopus eyes are very like ours, but the wires leading from their photocells don't point forwards towards the light, as ours do. Octopus eyes are, in this respect, more 'sensibly' designed. They have arrived at a similar endpoint, from a very different starting point. And the fact is betrayed in details such as this. (Dawkins, 1986, p 94-95, my italics)

Dawkins expressed a commonplace sentiment, rooted in a naive view of evolutionary theory. Dawkins propagated the illusion that evolution has something firm to say about nature.

Theorists use the transposition explanation at the level of molecules (e.g., leghemoglobin) and cellular organelles (e.g., eukaryotes), but would they also use it to suggest the transposition of major organs between higher life forms? Yes they would — and they have. In fact, they used it in precisely the case Dawkins is discussing, the eyes of cephalopods and vertebrates.

> While squid and vertebrate eyes differ in many details, they solve the same basic problems and each would benefit enormously from bits and pieces of plans interchanged. A continuous flow and interchange of gene parts 'on approval' would both explain and facilitate parallel evolution. (Anderson, N., 1970, p 1346)

In other words, one theorist (Dawkins) claims that identical convergence cannot happen, and another theorist (Anderson) proposes the transposition process whose specialty is explaining just such a situation. Evolutionary theory can be adapted to most anything. *Evolutionary theorists never have been restrained by an* *inability to experimentally demonstrate their theories.*

Transposition is simple in concept, vastly more elementary than convergence or natural selection. There is only one thing that has ever kept evolutionists from invoking it. And that is *pattern!* Evolutionists choose mechanisms only to the extent necessary to 'explain' the pattern, and that is all.

> The debate about lateral transfer does not center upon plausible mechanisms. .... The issue is not plausibility but relative frequency. Lateral transfer is intelligible and feasible, but how often does it happen in nature? This crucial question must be established by example, not by theory. (I have often emphasized ... that natural history is such a hard science because most of its key questions are debates about relative frequency, not matters of logic or mechanism. In our immense and multifarious world, issues of relative frequency are particularly difficult to resolve.) (Gould, 1986, p 18)

This has dramatic implications for the nested hierarchy. Because of the nested hierarchy, we know that life has not been substantially influenced by a transposition process. Nested hierarchy and transposition are incompatible patterns. As Gould points out, the success of Linnaean hierarchical classification argues against transposition:

> The major argument against high frequency [of lateral transfer] is a statement of simple common sense — obvious, but powerful. We have a fairly reliable Linnaean classification, at least for animals. Lateral transfer cannot be expressed in the hierarchical system of Linnaean nomenclature. If lateral transfer were rife in animals, we could never have constructed a workable classification for them by Linnaean criteria. (Gould, 1986, p 23)

In the article just cited, Gould considers the possibility that lateral transfer might be frequent in bacteria and fungi. He considers this possibility because of pattern. He points out that these kingdoms have so far frustrated our efforts at classification. He therefore leaves open the possibility of lateral transfer as an explanation for this difficulty. Gould is ready and willing to invoke transposition, if life's pattern ever lends itself to it. This case shows exactly what I am talking about. Mechanisms are invoked only to the extent needed to 'explain' life's pattern, then it is displayed as though it were a solid scientific theory.

One can offer no better example than this:

> *This* is evolution's grand prediction: that the patterns of similarities in the organic world are arranged like a complex set of nested Chinese boxes. .... But this is not the most important point. It is more important to see that the basic notion of evolution does have fundamental consequences that must be true if the very idea is correct. If we had failed to find this nested pattern of similarities interlinking all forms of life in our backyards, we would, as scientists, be forced by the rules of the game to reject the very notion of evolution. Evolution *is* predictive, and therefore thoroughly scientific. (Eldredge, 1982, p36-38)

Eldredge is clear and emphatic. Remember he is a punctuationist (one who is aware of the lack of clear phylogeny) and he is a leading hierarchy theorist and anti-creationist. His statement is from his anti-creation book, one of the first to follow the Arkansas creation-science trial. In the context of his statement, he is eager to show the public that evolution is real testable science, that it is vulnerable to empirical evidence. Therefore, he insists that without the nested pattern we would be forced to reject evolution.

His colleague, Gould, (in this instance not speaking directly to the creation versus evolution controversy) said the exact opposite. These are two top evolutionary scientists addressing the most fundamental of issues. This is evolutionary theory in action, as it really is. What the theory says depends on the situation at hand. Evolutionary theory predicts nothing, not even a nested hierarchy. Rather, the theory adapts to data like fog adapts to landscape.

The idea that 'evolutionary theory is solid science' is an illusion. The major device for achieving this illusion is silence, silence with a selective pattern. In making their public presentations, evolutionists only discuss those mechanisms that seem to *fit* the pattern of life — on the remainder of the evolutionary smorgasbord they are silent.

Selective silence is a powerful device for creating evolutionary illusions. For years you heard about common descent so exclusively it seemed to be the real evolutionary theory. Evolution never was limited to anything that minimal. Transposition is an ancient concept. It is still used today.

Convergence Explained

Nature contains an abundance of convergence. These are constructed in a manner most difficult for evolution to explain. Convergences are strikingly similar, *but not identical*. This is precisely as they should be to avoid looking like evolution.

This situation requires a delicate balance. If characters are too similar then they look like transposition, but if they are too different then they fail to demand special (and formidable) rationalizations like the evolutionists' convergence explanation. This delicate balance requires a designer.

- Convergence is a compelling way to unify diverse organisms together. It brings together disparate parts of the system of life into one unified whole. This sends the unifying message.

- Convergences help defeat the observer's attempts to identify phylogeny. This sends the non-naturalistic message.

- Convergences themselves look *unlike* evolution. They cannot be explained by common descent, *nor by transposition*. This sends the non-naturalistic message.

Convergence is one of the most difficult things for evolution to explain. It is therefore important in the biotic message.

One example is the Australian platypus, a mammal with a duck-like bill. The bill looks so much like a duck's that when it was first reported in Europe many scientists thought it a clever hoax. The platypus' bill is rubbery, not hard like a duck's. Unlike a duck's, it contains special bioelectrical sensors used for underwater navigation and sensing of prey. Because of features like these, the duck and platypus snouts cannot be explained by transposition. Instead, evolutionists must account for these with an implausible convergence explanation.

The Single Most Perfect Instrument

Two of evolution's most potent arguments were developed by Darwin: the argument from imperfection and Darwin's Riddle.

- The **argument from imperfection** — Nature contains odd, imperfect designs that a capable designer would not employ. Therefore, life was not fashioned by a designer. (This is also known as the *panda principle* after Gould's most widely known example, the panda's thumb. It is Gould's favored class of evolutionary evidence.)

- **Darwin's Riddle** — Why does nature sometimes use the same design for different purposes, and other times use different designs for the same purpose? A capable designer would use the *single most perfect instrument* in each case. Since life was not designed this way, life was not made by a designer.

Why would a designer have created in such an unexpected manner? Gould wields these arguments with great force:

> The 'various contrivances' that orchids use to attract insects and attach pollen to them are the highly altered parts of ordinary flowers, evolved in ancestors for other purposes. Orchids work well enough, but they are jury-rigged to succeed because flowers are not optimally constructed for modification to these altered roles. If God wanted to make insect attractors and pollen stickers from scratch, he would certainly have built differently. (Gould, 1983a, p 131-132)

> The message is paradoxical but profound. Orchids manufacture their intricate devices from the common components of ordinary flowers, parts usually fitted for very different functions. If God had designed a beautiful machine to reflect his wisdom and power, surely he would not have used a collection of parts generally fashioned for other purposes. Orchids were not made by an ideal engineer; they are jury-rigged from a limited set of available components. Thus, they must have evolved from ordinary flowers (Gould, 1980, p 20)

This is the riddle posed by every evolutionist since Darwin. They ask, Why such senseless variation? Why didn't the designer use the *same* design to accomplish the *same* function? Why not use the same design over and over? Once the designer had fashioned a given instrument, say a hand or an eye, then why not use it again?

> [A]n omniscient Creator shouldn't have to experiment with different designs. (Futuyma, 1983, p 199)

> But if the Divine Intellect has designed [flowering] organisms so that each is an effective mechanism for dealing with pollen transfer, why are there so many designs? Why did He not endow all species with the single, most perfect instrument? (Ghiselin, 1969, p 154)

352

Biochemists and physiologists, for example, find a red protein in vertebrates and certain insects. It performs the same function — carrying oxygen
— but the detailed structure of the hemoglobin protein, the sequence of
amino acids that make up the protein molecule, is entirely different in the
two groups. It really isn't at all the same molecule in insects and vertebrates. A creationist might suppose that God would provide the same
molecule to serve the same function, but a biologist would never expect
evolution to follow exactly the same path twice. (Futuyma, 1983, p 50)

[I]f all these forms [of cytochrome c] were created a short time ago by an
intelligent, rational creator, cytochrome c should have an identical structure
in all these forms. But it doesn't! So why is this enzyme different in the
various classes? .... I claim that the results of protein sequencing provide
some of the most significant evidence against creation and for evolution.
(Sonleitner, 1990, p 15)

*

The argument from imperfection was unraveled early in the book. A biomessage sender is constrained against using only perfect engineering designs.
Perfect design would look like the result of many designers acting separately.
Also, perfect design would not look like a message. Life's designer intentionally
created life to look like a message from a single designer. Therefore, the designer
had to use odd and curious design, which explains why some designs lack
perfect engineering elegance. This solves the argument from imperfection.

*

Now we turn to Darwin's Riddle. Why not use the *same* design over and over
again, whether good or bad, perfect or imperfect? The answer is utter simplicity.
If the designer had used the same design again, then it would have been trivially
easy for evolutionists to explain. They would say it was the result of simple
transposition. Nothing could be simpler.

The designer intentionally created life to look unlike the result of naturalistic
processes. Therefore, the designer was constrained from using the same design
again indiscriminately. No matter what the design, (be it good or bad) a biomessage sender is constrained against using it in an overall pattern that would
look like transposition.

The argument from imperfection and Darwin's Riddle were never evidence
for evolution, since evolution never predicted these. Evolutionists could adapt to
any outcome, merely by selecting the appropriate mechanisms from the smorgasbord. Instead, evolutionists used these riddles as evidence *against* a designer.
Message theory cleanly solves the puzzle.

Different Design — Same Function

To successfully send the biotic message, a designer must not indiscriminately use the same design repeatedly. Therefore, the designer is forced to sometimes use *different* designs to perform the same function. The wings of bats, birds, and pterodactyls make a classic example.

> When we compare the anatomies of various plants or animals, we find similarities and differences where we should least expect a Creator to have supplied them. Is it not strange that a Creator should have endowed bats, birds, and pterodactyls with wings made out of the same bony elements that moles use for digging and penguins use for swimming? Is it not stranger still that instead of modifying these bones for flight in the same way, the Creator should have decreed that the bat's wing be made by lengthening four fingers, the pterodactyl's by lengthening only one finger, and the bird's by shortening the hand and equipping it with feathers? ... an omniscient Creator shouldn't have to experiment with different designs. (Futuyma, 1983, p 199)

The bat's wing is made by lengthening four fingers, while the pterodactyl's wing is made by lengthening only one finger (what would be our little finger), and the bird's wing is made by diminishing the hand and providing it with feathers. Evolutionists claim these are evidence for evolution. They claim that a capable designer would not experiment with different designs.

The evolutionists are mistaken. A biomessage sender has every reason to design in this way:

- The similarity of these three organisms cannot be denied. They are variations on a theme, and possess a common body plan. This sends the unifying message.

- These organisms are systematically placed (regarding all other organisms) so their common possession of wings cannot be explained by common descent. This sends the non-naturalistic message.

- The wing designs are sufficiently different that they cannot be explained by transposition. This sends the non-naturalistic message. This is precisely their difficulty for evolution. If the wings were identical, then there would be no trouble rationalizing them by transposition.

The biomessage sender made these organisms difficult for evolutionists to explain. Evolutionists are left to account for the evolution of wings (and *flight!*) separately for each case. Rather than being evidence for evolution, these organisms are clean evidence for message theory.

The Simple, All-Natural Process

There is a reason to inventory the evolutionary smorgasbord. Certain dishes are highly prized because they complement the *observed* pattern of life. In all the hoopla, one can easily overlook many other dishes. There are entrees that are largely neglected because they do not fit the pattern of life. Yet some of these *neglected* ones are simple, all natural recipes. Is this not curious?

These neglected dishes at the evolutionary banquet have a special significance, for they hold the key to understanding why a biomessage sender should fashion life's peculiar pattern. Some of these simple, all natural recipes have a potent pattern-explaining potential. To send the non-naturalistic message the designer must avoid a pattern that looks like these.

Transposition is the most potent, most overlooked process at the evolutionary banquet. Yet it is an extremely simple process, much simpler than the scenarios commonly offered by theorists. Transposition has the potential to greatly aid an evolutionary explanation. If not properly avoided by a designer, it would have the power to destroy the biotic message. The next three sections examine transposition in depth.

Transposition as Scenario and Enigma

Transposition would provide a mechanism for rapid evolution.[4] New biological designs would not have to evolve separately each time they were needed. Instead, they could be transposed into new species, with the bad combinations eliminated by the executioner of the unfit (survival of the fittest). This is at least as good as the other scenarios you hear.

It could also potentially solve Haldane's Dilemma in one swoop. Transposition could break free of the small-scale step-by-step replacement process that Haldane's Dilemma is based on. Transposition would allow evolution to occur by leaps and bounds. Species participating in the process would acquire advantages over species that do not.[5] In this way, occasional transposition could add a new and important class of scenarios to evolutionary literature.

If nature possessed a pattern of transposition, then theorists would claim *the pattern itself* as evidence that the process has a substantial occurrence in nature. They would then feel free to invoke transposition in their scenarios.

To thwart this powerful class of scenarios a biomessage sender must avoid creating a pattern that looks like transposition. This effectively squelches would-be attempts to employ transposition scenarios.

---

[4] As suggested by B. R. Levin, 1984, p 461

[5] Also, transposition need not be voluntary. One can imagine a species occasionally stealing genetic material from other species. This could be achieved by stealing just one cell from another species. (Since each cell contains the genome of its entire multicellular organism.) The genome stealer could then use this newly acquired genetic material.

*

The avoidance of transposition accomplishes another important end by posing a serious explanatory problem for evolution. Why hasn't transposition had a major, widespread impact on the pattern of life? Why has transposition had an insignificant impact in nature? Transposition is a simple process compared with those the theorists routinely employ. Transposition could aid the evolution of species who possessed this capacity. So why isn't it here in abundance? Why isn't transposition everywhere?

Understand the difficulty this poses. Evolutionists readily offer scenarios for the origin of everything. They feel they can successfully explain the origin of complex features like hearts, brains, and intelligence. So why isn't transposition here too? By comparison, its origin and evolutionary benefit is easy to explain. By all rights, it should have a major impact on the pattern of life. Why doesn't it?

The answer is clear. By avoiding a transposition pattern the biomessage sender can effectively silence a potent naturalistic mechanism and simultaneously turn its absence into an evolutionary enigma.

*

The clearest and firmest of all evolutionary predictions indicates that sexual reproduction should not exist. Evolutionary theory would also indicate that organisms should sometimes acquire useful adaptations wholesale from other species by transposition. This would provide for the fastest, most easily explained evolution: (1) in the classical way, by gradual adaptation within a single asexual lineage; and (2) by acquiring fully-formed traits from other species. Yet the data refutes evolution on both points. Life is predominantly sexual, and lacks transposition of major biological traits.

This situation is evidence for message theory. Message theory correctly predicts the major patterns of life, while evolution predicts none.

Transposition is Ordinary Design Practice

We expect an ordinary designer to use the same design for the same purpose in different organisms. Any designer can easily do this by transposing designs. This is perfectly reasonable, commonplace design practice — we expect it from a designer.

Yet this expectation itself constrains a biomessage sender to do the unexpected. A biomessage sender is no ordinary designer. Rather, a biomessage sender must take conscious steps to make life look unlike the work of an ordinary designer. This is required if life is to *be* a message.

A transposition pattern would not look like a message at all, but would look precisely like the product of the typical designer doing typical design. It would look like the product of a designer who has no intention of sending a message.

Moreover, a transposition pattern would look like the casual product of an entire civilization. It could look like the product of multiple, separate designers sharing only a common technology base, but sharing no common design goal. By transposing entire technologies, one into another, our human cultures have enormously accelerated their development. Arduini points out that innovative design is contagious, it gets transferred by designers into other diverse created objects.[6]

> Grumman, Northrop, and McDonnel Douglas may be designing three individual air superiority fighters, but, if the specific design criteria so dictate, they can use the identical Pratt and Whitney engines for all three aircraft. This is not convergent evolution, but it *is* a fact of contemporary design. (Arduini, 1987, p 21)

A transposition pattern is a major identifying feature of a common technology base. For one broad example, consider books from a library. Many features of books are transposed from one to another, for example indexes, page numbers, tables of contents, photographs, formulas, footnotes, paragraphs, sentences, words, and grammar. These interlinking features show that the books are from a common civilization. Yet the books are the product of multiple designers working independently with no common goal.

Widespread transposition is a major indication that nothing out of the ordinary is happening. Transposition is the expected result of independent, multiple designers who are using a common technology base.

In summary, a transposition pattern would not look like a message, nor would it unambiguously look like the product of a single designer. It would not meet the requirements of the biotic message. This is a second reason why a transposition pattern should be avoided by a biomessage sender. Yet the most crucial reason remains.

---

[6] "[A]ircraft *have* evolved since Orville and Wilbur Wright took their first flights at Kittyhawk — but not in a manner that would allow construction of a phylogenetic tree." (Arduini, 1987, p 23)

Transposition versus Nested Hierarchy

Theorists say the nested hierarchy is the major evidence for evolution. We now stand that notion on its head. The nested hierarchy is not evidence for evolution, but its terminal downfall. The nested hierarchy allows us to ask those most embarrassing questions: Where are the ancestors? Where are the lineages? Where is the phylogeny? The absence of these has been a major dilemma for evolutionists from the beginning.

Transposition would provide an escape from this dilemma. By employing transposition, evolutionists would argue like this:

> The ancestors are *everywhere!* Genetic material has been transposed from many different sources, so species do not have unique, identifiable ancestors. This explains the absence of recognizable lineages.

Evolutionists would readily drop their allegiance to common descent, and perform a *volte-face.* They would scrutinize life for a pattern of transposition, and would use that pattern as *evidence* that transposition occurs in nature. Finally, they would claim that transposition is the reason phylogeny is not evident.

What is to keep evolutionists from doing that? What is to prevent them from invoking transposition? What, if anything, is to deter them from rationalizing the absence of phylogeny? There is only one answer: pattern. On the strength of life's pattern, the biotic message must resist all naturalistic explanations.

A major feature of the biotic message is the lack of phylogeny, yet this feature would be impotent if a prominent transposition pattern were visible. Transposition has the innate power to undermine the biotic message and destroy it totally. Transposition poses a threat to the biotic message, therefore a biomessage sender must vigorously pursue its undoing. A biomessage sender must avoid creating life with a substantial widespread pattern of transposition.[7]

Two major features of the biotic message are the absence of phylogeny, and a substantial amount of convergence. The absence of transposition allows these two features to come booming across, loud and clear. The designer used a nested pattern largely for what it is not. The nested pattern is not transposition.

---

[7] Transposition is not identified merely by discovering several examples of identical design, rather it is identified through a systematic pattern analysis. In a biotic message, there is nothing wrong with using an identical design in many different organisms. Not only is this allowed, it benefits the biotic message if done in the proper way. In addition, certain designs (such as specific bio-molecules) might be necessary for adequate survival in certain environments, and in such cases the re-use of these designs would be acceptable design practice. Yet message theory is precise about a general pattern of transposition: There is little to be gained by it and much to lose. A general pattern of transposition must be avoided.

Noise Immunity

There are many patterns that do not lend themselves to naturalistic explanation. These patterns would, at first, seem to qualify to be a biotic message. Let us discuss several.

Imagine a system of many organisms all standing in one great circle. In this configuration, each organism has two nearest neighbors, one on its immediate left and right. Imagine each organism possesses a set of similarities shared only with its two nearest neighbors. The entire system of life is then linked by an intricate pattern of shared similarities. Let us call this example the loop pattern.

We can imagine many other patterns based on a similar scheme. For example, figure-eight patterns, and triple-loop patterns, but they all suffer from similar problems. By discussing the loop pattern we will see their common downfall.

As a second class of examples, imagine a giant checkerboard or matrix of many rows and columns. Imagine each cell of this matrix contains an organism. Imagine there is a unique set of similarities possessed by all organisms in a given row. Every row of the matrix possesses a unique set of common similarities. Likewise, imagine a similar pattern for the columns. Every column of the matrix possesses a unique set of similarities possessed by no other organisms on the checkerboard. Call this the matrix pattern.

There are many patterns similar to the matrix pattern, for example in three or more dimensions instead of just two, but the matrix pattern will serve as a basis to discuss all of them.

Our third class of examples is the nested pattern, which you already know about. In this pattern, the organisms are arranged in subsets within subsets within subsets, with each subset possessing its own unique parcel of similarities shared by, all and only, its member organisms.

We then have three examples of biological pattern: loop, matrix, and nested. Each of these patterns would be quite striking and distinct. Each would link all organisms into one single system that demands a single common ordering force. (This sends the unifying message.) Also, each pattern would be impossible to persuasively explain as the result of any naturalistic process. (This sends the non-naturalistic message.) All three patterns convey both messages, so they all seem to have everything required of a biotic message.

Certainly, if life clearly adhered to any of these patterns we would probably attribute it to a single designer. The loop and matrix patterns appear to have a slight advantage because they do not even vaguely look like common descent.

This presents a puzzle. Why should a biomessage sender choose the nested pattern over the others? What possible advantage does a nested pattern have? This is the puzzle we now face.

The clear answer is in the concept of noise immunity. There exists no perfectly quiet medium of communication. All real messages must be conveyed through some communication medium that is noisy. There are many types of noise each with its own unique properties, and every communication medium has its own repertoire of noises.

A well-designed message takes into account the medium through which it must travel. A well-designed message is specifically designed to endure the expected noises and still be recognizable and decodeable by an observer. In the jargon of communications research, a well-designed message must be robust in the presence of noise, it must be resistant to noise, it must possess noise immunity.

What are the noise sources that a biotic message must face? There are two, a major and a minor one. The major noise source is that many created organisms will not be seen by the observer. Many organisms will go extinct; many organisms will not be fossilized; many fossils will not persist; many existing fossils will not be found; and most importantly, the observer might not possess the wherewithal to compile a total knowledge of the accessible data, living or fossil. In short, many organisms will be lost or unavailable. This is the major noise source that the biotic message must contend with. A biotic message must be designed to be resistant to lost data.

Noise immunity is a grievous downfall of the loop and matrix patterns. When the loop pattern is subjected to a little noise what does it look like? Removal of a few adjacent data points breaks the loop, and then it looks like a lineage. It now looks like evolution, and this after having lost only a few data points. As more data points are randomly removed, the situation worsens. It now looks like entirely separate unconnected strands of data points. Each strand can look like a separate lineage. Or, these unconnected strands can look like the result of multiple designers acting independently. Both situations are unacceptable for the biotic message. The loop pattern has extremely poor noise immunity.

The matrix pattern also suffers in the presence of noise. It is resistant for a while. Yet with more removal of data, two factors start to set in. Groups of data points become unlinked from the remaining system of life. These are perceived as several disconnected groups of organisms that are not united with other groups by shared similarities. Even more likely is the possibility the perceived pattern will lose its rigorous matrix structure and start to look like a pattern of random transposition. The "matrix + noise" pattern looks as if character traits have been randomly transposed between organisms. As already said, this perception would be fatal for the biotic message.

In summary, the loop and matrix patterns are fine when pristine and complete, but they perform poorly when faced with noise. They convey the message satisfactorily when unabridged, but not when data has been randomly removed. They fail to reliably convey the biotic message.

*

Perhaps you would try to remedy these problems by adding a universal set of similarities U. Every organism would then possess the U characters. Let us call these patterns "loop + U" and "matrix + U." The advantage of this scheme is obvious. The U characters cannot be interpreted as the result of multiple designers acting independently. Also, their universal occurrence makes them noise resistant. No matter how many organisms are removed, the remaining organisms all possess the U characters.

Nonetheless, universal characters U are easily explained by either common descent or transposition. The "matrix + U + noise" pattern tends to look like transposition, while "loop + U + noise" tends to look like common descent. The addition of the universal characters U has improved the noise immunity, but it is only a partial solution. It is just one step in the right direction, and this step was achieved by adding one level of nested hierarchy to the patterns. The "loop + U" and "matrix + U" patterns are now bi-leveled nested hierarchies where the U characters form the most general level. The move toward a nested hierarchy is impelled by the need for noise immunity. This move is a natural one.

*

The nested pattern has a unique and wonderful property: it retains its structure as data is removed. Virtually all the data can be eliminated and a nested pattern is still recognizably present. Take a large collection of organisms inter-related by the nested pattern. Place these into a paper bag. Then randomly pluck out a hundred or so. What pattern do they form? *Nested!* Are they all linked by the common possession of similarities? *Yes!* Is there a pattern of transposition? *No!* Are ancestors, lineage, or phylogeny present? *No!* The biotic message is still displayed in the available data. The nested pattern is thoroughly resistant to noise. It can successfully transmit the biotic message by a minimum of available data. There is no other pattern possessing this highly desirable property.

Visible Unity

The universal U characters pose a design constraint of their own. What character traits could be universal? What characters could be used by all organisms, of all types and sizes, in all environments? They could not be a backbone, a heart, or teeth. Bacteria do not need teeth. The universal characters are ultimately limited by the lowest common denominator of all life — single-celled organisms. Biochemical entities are ideal for the lowest, most general levels of life's nested hierarchy. DNA, RNA, the genetic code, ATP, metabolic pathways, membranes and so forth are ideal for linking organisms of all sizes and environments. This explains their use as biologic universals in the biotic message.

Though biochemical entities do a marvelous job of uniting all life, they suffer from their own universality. Because they are universal, they are forced to be microscopic traits. Because they are microscopic, they are effectively invisible. Therein is the drawback. It is counter-productive for a biotic message to be invisible.

The multi-leveled nested pattern resolves this limitation. The nested pattern extends from the microscopic world of bacteria all the way up to the very visible character traits of large organisms like dinosaurs. A multi-leveled nested pattern allows a designer to create a diversity of viable life forms while linking them together with shared character traits, many which are visible.

Besides the nested pattern, the unity of life is augmented with various features which subtly knit life together more visibly than biochemicals can. For example, mimicry, mutualism, symbiotic relationships, and convergences unite the system of life into one unified whole. Darwin was able to see this unity even though he had no knowledge of the universalities at the biochemical level.

This is one unified system of life; attributable to only one designer. The designer has gone to considerable lengths to ensure it is seen that way.

Mutation Noise

The matrix pattern has a bad side-effect. It places severe constraints on what each organism *must* possess and *cannot* possess. Different organisms face different environments with different needs. The row and column scheme criss-crosses too many ecological boundaries with an unrealistically restrictive design strategy. It ultimately limits the depth that the pattern can be embedded into each organism, thereby forcing the pattern to be superficial.

For example, imagine a given row of organisms possesses tusks. This is fine if the organisms happen to be large animals, but it is a problem if they are plants or bacteria. To remedy problems like this, place all the major designs into separate rows — bacteria, fungi, shelled animals, vertebrate animals, and so forth, each in their own row. Every row contains its own shared designs. However, every column now contains organisms of massively different design, and the matrix pattern requires that these organisms share some common similarity. This presents a problem. What character traits can all these diverse organisms share while remaining viable? The characters must be superficial in nature, like the colors blue, plaid, or pink polka dots. Thus, key elements of the matrix pattern would have to be carried by *superficial* biological designs.

This is where noise becomes important again. The biotic message must contend with mutation as a noise source. Mutations cause biological change, and the easiest things they noticeably change are the most superficial aspects of organisms. If a biotic message were carried by superficial designs, then it could easily become corrupted by mutation. A superficial biotic message would have poor immunity to mutation noise.

The nested pattern solves this problem. The nested pattern does not limit the depth that it can be embedded into organisms. The designer is free to use major designs, both for survival, and to carry the biotic message. Features such as a backbone, quadrupedal body form, an amniote egg, and a chambered heart, can serve a dual purpose. In this way, the designer can pack the biotic message deeply within the very essence of each organism. Each organism becomes fused with the biotic message; they become inseparable. The nested pattern allows the designer to avoid reliance on superficial character traits to convey the biotic message. One benefit of this is redundancy.

Redundancy is a simple way to make messages resistant to noise. Redundancy is a superabundance, surplus, or repetitiousness of a message. It is the sort of thing we do naturally without thinking about. Much of our oral communication is redundant, with repetitive variations of the same information. The redundancy allows us to communicate in a noisy environment.

Redundancy is increased by packing the biotic message into each organism. Greater redundancy means that organisms can endure a greater portion of mutation and still successfully convey the biotic message.

The nested pattern allows for high immunity to mutation noise, and life's designer has fully used that potential.

Balance Between Patterns

The biotic message has several characteristics:

- It avoids the appearances of phylogeny and transposition.

- It retains its structure when faced with noises due to the loss of data, and biological mutations.

- It unifies all life by shared similarities.

Those characteristics result in three types of pattern, which we call cladistic, phenetic, and convergence patterns. This poses a problem. How should these three patterns be balanced? Should any be given more emphasis?

To answer this we must understand convergence. Convergence cannot be seen in isolation. It can be seen only by reference to a data structure. The data structure serves as a backdrop that makes convergence visible.

Three types of data structure can make convergences visible: a cladogram; a phenogram; or a phylogeny. In the biotic message a phylogeny is forbidden, so cladograms and phenograms provide the reference frame for seeing convergence.

Life's cladograms and phenograms are primary or independent patterns. The observer sees convergence against the backdrop of these patterns. Convergence relies, for its visibility, on these two patterns. Convergence is therefore a secondary or dependent pattern.

The strength of a pattern is its ability to make itself perceptible. Some patterns are stronger than others in their ability to grip our perception and command our notice. A biomessage sender must correctly balance the strengths of the three patterns if they are all to be perceptible to an observer.

If a convergence pattern is too strong, it can obliterate the perception of the other two patterns, and by so doing, the overall pattern would become ambiguous. An overall pattern that is too strong in convergence can be interpreted in numerous unintended ways. Convergence can undermine the biotic message by overpowering the primary patterns upon which its very perception depends. A biomessage sender could err by using convergence too much.

Convergence is a trump card possessing great force, but it should be played sparingly. An abundance of convergence is desirable, but it must not overpower the primary patterns. This requires a balance among the three types of pattern.

For the biotic message to be perceived: (1) the cladistic and phenetic patterns should be strong and durable; (2) the pattern of convergence must be comparatively weaker; (3) a widespread transposition pattern should be minor at most. This balance is seen in nature. Message theory accurately accounts for the major patterns of life.

Darwin's Riddle Revisited

The first half of Darwin's Riddle was solved earlier this chapter.

> Darwin's Riddle: Why would a designer sometimes use *different* designs to accomplish the *same* purpose? Why would a designer sometimes use the *same* design to accomplish *different* purposes?

The second half remains to be solved: Why would a designer sometimes use the *same* design to accomplish *different* purposes? Evolutionists use this as evidence against creation.

> Forelimbs of people, porpoises, bats and horses provide the classic example of homology in most textbooks. They look different, and do different things, but are built of the same bones. No engineer, starting from scratch each time, would have built such disparate structures from the same parts. (Gould, 1980, p 248)

> [W]hy should the bones of man, bat, porpoise, and mole have the same nature and order? Such similarities help no one. Supporters of the argument from design were, therefore, compelled to fall back on suppositions that God had all sorts of subsidiary creative intentions, like the achievement of symmetry and order and harmony. Expectedly, such ad hoc suggestions convinced virtually no one. ... Adaptively valueless isomorphisms point to the fact that widely different organisms are descended from common ancestors. Natural selection has taken the ancestral form, molding it to different ends. (Ruse, 1982, p 41, 42)

The answer is simple. The designer must use the same design to accomplish different purposes because the nested pattern requires it. The nested pattern places demands on the occasions when a biomessage sender must use shared design, and when shared design is prohibited. Therefore, on occasion the designer is forced to use the same design for different purposes.

The designer is not suffering from lack of imagination (as accused by anti-creationists). Rather the designer is superbly creative, masterfully designing a planetary biosphere while mindful of the constraints of the biotic message. The anti-creationists are wrong — life's designer is a message sender, not a simple inventor, not a maladroit tinkerer.

Tattoos and Brands

Why didn't the designer use a tattoo or a brand, like cowboys put on livestock as a sign of ownership? Why not use a particular marking, like a rocking-horse or a bar-H? Why not use one on every organism to make the biotic message really stand out? It could be made heritable from generation to generation. It would unify all organisms together, in a manner difficult to explain naturalistically. It would seem to have everything necessary for a biotic message. Why not use a brand?

To unify all organisms, the brand must be on *every* organism, and this causes some difficulty. First, many organisms would be hindered by a brand, particularly those that are microscopic, or photosynthetic, or who rely on protective camouflage.

Second, mutation might alter these superficial markings, thus making them ambiguous. They could begin to carry the wrong meaning. They could begin to look like different brands, thereby implying different branders.[8] This would be unacceptable for the biotic message.

The third argument against brands is that a brand is ambiguous about the origin of the branded objects. For example, if the brand occurred along with the biotic message, then there would be no way to associate the brand with the biotic message. It would look as if two beings had been dabbling with life: one a creator-biomessage sender, and the other a brander. It would look as if the brander was *separate* from the biomessage sender. The observer could not know the two beings were the same. There would be no necessary link between the two.

The way around this is to avoid having major aspects of the biotic message carried by superficial aspects of life. Design so the message is integrated into the life forms, so it becomes an inextricable part of them. Design so the message cannot be separated from the organisms themselves. Design so the *message* and the *survival* of the organisms are the same. Build the message into the very fiber of the living beings. Sculpt it into their fins, their paws, their hooves, their feet. Forge it into their backbones, spell it into their genetic code, write it into their DNA. This makes it clear there was no passage of time between the creation of the organisms and the imprinting of the biotic message. These events had to have occurred simultaneously. In this way there can be no doubt. The biomessage sender and the creator of life are one.

Brands adequately serve our terrestrial purpose of signifying ownership, a message they convey very well. They are one form, of many possible forms, that messages can take. Yet they are ambiguous about the origin of the branded objects, so they fail to meet the requirements of the biotic message.

---

[8] The biotic message is highly resistant to mutation, because it uses a redundancy of unifying similarities all reinforcing the same unusual pattern system-wide. The biotic message has more noise immunity than does a superficial brand.

Apes and Tigers

Message theory makes specific predictions about the pattern of life. It predicts the form of the pattern while acknowledging that there are many ways to implement it. The theory does not completely explain "Why the ape?" or "Why the tiger?" It predicts a specific pattern of relationships between organisms, yet it does not specifically predict apes and tigers. With the help of an analogy, this factor can give additional insight.

Handwriting is unique and can identify messages written by various people. We can identify separate handwriters, even if the messages themselves are otherwise identical. That there are many possible handwritings allows us to identify the work of a single handwriter.

Likewise, the fact that there are many possible implementations of the biotic message allows a deduction. If there were two designers independently transmitting a biotic message, then the sum of the two patterns would be substantially different from either one taken alone. We could detect such a two-fold pattern if it were present. Thus, life on earth cannot be the result of multiple designers independently sending biotic messages. Rather, the pattern is the unified product of one designer.

Interbreeding

A designer could conceivably make life capable of wide interbreeding. An organism could then interbreed with most other life forms and give hybrid offspring. While that scheme is conceivable, there is good reason why a biotic message sender should not use it.

First, the continual interbreeding would fill in life's morphological gaps with countless hybrids. The pattern would then look like a smooth, gradual intergradation of life forms — and that would look like evolution. By constructing barriers to interbreeding, the designer prevented life from looking like evolution.

Second, if organisms could successfully interbreed widely, then it would be an easy, active, demonstrated mechanism of widespread DNA transposition — and that would harm the biotic message. By constructing barriers to interbreeding, the designer made life resistant to the transposition explanation.

Summary

Evolutionists claim that evolution theory would be in serious trouble if convergences were identical. This created the illusion that evolutionary theory makes a firm prediction. In reality, if convergences were identical, they would no longer be convergent — they would be transpositions. Evolutionists would simply change their story.[9]

Convergences are similar, but not identical. This is precisely as they should be to look most unlike evolution. This situation requires a delicate balance. If biological characters were too similar, then they look like transposition. Yet if they were too different, then they fail to demand special rationalizations like the evolutionary convergence explanation.

Evolutionists claim that evolution would be in serious trouble if life's nested hierarchy did not exist.[10] This created the illusion that evolutionary theory is testable science. Actually, evolutionary theory could easily accommodate a non-nested pattern. In fact, such a circumstance would be a great relief to evolutionists.

Evolutionary theory never did predict a nested pattern. Instead, evolutionists used life's nested pattern as evidence against a designer, then they accommodated the nested pattern by selecting common descent (and other mechanisms) from their theoretical smorgasbord.

Evolutionists are not committed to common descent. They are committed to 'Natural' Selection: they select the simplest natural processes necessary to 'explain' the data. Evolutionists have shown they are perfectly willing to select the transposition explanation. The transposition explanation is the simplest, most powerful process in evolutionary theory. Evolutionists use the transposition explanation whenever they feel it matches (and therefore explains) the data. In practice, evolutionists never have regarded a lack of experimental demonstration as an obstacle. They have shown that life's pattern is the only obstacle preventing them from using the transposition explanation. For these reasons, life's designer scrupulously avoided a transposition pattern:

- Transposition would provide a mechanism for rapid evolution. By avoiding transposition, the designer squelched this scenario, and turned the absence of this simple evolutionary mechanism into an evolutionary enigma.

---

[9] Identical convergence could also be re-interpreted and rationalized by the loss explanation. For more information see the chapter, Systematics and Classification.

[10] For example, see Raup, 1991, p 15-16

- Transposition is the expected design practice of an ordinary designer. It is also the expected result of a culture, or of multiple, independent designers who are using a common technology base. By avoiding transposition, the biomessage sender made life look like the product of a single designer who has unordinary intentions.

- Transposition would totally undermine the biotic message by allowing evolutionists to explain the absence of identifiable phylogeny. They would say that genetic material has been transposed from many different sources, thereby destroying any clear lineages. By avoiding transposition, life's designer defeated this scenario.

Life's nested pattern superbly conveys the biotic message:

- The nested pattern links all life into a unified whole. This sends the unifying message.

- The nested pattern looks unlike transposition. This allows the absence of phylogeny to take on real force. This sends the non-naturalistic message.

- The nested pattern serves as a backdrop that allows convergence to become visible. Convergence is an important pattern in the biotic message.

- The nested pattern requires few design constraints that conflict with survival. Biological characters can be nested and simultaneously be designed for survival. This allows the biotic message to be built deeply into each organism, thereby making the biotic message resistant to mutation noise.

- The nested pattern has a special property. It is resistant to lost, missing, or unavailable data. The nested pattern retains its structure as data is removed. The available data is: (1) nested; (2) unified; (3) it lacks phylogeny; and (4) it lacks transposition. The nested pattern can successfully transmit the biotic message with a minimum of available data.

Message theory is scientific. (1) It correctly predicts the major patterns of life and their relative strengths. (2) It refutes the argument from imperfection. (3) It cleanly solves Darwin's Riddle.

17

Embryology

The development of an organism from fertilized egg to adulthood is called its ontogeny. Embryology studies embryos and their ontogeny, and Darwin felt that it is "by far the strongest single class of facts" in favor of evolution.[1] Modern evolutionists still feel that embryology is one of their best evidences.

This chapter will remove more layers of evolutionary illusion, and show the remarkable willingness of evolutionary theorists to endorse any naturalistic explanation that seems to support their worldview. In particular, the chapter will trace the rise and fall of recapitulation theory, and demonstrate that evolutionary theory does not cope with embryology in a scientific way.

This chapter will also show that message theory illuminates the mysteries of embryology in substantial detail. The biotic message is clearly imprinted in the curious developmental pathways of life. Embryology is major evidence that life was designed as a biotic message.

Von Baer's Laws

Scientific laws are generalizations about the empirical world. Unlike a theory, a law summarizes observations without trying to explain them. For example, the law of gravity acknowledges the existence of gravity and describes it, without trying to explain it.

In 1828, the anti-evolutionist Karl von Baer generalized the observations of embryology into several laws that now bear his name. They remain today as our most broad and powerful summarizations of the data. Gould recognizes them as "probably the most important words in the history of embryology."[2] These are **von Baer's laws:**[3]

- The general features of a large group of animals appear earlier in the embryo than the special features.

- Less general characters are developed from the most general, and so forth, until finally the most specialized appear.

- Each embryo of a given species, instead of passing through the stages of other animals, departs more and more from them.

- Fundamentally therefore, the embryo of a higher animal is never like the adult of a lower animal, but only like its embryo.

---

[1]   As cited in Gould, 1977, p 70

[2]   Gould, 1977, p 56

[3]   As cited in Gould, 1977, p 56

Von Baer's laws indicate that the younger the embryonic stage, the more closely the distant classes of organisms tend to resemble each other. As embryos develop, they diverge ever further away from embryos of other species. For example, the human embryo is similar to the fish *embryo,* yet never identical to it. As human and fish embryos mature they become more unlike each other. Development is like the radial spokes of a wheel. Organisms start out near some central, common, starting point and diverge outward on a unique and distinctive path. There are similarities in development, and there are roughly parallel paths, but embryos tend to have a unique developmental path that diverges away from other species.

Von Baer's laws also indicate that embryonic characters appear in a peculiar sequence. The most generalized characters tend to appear earliest in ontogeny, followed by the less generalized characters, followed last by the most specialized. This series — from generalized to specialized — may be called the **von Baer sequence**.

*

The von Baer pattern of ontogeny is beautiful evidence for message theory. The pattern graphically indicates that organisms could not have come from many designers acting independently. Life must have originated from just one source. This sends the unifying message.

Also, species tend to have their own unique, distinctive ontogeny. This separateness of living forms sends the non-naturalistic message. The pattern of separate, diverging, radial spokes is awkward to explain in a naturalistic way.

The von Baer sequence posed a special difficulty for evolutionary theory. Natural selection cannot explain the von Baer sequence. Natural selection does not care whether characters are generalized or specialized. It does not see these attributes, therefore it cannot sort them into a special sequence.

People can see generalized characters, but evolution cannot. The concepts of generalized and specialized are seen only by reference to system pattern — they refer to the levels of life's nested hierarchy. The mechanisms of evolution are blind to system pattern and must operate without any such informed knowledge. There are no evolutionary mechanisms that can see generalized or specialized characters, much less sort them into a sequence.

Thus, the two dominant features of embryology — the radial spokes pattern and the von Baer sequence — are not easily explained by evolution.

Recapitulation Theory

In 1866, Ernst Haeckel published the biogenetic law, also known as the law of recapitulation, with its euphonious catch-phrase "ontogeny recapitulates phylogeny."[4] This law claimed that an organism's embryological development (its ontogeny) repeats (or recapitulates) the stages of the *adult* form of its ancestors. Numerous examples from nature were cited. Darwin too adopted the idea.

Haeckel referred to his concept as a law. He apparently used this name in an attempt to elevate its importance and overshadow von Baer. Yet it never truly was a law. Laws summarize our observations, and Haeckel's "law" claimed to summarize observations linking ontogeny with ancestry. Yet ancestry was not actually observed, since life has no identifiable phylogeny. Instead, Haeckel's concept was based on speculation, not observation. Thus, the biogenetic law never was a law.

*

Recapitulation was driven by the needs of evolutionary theory. Evolutionists sought to remake von Baer's laws into evidence for evolution, and recapitulation theory was the optimal way to accomplish this end.

With the Darwinian revolution, evolutionists needed evidence of phylogeny. Haeckel tried to provide the evidence by giving embryology a subtle twist. He sought to modify the von Baer pattern of distinct, diverging, radial spokes, and convert it into an evolutionary tree. There is a subtle difference, and it required that ontogeny be rerouted so that embryos follow the *same* developmental paths for a while before diverging.[5] Accordingly, embryos start at a common point — the base of the tree — and develop along the same path until groups of embryos branch off from each other. Each group follows on its path until it branches into smaller groups. This branching continues until each species finishes on its own twig. This 'ontogenetic tree' was central to Haeckel's concept.

The ontogenetic tree was explained in the following way. An organism traces a developmental path and then stops (at adulthood of course), yet its descendants tend to develop slightly further. The descendants evolve by a process of **terminal addition**, where new characters are tacked onto the end of the ancestor's developmental path. The early characters of ontogeny are kept and conserved. As new characters are continually added, the developmental process is accelerated to telescope it down to a reasonably short time. Recapitulation theory claims that most embryological characters are those of a distant ancestor

---

[4]   An idea like Haeckel's theory, only in a more primitive form, had been discussed for many decades.

[5]   According to Haeckel's drawings, in their earlier stages pigeons, dogs, and humans looked *identical*. (Milner, 1990, p 205) This erroneous portrayal favored Haeckel's attempt to coerce life's 'radial spokes' into an evolutionary 'tree.' "When critics brought charges of extensive retouching and outrageous 'fudging' in his famous embryo illustrations, Haeckel replied he was only trying to make them more accurate than the faulty specimens on which they were based." (Milner, 1990, p 206)

— that they are, in a deep sense, *identical* to those of a distant ancestor. The theory concluded that embryos retrace (or recapitulate) the *adult* form of ancestors.[6]

Terminal addition served a special purpose in Haeckel's theory. It added new characters to the end of ontogeny, in sequence. The newest evolved characters appear in ontogeny after the older characters. This process, together with the branching of common descent, would *force* the earliest ontogenetic characters to become the most widely distributed (or generalized) in nature, thereby creating a von Baer sequence.[7] Haeckel had specially constructed his theory to cause a von Baer sequence.

Haeckel's recapitulation theory was an attempt (I think the best possible attempt) at arbitrarily adapting evolutionary theory to von Baer's laws. It could have been devised in an armchair, without any further knowledge of embryology. Haeckel's theory took the von Baer pattern of distinct separate radial spokes and distorted it into an evolutionary tree. The process of terminal addition followed as the means to explain the von Baer sequence. Finally, the process of acceleration was needed to keep development time reasonably short. It was that simple.

*

There were huge theoretical difficulties with the processes of acceleration and terminal addition. Why should nature prefer these processes over other possibilities? Of all the processes that can be theorized, why should nature peculiarly follow these two? Theorists could easily suggest these abstract processes, but establishing a plausible theoretical basis was more problematic. The solutions to these problems were elusive.

Haeckel tried to explain terminal addition in the following way. He wholeheartedly endorsed Lamarckian evolution, the inheritance of acquired characteristics. According to Haeckel's view, only the adult stages of ancestors persisted long enough to acquire new characteristics, and so pass them on. Embryonic stages were too fleeting to acquire new characteristics. Thus, most new characteristics would be to the adult or late stages of ontogeny.

*

---

[6] Recapitulation theory said that embryos retrace the *adult* form of ancestors. This peculiar idea was not from observation. It was merely the logical conclusion required by the process of terminal addition. In turn, terminal addition was needed to 'explain' the von Baer sequence.

[7] Haeckel strongly emphasized that "Phylogenesis is the mechanical *cause* of Ontogenesis." (As cited in Gould, 1977, p 78, my italics) This curious statement perplexed many scientists. Some felt it was nonsense, while others thought it was mere rhetoric (Gould, 1977, p 421). Gould acknowledges the statement as a serious one, and dismisses it as the result of Haeckel's excessively severe commitment to "reductionism." But Haeckel's statement makes perfect sense when you realize that his explanation of ontogeny was indirect and implicit. We can make his explanation explicit as follows: Phylogenetic branching (together with terminal addition and the conservation of early ontogeny) *causes* the ontogenetic tree and the von Baer sequence.

Despite the glaring problems with the mechanisms of recapitulation, Haeckel focused his attention in another direction. He developed systematic tools for using his theory to *recognize ancestry* from observations of ontogeny. Gould notes that Haeckel "was far more interested in tracing lineages than in establishing the mechanism of recapitulation."[8]

In the end, recapitulation theory was accepted for overriding (though misplaced) reasons:

- The theory claimed that new adaptations are continually *accumulated* by terminal addition. This built on the popular but erroneous concept of naive natural selection. Also, it (and the industrial revolution in which it was embedded) bolstered hopes about the future.

- The theory claimed that development *accelerates* as evolution proceeds. This further bolstered hopes for the future.

- The theory claimed to identify ancestors and phylogeny from observations of ontogeny, thus providing evidence for evolution. This task was the goal and hope of Darwinians.[9]

- The theory claimed that early characters of ontogeny are kept and conserved. The most famous example was embryonic structures improperly known as human "gill slits."

In short, recapitulation theory filled the hopes of the day; it had structure; and at the time it seemed supported by examples.

Haeckel's recapitulation theory was buoyed up by the wave of Darwinist enthusiasm and carried far into the twentieth century. It has been taught in schools almost to the present day[10] and is still widely prevalent as folk-knowledge.

---

[8] Gould, 1977, p 83-84. Raff and Kaufman (1991, p 14) note that "Haeckel had no interest in embryology for its own sake: Embryology provided data for the working out of evolutionary histories, the construction of phylogenetic trees." "Haeckel hoped to use recapitulation as a guide to the reconstruction of phylogeny; he was strangely uninterested in its potential to provide insight into general mechanisms of evolution." (Gould, 1992f, p 159)

[9] "The importance of embryological data to late-nineteenth-century evolutionists was their phylogenetic content." (Raff and Kaufman, 1991, p 10)

[10] For example, "[T]he New York City public schools taught me Haeckel's doctrine, that ontogeny recapitulates phylogeny, *fifty years after it had been abandoned by science.*" (Gould, 1977, p 1, my italics)

The Downfall of Recapitulation

The acceptance of recapitulation was aided by illusions. Ontogeny allegedly recapitulates phylogeny, like this: the multi-cellular organisms gave rise to vertebrates, who originated the tetrapods, who evolved into the mammals, who descended into the primates, and finally humans. This "phylogeny" matches the sequence of human ontogeny (multi-cellularity, followed by vertebra, then four-legs, then mammalian characters such as hair and mammary glands, then primate characters). That sounds just like recapitulation. It also sounds like terminal addition, where newly evolved characters are tacked onto the end of development. This illusion helped sell recapitulation.

The illusion was effective because ontogeny actually goes from generalized to specialized, as do the alleged ancestors. The illusion uses nested supraspecific groups (such as vertebrates, tetrapods, mammals, and primates) as ancestors in a phylogeny. Since the phylogeny is an illusion, so is the alleged recapitulation.

In a similar way paraphyletic groups created an illusion of recapitulation. Imagine a "lineage" formed from paraphyletic groups. Each "descendant" group possesses characters that are absent in its "ancestor" group. Because of the von Baer sequence these characters appear in the embryo in the same sequence as the alleged ancestors. It seems like terminal addition, where newly evolved characters are tacked onto the end of development. This impression helped sell recapitulation. Once again, since the phylogeny is an illusion, so is the alleged recapitulation.

*

From the beginning, recapitulation theory was confronted with empirical counterexamples. As von Baer pointed out, embryos tend to look like the *embryo* (not the adult!) of other species.

Also, ontogeny sometimes leaves out sequences of presumed ancestors.

Also, many embryonic organs develop in a sequence that conflicts with their presumed ancestry. For example, the notochord, brain, eyes, and heart develop earlier than their appearance in phylogeny would warrant.[11]

Also, embryologists soon realized that morphology and morphological adaptations are useful and important during *all* stages of ontogeny, not just the adult stages. Adaptations are often specialized for early ontogeny and have little use later in life. This conflicted with Haeckel's explanation of terminal addition. Haeckel had presumed that adaptations are not specialized for early ontogeny, and that they are merely the accelerated appearance of the adaptations of ancestral adults.

As the counterexamples accumulated, the theorists tinkered with recapitulation theory to salvage it. The theorists de-emphasized Haeckel's original idea and supplemented it with many other embryological possibilities. Specifically, Haeckel's theory had only allowed for acceleration of development, so theorists added the possibility of *retardation* of development.

---

[11] Gould, 1977, p 82

Also, Haeckel's focus was on the whole embryo. So theorists allowed for dissociated body parts to have *independent* ontogenies.[12] Each organ could have an accelerated or retarded development, independently of other body organs. Each organ could have its own developmental history. Also, embryonic characters could be inserted into or deleted from ontogeny. This was the evolving body-parts scenario applied at the level of embryology.

> [R]ecapitulation ... was, instead, abandoned as a universal proposition and displayed as but one possible result of a more general process — evolutionary alteration of times and rates to produce acceleration and retardation in the ontogenetic development of specific characters. (Gould, 1977, p 206)

Even Haeckel's idea of using ontogeny to identify phylogeny fell into disrepute. Raff and Kaufman note that by 1894 a generation of embryologists was "frustrated by the lack of exactness in phylogenetic speculation."[13]

Haeckel's explanation of terminal addition was further undermined by the refutation of Lamarckian inheritance. His explanation got into additional trouble when Mendel's genetic research was rediscovered in 1900. The essence of Mendelian genetics is allele *substitution,* and this contradicted Haeckel's mechanisms of terminal *addition* and telescoping *acceleration.*

By the 1920s, recapitulation theory had been thoroughly invalidated.

> Haeckel's program of using the biogenetic law to search for entire ancestors in the embryonic stages of modern forms was pursued with much hope and fanfare, but led to few positive results and endless wranglings about untestable phylogenetic scenarios — all because the biogenetic law is basically false. By the closing years of the nineteenth century Haeckel's program had become a source of much ridicule, ... (Gould, 1992f, p 161)

> Surely the biogenetic law is as dead as a doornail. It was finally exorcised from biology textbooks in the fifties. As a topic of serious theoretical inquiry it was extinct in the twenties. (Thomson, 1988, p 273)

> Like so many ideas, [recapitulation] seemed like a good one at the time, but, as the creationists like to point out to us, the idea has long since been rejected. (McGowan, 1984, p 122)

> The [recapitulation] theory is now known to be invalid ... (Mayr, 1982, p 215)

> It [recapitulation] has now been disproven, at least in its classic form. (Ayala and Valentine, 1978, p 236)

---

[12]   Gould, 1977, p 89 & 235

[13]   Raff and Kaufman, 1991, p 17

The Illusion of Phylogeny

The revisions to recapitulation theory provided maximal flexibility for coping with the data. Evolutionary theory is now to the point where any embryological observation can be accommodated. Any similarities (in whole bodies or in body parts) between a descendant (embryo or adult) and a presumed ancestor or sister group (embryo or adult) can now be accommodated with an evolutionary scenario. This is the modern evolutionary embryology smorgasbord.[14]

Thus, recapitulation began as a structured theory with a real prediction about nature (embryos should resemble ancestral adults). Then, like the whole of evolutionary theory, it progressively collapsed into an unstructured jumble that could make no clear predictions about nature.

Though recapitulation theory had been discredited, it inspired the development of the embryology smorgasbord. Theorists continued to use these embryological mechanisms in a free-form manner to create the illusion of phylogeny.

For example, paedomorphosis is when an adult descendant displays similarities to the *juvenile* form of an ancestor. Thus, paedomorphosis is the exact opposite of recapitulation. Yet like recapitulation, the hypothesis of paedomorphosis was easily employed to bolster the illusion that phylogeny had been identified.

> It is unfortunate that most literature on paedomorphosis is cast in the same mold that bolstered recapitulation during the previous half century — speculative phylogeny of higher taxa. There is scarcely a major group of animals that has not inspired a paedomorphic theory for its origin. (Gould, 1977, p 277)

Paedomorphosis was also used in scenarios to explain fossil gaps. Paedomorphosis was claimed to generate new biological designs without creating intermediates.

> *The fossil record is notoriously uninformative on the origin of new morphological designs; usually, higher taxa simply appear in the record without clear antecedents or incipient stages (indeed, this abruptness has inspired most paedomorphic postulates, since promotion of a larva to adult status is one way to generate a new design without intermediates).* Since an ancestor with a larva ripe for paedomorphosis is almost invariably hypothetical, it need not have existed at all. The 'larval progenitor' could just as well have been an ancestral adult which later augmented its own ontogeny to evolve the modern animal now pressed into service as a model for the supposed ancestor. (Gould, 1977, p 280, my italics)

In these ways the embryology smorgasbord was used to create the illusion of phylogeny.

*

---

[14] Evolutionists emphasize two main processes of developmental change operating on individual body organs: acceleration and retardation. There is also an abundance of related processes and names: anaboly, archallaxis, cenogenesis, condensation, fetalization, gerontomorphosis, heterochrony, heterotopy, hypermorphosis, metathetely, neoteny, paedomorphosis, progenesis, tachygenesis. (compiled from Gould, 1977)

Though recapitulation theory is discredited, evolutionists continue to specially emphasize recapitulation and the biogenetic law. This creates the impression that they have an identifiable scientific explanation of embryology, when they do not.[15] It also kept the recapitulation myth alive.

For example, Cracraft argues, "The biogenetic law is not in disrepute; only Haeckel's capsule version of it ..." (Cracraft, 1984a, p 63)

Kent's college level comparative anatomy text mistakenly refers to von Baer's laws as "the biogenetic law." (Kent, 1987, p 18)

Isaac Asimov, when directly challenged on the matter, continued to defend recapitulation.[16]

> I don't know what aspect of embryological recapitulation is now 'thoroughly discredited' in the eyes of a creationist. (Asimov, 1981, p 83)

Lovtrup re-interpreted von Baer's laws under the name "von Baerian recapitulation."[17] This is an absurd term, since von Baer did not endorse recapitulation, and his laws cannot imply recapitulation because they say nothing about ancestors or descendants.

There are deep reasons why evolutionists continue to focus on recapitulation.[18] Recapitulation theory attempted to explain the von Baer sequence. Yet the explanation was implicit and unstated. It seems Haeckel did not actually address the problem. I have not found any case where evolutionists explicitly address it.

---

[15] Wallace Arthur acknowledges (1988, p 1 and 19) that the modern evolutionary synthesis lacks a coherent theory of embryological development, and his book proposes a theory that attempts to fill that need. His theory follows the modern trends in evolutionary thinking. His theory is pluralistic, that is, it uses a multitude of disjoint, conflicting mechanisms operating at many levels. Arthur tries to give structure to these mechanisms by using hierarchy theory, that is, by using the language and imagery of "hierarchy." Most notably, Arthur's theory emphasizes terminal addition and the doctrine of early ontogenetic conservation. These are always at the center of evolutionists' implicit attempts to explain the von Baer sequence.

[16] This quotation is from a written debate that Isaac Asimov had with the creationist Duane Gish in *Science Digest* magazine. Gish argued in the straightforward way, "The idea of embryological recapitulation ... is now thoroughly discredited and should be expunged from textbooks." Asimov responded, not by clearing the matter conclusively, but *by continuing to support recapitulation.*

[17] Lovtrup, 1987, p 378. Lovtrup offers a von Baer style of recapitulation this way: "During their ontogenesis the members of twin taxa follow the same course up to the state where they diverge into separate taxa." This is implicitly the classic Haeckel-style recapitulation. To make any sense it even requires Haeckel's mechanism of terminal addition.

[18] "But I am also convinced that the impression of an overwhelming dominance [of recapitulation over paedomorphosis] rests, *ironically, on cases that have nothing to do with recapitulation, but only mimic it in the workings of von Baer's laws.*" (Gould, 1977, p 234, my italics)

They draw no attention to this problem whose evolutionary solution is awkward at best. Their widespread silence on this important embryological phenomenon is remarkable.

Evolutionists universally handled the problem by misdirecting it. That is, they focused on it as a weapon against creation theory. They implicitly (and erroneously) interpreted the von Baer sequence as recapitulation, and used recapitulation as evidence against a designer. This approach focused attention away from the failings of recapitulation theory. Since evolutionists never did explain the von Baer sequence, they never had to explain why peculiar mechanisms — such as early ontogenetic conservation, terminal addition, and acceleration — were necessary. This approach hid the evolutionary difficulties and helped create the illusion of phylogeny.

*

In summary, modern evolutionists use the conflicting mechanisms of the embryology smorgasbord to 'explain' ontogeny and create the illusion of phylogeny. Paedomorphosis, for example, is the opposite of recapitulation, and is commonly employed in evolutionary scenarios as proof of phylogeny. At other times, evolutionists readily emphasize recapitulation. Evolutionists use ontogeny as evidence against a designer, even though they have no testable scientific theory for explaining it.

The Punctuationists

By the 1920s, Haeckel's recapitulation idea had been solidly discredited for its theoretical difficulties and for its failure to make clear, empirical generalizations about nature. Yet it hung around for a while, lingering in our textbooks and schools for nearly sixty more years. Why? Despite its problems, recapitulation served a purpose. It helped convey the illusion of phylogeny, and no evolutionist saw fit to finally remove it until there was a suitable replacement.

It is no accident of history this did not happen until 1977, when Stephen Jay Gould published his classic study, *Ontogeny and Phylogeny,* which sought to clear the matter once and for all. Five years earlier, Gould and Eldredge had produced their bold new vision of evolution, punctuated equilibria. They completely de-emphasized lineage, in favor of indecipherable bushiness. Haeckel's recapitulation theory, with its subtle endorsement of lineage, was now a hindrance and could be conveniently disposed of.

Thus, in the 1860s, Darwin and his followers sought evidence for evolution, and Haeckel's theory had risen to prominence as a tool for identifying ancestors and phylogeny. Yet for precisely that same reason the punctuationists had no need for Haeckel's theory. The identification of ancestors and phylogeny was antagonistic to punctuated equilibria. So, the punctuationists did not hesitate to knock down Haeckel's long discredited views.

Then, the punctuationists embraced von Baer's laws. They correctly emphasized that these laws are our best and broadest generalizations of embryology.
Punctuationists were comfortable with these because, unlike Haeckel's theory,
von Baer's laws do not require that ancestors or lineage be identified.[19]

*

The punctuationists retained a special portion of Darwin's thinking. They
called it Darwin's principle: the more similar the ontogenetic pathway, the closer
the organisms are to their common ancestor. This was the *unnamed common ancestor* ploy again, now at the embryological level.

> Though [embryonic features] *do not allow us to trace the actual course of our
> descent in any way,* they are full of evolutionary significance nonetheless;
> for, as Darwin argued, community of embryonic structure reveals
> community of descent.[20] (Gould, 1977, p 213, my italics)

The punctuationists used Darwin's principle as though it explains von Baer's
laws. But it fails to be an explanation. It does not deal with the von Baer pattern
of separate, diverging, radial spokes, and it does not even try to explain the von
Baer sequence. Ironically, the punctuationists had promoted the modern re-
emergence of von Baer's laws, and then virtually ignored them.

In one major respect the punctuationists approached embryology in the same
way evolutionists had ever since Darwin. That is, the von Baer sequence subtly
corroborates the nested pattern of life, and the nested pattern was used as
evidence against a designer.

Punctuationists tried to use the von Baer sequence as a weapon against a
designer, yet they also needed to conceal that they had no explanation of the
sequence. Because of these conflicting goals, they needed their argument to be
indirect and implied, rather than clear and explicit. Darwin's principle met those
needs. It accomplishes that by referring to the von Baer sequence implicitly,
rather than directly.[21]

In short, Darwin's principle created the impression that punctuationists had a
scientific explanation of embryology (when they didn't), and it was used as
evidence against a designer (when it wasn't). Darwin's principle is sufficiently
vague that it could be used for both purposes.

---

[19] Also, the von Baer sequence indicates that life's nested characters tend to show up *in
sequence,* beginning with the most general. Thus, von Baer's laws lend additional
support for the validity of life's nested pattern. Punctuationists apparently found this
encouraging, since it corroborated the nested pattern they now believed to be their
major evidence for evolution.

[20] "Darwin's principle also had a severe limitation: ... it offered no clues to actual
evolutionary lineages." (Gould, 1977, p 72)

[21] Evolutionists offer Darwin's principle as the justification for using ontogeny to identify homology, yet the von Baer sequence is the distinctive link between ontogeny and
homology. The von Baer sequence enables organisms to have similar ontogenies for as
long as reasonably feasible, and evolutionists interpret that long-term similarity
through Darwin's principle. Thus, in practice, Darwin's principle implicitly refers to
the von Baer sequence.

*

Punctuationists sought to explain the notorious gaps in the fossil record, and they looked to the embryology smorgasbord for the explanatory mechanisms. They suggested that a *small* change *early* in embryonic development can produce a large change in the adult organism. They felt this might explain the large gaps observed in the fossil record, since the fossils typically preserve adults, not embryos. By emphasizing *small* embryonic change, the punctuationists presented the beguiling image that they are not really all that different from neo-Darwinian gradualists.[22]

The punctuationists seemed unaware that their scenario, with its emphasis on change to *early* ontogeny, contradicted the doctrine of early ontogenetic conservation that evolutionists had traditionally relied on. This went unnoticed because evolutionists never had explained why the doctrine was necessary.

*

The punctuationists are pluralists, that is, they endorse an abundance of opposing mechanisms operating in conflict at various levels. They argue that the neo-Darwinian synthesis is incomplete. They have continually extended the evolutionary smorgasbord, and they have tried to give it the appearance of structure by classifying the mechanisms into a hierarchical relationship. Then, they try to defend this as legitimate science by attacking their perceived foe, reductionism.

Gould pursues that same program in *Ontogeny and Phylogeny.* He endorses many conflicting embryological processes, and generalizes them to maximize their flexibility and explanatory power. Then he tries to organize and classify them, thereby creating the impression that the embryology smorgasbord contains a structured theory. Finally, he takes a poke at Haeckel's "crude and confused reductionism."[23]

Many students view Gould's *Ontogeny and Phylogeny* as an isolated work, bearing no particular relationship to his other writings. Yet in major respects it is a precise continuation of the punctuationist's program begun five years earlier.

---

[22] For example, see Gould, 1977, p 409

[23] Gould, 1977, p 78-85

Humans Do Not Have Gill-slits

Human embryo "gill-slits" have been used since the mid 1800s as evidence for our evolution from fish. Most evolutionists still use that term — gill-slits — in their public presentations.[24] Yet it is untrue, and this fact has been known for many decades. Humans do not, at any time, breath through gills. Human embryos do not have slits passing inward through the side of the neck to the oral cavity. Most importantly, the structures possessed by the human embryo are very unlike the true gills of an adult fish.

Despite long-lasting protest by creationists, the myth thrives, due to its constant repetition.[25] Some technical embryology texts try to correct the error,[26] but there has been little attempt to publicly clear the matter. On the whole, evolutionists have unabashedly continued to use gill-slits to create illusion.[27] This misuse obscured the deeper issues.

Human and fish embryos pass through stages of development where they have *similar* (not identical!) structures in the neck region. These structures are properly known as **pharyngeal arches**, not gill-slits. As the fish embryo matures, these eventually turn into gills.

As long as human pharyngeal arches were called gill-slits, it was assumed they served the obvious useful purpose — respiration. With this error removed, evolution is faced with the obvious question: If pharyngeal arches do not serve a function, then what has maintained them for the 400 million years[28] since they last had a function? This is awkward to explain when you remember that evolutionists say humans rapidly lost an acute, functioning sense of smell.[29]

> How does the modern biologist explain the presence of gill arches in the ontogeny of mammals? To be frank, until the physiology and biochemistry

---

[24] For example, Gould, Luria, and Singer, 1981, p 581

[25] There are few places where evolutionists publicly acknowledge that the "gill-slits" do not ever function as gills. In one such place, Dobzhansky (1973, p 25-26) makes that acknowledgment, and then he immediately *continues to use the term "gill-slits"* in his arguments.

[26] Some textbooks, aimed at medical students, drop all reference to "slits" and *specifically disclaim* the existence of human gills. For example, "Since the human embryo never has gills — branchia — the term pharyngeal arches and clefts has been adopted for this book." (Langman, 1975, p 262)

[27] Because Texas is a large market for school textbooks, it tends to determine what is available throughout the United States. In 1990, creationists again argued before the Texas State Board of Education that the terms "gill slits" and "vestigial human appendix" should be dropped from the school textbooks about to be adopted by the state. Evolutionists convinced the board that these "were deemed to be not a significant enough part of the scientific consensus" to warrant changing the textbooks. (Hastings, 1991, p 22) So, these errors continue to propagate.

[28] Wesson, 1991, p 88

[29] Kitcher, 1982, p 73-74

of developmental systems is better understood, only a tentative answer is possible. One can suggest that the genetic program for development consists of a set of such complex interactions that it can be modified only very slowly. .... Once the genetic basis of a structure is thoroughly incorporated into the genotype and forms part of its total cohesion, it can be removed only at the risk of destroying the entire developmental system. It is less expensive to keep the complex regulatory system of mammalian embryogenesis intact, even though (as a by-product) it produces unneeded gill arches, than to break it up and produce unbalanced genotypes. (Mayr, 1982, p 475-476)

Evolutionists try to explain the situation with the doctrine of **early ontogenetic conservation**: early ontogenetic development is conserved by evolution.

[T]he early stages of embryology are extremely conservative and resistant to evolutionary change. (Gould, Luria and Singer, 1981, p 704)

This embryological doctrine has been prevalent throughout the Darwinian era. Evolutionists used it to explain that useless pharyngeal arches are present simply because early ontogeny is conserved.

Nonetheless, when the situation requires it, theorists tell scenarios that are exactly opposite. For example, Ayala and Valentine explain cases where similar adult forms have evolved quite different developmental stages.

Invertebrate species that are closely related but that live in different regions — tropical or polar — frequently have such distinctly different developmental stages, even though the adults resemble each other closely. Clearly this is because the early life stages have each become adapted to differences in the conditions that each must face, while the adults have similar modes of life. (Ayala and Valentine, 1978, p 236)

Other evolutionists have directly challenged the doctrine of early ontogenetic conservation. They point out that nature has many counterexamples to it, showing that early development is frequently not conserved.

Each class of vertebrates (in mammals we might almost say each particular order) develops and then loses its own set of temporary structures — like the parade ground "formations of maneuver" — during this period. *The plain fact is that evolutionary divergence has taken place at every stage in the life history, the earliest no less than the latest.* (Ballard, 1976, p 38, my italics)

It is clear that a casuality of these arguments is the 19th century concept that early development must be an evolutionarily conserved process. (Davidson, 1990, p 384)

Thus, the evolutionary explanation of pharyngeal arches is nothing more than a convenient just-so story: its essential doctrine is contradicted by numerous cases.

Yet evolutionists could avoid stating their scenario as long as they referred to pharyngeal arches as gill-slits. This label hid the evolutionary difficulties.

*

382

Most importantly, the term "gill-slits" distorts the data. The term makes human pharyngeal arches seem *identical* to structures in an *adult* fish, thus making them seem like recapitulation. The term "gill-slits" subtly distorts the public's perception of the data in favor of evolution.

Embryos of fish and humans are merely similar, never identical. This subtle distinction — between similar and identical — makes all the difference. This is why embryology is not evidence for evolution.

*

In summary, evolutionists have known for many decades that the human embryo does not have gill-slits. Yet they continued to use the term. (1) The term hid the theoretical difficulties for evolution. (2) The term distorted the data in favor of recapitulation theory. (3) The term amplified embryology as a weapon against a designer.

The Biotic Message in von Baer's Laws

Message theory expects that ontogeny helps convey the biotic message. The multi-leveled nested pattern of life extends from the molecular level of biochemical universals, all the way up to the large *visible* traits of organisms. Embryonic traits occupy a range in-between. The embryological similarities serve to directly unify life on a broader scale than can be conveyed by adult organisms alone. The system of life was designed to be unified, and the biomessage sender has gone to great lengths to ensure it is seen that way.

This fact was not lost on the scientists of the seventeenth through nineteenth centuries. Through their primitive microscope lenses, they could see detailed embryological similarities between species that are quite different as adults. These workers compiled an encyclopedic knowledge of this fact. It was the pinnacle of this kind of research. The examples are striking.

> There would seem a world of difference between a jellyfish and a coral, but the connection between them is clearly shown by their life histories. (McGowan, 1984, p 77)

> Have [sea squirts] got any convincing chordate features at all? None. Here we have a regular-looking invertebrate. However, the larva of the sea squirt looks just like a small tadpole, and possesses ... a notochord, a hollow dorsal nerve cord, and a pharynx, usually with one pair of gill slits. Here is persuasive evidence for the invertebrate-vertebrate connection. (McGowan, 1984, p 76)

> In fact, if one looks at the major divisions such as annelid worms, molluscs and arthropods, the early developmental stages are virtually indistinguishable. (Halstead, 1984, p 250)[30]

---

[30] See also Stebbins, 1982, p 267-268

Thus, embryology makes the biotic message visible to low-tech observers. Many impressive embryological similarities are visible to the naked eye. The human fertilized egg (the zygote) is the size of a pinhead. In the human embryo, the commonly cited embryological evidences are visible as it grows from 3 to 20 millimeters in length.[31] At the stage where pharyngeal arches occur, the embryo is roughly 7 millimeters long and easily within range of our vision.

Because of this easy visibility even the Ancients were aware of the widespread similarities in development. Anaximander, Anaximenes, Democritus, Empedocles, and especially Aristotle used these embryological similarities in their cosmologies.[32]

> As far back as the Greeks, it had been recognized that there was some sort of parallel between the seriation of stages in the growing embryo and the seriation of organisms from the lowest to the highest (Mayr, 1982, p 471)

Embryological similarities were *visible* to the Ancients, and provided powerful evidence for the unity of life.

This explains the intriguing ontogenetic procession identified in the von Baer sequence. As the observer's vision is tuned to ever higher magnification, earlier stages of ontogeny can come into view; diverse specializations are stripped away; and successively broader layers in the unification of life are nakedly displayed. The observer might be unable to actually see down to the level of molecules, but the trend is unmistakable: life, in all its incredible diversity, is unified.

Let me re-emphasize this. The von Baer sequence indicates that the more generalized characters tend to appear earliest. *One could not ask for a pattern more effective at unifying life in a broad and visible way.* This accomplishes the utilitarian goal of efficiently developing each organism, while simultaneously serving the goals of the biotic message. *Diverse organisms tend to have similar ontogenetic pathways for as long as reasonably feasible before attaining their unique specializations.* The von Baer sequence, from generalized to specialized, is central to this visibility.

---

[31] For a series of photographs of human ontogeny see Torrey, 1967, p 130-137.

[32] For discussion see Gould, 1977, p 13-17

Embryology versus Transposition

Ontogeny accomplishes its task while disposing with a most dangerous threat to the biotic message: transposition. Von Baer's laws identify compelling trends that argue against transposition.

- The developmental pattern of separate, diverging, radial spokes is evidence that transposition between lineages could not have had a major effect.

- The von Baer sequence is a special non-random pattern. It is evidence that embryological characters have not been randomly transposed among life forms.

These two trends would be destroyed by transposition. Therefore, the existence of these trends indicates that transposition is not a significant part of nature.

In specific cases, embryology offers additional evidence against transposition. For example, cephalopods (such as the octopus and squid) and vertebrates have similar eyes. Yet, the eyes of these two groups develop from different embryonic tissue types. Embryologists acknowledge this as a major difference in development, showing that the similar eyes of cephalopods and vertebrates are not the result of transposition. Moreover, the blood vessels that supply the retina come from the front side of the retina in vertebrates, and from behind the retina in cephalopods. This substantial difference in structure is additional evidence against transposition.

*

Evolutionary systematists tried to develop methods for using embryological data as an aid in identifying phylogeny. Nonetheless, embryology has a demonstrated ability to thwart those attempts. Convergence at the embryological level confounds the observer's attempts to construct phylogeny.

> Generally speaking, the developmental stages of species belonging to the same major animal group resemble each other somewhat; starfish larvae tend to resemble each other more than they resemble snail larvae, and so on. Yet *the effects of convergence and divergence in larval forms is often greater than upon adults, and one must use caution in inferring phylogenies from early stages of life histories.* (Ayala and Valentine, 1978, p 236, my italics)

By displaying numerous convergences, embryology sends the biotic message. These convergences are carefully constructed so they look unlike transposition. This requires intelligent design.

Odd and Curious Development

The embryos of ant-eaters and baleen whales develop teeth-like structures that are re-absorbed into the jaw before birth.[33] These "embryonic teeth," as they are called, lack the detailed structure, biting surfaces, cusps and roots that we commonly associate with teeth. They are ambiguous forms, though similar to structures in other embryos that eventually do develop into teeth.

Evolutionists claim that such developmental pathways are imperfect and therefore are evidence against a designer.

Creationists have argued that the embryonic teeth serve useful purposes by helping to align the developing jaw. They point to several animal studies which show that if the teeth do not develop properly, a feeble jaw results.

Yet transitory embryonic teeth are an odd way to align the jaw nonetheless. It is an odd and curious developmental pathway, and this is precisely a requirement of the biotic message. Structures like these testify that life is from *one* designer whose embryological designs are recognizably different from those of multiple, perfect designers acting independently. This sends the unifying message.

In addition, these odd developmental pathways do not lend themselves to a transposition explanation. This sends the non-naturalistic message.

In every respect, they meet the predictions of message theory.

Deviations from von Baer's Laws

Von Baer's laws are generalizations about the observed pattern of ontogeny. These generalizations are powerful and broad. In this effort they have no serious rival. Yet von Baer's laws are not perfectly true for all organisms. Rather, they are wide-ranging generalizations of the facts. There are numerous deviations from these laws. Message theory goes beyond von Baer's laws, to explain these previously unruly cases. Specific variations from von Baer's laws are expected by message theory.

The von Baer sequence is ideal for visibly uniting organisms on a broad scale, thereby sending the unifying message. Nonetheless, a strict von Baer sequence would have a weakness. If life had perfectly displayed the von Baer sequence, then evolutionists would have consistently explained it as a result of early ontogenetic conservation, terminal addition, and branching common descent. Theorists would claim *the pattern itself* as compelling evidence that early ontogenetic conservation operates in nature.

In fact, evolutionists invented the doctrine of early ontogenetic conservation based on no other evidence than that it 'explained' the predominant von Baer pattern. This is why Haeckel built the doctrine into the foundations of recapitulation theory. The von Baer sequence had to be explained, and Haeckel was implicitly trying to explain it. This is why notions of early ontogenetic conservation continue to interest evolutionists.

---

[33] For example, Futuyma, 1983, p 199

The biomessage sender had to defeat this simple evolutionary doctrine, and this required deviations from a strict von Baer pattern.

For example, the vertebrates differ somewhat from von Baer's laws. The vertebrates start from various eggs and go through different early stages. Then, *they all converge* toward a remarkably similar pharyngula stage: the stage where pharyngeal arches are visible.

> [F]rom very different eggs the embryos of vertebrates pass through cleavage stages of very different appearance, and then through a period of morphogenetic movements showing patterns of migration and temporary structures unique to each class. All then arrive at a pharyngula stage, which is remarkably uniform throughout the subphylum, consisting of similar organ rudiments similarly arranged (though in some respects deformed in respect to habitat and food supply). (Ballard, 1976, p 38)

After converging together, the embryos then gradually diverge away from each other in the classic von Baer pattern of diverging radial spokes.

> After the standardized pharyngula stage, the maturing of the structures of organs and tissues takes place on diverging lines, each line characteristic of the class and further diverging into lines characteristic of the orders, families, and so on. (Ballard, 1976, p 38)

This dramatic pattern meets the needs of diverse vertebrates in diverse environments, while still meeting the objectives of the biotic message. Specifically, it forces evolutionary theorists to allow that the earliest stages of ontogeny are plastic and changeable. In short, it defeats the doctrine of early ontogenetic conservation.

> [E]mbryonic patterns are as subject to evolutionary change as adult form ...
> (Gould, 1991, p 26)

This creates an enigma for evolutionists. Why do vertebrates all have a stage with pharyngeal arches? "Why should species that ultimately develop adaptations for utterly different ways of life be nearly indistinguishable in their early stages?"[34] What evolutionary mechanism could have driven the ontogeny of all vertebrates to converge on this remarkable pattern and maintained it for hundreds of millions of years? Natural selection could not do this because:

> There are no design constraints that require sharks and humans to have similar embryos and yet develop into completely different organisms. (Futuyma, 1983, p 225)

Moreover, the similarities cannot be due to a process of early ontogenetic conservation. The vertebrates themselves show that the earliest ontogeny is not conserved. Evolution is unable to cope with this problem in a meaningful way.

---

[34] The quotation is from Futuyma, 1983, p 48. He further asks, "How does God's plan for humans and sharks require them to have almost identical embryos?" He is attempting to use this embryology as evidence against a designer. I show that he is mistaken.

*

Here are three examples of unusual patterns of development.[35] (1) Digits (the fingers and toes) are formed in different ways in amniotes and amphibians. In amniotes they are formed by cell death in the regions between the digits. In amphibians they are formed by cell division at digital growth points. These are substantial differences in development that result in the *same* external form: digits. (2) The salamander's limb bones are developed through a peculiar pattern of cartilage formation. This limb development is utterly different from other tetrapods, yet the final form of the limbs is so similar that evolutionists feel it must be the result of common descent. (3) The cytoskeleton of the ciliate protozoan *Tetrahymena* is visibly the same among species, but it is formed from proteins that differ greatly.

Evolutionists accommodate these cases only by denying the doctrine of early ontogenetic conservation and then giving a just-so story.

> [T]he structures of different organisms can be homologous even though their developmental pathways have come to differ substantially; form can be more conservative than the developmental route by which it is achieved. .... [A] developmental pathway may evolve while the form of its product is retained. .... Many of the parts of an organism, then, are so integrated that their form retains an identity through evolutionary time despite changes in their molecular constitution or developmental pathway. (Futuyma, 1986, p 436)

Evolutionists say development in these cases is not conserved, but the organism's outward form and function are conserved. This is awkward for evolutionists to explain. These cases cause evolutionists to reveal that their explanation of embryology has no structure. Yet these cases make perfect sense with message theory.

*

In summary, the exceptions to von Baer's laws serve legitimate purposes in message theory. They efficiently develop diverse organisms in diverse environments. They help show the unity of life. Yet they thwart naturalistic explanations.[36]

---

[35] These three examples are cited from Futuyma, 1986, p 436

[36] This illustrates an additional point. The pattern of life is complicated because evolutionary theory is complicated. Evolutionary theory is a vast smorgasbord of naturalistic mechanisms, and all of them must be defeated by the biomessage sender. Seemingly inconspicuous mechanisms — like early ontogenetic conservation — must be defeated, and so have a *reverse* impact on the pattern of life. The more potent the evolutionary mechanism, the more of life's pattern is devoted to defeating it.

Summary

Evolutionary theory approaches embryology with an unstructured smorgasbord of naturalistic mechanisms. Theorists merely select those mechanisms that seem to explain the data. As a result, there is nothing in embryology coherently predicted by evolution. Evolutionists primarily used embryology as evidence against a designer.

A classic example is the evolutionists' misuse of the term "gill-slits." This misnomer concealed the theoretical problems of evolution; it distorted the public's perception of the data in favor of recapitulation theory; and it was used as a weapon against a designer. The persistence of gill-slits — properly known as *pharyngeal arches* — is actually an evolutionary enigma.

Though recapitulation theory had been solidly discredited by the 1920s, it was widely taught in schools until recently, and remains today as folklore of evolution. Recapitulation theory aided the illusion of phylogeny, and gave the impression that evolutionists possessed a structured scientific explanation of embryology. For these reasons, evolutionists were reluctant to overthrow it.

Recapitulation theory was eventually overthrown in 1977 by the punctuationists. It conflicted with their new de-emphasis of identifiable phylogeny, so they wasted no time disposing of it. The punctuationists then correctly re-emphasized von Baer's laws as our most general observations of embryology. They tried to use von Baer's laws as evidence for evolution, even though they had no coherent explanation of these.

Von Baer's laws are an outcome of the biotic message:

- Von Baer's laws indicate that life forms tend to begin near a common point and diverge outward, each on its own unique path, like the diverging spokes of a wheel. This pattern unifies life, showing that life could not be from multiple sources. Moreover, the similar, *yet separate* developmental pathways are awkward for evolution to explain.

- Von Baer's laws indicate that life forms tend to develop in a sequence from generalized to specialized. Organisms look similar for as long as reasonably possible before they develop their unique specializations. This sequence is ideal for visibly displaying the unity of life. Moreover, this sequence is difficult for evolution to explain, and is the fundamental reason why evolutionists continue to emphasize notions of terminal addition and recapitulation.

Embryological similarities unify nature in a *visible* way that biochemical universals cannot, and in a *widespread* way that adult forms cannot. They are an obvious attempt at convincing the observer that life, in all its diversity, is the intentional product of a single designer. Because of this even low-tech observers like the ancient Greeks were aware of life's underlying unity.

Embryology was also designed with odd unifying features, showing that life was not created by an ordinary designer. Life was created by a designer with unusual intentions, as a biotic message.

Embryology was also designed to resist simple naturalistic explanations, such as transposition and early ontogenetic conservation. The subtle details of embryology are the undoing of these two evolutionary mechanisms.

Embryology also thwarts the construction of phylogenies. Embryonic "convergences" serve to defeat the observer's efforts to identify phylogeny.

The metamorphosis of the butterfly is spectacular ontogeny. This peculiar developmental pathway could hardly be more difficult for evolutionists to explain. Even a casual observer cannot avoid the impression it was intentionally designed with this goal in mind.

Embryology is solid evidence for message theory. Embryology shows the straightforward extension of the biotic message into the theater of development.

18

Vestigial Organs

Vestigial organs are biological structures that have no function.[1] They are sometimes called rudimentary, degenerate, or atrophied organs. Darwin argued that vestigial organs are the useless remnants of organs that previously had a function, thereby indicating an ancestral history. Darwin further argued that a competent designer would not have used such useless designs.

The argument from vestigial organs was carried to its height by the eighteenth century German anatomist, Wiedersheim, who listed eighty-six vestigial organs in humans, plus many more he considered retrogressive. Wiedersheim's extensive list has not withstood scientific research. A modern evolutionist, Scadding, divides Wiedersheim's list into four categories that offer little, if any, support for evolution.

- Organs clearly incorrectly identified as 'useless,' and which in fact have very important functions. (e.g., the pineal gland, pituitary body, lachrymal glands)

- Structures of limited or minor function. (e.g., phalanges of the 3rd, 4th, and 5th toes; wisdom teeth; certain valves of the veins; the area scroti)

- Structures that only function during the embryonic period. (e.g., the notochord, and parts of the embryonic circulation system such as the posterior cardinal veins and ducts of Curvier)

- Organs which are remnants of the reproductive structures of the opposite sex. (e.g., nipples and Mullerian ducts in men; and the Wolffian duct in women) These structures are due to the fact that the human fetus begins its development in a sexually neutral condition with structures characteristic of both sexes. These are not evidence of evolution because no one supposes that one mammalian sex evolved from the other. (Scadding, 1981, p 174)

Scadding further refutes the few cases that remain in modern folklore. He concludes that vestigial organs have not provided evidence for evolution.

> As our knowledge has increased the list of vestigial structures has decreased. Wiedersheim could list about one hundred in humans; recent authors usually list four or five. Even the current short list of vestigial structures in humans is questionable. Anatomically, the appendix shows evidence of a lymphoid function since the submucosa is much thickened

---

[1] "Vestigial organs are formerly useful structures now without function. Why do snakes maintain rudimentary and apparently useless leg bones?" (Gould, Luria and Singer, 1981, p 580)

and almost entirely occupied by lymphatic nodules and lymphocytes. There is experimental evidence as well, that the vermiform appendix is a lymphoid organ which acts as a reservoir of antibody producing cells. The coccyx serves as a point of insertion for several muscles and ligaments including the gluteus maximus. The semilunar fold of the eye is simply that portion of the conjunctiva at the medial corner of the eye and as such aids in the cleansing and lubrication of the eye ball. ....

I conclude that 'vestigial organs' provide no special evidence for the theory of evolution. (Scadding, 1981, p 175, 176, my italics)

Loss of Function

An often cited example of vestigial organ is the blindness of animals that live continually in caves. Loftin cites these as "some of the most clear and convincing examples of vestigial organs one can find anywhere."[2]

Blindness was always poor evidence for evolution, since a loss of function is easy to accomplish and offers no support for the overall improvement necessary for amoeba-to-man transformation.

Today, most cave blindness is recognized as a loss due to mutation and inbreeding. In several cases we have experimentally demonstrated that the condition is due to harmful mutations of a few specific genes. Moreover, blind cave animals are typically similar to their non-blind relatives living in the open, and often these two groups can interbreed. Taken altogether, the evidence gives no support for large-scale evolution.

This matter is entirely consistent with the creationist worldview. The modern creationist embraces biological change wholeheartedly, but not recklessly. In the time since life forms were created, real change has occurred. The change has been small compared to the large morphological gaps in life, and most change has been harmful, resulting in reduced or lost function.

Genetic Throwbacks

The sudden re-appearance of an ancestral character is called a throwback, reversion, or atavism. The concept was popular in the early Darwinian era, before we had any understanding of genetics. The idea eventually fell into disfavor, though it has remained part of evolutionary folklore.

Occasionally, some evolutionists still employ it. For example, Laurent wraps it in the modern garb of "suppressor regulatory genes" to explain the origin of eyes in snakes.

---

[2]   Loftin, 1988, p 26. Futuyma (1983, p 207) likewise tries to use the "rudimentary" eyes of blind cave animals as evidence for evolution.

Indeed, complex organs may well reappear sometimes, if their former disappearance resulted from the action of a suppressor regulatory gene(s), that in turn disappears. The catch is that the structure had not really disappeared; it was still there, genetically. .... According to Walls' (1942) theory of the origin of snakes, the eyes have been atrophied in their fossorial ancestors, only to reappear, although somewhat different in the flourishing descendants. Again, the suppression of a suppressor is a likely explanation. (Laurent, 1983, p 75)

This shows once again that evolutionists are willing to use any conceivable mechanism as a facile explanation — even when they cannot experimentally demonstrate it. The next chapter will examine genetic throwbacks in more detail.

*

Despite powerful evidence against genetic throwbacks and a lack of substantial experimental support, evolutionists still occasionally employ them as evidence when it seems convenient. Only now they are changing the name.

Vestigial organs have slowly been refuted by modern science. As scientific research progressed, the argument from vestigial organs slowly degenerated. With time, there were fewer examples, and they carried ever less weight as evidence for evolution. So, a few modern evolutionists have tried to reinvigorate the argument by redefining (and misusing) the term vestigial organ.

For example, Strahler asserts that vestigial organs *do not occur normally* in a given species, but only occur anomalously and rarely.[3] He therefore argues that the appendix and tonsils are not vestigial.

[The appendix and tonsils] are not, however, acceptable under the title of vestigial organ as the evolutionists define the term. One reason is that the appendix and tonsils occur in nearly all human individuals, whereas a true vestigial organ occurs infrequently or rarely. .... because everyone has tonsils, they can scarcely be called vestigial organs. (Strahler, 1987, p 442)

That contradicts what evolutionists had been claiming for a century.[4]

Strahler's explanation of vestigial organs requires an unmasking process, whereby a previously masked genetic character becomes unmasked. Strahler is reviving the concept of genetic throwback under the label "vestigial organ." In effect, Strahler argues that a vestigial organ represents a rare genetic throwback from a distant ancestor — the organ shows up on occasion as a useless aberration.

The classic example of genetic throwback was the human "tail."

---

[3] Strahler, 1987, p 442

[4] Strahler's position is also conveniently in line with growing evidence that the classic human "vestigial" organs — the appendix, tonsils, and pineal gland — all have useful functions.

Humans Do Not Have Tails

On very rare occasions human babies (neonates) are born with a so called "tail," a narrow fibrous filament of skin near the buttocks region. This was the classic example of genetic throwback.

Ernst Haeckel used the human neonate "tail" to support evolution. In 1874 he wrote, "It is the rudiment of an ape tail, the last hereditary relic of a long hairy tail, which has been handed down from our tertiary primate ancestors to the present day."[5] In *The Descent of Man,* Darwin likewise cited cases as evidence for his reconstruction of human ancestry. Many cases of human neonate "tails" were reported between 1850 and 1900, because they seemed to corroborate the then fledgling concept of evolution. Once evolutionary theory became established, the issue was neglected and became part of the evolutionary folklore.[6]

*

The issue of human tails resurfaced in the modern origins debate. In 1982, at the height of furor over the Arkansas creation-science trial, a case occurred in the Boston area. Dr. Ledley looked on the case as evidence for evolution, sensationalizing it in *The New England Journal of Medicine.* The article, "Evolution and the Human Tail: A Case Report," was quoted widely around the country. The article sometimes referred to the malformation by its medical description, caudal appendage.

> There is something seemingly unhuman about the presence on a human infant of a "tail" like the tails found on other primates. ....

> This report describes a case of a child with a well-formed caudal appendage and explores archaic and modern explanations for this malformation. The human tail serves as an example of modern concepts of ontogeny and phylogeny and presents a striking clinical confrontation with the reality of evolution. ....

> [We] are rarely confronted with the relation between human beings and their primitive ancestors on a daily basis. The caudal appendage brings this reality to the fore and makes it tangible and inescapable. (Ledley, 1982, p 1212, 1215)

Despite Ledley's sensationalized account, most of the data necessary to refute him is present in his article. The infant was normal in every respect except for the malformation, which was 5.5 cm long with a diameter of 0.7 cm at its base. It was located 1.5 cm to the right of the end of the backbone. Thus, it was located near but not at the place where a tail would occur. It had no connection with the

---

[5] As cited in Gould, 1982d, p 41

[6] Historically, genetic throwbacks were associated with recapitulation theory, though the connection is a loose one. Recapitulation theory said that early ontogenetic characters tend to be kept and conserved within the genome. Supposedly these can become masked so they are not expressed in the phenotype, and then a genetic throwback occurs when they are unmasked.

backbone, and possessed no bone or cartilage. These findings are contrary to virtually all normally occurring tails.[7] This strongly indicates it was not a tail. Its resemblance to a tail was superficial. The exact cause of this malformation is unknown, but since it has never been reported to recur in families it is unlikely to be genetic in origin.

Ledley's article caused a public clamor. Creationists responded by arguing that the appendage is neither a genetic throwback nor a tail, but merely an abnormality of development. They further argued that evolutionists are arbitrarily selecting this malformation as important. The caudal appendage is only one rare abnormality in a world that provides abundant types. For example, on rare occasions human females are born with breasts in abnormal numbers or locations, such as on the back, under the armpits or in the groin. What do evolutionists make of these? What about the other malformations that are just as mysterious and misunderstood? What about spina bifida, hypodactyly (less than the normal number of digits), heterotopic anus (misplaced anus), chondrodystrophy (dwarfism), or cleft palate to name a few? What about cows born with two heads? Are theorists to give these an evolutionary interpretation also? Evolutionists have never provided a coherent method for discriminating between genetic throwbacks and ordinary abnormalities.

Ledley allotted a special significance to this case[8] as a confrontation with the fact of evolution. He claimed it as "testimony to the preservation of the structural elements necessary for tail formation in the human genome." To all appearances, Ledley was reviving this long overlooked argument to use in the origins debate.[9]

The public interpreted the case as a genetic throwback — one of the classic evidences for evolution. So Gould clarified:

> This impression is quite wrong, for a simple reason: *all normal human embryos have tails.* They appear early in the embryology of all mammals. (Gould, 1982d, p 41)

Gould said the case is not an example of genetic throwback, because *all* human embryos have tails — it is not a throwback if it *always* occurs. The human "embryonic tail" (as opposed to the human "neonate tail") may contain up to

---

[7] Ledley acknowledges "It is possible that this structure is merely a dermal appendage coincidentally located in the caudal region. This possibility cannot be excluded." (Ledley, 1982, p 1213)

[8] Ledley drew detailed comparisons between the baby's boneless appendage and the tails of other organisms (such as the boneless tails of a rare breed of mutated laboratory mice). The purpose of that comparison is confusing at best, and it misled many readers into thinking there is a basis for viewing the caudal appendage as a legitimate tail.

[9] Stephen Jay Gould had consulted on Ledley's paper before its publication, so he was besieged with calls from reporters asking for comment. Gould (1982d, p 40) records that "these calls amazed me because the inquirers had so completely magnified and mistaken the interest of this tale." Given the history of this subject and the way it was presented, I fail to see how the public could have interpreted the matter any other way than how they did.

twelve vertebrae at the sixth week but by the eighth week these begin to fuse, forming the coccyx at the end of the spine. However, the tip of the embryonic tail contains no vertebrae, and Gould correctly suggests that the boneless caudal appendage on newborns may merely be the *abnormal preservation* of this tip. He says, "Tails of human neonates are probably rare retentions of the normal embryonic structure."[10]

Thus, the caudal appendage is a simple malformation of normal development, not a genetic throwback. Despite the sensationalism, Ledley's case has no legitimate impact on the origins debate.

Gould points out that during development *all* human embryos have an embryonic tail. First, we must clarify that term. The embryonic structure is not a tail. It is nothing more than the tip of the spinal column. The spinal column develops early and becomes a conspicuous part of the embryo. It protrudes substantially, and then fuses together as the growth of the remaining embryo catches up. The so called human "embryonic tail" is never a tail, just as human "gill-slits" are never gills or slits.

As Gould later argued, the real focus of the matter is that normal development (including the formation of the vertebrate backbone and embryonic tail) reflects von Baer's laws of embryology. Human ontogeny supports von Baer's laws, and Gould mistakenly believes that von Baer's laws support evolution.

Once the confusing labels and misleading arguments are cleared away, the entire issue of human tails disappears. The issue boils down to von Baer's laws, and these are evidence for message theory, not evolution.

Odd and Curious Designs

The argument from vestigial organs has devolved into a relic of its former self. All that remains is the argument from imperfection. Life has odd and curious designs, and evolutionists argue that a capable designer would not use such designs.

Yet odd and curious designs are predicted by message theory.

The "vestigial hind legs" of snakes (such as pythons) and the "hips" of some whales are the classic examples. These structures are not legs or hips as you would commonly interpret those words. Rather, they are much simpler structures resembling legs or hips mostly in their location. These structures are believed to perform useful functions for snakes and whales by supporting internal organs and providing attachment points for muscles. Yet they are odd and curious nonetheless. These designs show that life is the work of one unordinary designer, a designer who is intentionally signaling that fact.

Moreover, these odd and curious designs resist the transposition explanation. Thus, in every respect they comply with the goals of the biotic message.

---

[10] Gould, 1982d, p 41

Summary

Modern science has refuted the evolutionary argument from vestigial organs.

- Most classic cases of vestigial organs have a legitimate function that was previously unrecognized. These cases are not evidence against creation or for evolution.[11]

- Some vestigial organs once had a function, but lost it through mutation and inbreeding. Blindness in cave animals is a classic example. While these may be evidence for biological change: (1) they are not evidence for biological improvement; (2) they are not evidence for large-scale amoeba-to-man transformation; (3) such cases are fully compatible with creation theories.

- Some so called vestigial organs are remnants of the reproductive structures of the opposite sex. These are not evidence for evolution because it would indicate, for example, that one mammalian sex evolved from the other, which is clearly untrue.

- Some so called vestigial organs have a function, but are *odd* designs nonetheless. Message theory predicts that they should exist.

The progressive failure of the argument from vestigial organs led some evolutionists to redefine it in terms of genetic throwbacks. Evolutionists never had a coherent method for distinguishing genetic throwbacks from ordinary malformations of development. So evolutionists selected as "throwbacks" those malformations that happened to look ancestral. The human baby with a so called "tail" is the classic example. Some evolutionists still try to use it as evidence for evolution:

- The human born with a "tail" is a rare but ordinary malformation, not an inscrutable genetic throwback to a time 25 million years ago when our supposed ancestors had tails.

- The so called tail on the human *embryo* is not a tail. It is nothing more than rapid growth of the embryonic spinal column.

- The entire affair about the human tail boils down to one thing: *human embryology follows von Baer's laws.* Von Baer's laws are evidence for message theory, not evolution.

The argument from vestigial organs, in all its forms, offers no coherent evidence for large-scale evolution.

---

[11] Numerous vestigial organs are refuted in the book by creationists Bergman and Howe called, *"Vestigial Organs" Are Fully Functional,* Creation Research Society Books, Terre Haute, Indiana

19

Molecular Evolution

Molecular evolution is biological evolution as it occurs at the level of genes and molecules. Our first view of molecular evolution came in a crude way through the study of serology, the branch of science dealing with serum, especially specific immune or lytic serums.

Serology provided evolutionary evidence that was once quite popular. Immunological cross-reactions were measured between the serums of various organisms. This pairwise measurement determined the similarity of the serums, and was believed to indicate the closeness of evolutionary ancestry.[1] The typical examples featured the blood serums of horses, pigs, chickens, apes and humans. The serums of humans were most similar to apes; less similar to horses and pigs; and still less similar to chickens. These molecular phenograms from serology were displayed as compelling evidence of common descent.

With the advance of science, the serological approach has been called into doubt.

> There has been a time, more than half a century ago, when somebody hoped that serological reactivity would be a sort of philosophers' stone of evolutionary systematics. .... Unfortunately, the molecular bases of serology were scarcely understood at that time, the technique was rather approximate and data processing very arbitrary. The results were, therefore, hardly justified by the actual experimental evidence. (Cristofolini, 1980, p 270)

> In the reconstruction of evolutionary history the usefulness of data derived from immunological cross-reactions involving proteins is generally viewed as depending on a correlation between such data and amino acid sequence difference. The available evidence suggests that this correlation is at best very approximate. (Friday, 1980, p 289, my italics)

---

[1] This pairwise measurement of overall similarity is the key part of the systematic method known as phenetics. Thus, the classical evolutionary evidence from serology was merely the phenetic method applied to serums. No ancestors were identified.

Like so many other things, serology works when it works, and doesn't work when it doesn't. Serological reactions correlate with other features often enough so that they must be taken seriously by taxonomists, but they so often fail to correlate that they can never be taken as definitive. They provide a partially independent check on taxonomic systems that have been developed on morphological bases. If the serological data fit, fine; if not, one should take notice and see if there is cause to reconsider. (Cronquist, 1980, p 17-18)

During the late 1960s and early 1970s there was a wide-spread assumption that taxonomic data from chemical analyses of plants and animals would suggest classifications similar to those based on anatomical and morphological data. .... Confidence in [this hypothesis] is now waning. (Harris and Bisby, 1980, p 305-306)

Serology does not offer the clear support for evolution that theorists had once claimed. This went largely unnoticed because serology was overshadowed by a new technique, called electrophoresis, that more accurately measured the overall similarity of proteins. Soon, there were also techniques for directly sequencing proteins and genetic material. These modern techniques can now determine the precise sequences of amino acids and nucleic acids.

With these developments there was a rush to the new pastures of data, to harvest it as evidence for evolution. The serology data receded into the background and was never clarified for the public. It just hung around as folklore of evolution.

Molecular Sequences and Phylogeny

Modern techniques brought a wealth of information at the molecular level, and evolutionists immediately tried to use this information to identify phylogeny. After the initial enthusiasm abated, they saw that the new molecular data failed to clarify phylogeny.

> The possibility of identifying variation in gene products by such techniques as electrophoresis seemed at one time a logical and easy solution to taxonomic problems. This has not proved so: ... (Berry, 1980, p 147)

> The glib phrases of those who sought a 'natural' phylogenetic classification through genic evolution have been found wanting; enzyme variation is a useful — possibly a necessary — tool in the systematist's kit, but it is not the answer to all his difficulties. .... it can be seen that no amount of data about protein and enzyme variation is going to solve taxonomic problems at a stroke, and that protagonists of phylogenesis as the El Dorado of systematists have had their bluff called. (Berry, 1980, p 148)

> Despite the active compilation of biochemical information in the last 20 years, small molecule chemical characters have only really ever been evaluated in a vague manner, typical of narrative evolutionary biology. (Humphries and Richardson, 1980, p 354)

> I think that we would agree that reliable phylogenies cannot yet be deduced from this sort of data, partly because of the shortcomings of the data itself and partly because of the unacceptable assumptions which are involved in the data handling.[2] (Joysey, 1980, p 424)

The theorists' attempts to construct phylogeny were frustrated by convergence — this time at the molecular level.

> [T]he pervasive parallelism which confounds our efforts to produce a natural system of classification of angiosperms extends to chemical as well as morphological characters. (Cronquist, 1980, p 5)

> [P]arallel evolution is rampant at both the morphological and the chemical level (Joysey, 1980, p 420)

> Most morphological characters are so riddled with convergences, polyphyly, and mosaic evolution that they are very vulnerable as raw material for numerical analysis. Convergence and polyphyly occurs also in the evolution of macromolecules, and presumably in that of DNA ... (Mayr, 1982, p 245)

> Initial results obtained by using amino acid sequences of vertebrate cytochrome c led to an outline of the phylogeny of the vertebrates which was similar to that derived from fossil evidence. This very encouraging start

---

[2] Joysey was summing up the papers delivered at a chemosystematics symposium.

was soon to change to a less satisfactory one as the results from other pro-teins were assembled. Amino acid sequence data sets of different proteins did not always lend themselves to the same phylogenetic interpretation or agree with the accepted phylogeny obtained mainly from fossil or morpho-logical characters. Whilst it is clear that facets of protein structure should provide excellent taxonomic characters, it now appears that they are subject to the same limitations of interpretation, when used to reconstruct phylo-genetic relationships, as are other characters of present day organisms. The main reason for this in the case of amino acid sequence data sets is that they contain many parallel substitutions ... (Boulter, 1980, p 235-236)

In our opinion cases where there is severe incongruence between chemical and morphological data do exist and such cases do pose both fundamental and practical problems for taxonomists. (Harris and Bisby, 1980, p 308)

Incongruence between data sets has been established in some taxa and has introduced a major problem in the seemingly simple taxonomic task of using chemical data in the recognition and delimitation of taxa. (Harris and Bisby, 1980, p 325)

*

Although the molecular data resisted attempts to identify phylogeny, evolu-tionists began to display the data in special diagrams known as phenograms and cladograms. These diagrams have a tree-like structure, which evolutionists com-monly (and mistakenly) call phylogenies. This created the widespread illusion that phylogeny had been revealed by the molecular data.

Ironically, these diagrams are not evidence for evolution. Instead, they are key evidence against transposition.

- The cladograms of life show that life has a strong nested pattern. Subsets are nested within subsets, where each subset has biological characters unique to itself.

- The phenograms of life show that life forms are not arbitrarily designed, but have a peculiar pattern known as theme and variation. Moreover, the phenograms of different biomolecules tend to corroborate each other.

- The cladograms and phenograms of life tend to coincide. If organisms are close together on cladograms, then they tend to be close together on phenograms.

These highly peculiar patterns would be obliterated if DNA were transposed across the system of life. The molecular phenograms and cladograms convincingly show that transposition is a negligible evolutionary mechanism at the molecular level, particularly in multicellular organisms.

Evolutionists and DNA Transposition

Evolutionists contradict each other concerning evolution at the molecular level. For example, John A. Moore is pleased by the molecular evidence.

> The field of molecular evolution is now in a period of validation. Its discoveries are in accord with what previous methods have established as the major concepts of evolutionary biology — *we would be in serious trouble if that had not been the case.* (Moore, 1984, p 519, my italics)

Moore's statement is from a lengthy article directed against the creationists. In his article, he wants to show that the molecular data meets the predictions of evolution. To do that he (apparently unknowingly) overlooks the possibility of transposition and predicts a nested pattern; he therefore feels comforted by the data (since it generally lacks transposition); and he argues that this situation is evidence for evolution. Moore mistakenly assures us that evolution would be in "serious trouble" if this had not been the case.

Yet at the same anti-creation meeting[3] Moore was contradicted by Levin (apparently unknowingly by either of them).

> I personally would not be at all surprised, if the results of DNA sequence studies provide evidence for a *significant role* of infectious inheritance [DNA transposition] in evolution and adaptation of *multicelled eukaryotes.* (Levin, 1984, p 462, my italics)

Levin was reviewing recent directions in evolutionary theorizing. He was eager to find evidence of DNA transposition, since it would provide a mechanism for rapid evolution. Levin is willing to allow a significant role to transposition if only the data would substantiate it.

This is another example of how theorists draw from the evolutionary smorgasbord what they wish to meet their immediate ends. Moore and Levin had different objectives and this resulted in their contradicting each other about the fundamental expectations of molecular evolution.

*

Evolutionists are not committed to common descent, they are committed to naturalism and 'Natural' selection. The absences of gradual intergradations and phylogeny have always been a mortifying embarrassment. Evolutionists would drop common descent in an instant, but the data allows no better naturalistic alternative.

There is nothing evolutionists would more like to see right now than a widespread pattern of transposition at the molecular level. They would immediately grab hold of it and weave a scenario in a moment. "DNA transposition," they

---

[3] The proceedings of the symposia were reprinted under the title, "Science as a way of knowing — Evolutionary Biology." originally published in *American Zoologist* (1984, Vol. 24, No. 2).

would say, "has obscured any semblance of phylogeny." "DNA transposition," they would argue, "has produced the large morphological gaps in the record of life."

Evolutionists would not hesitate to endorse DNA transposition as a major mechanism of evolution. The idea had been supported by some theorists in the 1970s under the name "lateral gene transfer," but they soon dwindled and only a few proponents remain. By 1989 Micheal Syvanen was the remaining leading proponent of this view. He argues that lateral transfer may be a major evolutionary mechanism in multicellular organisms (called higher eukaryotes), though he cautions that the idea is presently "unorthodox," "very speculative,"[4] and "most strange."[5] A major impetus for his view is the large fossil gaps and the lack of clear lineage, particularly the prevalence of parallelism and convergence.

> The cross-species gene transfer model could help explain many observations which have puzzled evolutionists, such as rapid bursts in evolution and the widespread occurrence of parallelism in the fossil record. (Syvanen, 1985, p 333)

In his earlier papers, Syvanen speculated a greater emphasis on the lateral transfer of whole genes. Yet by 1987 he notes, "only a few cases of whole genes being transferred across animal species barriers have been reported."[6] He now believes that transfer of parts of genes may be more important — perhaps tens of nucleotides rather than entire genes.[7] In this way, his idea has already been seriously constrained by the data.[8]

Evolutionists have fully demonstrated that they would endorse DNA transposition, if only the data would support it. This shows, again, that evolutionary theory never predicted a nested pattern. The absence of transposition — all the way down to molecular phenograms and cladograms — is potent evidence against evolution and for the biotic message.

---

[4]   Syvanen, 1986, p 63

[5]   Syvanen, 1987, p 21

[6]   Syvanen, 1987, p 16

[7]   Syvanen, 1987, p 16-17

[8]   Syvanen's conjecture is opposed by most specialists in the field. For example, Walter Fitch is a leading expert at the sequencing and comparison of biomolecules. His work led him to argue that lateral gene transfer is probably not a significant mechanism of evolution in multicellular organisms.

DNA Transposition in Bacteria

Bacteria can sometimes incorporate a portion of foreign DNA and pass it on to the next generation. This DNA transposition can happen in three ways, known as conjugation, transformation, and transduction.

Conjugation is the bacterial equivalent of sex, where bacteria of two different 'sex types' unite and one receives genetic material from the other.

Bacteria can incorporate short pieces of foreign DNA (a few tens of nucleotides), either from the environment directly (transformation), or with the aid of a virus (transduction). Transformation and transduction occur extremely infrequently, but this rarity can be offset somewhat by the enormous population sizes that bacteria can achieve, especially under laboratory conditions.

By those three methods bacteria can acquire DNA that alters their survival. This can sometimes improve bacterial survival in novel environments containing heavy metals, radioactivity, acids, salts, extreme heat or cold. These seemingly dramatic results occur by affecting relatively minor cellular properties. For example, DNA transposition can result in reduced permeability of the cell wall to certain substances, sometimes providing an increased resistance to antibiotics.

Message theory claims that life meets two goals. (1) Life was reasonably designed for survival. (2) Life was designed as a biotic message. The designer had to balance between these two goals, and for single-celled life the balance is altered slightly.

First, single-celled organisms are the earth's go-anywhere ecological clean-up crews. They recycle waste, prepare environments for higher life forms, and serve as the bottom of the food chain. To do their task they must survive in many novel environments. DNA transposition allows them to acquire (or re-acquire) an ability to survive in various environments. In this way, it helps meet the first goal of message theory.

Second, single-celled organisms inherently lack a detailed fossil record, and therefore their lack of a fossil phylogeny cannot be seen. Because of this an observer will likely assume that the missing fossil data contains a phylogeny for microorganisms, since the fossil data is too sparse to refute that assumption. Therefore, the presence of some DNA transposition in microorganisms does no further harm to the biotic message.

Although DNA transposition is significant in bacteria, it is not all-powerful. It has not allowed bacteria to arbitrarily swap major innovations such as the use of chlorophyll or flagella. The major features of microorganisms fall into well-defined groups that seem to have a nested pattern like the rest of life.

Thus, DNA transposition in bacteria does not adversely affect the biotic message, and it helps these essential organisms survive in novel environments.

The Molecular Clock Hypothesis

The molecular clock hypothesis was proposed in the mid 1970s. The hypothesis suggested that amino acids are substituted into proteins at a nearly constant rate *per year*. Supposedly, this regularity could be used to infer the date of branching between two evolutionary lineages, based on the degree of difference of their molecules. At the time, the preliminary data on proteins seemed to support the idea. Proponents of the idea, particularly Sarich and Wilson, claimed it as evidence for evolution and used it in debates against creationists.

Nonetheless, the hypothesis subtly conflicted with the theories of molecular evolution. Evolutionary genetics and the theory of neutral evolution both indicated that substitution rates depend on generation length, and should not be constant per year.[9] The clock hypothesis claimed that substitution rates are independent of generation times and are constant per year. This theoretical discrepancy was never satisfactorily solved.

The proponents of the clock hypothesis were willing to overlook the theoretical and experimental difficulties merely because they perceived a pattern in nature that they felt supported evolution. As always, evolutionists used the perceived pattern itself as the only evidence for an evolutionary mechanism, in this case a clock mechanism.

Their perception was undone by a clearer view of the data. As the molecular data came into view, the clock hypothesis slowly unraveled. There are considerable discrepancies between dates of branching points calculated by the molecular clock and those calculated from the fossil record.[10] Moreover, according to evolutionists, the rate of substitution is different for different proteins and is often not even constant for the same protein over time. Comprehensive studies by evolutionists now show that the molecular clock is nonexistent.

> Considering the strong demands usually applied in experimental biology, it is hard to understand why the [molecular clock] concept survived such a long period at all. It can neither be used as a tool for dating phylogenetic splits nor as reliable supportive evidence for any particular phylogenetic hypothesis. .... A reliable molecular clock with respect to protein sequences seems not to exist. .... It is concluded that the protein molecular clock hypothesis should be rejected. (Scherer, 1990, p 102-103)

---

[9] According to evolutionary genetics and the theory of neutral evolution, organisms with shorter generation times achieve faster substitution rates. Nonetheless, neutralists desperately tried to alter their theory to fit the molecular clock hypothesis.

[10] Mayr, 1982, p 577

The Unmasking Process

The essential underlying process behind genetic throwbacks, reversions, and atavisms is an unmasking process. The process would provide a simple, powerful mechanism of evolution. In theory it would operate as follows. A genetic trait could become masked, (or it could be copied first and then masked). Large libraries of such traits might exist within the organism in a masked condition inherited from generation to generation. Then they could become unmasked, either alone or in various combinations. The reappearance of those traits into a distant descendant (perhaps a modified descendant or one living under new environmental conditions) might look like the sudden, abrupt appearance of a *new* biological design.

In theory the unmasking process could accomplish results that look like transposition. The unmasking of the same genetic material into two different descendant lineages could look as though genetic material had been transported directly between separate lineages.

The unmasking process is even simpler than transposition because no genetic material is ever transported outside the direct line of inheritance. It is completely compatible with the theories of common descent and descent with modification.

The unmasking process is a potent explanation of fast, abrupt evolution. It is so simple it might have been suggested by anyone. It doesn't require any detailed knowledge of genetics. It easily could have been proposed by early Darwinians. It would have added a powerful new class of scenarios to evolutionary theory.

Yet virtually no textbooks or leading evolutionists have ever endorsed it as a significant mechanism of evolution.[11] Why? Simply because the pattern of life doesn't look like it.

Once again the pattern of life seems designed to resist evolutionary explanation. Pick any major biological design — the spinal column, the tetrapod limb, the feather, the whale's body plan, or the tortoise shell for example — and it is so different in character from any previous designs that an unmasking process is little help in explaining it.

If only the molecular data would cooperate, evolutionists would immediately grab hold of it and invent a scenario. "The masking and unmasking of genetic libraries," they would say, "has obscured phylogeny and abruptly produced the large morphological gaps in the record of life." The punctuationists especially would latch onto an unmasking process as their long sought mechanism of macromutation. They would effortlessly add it to their theory. They would say, "An unmasking process occurs abruptly and in a random direction from a parent species, and this is why phylogeny is not visible." If only the data would cooperate, evolutionists would easily explain away the absences of phylogeny and gradual intergradation.

---

[11] For example, Stephen Jay Gould is known for his pluralistic approach of embracing any process that can lend flexibility and expand the explanatory power of evolutionary theory. Yet he nowhere endorses atavism (i.e., an unmasking process) as a mechanism of importance.

Precisely because the unmasking process is so simple, plausible, and powerful, the biomessage sender had to vigorously pursue its undoing. That pursuit continued down to the molecular level.

According to evolutionists, the phenogram of a trait (such as hemoglobin) displays the evolutionary 'distance' between modern organisms and their common ancestors. Each trait has a phenogram, and the various phenograms all display a smooth, consistent pattern that evolutionists claim as evidence for evolution. We now turn that notion on its head.

Phenograms demonstrate that an unmasking process has not had a significant effect in evolution. The argument is especially forceful at the molecular level. For example, imagine that a hemoglobin gene from an ancient organism was unmasked into a modern organism. The modern organism would have ancient hemoglobin, and when displayed on a phenogram with other hemoglobin (from modern organisms) it would stick out like a sore thumb.

Molecular phenograms strongly corroborate each other (and the cladograms of life). They form a smooth, regular pattern that would be dramatically disturbed if an unmasking process were operating. The phenograms proudly displayed in evolutionary textbooks are not evidence for evolution. They are key evidence against one of evolution's simplest and most powerful mechanisms, an unmasking process. Because that situation is predicted, they are evidence for message theory.

Combined Processes

A strict unmasking process would transpose traits through time into a distant descendant, whereas a strict transposition process would transpose traits into other lineages that exist only at the same time. The combination of the two processes could, in theory, transpose traits between any two organisms. The smooth correspondence between life's many molecular phenograms and cladograms demonstrates that such processes have not operated.

Contrary to evolutionists, the molecular evidence is a major setback to evolution. It displays the balanced design predicted by message theory. Take hemoglobin for example. The similarity of life's hemoglobin molecules testifies that they must have come from a common source (i.e., a common designer). If they had all been identical, however, they would have been trivially easy for evolutionists to rationalize.

On the other hand, what if there were no similarities between the molecules of life? What if life forms all used completely different genes and proteins? What if there where no molecular pattern at all? Evolutionists would have said it was the result of a riot of processes operating at the molecular level. They would take it as evidence for a rowdy mix of transposition, unmasking, distant hybridization, mutation, loss, and replacement. Then they would use that to explain away the absences of gradual intergradation and phylogeny.

To defeat evolutionary interpretations the biomessage sender had to construct a special, distinct, molecular pattern. The pattern of distances[12] (as displayed in phenograms) and the pattern of nested distribution (as displayed in cladograms) refute evolution's simplest and most powerful mechanisms. That pattern — repeated throughout the biomolecular world — makes a compelling case. The pattern of life, visible at the macroscopic level and reinforced at the molecular level, allows the absences of gradual intergradation and phylogeny to take on real force. This cannot be the result of happenstance. It had to be designed.

Summary

Molecular data has been systematically compiled for several decades, resulting in the molecular phenograms and cladograms that everywhere adorn evolutionary textbooks. These diagrams are commonly mislabeled as "phylogenies." In reality they are detailed evidence against two plausible, simple, powerful evolutionary mechanisms: DNA transposition and unmasking processes. Evolutionists have shown their willingness to endorse these processes. The major thing stopping them is that the phenograms and cladograms compellingly argue against it.

The molecular pattern is not evidence for evolution because evolution does not predict it. It is predicted by message theory because it is compelling evidence against key evolutionary mechanisms. The molecular data (whether from serology, proteins, RNA, or DNA) follows message theory precisely.

---

[12] In addition, biomolecules span considerable phenetic 'distances' that are awkward for evolutionary geneticists to explain with current models of the evolutionary process. For details see the chapters on Haldane's Dilemma and the Neutral Theory of Evolution.

20

Illusions of Fossil Sequence

The sequence of fossils up through the earth's crust is traditionally offered as a major evidence for evolution. The sequence is real, but the evidence for evolution is an illusion. The illusion is created when evolutionary literature depicts fossil progressions as though they are lineages. The public is often left unaware that these portrayals are not real lineages. David Raup acknowledges that even well-trained scientists have been misled.

> A large number of well-trained scientists outside of evolutionary biology and paleontology have unfortunately gotten the idea that the fossil record is far more Darwinian than it is. This probably comes from the oversimplification inevitable in secondary sources: low-level textbooks, semipopular articles, and so on. Also, there is probably some wishful thinking involved. *In the years after Darwin, his advocates hoped to find predictable progressions. In general, these have not been found — yet the optimism has died hard, and some pure fantasy has crept into textbooks.* (Raup, 1981, p 289, my italics)

Fossils are frequently displayed as a lineage, even though they are not chronologically successive in time.

> Non-paleontologist readers ... should be aware of several common occurrences within the professional paleontologic literature which could conceivably be confusing. .... for instructional purposes, *some authors illustrate a series of fossils which show a progression in morphology, but which are not chronologically successive. These therefore are not evolutionary sequences, even though they resemble such.* (Cuffey, 1984, p 264, my italics)

On the other hand, *selected* chronologically successive fossils are often displayed as a lineage, even though they are quite doubtful as ancestor-descendant relationships.

> [M]any "trends" singled out by evolutionary biologists are ex post facto renderings of phylogenetic history: biologists may simply pick out species at different points in geological time that seem to fit on some line of directional modification through time. Many trends, in other words, may exist more in the minds of the analysts than in phylogenetic history. This is particularly so in situations, especially common prior to about 1970, in which analysis of the phylogenetic relationships among species was incompletely or poorly done. (Eldredge, 1989, p 134)

Illusion is also created with misleading claims about the fossil sequence.

> Never has a single fossil been found out of stratigraphic sequence (Schafersman, 1983, p 223)

The public is left with the clear impression that no fossils are out-of sequence.

Yet how would you know if a fossil is out-of-sequence? It surprises people that an out-of-sequence fossil would be quite difficult to authenticate. This is because evolutionary theory is insulated from the fossil sequence by potent devices for explaining away out-of-sequence fossils. This chapter examines those devices.

Radiometric Dating

In practice, radiometric dating offers little help in determining an out-of-sequence fossil, because fossils primarily occur in sedimentary rocks that typically cannot be dated by radiometric techniques.

> [Radiometric dating] is ruled out for most sedimentary rocks, ... because their component minerals either are not radioactive or are present as old particles washed into a depositional basin that is much younger than they. (Stanley, 1981, p 81)

Also, radiometric dating has problems resolving the details of fossil sequence.

> The use of radioactive isotopes in geologic dating has many problems. The methods are inexact and contain many sources of error. .... a series of dates run on a single rock may produce quite different results ... (Raup, 1983, p 155)

Because of these difficulties, radiometric dating is rarely used to date fossils, a point emphasized by geologist Derek Ager:

> Ever since ... the 19th century, fossils have been and still are the best and most accurate method of dating and correlating the rocks in which they occur. .... As for having all the credit passed to the physicists and the measurement of isotopic decay, the blood boils! Certainly such studies give dates in terms of millions of years, with huge margins of error, but this is an exceedingly crude instrument with which to measure our strata and I can think of no ocassion [*sic*] when it has been put to an immediate practical use. Apart from very 'modern' examples, which are really archaeology, I can think of no cases of radioactive decay being used to date fossils. (Ager, 1983, p 425)

Stratigraphy, Transgression, and Reworking

The relative sequence of two fossils usually cannot be determined by a direct comparison. This is because they rarely exist in a single rock exposure, one above the other. Instead, the fossils we seek to compare are typically in different rock exposures in different parts of the world.

In most cases, fossil sequence is determined by fossil stratigraphy: an indirect line of reasoning that involves the correlation of partial fossil sequences from around the world.[1] Fossil stratigraphy does have problems and limitations.

---

[1] "Nowhere is the entire sequence, from Cambrian to recent, displayed conformably in a single locality. Nevertheless, many regions contain conformable sequences that include up to one-fourth or one-third of the total record." (Stebbins, 1982, p 106)

[T]he bodies of rock representing the time units are not perfectly delimited throughout the world. In Western Maryland, I direct my students' attention to the seemingly plain face of a particular limestone quarry and tell them that somewhere in that rock wall lies the boundary between the Silurian System and the Devonian System. The level of the boundary is estimated from the study of fossils harbored within the limestone, but the Silurian and Devonian are intervals defined across the Atlantic in Britain, where the fossils are not exactly the same. *The truth is that we do not know exactly where to draw a boundary line on our quarry wall in the Appalachians.* (Stanley, 1981, p 81, my italics)

*

The determination of fossil sequence is also difficult due to a phenomenon called transgression. Imagine that a distinctive looking material is being deposited at a shoreline. Imagine that the shoreline is slowly sinking or subsiding over millions of years. As this happens the water slowly advances horizontally over the land. This process, called transgression, has an unusual consequence. Suppose two fossils reside at the same level in the same distinctive rock strata but are separated from each other horizontally by several tens of kilometers. Normally we would assume these fossils are the same age. Yet if transgression is involved, then they could be dramatically different in age, contrary to our intuition. The phenomenon of transgression could distort the relative sequence of fossils.

*

Fossil reworking occurs when fossil material is eroded from its original location and redeposited at a new location. In this way, fossils can come to reside out-of-sequence with their normal occurrence. This phenomenon causes a problem for fossil stratigraphy.

Organisms are seldom fossilized in a pristine, unspoiled condition. They are frequently damaged before, during, or after the fossilization process. Reworked fossils undergo additional destruction due to weathering and transport processes. This additional destruction beyond what is normal is said to be a key indicator that reworking has occurred.

Some fossils (such as pollen) are hard or small, so they are especially resistant to destruction. In such cases the predominant tip off that reworking has occurred is when the fossils themselves are not in the normal sequence.

In a few cases, some particularly resistant structures ... may show little physical evidence of reworking. Intimate knowledge of the normal biostratigraphic successions must then be employed to interpret the anomalous occurrences. (Glenister and Witzke, 1983, p 77,80)

Thus, the argument of fossil reworking can lead, in some cases, to circular reasoning, where reworking is identified by fossils not in their "normal" stratigraphic positions.

411

Overthrusts

An overthrust can take a sheet of rock and slide it hundreds of kilometers on top of another rock layer. (The overthrusted rock is perhaps many hundreds of meters thick and thousands of square kilometers in extent.) Surprisingly, this often leaves the rocks nearly unblemished above and below the contact plane where the layers meet. Often these rocks are not readily distinguished from rocks that had not been dramatically overthrusted.

In some cases of overthrusting, the relocated strata are later smoothly eroded down to a fraction of their original thickness, then further sedimentation continues on top. In this way, entire fossil strata can come to lay smoothly out-of-sequence. In these cases, the predominant tip-off that overthrusting has occurred is when the fossils themselves are not in the normal sequence.

> A bedding thrust may be difficult to identify in the field, but its presence must be inferred when an older group of strata overlies a younger group, as shown by their respective fossil contents. (Strahler, 1987, p 385)

> Not uncommonly, however, demonstrably young rocks are found *beneath* older rocks. .... the geologist feels confident in interpreting a reversed sequence as the result of faulting even when the actual evidence of the fault cannot be found in the particular case. This practice is dangerous, of course. The interpretation of such discordant sequences could be in error, but the geologist is comfortable with the reasoning ... (Raup, 1983, p 160-161)

Overthrusts actually exist, but the physical mechanism and geological circumstances behind them are enigmas of active interest to creationists and evolutionists.[2] The problem is mechanics. The massive rock layers must be moved horizontally over great distances, but the known pressure and friction between the layers make this motion highly implausible.

> The problem of sufficiently reduced friction between the gliding layer and the base on which it moves remains to be solved. (Strahler, 1987, p 391)

---

[2] Curiously, the 'roots' or sources of the relocated rock strata are "rarely discernible and invite much speculation." (Strahler, 1987, p 389)

Separate Ancestry and Incompleteness

So far, this chapter has identified several devices that evolutionists use to cope with out-of-sequence fossils:

- Perhaps the radiometric dating techniques were misapplied or are substantially in error.

- Perhaps the complicated sciences of fossil stratigraphy and transgression were misapplied.

- Perhaps there was fossil reworking or an overthrust that artificially altered the fossil sequence.

These devices can cause real difficulty for the determination of fossil sequence. Yet they are relatively minor in significance. These devices can be tested (with some difficulty and expense) by studying the local vicinity of a problematic fossil. Since these devices can potentially be refuted, theorists cannot use them so freely to explain away problematic fossils.

Yet the two most powerful devices remain. These two are simple in concept. They are immune to dating techniques of any type. They cannot be tested by studying the vicinity of a problematic fossil. They are general in application and are available under the widest of circumstances. They are also the most difficult to counter-argue. These two devices are the evolutionist's most powerful tools for explaining away out-of-sequence fossils. We study these next.

Suppose you found two fossils in the wrong sequence. The evolutionist can respond in the following way. The two fossils do not have an ancestor-descendant relationship, they have separate ancestry (they are often called sister groups). Therefore, the two organisms may appear in the fossil record in any relative order. Any sequence would then be acceptable to evolutionary theory.

This device is especially powerful because the modern evolutionist does not identify ancestors or lineage. Instead, the modern evolutionist emphasizes a highly branching, bushy pattern of evolution, with sister groups and hypothetical common ancestors. By failing to identify specific ancestors, the evolutionist has a simple device for maximally adapting to the fossil sequence.

Understand the enormous advantage this device gives the evolutionist. To show that fossils are out-of-sequence, you must first identify a clear-cut phylogeny in morphology space. Then you must show that the organisms of the phylogeny appear in the wrong fossil sequence. The enterprise neatly reverses the roles between evolutionist and opponent. The burden falls on the anti-evolutionist to show a clear-cut phylogeny! Since this showing cannot be made, it insulates evolutionary theory against out-of-sequence fossils. It protects the theory in a most disarming way. The evolutionist need only claim that the organisms in question do not have an ancestor-descendant relationship. ... And who could argue with that?

The final device for explaining away out-of-sequence fossils is so simple it seems harmless. That device is the alleged incompleteness of the fossil record. Out-of-sequence fossils can be dismissed with the claim that the fossil record is incomplete and therefore we have not found the earliest occurrences of the truly earlier species. Evolutionists can use this device freely, under the widest possible circumstances.

In summary, evolutionists have an assortment of devices for coping with out-of-sequence fossils. Two of these devices are powerful at insulating evolutionary theory from the fossil sequence:

- Perhaps the fossils in question do not have an ancestor-descendant relationship.

- Perhaps the fossil record is incomplete.

Misuse of Terminology

Evolutionists use terminology to create illusion. They use words that sound like evolution, but defined in peculiar ways that are immune to the fossil sequence. The terms *intermediate* and *transitional form* are examples. According to evolutionists, an intermediate can occur before, during, or after a descendant.

> Creationists cannot understand that intermediates may occupy positions at the ends of branches and can thus be found in strata of the same age, or younger age, than the descendant form. (Strahler, 1987, p 419)

> In a branching hierarchical system an intermediate and one of its descendants can coexist in the same time plane, along with descendants of the common ancestor of both of them. (Strahler, 1987, p 423)[3]

Strahler defines the intermediate so that it may be older, younger, or the same age as the descendant form. This peculiar definition is not how the public interprets the words. Straher's definition conveys the imagery of evolution while being immune to the data.

Another example of this misleading terminology is given by McGowan.

> [*Seymouria*] has long been held as a perfect transitional form between [amphibians and reptiles]. The only problem is, though, that *Seymouria* is Permian in age, whereas the first reptiles appeared in the preceding Carboniferous Period. [This argument] misses the point that *Seymouria* is only one member of a group of amphibians, a group that first appeared in the Carboniferous Period. (McGowan, 1984, p 157-158)

---

[3] As seen in the quotation, Strahler bases his definition of *intermediate* not on lineage, but on nested hierarchy. This reflects the evolutionists' strategic shift in emphasis documented in earlier chapters of this book.

414

McGowan uses the fossil amphibian *Seymouria* as a transitional form, even though he admits it has the wrong fossil sequence. His use of this term is immune to fossil sequence.

To understand fossil sequence, Strahler recommends a change in terminology away from the term "ancestor."

> In a more practical vein it may also help to substitute the words "descendants of a common ancestor" at every point where a creationist uses "ancestor." (Strahler, 1987, p 422)

Strahler has uncovered the evolutionists' strategy. Evolutionists de-emphasize "ancestor" and emphasize the hypothetical "common ancestor." They say every organism is a descendant of something, but they do not identify just who that something was. By avoiding direct discussion of ancestors, evolutionists insulate their theory from difficulty with the data.

The Old Tradition

Classical Darwinians expected to find clear-cut lineage, and paleontologists of that era were eager to provide it. Their efforts were soon frustrated, so they turned to the fossil sequence for help in identifying ancestors. This practice was most prevalent until the 1970s.[4]

The old tradition used a bold approach. Paleontologists used the fossil sequence itself to determine ancestors from descendants. The earliest fossils were defined to be the ancestors.

> One of the factors contributing to the controversy within contemporary paleontology over the identification of transitional forms has been the historical predisposition of paleontologists to lend more weight to the stratigraphic sequences of their fossils than to their comparative systematics. Thus, *some paleontologists have used stratigraphic position as an important criterion for identifying ancestral taxa.* (Cracraft, 1984, p 202, my italics)

> Traditionally, paleontologists, ... have had a conviction that the stratigraphic position of fossil taxa is a primary criterion with which to postulate ancestral-descendant relationships, whereas recent critics of this methodology have stressed the importance of a critical analysis of morphological characteristics (Cracraft, 1983a, p 179)

> [I]t is only the analysis of morphology which can reveal the pattern of evolutionary relatedness among organisms. Nonetheless, ... dating has been regarded as being of the essence. If a form is early in time, the myth runs, it can, if there is nothing really remarkable in its morphology to

---

[4] The use of fossil sequence to identify ancestors was most common until the 1970s. Then it became overshadowed by cladistics and punctuated equilibria, neither of which had any need for identifying ancestors.

415

prevent it, be conveniently plugged into the scheme as an ancestor. If it occurs late, then it qualifies with little more ado to be a descendant. (Eldredge and Tattersall, 1982, p 108)

There are various methods, including a study of the fossil record, by which either one or the other polarity can be made probable, but the fact remains that an unequivocal determination of the ancestral condition is at present often impossible. (Mayr, 1982, p 228-229, my italics)[5]

This practice led to circular reasoning. The fossil sequence was used to identify ancestors—then the perfect corroboration between ancestors and fossil sequence was claimed as evidence of evolution. That was a no-lose proposition. Whatever the fossil sequence was, paleontologists would claim that the fossil record always has the ancestor-descendant sequences predicted by evolutionary theory.

In-Sequence Fossils

Fossils can be in-sequence only if they form a lineage and have the proper chronological succession. Darwinism predicted that fossils should be in-sequence, yet the fossil record shows that virtually no fossils actually are.

[I]t should come as no surprise that it would be extremely difficult to find a specific fossil species that is both intermediate in morphology between two other taxa and is also in the appropriate stratigraphic position. (Cracraft, 1983a, p 180)

Species that were once thought to have turned into others have been found to overlap in time with these alleged descendants. In fact, the fossil record does not convincingly document a single transition from one species to another. (Stanley, 1981, p 95)

Evolutionists claim that no fossils are found out-of-sequence. That claim is misleading in two ways:

- Evolutionists have powerful devices for explaining away out-of-sequence fossils.

- The claim suggests that most fossils are in-sequence, which is gravely untrue.

Thus, the evolutionists' claim creates an illusion that masquerades as scientific evidence for evolution.

*

---

[5] Mayr (1982, p 228) recognizes that determining the polarity of ancestor-descendant relationships is a "formidable difficulty." This would not be the case if phylogeny were clear-cut.

Another classic illusion is when evolutionists claim that evolution predicts that fossil mammals will not be found in Paleozoic rocks. Evolutionists commonly use that argument to show that evolution is scientific.

> Our creationist detractors charge that evolution is an unproved and unprovable bit of secular religion masquerading as science. They claim, above all, that evolution generates no predictions, never exposes itself to test, and therefore stands as dogma rather than disprovable science. This is nonsense. We make and test risky predictions all the time; our success is not dogma, but a highly probable indication that evolution is true. As in any historical science, most predictions are about an unknown past (technically called postdictions in the jargon). For example, *every time I collect fossils in Paleozoic rocks (225 to 550 million years old), I predict that I will not find fossil mammals — for mammals evolved in the subsequent Triassic period* ... If I start finding fossil mammals, particularly late-evolving creatures, such as cows, cats, elephants, and humans, in Paleozoic strata, our evolutionary goose is cooked. (Gould, 1992e, 18, my italics)

First, evolution does not predict mammals *ever*. Most evolutionists (especially Gould) emphasize that evolutionary theory never predicted any particular organisms. Mammals happen to be here, and evolutionists merely accommodate that fact.

Second, evolutionists often use geological age of appearance to identify ancestors from descendants. This remains an important criterion for many groups, including those at issue here, the mammal-like reptiles.[6] The origin of reptiles is obscure,[7] and even Gould acknowledges that no fossil amphibian is clearly ancestral to the fully terrestrial vertebrates (such as reptiles, birds, and mammals).[8] The ancestor of amphibians is just as mysterious, as Wesson notes, "The stages by which a fish gave rise to an amphibian are unknown. .... [A] dozen orders of amphibians suddenly appear in the record, none apparently ancestral to any other."[9]

Quite simply, Gould is using circular reasoning. Mammals are not found earlier than the Triassic, so Gould conveniently claims they will not be found earlier — and he creates the illusion that evolution predicts this. It is merely a claim of evolutionists, not a prediction of evolutionary theory. The only time the theory has anything to say about fossil sequence is when there is a clear-cut phylogeny, then it says the ancestors will appear before the descendants. Since there is no clear-cut phylogeny (as tacitly acknowledged by Gould in his theory of punctuated equilibria), any sequence is acceptable to evolutionary theory.

Third, modern history shows that evolutionary theory is plastic and can accommodate dramatic changes in our knowledge of the fossil sequence. For

---

[6] Kemp, 1982, p 12

[7] Wesson, 1991, p 41

[8] Gould, 1991, p 25

[9] Wesson, 1991, p 50

example, Eldredge (1982, p 65-66) uses *Peripatus,* (a lobe-legged, wormlike creature that lives in rotting logs in the Southern Hemisphere) as an intermediate between two of the major phyla on earth today — the segmented worms and the arthropods. Evolutionists felt it was so clear that they traditionally used it as evidence for evolution. They used it as evidence where they desperately needed it — as an intermediate form between higher levels of the Linnaean hierarchy. Nonetheless, new fossils from the Cambrian era have now forced evolutionists to change their position. Gould (1992c) removes *Peripatus* from its status as an intermediate. He argues that *Peripatus* (and its group, the Onychophora) represents, not an intermediate, but a separate unique group whose closest relatives appeared far earlier, in the Cambrian explosion. Thus evolutionists have dramatically altered their conceptions of ancestry to accommodate new evidence from fossil sequence. This happens often, without anyone even raising an eyebrow. It happens because there is no clear-cut phylogeny, so evolutionary theory can accommodate any new discoveries about fossil sequence.

Fourth, if mammals were found in the Paleozoic, it would hardly be more remarkable than the organisms that are found there now. The Cambrian explosion (at the beginning of the Paleozoic) shows the abrupt appearance of almost all the animal phyla, many of them every bit as complex as mammals. These organisms appear suddenly and abundantly into a fossil record that is nearly empty. The Cambrian explosion already is a huge evolutionary enigma, with or without mammals.

Fifth, contrary to Gould, if mammals were found in Paleozoic strata it would not falsify evolution. It would be astounding … at least for a while. It would make headlines. But it would not refute evolution. Instead, (as the next chapter shows) it would open the door to different (and easier) evolutionary stories. Evolutionists would merely change their story.

The Vector of Progress

There is a popular belief that fossils show a vector of progress, a clear progression from simple to complex. Yet David Raup calls that a "mistaken notion."[10]

> [T]here is no recognizable trend toward increased complexity that is clear enough to use for dating purposes. .... increasing complexity through time is elusive at best. (This is one of the interesting aspects of evolution: the process is not clearly directional.) (Raup, 1983, p 154, my italics)

Newell substantially agrees.

> The old Darwinian view of evolution as a ladder of more and more efficient forms leading up to the present is not borne out by the evidence. .... Most changes are random rather than systematic modifications, until species drop out. There is no sign of directed order here. Trends do occur in many lines, but they are not the rule.[11] (Newell, 1984, p 10)

Gould acknowledges that the absence of a vector of progress is a major dilemma for evolutionists.

> Stepping way back and looking at too broad a scale, one might discern some sort of progress in life's history .... But the pattern dissolves upon close inspection. Most structural complexity entered in a grand burst at the Cambrian explosion, and the history of Phanerozoic life since then has largely been a tale of endless variation upon a set of *Bauplane* [basic body plans]. We may discern a few "vectors" of directional change — thickening and ornamentation of shells ... — but these are scarcely the stuff of progress in its usual sense. (Gould, 1985a, p 3)
>
> I believe that our failure to find any clear vector of fitfully accumulating progress ... represents our greatest dilemma for a study of pattern in life's history. (Gould, 1985a, p 4)

Thus, the fossil sequence provides little evidence of a clear progression from simple to complex.

---

[10] Raup, 1983, p 155

[11] Newell includes an ambiguous remark, "We now know that *some* of the assemblages at successively *higher levels* exhibit changes that are increasingly complex." (Newell, 1984, p 10, my italics) He then refers cryptically to a figure showing the usual vague transitions: invertebrates, fish, amphibians, reptiles, birds, mammals -- All of them diverse, supraspecific or paraphyletic groups. He would have difficulty showing, for example, that the typical mammal is more complex than the typical fish.

Adaptive Radiation

Adaptive radiation is an evolutionary term for the abrupt appearance of diverse fossil organisms that are based on a new common design plan. Evolutionists try to explain adaptive radiation by employing *vacant niches* and *empty ecospaces*.

> Adaptive radiations may occur whenever organisms invade an empty ecospace, either an unoccupied territory, as when a group first reaches an isolated island, or a previously unexploited mode of life, as when insects became the first flying creatures more than 300 million years ago. (Gould, Luria, and Singer, 1981, p 646)

Organisms are said to rapidly evolve into a vacant ecospace, filling it with diversity.

The vacant ecospace scenario fails for numerous cases. The classic examples are whales, porpoises, seals, penguins, and ichthyosaurs. Evolutionists say these are separate radiations from a quadrupedal land-based existence back into an environment already teeming with super-efficient marine life forms. Each of these radiations would have been awkward and directly at odds with the vacant ecospace scenario.

Vacant ecospaces are nebulous, so they can be artificially created and deleted, as needed by evolutionary storytelling. Some evolutionists say the *existence* of a species proves there was an available empty niche. Yet that approach begs the question. The question is not the existence of whales, ichthyosaurs and the rest. The question is their presumed origin, their mad traverse across a convoluted and unpredictable fitness terrain. Evolutionary theory fails to illuminate this matter.

*

An inadaptive valley in the fitness terrain can prevent evolution and cause extinction. Evolutionists do not hesitate to suggest this mechanism, when it suits the needs of an evolutionary scenario. For example, Stebbins feels this mechanism explains why shelled cephalopods went extinct rather than evolve paddles, fins or flippers.

> Once this [jet propulsion] method of locomotion had been the common property of the class for 200 million years, a shift to the paddle-flipper method *would have involved crossing so deep an inadaptive valley that it was essentially impossible, particularly in the face of the immediate challenges posed by animals that had already perfected this method.* Consequently, as selective pressure from competitors increased, all the shelled cephalopods succumbed and became extinct. (Stebbins, 1982, p 257, my italics)

Thus, evolutionists claim: (1) that an inadaptive valley prevented marine cephalopods from evolving, and drove them to extinction; and (2) that the inadaptive valley did not prevent four-legged land creatures from undergoing a complete overhaul for sea-going existence. These scenarios show that evolutionists pretend to possess an insuperable knowledge of the fitness terrain. Moreover, these scenarios contradict each other.

420

*

What causes evolution? Evolutionary scenarios reveal a hodgepodge of conflicting explanations:

- In some cases, competition or predation is said to *hasten* evolution. While in other cases, these *prevent* evolution or cause extinction.

- Vacant ecospaces (with a general *absence* of competition and predation) can be artificially conceived, to explain evolution. While in other cases, an occupied ecospace can be artificially deleted, to explain extinction.

Any case affords a facile answer. Evolutionary theory fails to make clear predictions because it lacks coherent structure.

Summary

The evolutionary evidence from fossil sequence is an illusion.

Illusion is created by the way evolutionary literature depicts fossil progressions. Even well-trained scientists are often unaware that the portrayals could not possibly be real lineages.

- Fossils are portrayed as a lineage, even when they are not chronologically successive.

- Chronologically successive fossils are portrayed as a lineage, even when they are not ancestor-descendant relationships.

Illusion is also created with terminology:

- The words *intermediate* and *transitional form* convey the imagery of evolution, yet they have been redefined in ways that are contrary to public perception. The redefinitions make them immune to fossil sequence.

- The words *common ancestor, descendants of a common ancestor,* and *sister groups* convey the imagery of evolution, while being immune to fossil sequence.

Illusion has been created by circular reasoning. Darwinians have frequently used the fossil sequence to identify ancestors from descendants. Ancestors were identified by the fossil sequence — then the perfect match between ancestors and fossil sequence was claimed as evidence of evolution.

Evolutionists claim that no fossils are found out-of-sequence. That claim creates illusion in two ways:

- Evolutionists have powerful devices for explaining away out-of-sequence fossils.

- The claim suggests that most fossils are in-sequence, which is profoundly untrue. Few fossils are in-sequence with Darwinian expectations.

There are numerous devices for coping with abnormalities of the fossil sequence. Most of these devices merely cause difficulty for the researcher. Yet two of the devices are powerful at insulating evolutionary theory from the fossil sequence:

- Perhaps the fossils do not have an ancestor-descendant relationship.

- Perhaps the fossil record is incomplete.

These two devices are available under the widest circumstances for explaining away out-of-sequence fossils.

Modern evolutionists do not identify lineage. Instead, they emphasize a highly branching, bushy pattern of evolution, with sister groups and hypothetical common ancestors. By failing to identify specific ancestors, evolutionists have a simple device for maximally adapting to the fossil sequence.

Evolutionary theory does not scientifically account for adaptive radiations, such as whales, porpoises, seals, penguins, and ichthyosaurs. Evolutionists allege that these organisms rapidly evolved a sea-going design from land-based ancestors. That would be difficult enough to believe under normal circumstances. Yet the abrupt appearance of these groups occurs *after* the seas held swarms of highly refined predators and competitors. This fact is problematic for evolution.[12]

Finally, the fossil sequence provides little evidence of a clear progression from simple to complex.

Taken altogether, the fossil sequence is not evidence for evolution.

---

[12] These organisms — whales, porpoises, seals, penguins, and ichthyosaurs — are significant. (1) They are dramatic examples of so called "convergence." (2) In each case they fail to provide a clear lineage. (3) Their abrupt appearance into the record (otherwise called "adaptive radiation") occurs *after* the seas contained numerous highly refined predators and competitors. All these facts support message theory.

21

Fossil Sequence and Message Theory

Evolutionary textbooks display orderly fossil progressions, and many creationists therefore tried to explain these. David Raup sees this as ironic, since the classic evolutionary progressions are mistaken. He sees that creationists tried to explain something that is really a textbook myth.

> One of the ironies of the evolution-creation debate is that the creationists have accepted the mistaken notion that the fossil record shows a detailed and orderly progression and they have gone to great lengths to accommodate this 'fact' in their Flood geology. (Raup, 1981, p 289)

The fossil sequence is not the orderly lineages erroneously portrayed in evolutionary textbooks, nor is it haphazard or mixed-up. The fossil sequence has a distinctive structure that is real, not simply a product of evolutionary circular reasoning. That is the pattern that message theory will explain in this chapter.

Sequential Release

Life's designer could influence the fossil sequence in many ways. For the sake of discussion let us assume a simple method: sequential release. Fossil sequence can be influenced by sequentially releasing organisms into the biosphere.[1] As organisms are released, their population size would begin to increase, and they would disperse. Then they would become preserved in the earth. The fossil sequence would then reflect the sequence of release.

Through competition and predation, some life forms would affect organisms released earlier, thereby driving them to extinction. So, sequential release would, in many cases, cause the extinction of organisms from the fossil record.

On the other hand, some newly released organisms might be inhibited by earlier ones. In such cases, the newer organisms would be limited to small populations until the earlier ones go extinct. Global temperature changes, volcanism, and asteroid impacts are some of the processes said to cause such extinctions. When the earlier organisms go extinct, the newer organisms would multiply, disperse, and begin to show up in the fossil record.

The detailed mechanisms of extinction remain speculative, and are not particularly important here. It is enough to note that sequential release would strongly affect the first fossil appearance of organisms, and to some extent their last appearance. With this simple mechanism, life's designer could accomplish several goals predicted by message theory.

---

[1] Message theory requires that the designer somehow influence the fossil sequence, but does not limit how that must be accomplished. There are several ways. For example, life's designer could control: (1) the biological design of organisms (which affects their rate of reproduction and dispersal); (2) the time of release; and (3) the place of release. These factors would then influence the fossil sequence.

System Bootup

Why would a designer intentionally release life forms in a particular time sequence? One answer is system bootup, the process whereby a complex system moves through a sequence of stable stages as it rises up to full function.

The classic example of bootup is a computer system. When a computer is switched on, it does not begin normal operation immediately. Rather, the computer goes through a bootup sequence of distinct stages. Various hardware and software entities are initialized in turn; some self-testing is done; different portions of the operating system are loaded; and finally the computer is ready for its normal functioning.

We can see small-scale cases of bootup in nature. For example, after a forest fire the land does not immediately grow a new forest. Rather, the land goes through a series of ecological stages involving distinctly different sets of plants and animals. Ecologists have studied this bootup process in a variety of situations, including newly formed volcanic islands and the aftermath of eruption at Mount Saint Helen.

The bootup of an entire planetary biosphere would have spectacular problems. Perhaps the designer had to solve these problems by releasing organisms in a particular time sequence. This would provide for a sequence of stable ecological stages, each stage building on previous ones.

For example, higher animals should not be released first. What would they eat? The system would not have been stable, because the food pyramid must be built from the bottom up. In addition, waste and decomposition products must be recycled if the system is to be stable, and this task is accomplished predominantly by single-celled organisms.

Message theory says life was reasonably designed for survival, and sequential release provides for survival by solving the problems of system bootup. Message theory says life was also designed to convey a biotic message. This chapter will show that the fossil sequence itself is essential to the biotic message.

The Simple Space Scenario

Before we approach the problem of fossil sequence, let us warm up by reviewing the origin of life. The origin of life proved difficult to explain naturalistically, so several renowned theorists eventually suggested that it came from Space.

One of these theorists is Francis Crick, a Nobel prize winner and co-discoverer of DNA. He and Leslie Orgel proposed directed panspermia, the idea that simple one-celled organisms were sent here from some civilization in outer space. Crick's book on the subject was widely promoted. Some evolutionists viewed the idea as an ace in the pocket to be used if all other naturalistic explanations failed.

> [I]f there are problems with demonstrating how life on earth could arise by chance within a naturalistic framework (perhaps because our planet is not old enough), the directed panspermia hypothesis offers a possible solution. (Edwords, 1982a, p 42)

Hoyle and Wickramasinghe offered a more extensive version of directed panspermia. In their widely circulated books, they suggested that genes and viruses have been sent to Earth to rain down from the stratosphere and be incorporated into organisms. This, they said, accounted for the presence of life on Earth and the subsequent development of higher life forms.

These theorists are respected members of the scientific community. It makes no difference here whether you agree with their speculations. The point is that "It came from Space" is an indelible part of the evolutionary smorgasbord. Reputable scientists are willing to use it to explain life on Earth.

We are now ready for the problem at hand, the problem of fossil sequence. We ask, What would evolutionists have said if there had been no fossil sequence? No sequence whatever? The fossils just appearing in the record suddenly all together, all at once, with no sequence? How would theorists have explained life? ... They would have said, "It came from Space."

The Simple Space Scenario is easy. For example, an interstellar spacecraft lands on the planet and unloads its cargo of life forms. The space beings might have been conservationists interested in the greening of the universe. Or they might have been conducting ecological research on a planetary scale. Or they might have been cultivating planets, like a farm. Or they might have been starting a space colony. Or perhaps a planetary prison system. It is the theme of a thousand science-fiction plots. It is simple, straightforward, plausible. It would have left no fossil sequence, just a sudden onset of all fossils together.

A major feature of the biotic message is that life lacks ancestors. Yet this would lose all impact without a distinct fossil sequence. The theorists would simply say, "The ancestors were left behind!" Then they would dust off their hands and walk away — "Problem solved!" they would declare over their shoulder. I say they would do it, and they would not flinch once. It is completely consistent with their method of operation.

A designer could create a fossil sequence by releasing organisms into the bio-sphere in a time succession. The resulting record in stone serves a purpose. The biotic message is bonded to the planet, visibly wedded to its rocks. The biotic message must be dealt with as it stands. Life cannot be put out onto another planet, or casually passed off with the claim that It came from Space. Life's pattern (with its lack of ancestors) takes on real force. The designer did not produce the fossil sequence to look like evolution (as accused by the anti-creationists). Rather, the fossil sequence eliminates the trivial explanations.

The Earth-bound Explanations

If life had appeared in the fossil record all at once — with no sequence — then it could have been explained by several fully naturalistic earth-bound explanations.

- Perhaps life evolved on earth but tectonic activity erased the sequence from the fossil record. Continental drift subducts entire plates of surface rocks into the depths of the earth, thus wiping clean the fossil record.

- The older the fossil, the greater the chance it will be destroyed by random processes of heat, pressure, erosion, chemical action, quakes and such. These mechanisms would preferentially destroy the oldest fossils.

- Perhaps the conditions of atmosphere, sedimentation, or chemistry on the ancient earth were not conducive to producing fossils.

These mechanisms are part of the smorgasbord of naturalistic mechanisms. Evolutionists have used these in the past,[2] and still use these today in a limited form. These mechanisms claim that the fossil record is incomplete.

Again, it behooves a biomessage sender to produce a fossil sequence of some type. This is required if the biotic message is to have its full impact. The origin of life, the systematically placed morphological gaps, the lack of phylogeny, and the entire biotic message would all cease to be issues if there had been no fossil sequence.

---

[2] Darwinians have used numerous naturalistic mechanisms to rationalize the absence of fossil lineages. A notable example was the absence of Precambrian fossils. Some Darwinians claimed this was due to a universal metamorphism that had destroyed all Precambrian fossils. Other Darwinians suggested that Precambrian creatures lacked fossilizable hard parts. Darwin had suggested that the vast Precambrian oceans had no source of sediments for fossilization because there were no continents nearby. Walcott suggested the infamous *Lipalian interval*: a world-wide interruption in acces-sible marine sedimentation, just during the critical interval of extensive Precambrian evolution. Walcott felt that the Precambrian fossils might be inaccessible to us, under miles of deep ocean. (For discussion see Gould, 1989, p 273-274)

The Advanced Space Scenario

The Advanced Space Scenario goes like this. Ancient space beings land on the planet and construct all the life forms slowly over time. They create the life forms in a sequence that meets the demands of stable system bootup. In short, they are reasonable designers, doing precisely what reasonable designers would do. They have generous latitude in selecting the sequence of their creations, because they are limited solely by the minimal constraints of system bootup. This results in a fossil sequence.

Suppose you are the ancient astronaut who has just landed on a barren planet. Suppose you are to create all the earthly life forms from scratch. In what sequence would you create them? There are countless sequences you might choose. Perhaps you would take care of system bootup, and then you would straightaway create your favorite animals such as a dog or cat. Perhaps you would then create your favorite bird, followed by your favorite herbivorous dinosaur. Or perhaps you would follow with the more useful work animals such as oxen, horses, llama, or camels. Then your favorite fish. There are countless ways to do it, depending on whim. Whatever sequence you have chosen, keep it in mind through this next discussion.

A biotic message is no ordinary creation, and cannot look like an ordinary design effort. It must be distinctly different if it is to be perceived as a message. This places a special restriction on a biotic message. The sequence of fossils must be unlike any sequence expected from an ordinary designer.

The biomessage sender has met this restriction. The Earth's fossil sequence has an intricate structure, unexpected from an ordinary designer. (For example, compare it with the one you casually thought up.) This pattern eliminates the possibility that it is the haphazard, unintended, or aimless result of ancient space beings. The pattern can only be explained as the result of a unified, purposeful and intentional biomessage sender.

As a result, the Advanced Space Scenario is faulted so badly it does not occupy any turf on our intellectual landscape. There are no scientists who seriously endorse it.

Abrupt Appearance

A slow gradual transition is easy to explain in evolutionary terms. Therefore, the biomessage sender used fully-formed abrupt appearances, since these look like creation while making evolutionary interpretation difficult.

Abrupt appearances are a major feature of the fossil sequence.

> The record certainly did not reveal gradual transformations of structure in the course of time. On the contrary, it showed that species generally remained constant throughout their history and were replaced quite suddenly by significantly different forms. New types or classes seemed to appear fully formed, with no sign of an evolutionary trend by which they could have emerged from an earlier type. (Bowler, 1984, p 187)

427

> [This is] one of the most striking and potentially embarrassing features of the fossil record. The majority of major groups appear suddenly in the rocks, with virtually no evidence of transition from their ancestors. (Futuyma, 1983, p 82)

> [E]nthusiastic palaentologists in several countries have claimed pieces of this missing record, but the claims have all been disputed and in any case do not provide real connections. That brings me to the second most surprising feature of the fossil record. ... the abruptness of some of the major changes in the history of life. (Ager, 1981, p 20)

> [W]e have long known about stasis and abrupt appearance, but have chosen to fob it off upon an imperfect fossil record (Gould, 1985a, p 7)

> [A]ll through the fossil record, groups — both large and small — abruptly appear and disappear. .... The earliest phase of rapid change usually is undiscovered, and must be inferred by comparison with its probable relatives. (Newell, 1984, p 10)

Stephen Gould acknowledges the prevalence of abrupt appearance. Ironically, he brushes up against the biotic message. He unknowingly touches its goal (to frustrate naturalistic interpretations) and its central metaphor (nature as message).

> [W]hen fossils are most common, evolution is most rarely observed. .... Again, we note the paradox: nothing much happens for most of the time when evidence abounds; everything happens in largely unrecorded geological moments. We could attribute this pattern to either a devious or humorous God, out to confuse us or merely to chuckle at our frustration. But I choose to look upon this phenomenon in a positive light, for it is trying to tell us something important. There is a lesson, not merely frustration, in the message that change is concentrated in infrequent bursts and that stability is the usual nature of species and systems at any moment. (Gould, 1988b, p 14)

Before Darwin, creationists saw the abrupt appearances in the fossil record, and correctly viewed it as evidence favorable to creation. Modern creationists aptly called it the abrupt appearance model, but they could not turn it into a testable theory because they were vague about the designer's intentions. Message theory solves this by providing a clear and consistent view. This self-same theory offers a uniform scientific basis for understanding the fossil sequence as well as the biological patterns of life.

Adaptive Radiation

Evolutionists try to link organisms into time-sequential lineages. The bio-message sender thwarted their attempt by introducing a burst of diversity precisely at the place where evolutionists least want it — near the introduction of major new biological designs. The new organisms share a common design plan, yet they appear in a burst of diversity that frustrates attempts at constructing lineages. Near the time where theorists would love to draw a lineage, there is too much diversity to accomplish the task.

A sudden burst of diversity among organisms with a common design plan is what evolutionists call adaptive radiation. Evolutionary theory provides no coherent explanation of this phenomenon. The adaptive radiation of many organisms — such as whales, seals, and ichthyosaurs — is problematic for evolution, since these occur *after* the seas contained many highly efficient predators and competitors.

Creationists sometimes use the term "adaptive radiation" because it is widely embedded in the literature as a description of the data, however, they do not endorse any evolutionary explanation associated with the term.

Adaptive radiation describes a major feature of the fossil sequence that has always been a difficulty for evolution.

> Zoologists divide the animal kingdom into about 25 major phyla. These phyla do not form a ladder of increasing advancement or complexity; rather, their origin is the result of a few successive adaptive radiations. .... the pathways of their divergent radiations probably will never be accurately traced. (Stebbins, 1982, p 265)

Morphological Space-Time

Adaptive radiation is a problem for evolutionists because it calls attention to the lack of lineage. When a burst of diversity occurs near the same time horizon, then the fossil sequence offers little help in constructing lineages. It says emphatically, "If you are going to look for a lineage, then you will have to look right *here!*" It tells you exactly where to look, then it defies you to find the lineage.

Let me illustrate this with an analogy. Newtonian theory viewed space and time as separate entities, and explained kinetic motion in those terms. Einstein took a different view.

Einstein recognized that space and time are not entirely separate, but may be viewed together as a space-time continuum. It was a subtle distinction, but it had powerful implications. In his view, time became the fourth dimension (albeit a special dimension) of kinetic motion. These four dimensions are orthogonal to each other. They are at right angles. (The term *orthogonal* has a clear meaning concerning multi-dimensional spaces.) These four dimensions are independent, yet they have a special relationship to each other. Einstein proposed that objects (in motion or at rest) left unperturbed in a gravitational field follow a straight line trajectory within the space-time continuum.

429

My analogy is a simple one. Lineage takes place in a space-time continuum, except it is morphology space rather than physical space. Morphology space is the multi-dimensional space totally enclosing all characteristics of all organisms. Lineage is a trajectory within this morphological space-time continuum.

Theorists want to find lineage, and they approach this task by either including or excluding time information.

For example, theorists may exclude the time information and try to construct lineages exclusively within morphology space by connecting the dots of morphological data. They try to identify lineages entirely from morphological data alone, irrespective of its occurrence in time. The biomessage sender has frustrated their attempt by using morphological diversity to destroy lineage. Any lineage can be destroyed by diversity at a suitable distance orthogonal to the lineage. This diversity fails to form a clear trajectory through morphology space. The pattern is too nondescript, too bushy to be a lineage.

Alternatively, a theorist may include the time information into attempts at lineage construction. This approach is reasonable because lineage must occur within a morphological space-time continuum, and all real lineages must have a trajectory along the time-dimension.

How may lineage be thwarted in this morphological space-time continuum? The answer is the same as before: by placing a diversity of data points at the proper distance orthogonal to any conjectured lineage.

In the stratagraphic record, time's arrow points vertically. The higher a fossil occurs in the record, the more recent it is. The time dimension is vertical. When a burst of diversity occurs near the same time horizon then it is orthogonal to the time dimension. Since this diversity is orthogonal to the time dimension it is orthogonal to any presumed lineage. This diversity thwarts the attempt to construct lineage.

In short, the abrupt bursts of diversity in time are merely a manifestation of the very same design strategy seen within morphology space. It is the very same design strategy undertaken for the very same objective: diversity thwarts phylogeny. This pattern manifests itself in the fossil record as abrupt bursts of diversity based on a unifying design plan.

The concept of a morphological space-time continuum illustrates this unified pattern. The separate patterns observed within morphology space and fossil sequence are merely different views into the same underlying pattern, the same design strategy.

Evolutionists want to construct lineages. They typically begin their effort by choosing one of the two available methods, and when they run into difficulty they turn to the other for help. When they do, they find little relief because the biotic message is devised to thwart both methods simultaneously. Whichever approach is chosen, lineages may be constructed only by selecting certain data points while arbitrarily ignoring many others. That is precisely how classical evolutionists contrived the illusion of lineage.

The Completeness Problem

We never have all the data. Yet we always try to model the available data as a pattern. The pattern can be an accurate reflection of reality. Or it can be a distorted view, due to the scarcity of data at hand.

Since we never have all the data, how can we know when we have compiled a reasonably complete and reliable model of reality? Curiously enough, we determine this by the pattern itself, based on its ability to be distinctive, consistent, repetitive, ordered, structured and informative.

Suppose you took all the known life forms, shuffled them up like a deck of cards, and dealt them into a virgin biosphere, one at a time over the history of the planet. Every major group of life would be scattered throughout the fossil record. The resulting fossil sequence would be random.

Yet an unacquainted observer would not know it was random. Rather, an observer would reasonably attribute the perceived randomness to a scarcity of data. Spurred by this interpretation, the observer would then collect more fossil samples. Yet the newly revealed data would not resolve the pattern into something recognizable. Again the observer would return for more data, only to find that the pattern still failed to resolve. The new data would reveal new information but it would not make a dent in unraveling a pattern. Eventually a reasonable observer might conclude that the available data is massively incomplete and the observed randomness is merely a garbled view of some unknown pattern. This perception would undermine the biotic message at its very foundations. The observer would be free to interpret the "missing data" and the pattern in any way. If evolutionists were confronted with this pattern, they would claim the missing data contains the phylogeny and gradual intergradations required by their theory.

As another example, suppose you took all the known life forms and shuffled them up like a deck of cards. Except this time you dealt them many at a time into the biosphere, like dealing ten cards at a time from a large deck. Organisms would appear in the record in random unrelated groupings. How would an observer perceive this?

Like a movie, all the sudden appearances of groups would blend into one smooth motion of random appearances. The observer might still interpret this nondescript pattern as the result of incompleteness in the data.

On the other hand, the patterns could be viewed as the result of the Advanced Space Scenario: random groupings of organisms periodically escape (or are released) from the zoos and laboratories of the ancient space beings. An unstructured scenario like this works precisely because the pattern is so unstructured. It is an effortless explanation.

*

Any message sender must try to ensure that the message is perceived as complete and reliable, otherwise the recipient might misread the message or cast it aside as noise. For example, when we write a note on paper, the paper ensures that the message will be perceived complete as one unit.

The biomessage sender cannot put the fossil record on paper to ensure its reception as one complete unit. Some fossils will always remain undiscovered. How can the meaning of the fossil record be made resistant to lost or undiscovered data? This is the completeness problem.

The examples above show that the solution requires a fossil sequence with identifiable structure. A fairly repetitive structure of intricacy and consistency so an observer is prevented from pleading wanton incompleteness in the data. The biomessage sender must induce the observer to buy into the sequence as a real pattern, separate from noise, and sufficiently complete to carry reliable meaning. The pattern must say of itself, "I am a *complete* pattern, not to be substantially altered by the discovery of further data."

This requirement of a pattern to pronounce itself "complete" is a major difficulty. It is a subtle constraint on the biotic message, and the structure of the fossil sequence has been intentionally produced for solving it.

The Completeness Solution

The trends of abrupt appearance and adaptive radiation are important because they are difficult for evolution to explain. Yet they cannot stand alone. They would be invisible and impotent if the fossil record were perceived as seriously incomplete.

Nonetheless, the two trends work together in the designer's solution to the completeness problem. They are part of an overall pattern that validates itself. The pattern says, "I am a complete pattern. You cannot discount me. I must be explained!" Here is how the fossil sequence accomplishes this essential feat.

Suppose an observer sets forth to examine the earth's fossil record for the first time. The observer then finds an abrupt appearance of many life forms — a choreographed appearance of many diverse yet unified forms. This is an improbable concurrence of events, and demands an explanation. A reasonable observer can be forgiven for suspecting that the data is incomplete. The observer may feel the missing lineages are absent due to the serendipitous loss of data at that particular time in fossil history. However, additional examination shows that the same pattern appears over and over throughout the record. Again and again, the observer finds this same highly improbable pattern. Repeatedly, the observer finds the sudden appearance of a burst of diversity among organisms built on a unifying design plan. The observer cannot continue to maintain that the data was accidentally lost precisely at all the critical points. Instead, the incompleteness plea loses its force due to the consistent recurrence of this intricate pattern. The thoughtful observer is compelled to acknowledge a good measure of completeness to the pattern. In short, the observer will never possess all the data, but the pattern is seen as substantially complete nonetheless.

That pattern was able to move even the most committed evolutionists, such as G. G. Simpson.

> [Simpson noted that] gaps between families and taxa of even higher rank could not be so easily explained as the mere artifacts of a poor fossil record. (Eldredge, 1989, p 22)

> To explain discontinuities, Simpson relied, in part, upon the classical argument of an imperfect fossil record, but concluded that *such an outstanding regularity could not be entirely artificial.* (Gould, 1983d, p 81, my italics)

Think about this again. When a burst of diversity taunts you to "Look right *here* for a lineage if you can!" it has simultaneously moved you closer to accepting the completeness of the pattern. This circumstance, repeated many times, makes a convincing case. The fossil record is significantly complete and reliable.

This makes the absences of phylogeny and gradual intergradations embarrassing for evolution. This also puts the *abrupt* into "abrupt appearances." These two trends of the fossil sequence would be nothing without the proper foundation on which to stand.

Evolution is the theory with ten thousand faces, and the biotic message must look unlike all of them. Just as importantly, it must convey to the observer a high level of confidence that the perceived pattern is real, complete, and reliable, not merely a garbled view of one of evolution's many apparitions. This requires a pattern of meticulous care. The fossil sequence embodies this in three ways:

- The fossil sequence shows an improbable concurrence of events — the abrupt appearance of a diversity of life forms based on a new unifying design plan.

- The fossil sequence shows a recurrence of this circumstance many times.

- The fossil sequence shows a reasonable consistency of this circumstance throughout the record.

These three work together. If the pattern fell short on these, then the observer would have the latitude to misperceive it as an indication that the data (and the pattern) are fragmentary.

The fossil sequence admirably serves its objective. It pursues the unrelenting task of convincing the observer that the pattern is complete.

From Darwinism to Punctuationism

Classical Darwinians expected gradual evolution through identifiable lineages, and when the fossil record failed to accommodate, they claimed "Incompleteness!" Evolutionists are now surrendering this claim, with the greatest reluctance.

> We must learn to accept the fossil record at face value and construct our theories around it, not the other way round. Too often we have endeavoured to force it into a particular mould or to ignore awkward facts contained in it. .... We still have a long way to go before we look at the fossil record for what it is and not for what we would like it to be. Historically, from Lyell and Darwin onwards, people have looked at the fossil record with a particular pattern in mind. They have failed to find the pattern they sought and have appealed to the incompleteness of the fossil record to explain away this anomaly. We are still doing this ... (Paul, C.R.C., 1982, p 115-116)

> The fossil record is much less incomplete than is generally accepted. (Paul, C.R.C., 1982, p 75)

Modern evolutionists have been forced to accept the substantial completeness of the fossil record. Led by the punctuationists, they have been forced to read the fossil record literally. Therefore, they had to accept abrupt appearances, stasis, large morphological gaps, and lack of identifiable phylogeny as real.

This is a major requirement (and success) of the biotic message. The fossil sequence plays a crucial role in the biotic message, providing a dimension impossible to achieve by purely biological means. Again there is irony. Life was not constructed to look like evolution, but to denounce it.

The Cambrian Explosion

> The fossil record had caused Darwin more grief than joy. Nothing distressed him more than the Cambrian explosion, the coincident appearance of almost all complex organic designs ... (Gould, 1980, p 238-239)

Nowhere is the fossil sequence more stunning than at the base of the Cambrian strata, where highly complex multicellular organisms appear abruptly and fully formed into a nearly empty fossil record. This is known as the Cambrian explosion. Ernst Mayr notes that since the Cambrian not one new morphological type (or phylum) has appeared.[3]

> Modern multicellular animals make their first uncontested appearance in the fossil record some 570 million years ago — and with a bang, not a

---

[3]   Mayr, 1991, p 160

protracted crescendo. This "Cambrian explosion" marks the advent (at least into direct evidence) of virtually all major groups of modern animals — and all within the minuscule span, geologically speaking, of a few million years. (Gould, 1989, p 23-24)

Trilobites, for example, show up fully formed. They were complex animals, not arguably less complex than lobsters.[4] The trilobite's hard exoskeleton is excellent for leaving fossils. Yet trilobites, like all the life forms of the Cambrian explosion, fail to have a significant prior fossil history, and nothing that would qualify as an ancestral lineage.

*

Classically, Darwinians claimed the Cambrian explosion is not real, but merely an artifact of a poor fossil record. This is called the artifact theory.

Darwinians tried to support the artifact theory with a scenario. Some said the ancestors of the Cambrian fauna were soft-bodied and therefore failed to be preserved in the Precambrian rocks.

This rationalization has been overturned by fossils from the Ediacara[5] (a time barely preceding the Cambrian) and the Burgess shale (a time immediately after the Cambrian explosion). These show that delicate soft-bodied organisms left finely preserved fossils in rocks from that era. So, the absence of ancestors for the Cambrian fauna cannot be blamed simply on poor fossil preservation.[6]

The punctuationists reject the artifact theory and read the fossil record literally. They say the Cambrian explosion is the result of rapid adaptive radiation, which they call the fast-transition theory. Stephen Gould recognizes the peculiarities of fossil sequence as the evidence that destroys the artifact theory.

> If evolution could produce ten new Cambrian phyla [in the Burgess shale] and then wipe them out just as quickly, then what about the surviving Cambrian groups? Why should they have had a long and honorable Precambrian pedigree? Why should they not have originated just before the Cambrian, as the fossil record, read literally, seems to indicate, and as the fast-transition theory proposes? This argument, of course, is a death knell for the artifact theory. (Gould, 1989, p 273)

Since the Cambrian explosion cannot be explained away by the artifact theory, it is now more of an evolutionary problem than ever.[7]

---

[4]   Gould, Luria, and Singer, 1981, p 638

[5]   Gould, 1989, p 58-59

[6]   Gould, Luria, and Singer, 1981, p 651

[7]   The fast transition theory (like punctuated equilibria) can be 'refuted' only by finding convincing evidence that evolution happened slowly. This is a no-lose proposition for evolution, and shows again that evolutionary theory (as practiced by its proponents) is not scientific.

Summary

A biotic message cannot succeed when written solely in biological terms, because it would be short-circuited by two simple non-biological explanations of life. (1) It came from Space. (2) The fossil record is incomplete. Life's designer used the fossil sequence for the undoing of these two classes of explanation.

In detail, message theory identifies six requirements of the fossil sequence:

- Stable system bootup — This is a reasonable design goal, yet it (together with the other requirements) inherently results in a fossil sequence with ecological stages.

- A fossil sequence with many discrete steps — This defeats the Simple Space Scenario and the earth-bound naturalistic explanations that would rationalize an absence of fossil sequence.

- A sequence unexpected from an ordinary designer — This defeats the Advanced Space Scenario.

- Abrupt appearances of fully formed biological designs — This is difficult for evolution to explain.

- Sudden bursts of diversity among organisms built on a unifying design plan, (evolutionists call this "adaptive radiation") — This thwarts the observer's attempt to construct identifiable lineages.

- A pattern that proclaims itself complete — This essential objective prevents the observer from misreading the data or casting it aside as noise.

Morphology space and *fossil sequence* are merely two different views into the morphological space-time continuum. They show the same unified design strategy: Diversity thwarts phylogeny.

- Morphological diversity inhibits the identification of lineages in morphology space.

- A burst of diversity near the same time horizon inhibits the identification of lineages in the fossil sequence.

Lineages may be constructed only by selecting certain data points while arbitrarily ignoring others. This is how Darwinians often created the illusion of phylogeny.

The fossil sequence is not an unresolvable, nondescript or vague pattern. It is a dramatic pattern, readily capturing one's eye and interest. Easily calling attention to itself by shouting, "Explain me. I am distinct and coherent. You must explain me!" Its intricate and consistent structure thwarts all casual, haphazard, or aimless explanations. The fossil sequence aptly serves the goals of the biotic message.

22

Biogeography

Biogeography studies the geographical distribution of organisms. In the era of Darwin and Wallace, scientists believed this field provided important evidence for evolution. Through the years, however, this assessment has slowly eroded. In the origins debate, one hardly hears about it anymore.

> Perhaps the best that can be said for this period [after 1900] is that biogeography suffered progressive degeneration, until a large number of the scientists supposedly active in this field became fixed in their adoration of what must have seemed to them the ultimate pinnacle of achievement made manifest by Darwin. (Nelson and Platnick, 1981, p 392-393)

One reason for this erosion was the 1960's development of plate tectonics and continental drift. This development radically changed the picture, and forced evolutionists to rapidly restructure biogeographical ideas away from the fixed continents axiom of Darwin and Wallace. The biogeographers tried to reconcile their data with the new concepts of movable paleogeography. The plasticity of evolutionary biogeography was nakedly revealed by its ability to suddenly adapt to the dramatic shift in geologic understanding.

Because of this shock, scientists recognized that just-so scenarios permeate the literature of biogeography just as much as in the literature of evolution.[1] Scientists began to complain about the untestability of biogeographic narrative, and they sought rigorous methods of pattern analysis that were free of such facile ingenuity.

Fortuitously, in the 1960s several new methods of pattern analysis were available, including phenetics and cladistics as applied to biogeographical areas. Scientists realized that phenetic and cladistic methods could be applied to 'biogeographical areas' of the globe just as these had been applied to 'species' in morphology space. These methods provided new ways to analyze biogeographical pattern. After the trauma caused by the theory of continental drift, these new methodologies gained acceptance and began to vie for the attention of biogeographers.

The field of biogeography is now undergoing great upheaval.

> [B]iogeography, [is a] discipline notorious for idiosyncrasy, or lack of an agreed method. (Patterson, C., 1982a, p 117)

> There is probably no other branch of biology as rich in controversies as biogeography. Why should this be the case? It is now becoming increasingly evident that it is largely because authors have based their conclusions on one particular group of organisms but that different organisms differ greatly from each other in their dispersal propensities and colonizing abilities. (Mayr, 1984, p 252)

---

[1]   Patterson, C., 1983, p 5

Yet the status of biogeography as evolutionary evidence has been in doubt for some time. All that remains is the piecemeal citation of a few old selected examples. There exists no modern book that surveys this field as evidence for or against evolution. Some evolutionists flatly reject its relevance to the origins debate.

> We conclude, therefore, that biogeography (or geographical distribution of organisms) *has not been shown to be evidence for or against evolution in any sense.* (Nelson and Platnick, 1981, p 223, my italics)[2]

Biogeographic study often has little to do with evolution, and is concerned instead with methods of data collection, mapping and systematics, or with problems of organism dispersal, extinction, and ecology. These issues have little impact as evidence for large-scale evolution.

*

Suppose a given species exists only in region X. Several explanations are possible:

- Did the species originate in region X? If so, then what non-X region did its ancestor come from? This problem is obscured by "the unwillingness of palaeontologists and phyleticists to designate ancestral species with any conviction." (Patterson, C., 1983, p 23)

- If the species changed while living in region X, then this is not necessarily evidence for large-scale evolution. In most cases, the evidence from biogeography fails to span the large morphological gaps in life. This seems to be the case with the finches, turtles, and iguanas that Darwin made famous from the Galapagos Islands.

- If a species exists *only* in region X, then this may simply be because it died out everywhere else. Perhaps a species exists only in region X because its predators and competitors do not exist there. Perhaps the absence of its predators and competitors allowed the species to survive.

That last phenomenon may well have occurred on the continent of Australia where marsupials lived without competition from eutherian mammals until recently. The introduction of eutherian mammals, such as dogs, had a devastating effect on Australia's natural ecology. Even non-ferocious herbivores such as rabbits have multiplied so rapidly they have become a national pest by crowding out the native marsupials that are the pride of that continent's ecology. Dramatic steps had to be taken to control these mammalian invaders.

---

2 Nelson and Platnick continue: "The significance of biogeography has been merely that biogeography has raised the possibility of agreement between cladograms as considered in the geographic dimension—a possibility that has been little studied ..."

Fossils show that marsupials lived on all other continents. Possibly the marsupials survived predominantly in Australia precisely because the eutherian mammals did not find their way there. In this way, the solution to biogeographic problems can have more to do with ecology and extinction than evolution.

Presently, these matters must go unresolved while awaiting further developments. In the origins debate, biogeography has long been a defunct body of evidence.

> Biogeography, as a topic for discourse or discussion, is in some ways like religion: both topics lend themselves to ever more complicated treatment in the abstract, which is apt to border even on the miraculous, but which is apt to crumble in confrontation with concrete facts of life. (Nelson and Platnick, 1981, p 375)

23

Cosmological Issues

In this chapter message theory gives some insights into geological and cosmological processes and hence into the capacities of the designer.

Geology

Can message theory be extended from biology into geology? Two curious
facts of geology are pertinent here.

First, the theory of continental drift indicates that continents were once all
joined as a supercontinent. There is something uncanny about it, like a fairy tale.
It is extremely curious. Unexpected coincidences like this draw our attention.
Possibly the supercontinent served as a convenient means of dispersing organisms. Or maybe its meaning is deeper still. Perhaps this matter will someday
figure in an extension of message theory into geology.

The second curious fact is simply that fossils are found on land — *marine
fossils on land*. There has always been something disturbing about it. All those
fossils, most of them *marine* invertebrates, are stacked up on land staring at us.
Most places on earth, from the lowlands to the tops of mountains, have sedimentary fossil-bearing rocks. The pre-Darwinian knowledge of the geologic column
was constructed by scientists marching around Europe with a pick-ax and
shovel. (Even modern technologies of mining, drilling, and sea-floor exploration
have not substantially altered that picture of the geologic column.) The geologic
column was visible to ordinary people with no special tools.

When organisms die, they rapidly decompose, unless soon buried. Many
chemical processes can interfere with the fossilization process, and many geological processes can destroy fossils or conceal them from view. So why should
fossils exist at all? Why are they not hidden at the bottom of the sea? Or hidden
ten kilometers beneath the crust? Or destroyed altogether by the tectonic
subduction of crustal plates into trenches? Or eroded into dust? Or only the
topmost, most recent fossils accessible, like the outside layers of an onion?

Earth is a peculiar planet. Why are there sedimentary fossils high and dry on
land? In such prodigious quantities? Utterly unavoidable to anyone who looks
at rocks? Why this tremendous fossil record so easily and so conspicuously
within reach? Is this mere happenstance?

No other known planet has geologic processes suitable for preserving an
abundant fossil record. On the giant gaseous planets if you dropped a clam shell,
it would not stop sinking until it reached the planet's center. Other planets lack
enough liquid to create sedimentary fossils. The inner planets have extremes of
heat and cold that would make fossil preservation difficult. Some of the planets
have weather systems and atmospheres (such as sulfuric acid) that would be
corrosive to fossils. The Earth alone can maintain and display its fossil record.

Thus, the Earth itself meets the goals of message theory:

- The Earth seems designed for the survival of life. These features include its mass, density, nearly circular orbit, distance from the Sun, tilt of the axis, magnetic field, chemical makeup, temperature, and abundance of water.

- The Earth seems designed to successfully convey the biotic message. Its peculiar balance of tectonic processes preserves and displays the fossil record. That ability was essential to the biotic message.

Extraterrestrials

Some creationists presumed that life's designer wanted to create as much beauty, variety, magnificence, and "glory" as possible. They therefore expected an abundance of life in Space.

Message theory says that such presumptions are mistaken. The designer had a different goal in mind. The designer fashioned life to tell where life came from. That goal would be ruined by other intelligent life in the universe, since they might be mistaken for the designer. An observer might attribute earthly life to the wrong being. A biomessage sender would take steps to prevent that misinterpretation, and thus would not create intelligent life indiscriminately. A biotic message sender would create the minimum number of intelligent life forms.

Moreover, life was made to look like the work of a single designer, and that goal would be ruined by the existence of extraterrestrial life.

- Suppose the designer were to make extraterrestrial life *unlike* life on Earth. The universe's life forms would then look like the result of multiple, separate designers, (and that would defeat the biotic message). Or, it would look as if the result of multiple separate origins and evolutions of life — and that is precisely what evolutionists would claim. They would use this pattern as evidence for evolution.

- On the other hand, suppose the designer made extraterrestrial life virtually *identical* to life on Earth. Many evolutionists would use this as evidence that the origin of life is biochemically predestined and that evolution proceeds only along specific pathways. (Some evolutionists already make that claim, but they presently have no evidence to base it on.) Other evolutionists would claim this situation as evidence that life evolved elsewhere and was brought to Earth by extraterrestrials, or by directed panspermia (as in Francis Crick's theory), or by viruses (as in Hoyle and Wickramasinghe's theory).

In either case, evolutionists would use extraterrestrial life as evidence in their favor. Extraterrestrial life would harm the biotic message and so would not be created by a biotic message sender.

441

The Supernatural

Message theory does not inherently assume the existence of the supernatural. Nonetheless, evidence now suggests that the biotic message sender is supernatural.

- The system of life shows that it was designed for survival and to convey a biotic message. This required intelligence and technology far beyond our own. In addition, the fossil sequence shows that mankind was not present until virtually the end, and this further indicates that mankind could not have been the designer of life. No life on earth had both the capacity and the opportunity to be the designer. Thus, the absence of extraterrestrials points toward the supernatural as the remaining possibility for life's designer.

- The fossil sequence bonds the pattern of life to the Earth's crust. Together with the absence of extraterrestrial life, these prevent the observer from disposing of evolutionary problems by shifting them out into Space. In addition, the Earth has many rare properties necessary for life and it has the especially peculiar ability to preserve and display its fossil record. These properties were essential to the biotic message and they indicate that the biomessage sender possessed powers that are at least cosmological in scope.

- The universe itself has many highly improbable properties that are necessary for life. (Evolutionists try to explain away these properties with the anthropic principle.) The universe also has peculiar properties necessary for the success of the biotic message. These include an inability to yield a naturalistic origin of life, and an absence of extraterrestrial life. These properties suggest that the universe was designed to assist the biotic message.

- In combination, the Big Bang, the Laws of Thermodynamics, and Paley's theory of life, scientifically indicate that a supernatural agent has performed a creative act in the universe.

If the data had failed in any number of ways it would have allowed other interpretations. Yet the data is intricately constructed to point consistently to one conclusion. The evidence suggests that the biomessage sender is supernatural and has intentionally signaled that.

Summary

The Earth has many unique properties necessary for life. Yet it also has the capacity to form a substantial fossil record, and the special balance of tectonic forces necessary for displaying it. These peculiar features are essential to the biotic message.

The existence of extraterrestrial life would harm the biotic message, and so would not be created by a biomessage sender.

The universe itself has features that help convey the biotic message.

24

Discontinuity Systematics

Creationists recognize that organisms change and vary, yet they also see that life's predominant pattern is discontinuity. Life has a pattern of large morphological gaps and an absence of large-scale phylogeny. This pattern is now the central issue in the question of biological evolution or creation.

Evolutionists believe in a fundamental continuity of life. They believe life is interrelated by evolutionary processes, the foremost being descent with modification. Accordingly, they expected life to show phylogeny and gradual intergradations of life forms. Since the mid 1970s, however, evolutionists have increasingly acknowledged the existence of discontinuity. They proposed punctuated equilibria as an evolutionary theory consistent with that perception. Therefore, the pattern of discontinuity is an increasingly important matter, even to evolutionists.

Despite the significance of discontinuity there was, until recently, no systematic method for studying it. Traditional systematic methods are completely insensitive and blind to discontinuity. Hennigian cladistics and Darwinian taxonomy assume the continuity of life and question the matter no further. All the traditional methods focus on the identification of hierarchical data structures such as phenograms or cladograms. These have the shape of a tree, yet the life forms are located only at the tips of the branches, not along the branches. These data structures never place life forms into a phylogeny of ancestor-descendant relationships and never identify continuity or discontinuity.

A new method,[1] Discontinuity Systematics, helps scientists probe the pattern of common descent. It also provides a coherent method of communicating and constructing knowledge. Lastly, it enables creationists and evolutionists to identify and debate their differences.

Definition of the Method

Discontinuity Systematics seeks to identify the boundary between common descent and discontinuity. It views all available scientific evidences as legitimate, with two explicit clarifications. First, Discontinuity Systematics performs its task independently of creation theories. The method tries to discern life's pattern as seen by a neutral scientific observer.

Second, Discontinuity Systematics holds that cladograms and phenograms are inconclusive as evidence of evolutionary continuity. There are at least three reasons for this:

---

[1]   ReMine, 1990

- Evolution does not predict a hierarchical pattern. Simple processes of loss, replacement, anagenesis, transposition, unmasking, or multiple biogenesis would prohibit such a pattern. Since hierarchical patterns (such as cladograms or phenograms) are not predicted by evolution they are not evidence for evolution.

- Life's hierarchical pattern (as displayed in cladograms and phenograms) is too indirect to establish even the special case of common descent. The conclusive evidence must come from other sources, such as clear-cut phylogeny, gradual intergradations, or biological experiments.

- Lastly, Discontinuity Systematics rejects cladograms and phenograms so that it may focus on another type of pattern. The three systematic methods — transformed cladistics, phenetics, and Discontinuity Systematics — study different, non-overlapping aspects of the pattern of life. They are like three types of film — infrared, ultraviolet, and x-ray — for studying different types of pattern. They are sensitive only to certain patterns and they are reasonably free of theoretical bias. Properly used, they are well-defined, neutral, unbiased methods for studying nature. Scientists may then interpret and debate the results.

Thus, Discontinuity Systematics classifies organisms into groups, but unlike traditional classifications it is not hierarchical. It is defined as follows. Discontinuity Systematics tries to identify the boundaries of evolutionary continuity by emulating a neutral scientist who (1) has no detailed knowledge of creation theory, and (2) views phenetic and cladistic patterns skeptically or agnostically.

The Terminology

The terminology allows scientists to state their research experience as hypotheses about groups of organisms. There are four types of groups. Each is defined from the observer's point of view.

Holobaramin — A complete set of common descendants. A group containing *all and only* organisms related by common descent. (From a theorist's point of view this represents one or more organisms directly originated as a highly integrated or inter-reproductive group, together with all their descendants.)

Monobaramin — A group containing *only* organisms related by common descent, but not necessarily all of them. A group sharing a common ancestor. (A group comprising one entire holobaramin or a portion thereof.)

Apobaramin — A group containing *all* the ancestors and descendants of any of its members. A group not sharing an ancestor or descendant with any organism outside the group. (A group comprising one or more entire holobaramins.)

Polybaramin — A group not sharing a common ancestor. (A group containing members of more than one holobaramin.)

Note: The terminology is defined from the observer's point of view and thus always refers to known data, rather than speculation or hypothetical reconstructions. When a group is said to include "all" organisms of a certain type, it is referring only to known data (fossil or living). Obviously, as new organisms are found, some groupings would need to be adjusted accordingly.

The plural form of the terms is made by adding -s, as in holobaramins. The adjective form is made by adding the suffix -ic. For example, the mammals are apobaraminic; lions and tigers are a monobaraminic group.

Group membership is communicated by listing the members' names. Or, well-characterized groups can be given a group name. For example, placental dogs, coyotes, wolves, foxes, and jackals might be called a *Canidae* monobaramin. Most well-characterized groups already have scientific names. For consistency and convenience these should be used in Discontinuity Systematics. There will rarely be a need to create new names.[2]

The terms can be combined with a time modifier to make statements about organisms at a specific time horizon. For example, the "living *Canidae* monobaramin," or the "Devonian crab apobaramin." Many additional statements are easily communicated with this terminology.

The definition of each term is the primary, most fundamental meaning of the term. It is used when identifying groups and when making arguments for or against specific groupings.

Each of the above terms also has a meaning enclosed within parentheses. The parenthesized meaning is secondary, since it can be derived from the definitions of the four terms in combination. The derived meaning expresses the relationship

---

[2] A biological species has many theoretical definitions. Yet in practice the taxonomically recognized species are typically identified by interbreeding or by experimentally-based "measuring stick" criteria of some type. Thus, most species are monobaramins, and discontinuity systematics is not interested in dividing them into smaller groups such as subspecies, populations, or demes. With few exceptions a discontinuity classification is concerned with groups at, or above, the species level. In most cases, these groups already have suitable names.

of each term to the other terms (and ultimately to some theory of origin). It states how the terminology is interconnected.

Thus, each term has two meanings, the defined meaning and a somewhat different derived meaning. Both meanings are valid, and we can legitimately transform from one to the other. This allows us to identify groups (by their definition), and then transform the group's significance in a way that allows construction of further knowledge. The terms are not isolated definitions, rather they are interconnected. The terms work together to provide a systematic method of knowledge construction.

Ease of Communication

The discontinuity systematist examines the specimens of life (fossil or living) and classifies them into groups that meet the above definitions. The systematist communicates this research to others by means of the terminology. The terminology then provides a precise, compact way to debate the groupings.

For example, one researcher may claim that organisms X, Y, and Z form a holobaramin (let us call it group XYZ). Another researcher may challenge that hypothesis in the following language:

> "XYZ is not holobaraminic because W should also be included in that group. The holobaramin should be WXYZ."

Or another researcher may challenge in the following language:

> "Group XYZ is polybaraminic and should be divided into two monobaramins, X and YZ."

The researchers would then debate by providing arguments and evidence.

Identification of the groups is a tentative scientific hypothesis subject to further test. A systematist may propose that a certain group is a holobaramin, and later the group is shown to be incomplete (and therefore not a holobaramin). Or perhaps the group might be shown to be polybaraminic (and therefore not a holobaramin). This can happen when new specimens or experimental techniques change the picture, thereby forcing the researcher to modify previous findings. Like all science, Discontinuity Systematics is a tentative and self-correcting process.

Some groupings will prevail as the most scientifically tenable, and these groupings can then be used to construct new knowledge due to the special interconnection of the terminology. In this way the terms provide a convenient means to study nature, communicate and debate the results, and construct further knowledge.

The Method of Knowledge Construction

Science (and systematics in particular) is a knowledge building process — a cumulative pooling of knowledge from various researchers. The knowledge need not be perfect, and it need not be complete, but it can be important effective science when pooled together. Discontinuity Systematics therefore provides a method for constructing knowledge. The method allows research results to be compiled together in a practical way.

Discontinuity Systematics seeks to classify organisms into identifiable groups. It seeks to eliminate all polybaraminic groups, and instead identify groups that are monobaramins, apobaramins, or better still, holobaramins. The ultimate goal is the identification and description of all holobaramins.

The terminology places boundaries on the size of a group. The size of a holobaramin is complete and 'bounded' on both sides, since it contains *all and only* organisms related by common descent. (The prefix *holo-* means "entire, whole, and complete," indicating that the group is complete.)

Monobaramin and apobaramin, on the other hand, are open-ended and unbounded on one side. They provide a way to communicate incomplete knowledge, (an important task in any developing science). These terms allow for a less restrictive type of hypothesis. They allow the researcher to convey hypotheses that identify group boundaries on one side only.

Discontinuity Systematics judiciously seeks to increase the size of monobaramins and decrease the size of apobaramins. This process is called successive refinement. Theoretically, a monobaramin is a subset of a holobaramin. So, a holobaramin is approached as a monobaramin is successively increased in size. On the other hand, an apobaramin is a superset of a holobaramin, so a holobaramin is approached as an apobaramin is subdivided into smaller apobaramins. A holobaramin is bounded on one side by monobaramins and on the other by apobaramins. Since the holobaramin is confined between these two limits, successive refinement converges on it. When we have identified a monobaramin that is also an apobaramin, then we have achieved the goal of recognizing a holobaramin.

*

The knowledge building process works as follows. A systematist might propose that placental dogs, coyotes, wolves, foxes, and jackals form a monobaramin because they can interbreed. The systematist is saying that these organisms are related by common descent, that the group is definitely unified together. (The prefix *mono-* signifies this unity.) Yet the systematist might hold back from claiming that the group is a complete set of common descendants: a holobaramin. The systematist might withhold such a conclusion because he or she does not have sufficient knowledge concerning organisms outside the group. This is expected in practice, since any researcher has only limited knowledge and experience.

The concept of monobaramin allows groups to be constructed by addition. Suppose a researcher finds that organisms Y and Z form a monobaramin. Suppose a second researcher finds that X and Z form a monobaramin. On hearing these results, a third researcher may compile the two monobaramins additively into one monobaramin: XYZ. In this way, knowledge can smoothly increase as each researcher makes a contribution.

The term apobaramin is important for Discontinuity Systematics. It has no parallel with any previous evolutionary term. The prefix *apo-* means "away from" or "separate from" and signifies that an apobaramin is separate and away from all other groups — it is a distinct group. An apobaramin is a group of organisms that appears evolutionarily disconnected from any other known organisms.[3]

The concept of apobaramin allows groups to be constructed by subtraction. Suppose a researcher finds that organisms W, X, Y, and Z form an apobaramin. Suppose a second researcher finds that Y and Z form an apobaramin. On hearing those results, a third researcher may combine them by subtracting the smaller apobaramin from the larger, thereby refining the larger apobaramin WXYZ into two smaller apobaramins WX and YZ. This is a useful result because the smaller the apobaramin the closer it is to being recognized as a holobaramin (the ultimate goal of Discontinuity Systematics). Again, these concepts allow knowledge to smoothly increase by building on each researcher's contribution.

The knowledge building process can also combine information about monobaramins and apobaramins. For example, suppose one researcher shows that group XYZ is a monobaramin, and a second researcher shows that group WXYZ is an apobaramin. A third researcher can then combine those two results into a new conclusion: either group WXYZ is a holobaramin, or there are two holobaramins (W and XYZ). This would then suggest directions for new research.

The terminology easily communicates research results and the methodology then compiles these in new and revealing ways. The methodology can take open-ended statements about apo- and mono- baramins and convert them into closed, bounded statements about holobaramins.

The Continuity Criteria

The terminology defines four types of groups, but it does not completely lay out the continuity criteria used to determine membership in the groups. From a practical viewpoint, the terminology is not exhaustively specified. This circumstance is desirable since the continuity criteria will change somewhat as our scientific technology increases. The terminology is free of a strict dependence on changeable criteria, so it can still be used as the criteria develop.

---

[3] Conceivably, an odd assemblage of organisms could be named as an apobaramin. As an extreme example, the group composed of molluscs together with primates would meet the requirements of an apobaramin since these organisms cannot be definitively linked with any other group by a naturalistic process. However, such mixed groups fail to form coherent natural groups, so they quickly attract the attention of systematists. Discontinuity systematists would rapidly refine such mixed groups into a number of smaller apobaramins.

For example, modern techniques can measure the overall DNA similarity between two organisms. Yet the meaning of overall DNA similarity is presently a matter of debate. Here are two contrasting cases. There are two species of flies (*Drosophila*) that look alike but have only 25 percent of their DNA sequences in common. Yet the DNA of humans and chimpanzees share 97.5 percent. This means the DNA of two virtually identical flies is 30 times more different than that between humans and chimpanzees.[4] The DNA data conflicts with the morphological data.

There are many questions about this matter. Are these typical cases or is there something peculiar about the DNA of one of the fly species? What is the relationship between DNA and morphology? How noisy are DNA similarity measurements? How much DNA is junk? Do some species have more junk DNA than others? By itself can DNA similarity indicate membership in monobaramins or apobaramins? Is DNA similarity sufficiently consistent to be a useful systematic criterion for demarcating groups? What does DNA similarity mean? It is too early to answer those questions. Systematists can debate such a DNA-based criterion without the outcome requiring that the terminology be replaced. That is an advantage of the terminology. It is defined in a durable manner.

*

The continuity criteria identify evolutionary continuity (and its absence) without using phenetic or cladistic evidences. There are presently three such criteria, any one of which can establish the common descent of two organisms: (1) the ability to interbreed; (2) experimental demonstrations; or (3) clear-cut phylogeny. These are discussed next.

Reproductive Viability

Reproductive viability is the ability of two organisms to successfully interbreed. This continuity criterion is already widely used by taxonomists since it plays a key role in the concept of species. When two organisms interbreed (with or without human assistance) and produce viable, fertile hybrids, it is sufficient evidence that they are in the same monobaramin.

Hybrid offspring can sometimes be viable but infertile. This occurs, for example, when a horse and donkey produce a mule. (The mule is healthy, but sterile.) This still seems sufficient to place the horse, donkey and mule in the same monobaramin.

Cases are more difficult to assess when hybrids do not even survive until birth. These cases need more research.

Far less compelling are cases where the hybridization involves fragments of DNA. For example, modern laboratory techniques can artificially place human genes into bacteria. Viruses likewise can sometimes transfer short segments of genetic material from one species to another. These genetic combinations are fragmentary and involve only minor parts of genomes. Presently, such fragmentary hybridization fails to establish common descent.

---

[4]   Stebbins, 1982, p 129-130; see also Dover, 1980, p 246, and Mayr, 1982, p 241.

In summary, hybridization has a variety of outcomes. Listed in decreasing order of importance they are: (1) viable and fertile offspring; (2) viable and infertile offspring; (3) inviable offspring; and (4) fragmentary hybridization. More research must be done to further develop this continuity criterion.

Using reproductive viability as a criterion, here are several examples of monobaramins:

- horses, mules, asses, zebras, and onagers

- lions and tigers

- cattle, buffalo, yaks and bison

- mallards and pintail ducks

- placental dogs, wolves, coyotes, jackals, and foxes

One of the first tasks for Discontinuity Systematics should be the documentation of all such inter-reproductive groups.

Experimental Demonstrations

Biological experiments are the measuring stick for gauging life's morphological gaps. The gap between two organisms is "small" if it is bridged by experimental demonstrations. Such a circumstance offers strong evidence for evolutionary continuity.

A good example of biological change is color. With breeding experiments we can demonstrate new color patterns in organisms as diverse as birds, flowers, insects, and fish. Such color change is common, widespread, and often dramatic. This suggests that if two organisms differ mostly in their coloring, then they probably belong in the same monobaramin.

Experimental demonstrations often apply far beyond the species for which they were achieved. However, they need not (and frequently cannot) be applicable to all organisms. Some demonstrations will be limited to certain types of organisms. For instance, demonstrations of biological change in plants might be irrelevant, undefined, or inapplicable to fish. Research will be needed to assess how widely to apply a given experimental result.

Experimental demonstrations can be applied in the following ways. If a breeding experiment creates a diversity of morphology that overlaps an untested organism, then there is evidence that the untested organism belongs in the same monobaramin with the others.

That idea can be cautiously extended to fossils. If a breeding experiment produces a range of morphology greater than the difference between two fossil organisms, then there is evidence that the two fossil organisms belong together in a monobaramin. (This idea is not new. Taxonomists already use such comparisons to identify extinct fossil groups as species.[5]) The idea is also extended to asexual groups, who are called "species" even though they do not interbreed.

In summary, if the difference between two organisms is sufficiently small, or the magnitude of our experimental demonstrations is sufficiently large, then the two organisms are in the same monobaramin.

Phylogeny

A lineage is not clear if it is just two organisms, a starting and an ending organism. A lineage is not an obscure cloud of organisms. A lineage has a special pattern within a multidimensional morphology space. It curves through that space with ancestors and descendants in succession. A clear lineage is a reasonably filled trail of organisms, long and narrow, with a void in the adjacent regions.

A phylogeny is merely discrete lineages connected into a tree-structure of evolutionary descent.

A clear phylogeny between two life forms is strong evidence that they are in the same monobaramin. This is true even if there are large morphological distances between the organisms making up the phylogeny. In principle, this criterion could span large morphological gaps in the record of life. This criterion, unlike any other, is completely independent of experimental support, and therefore relies entirely on the clarity of the pattern for its strength.[6]

A clear-cut phylogeny is strong evidence for evolutionary continuity. Yet phylogeny (and its absence) is the most under studied pattern in nature. When evolutionists sought phylogeny and failed, they fell back on phenetic and cladistic evidences. The absence of phylogeny typically went unreported, and in any case it was not systematically compiled. That cannot happen in Discontinuity Systematics, for phylogeny (and its absence) is the most central object of study.[7]

---

[5] We cannot tell whether a fossil group could interbreed. Instead, groups are identified as fossil species because they show roughly the same morphological diversity as living species. This demarcation does not seem to be arbitrary. Fossil organisms do fall into distinct groups like living species.

[6] Evolutionists often claim they have identified a phylogeny. Yet they rarely discuss whether the phylogeny is clear. They fail to discuss whether a given lineage is long and narrow, whether it is significantly filled in, or whether there is an appropriate void adjacent to the lineage. This is a serious oversight in evolutionary literature.

[7] In the origins debate, there is sometimes argument about where an organism should be classified. (Should *archaeopteryx* be classified as a bird or a reptile, for example.) That issue is irrelevant here. Discontinuity systematics is not concerned with the rigors of tree-structured classification schemes. Rather, the pivotal issue is whether there is a clear phylogeny.

The Identification of Apobaramins

Continuity and discontinuity are related observations. You cannot see one without having eyes to see the other. The continuity criteria provide this vision. They are scientific tools for identifying common descent and its boundaries. They identify the continuity within monobaramins, and these same tools identify the discontinuity between apobaramins.

We have already discussed several criteria, any one of which is sufficient to show continuity. Discontinuity is the observed absence of continuity. It is merely the failure to meet the continuity criteria.

A group is an apobaramin if there is discontinuity between it and all organisms outside the group. If members of the group are not interfertile with non-members, and the morphological gap between members and non-members dwarfs our experimental demonstrations, and there is no clear phylogeny uniting members with non-members, then the group is very probably an apobaramin. An apobaramin is recognized by an empirical failure to establish the origin of the group from any other group.

Evolutionists say all known organisms are common descendants, so theoretically there can be only one apobaramin. Creationists say there are many. By identifying these groups, systematists can identify the observable boundaries of the origins controversy.

Objectivity versus Subjectivity

History has shown that traditional systematic techniques (such as phenetics or transformed cladistics) are built on reasonably clear principles that when pushed to their limits ultimately become a discouragingly subjective enterprise. Endless debates arise between the lumpers and the splitters, or between systematists who claim they have the only truly objective method. Such claims of total objectivity always ended in frustration. History shows that systematics is not a totally pure objective enterprise. Systematics accomplishes its task in a world of partial knowledge and ambiguous interpretations. The views of systematists often reflect this uncertainty. Subjectivity is unavoidable in all traditional systematics.

In the same way, subjectivity cannot be eliminated from Discontinuity Systematics. Experimental demonstrations improve with time, and our interpretation of them alters as we learn. The meaning of a given experimental result is not always clear at the time it is first achieved. This means the measuring stick is not rigid, but changes as our knowledge increases. Also, as a given result gains observational support, it becomes more stable, secure, and useful for extension to other cases.

At any given time the precise interpretation of the measuring stick will foster active debate, and that will be reflected in differences of opinion about which organisms belong in a given group. Such debate is a natural outcome of the growth in knowledge.

Nonetheless, confidence in this useful systematic method can increase with experience. As happened with phenetics and cladistics, our confidence grows when the pattern under study is seen as real, coherent, and informative.

Summary

Discontinuity Systematics seeks to identify the boundaries of common descent. It is a neutral, scientific method for studying nature, communicating the results, and compiling those results into greater knowledge. It is also the major tool for resolving the debate over biological origins.

25

Systematics and the Origins Debate

This chapter discusses systematic methods, their justification, and their relationship to the origins controversy.

Transformed versus Hennigian Cladistics

Transformed cladistics is a neutral, theory-free method to examine nature for a nested pattern. Its proponents argue (correctly) that no further justification is necessary.

Hennigian cladists disagree and argue as follows.[1] Evolutionary theory, they say, is required to "justify" the cladistic method. Cladistics examines life's nested pattern, which is the major evidence of evolution. It is senseless to separate observations from the only theory that explains those observations. Moreover, evolutionary theory can give useful insights for applying the cladistic method. Hennigian cladistics is "justified," they conclude, and transformed cladistics is without justification.

That justification for Hennigian cladistics has now collapsed. Life's nested pattern is not evidence for evolution, but major evidence against its most powerful mechanism — transposition. Evolutionary theory does not provide useful insights to its practitioners, rather it is an obstacle to their vision. Hennigian cladistics is without justification.

Therefore, scientists should use transformed cladistics (and phenetics) to study life's hierarchical patterns and produce useful hierarchical classifications. But these no longer help evolutionists. _Discontinuity Systematics is now the only biosystematic method that could conceivably provide evidence for evolution._

Empirical Justification

Discontinuity Systematics is justified on theoretical grounds, and as a tool for studying nature. It is also justified by the data — The pattern of discontinuity is real.

First, there is a correlation between apobaramins and major designs. Name any major design and that group seems to be an apobaramin, that is, it lacks experimental demonstrations, gradual intergradations, phylogeny, and interfertility that would link it with non-members. For example, whales, bats, turtles, spiders, crabs, or flies each seems to be an apobaramin. The consistency of this pattern is major evidence for creation.

---

[1]   Ridley, 1986

Second, the higher you look in the Linnaean hierarchy — at orders, classes, or phyla — the more dramatic the pattern of discontinuity tends to be. The major evolutionary transitions in design curiously have the most evidence for discontinuity.

Third, if evolutionists could identify continuity, they would have. Instead, they used many devices to create its illusion.[2] That universal practice on their part is now material testimony that the pattern of discontinuity is real.

Creation Systematics

Though Discontinuity Systematics does not contain message theory, there is a tight logical connection. Message theory scientifically explains why a designer would create: (1) large morphological gaps; (2) absence of phylogeny; (3) barriers to interfertility; (4) phenetic patterns; and (5) cladistic patterns. In each case these serve the goals of the biotic message. Discontinuity Systematics acknowledges the existence of 4 and 5, and formally sets them aside in order to focus clearly on 1, 2, and 3.

Moreover, message theory neatly explains the holobaramins of Discontinuity Systematics. Holobaramins were intentionally created so the observer can see them as evolutionarily disconnected from other groups.

Discontinuity Systematics is a neutral method for studying life's key pattern, and message theory scientifically predicts and explains that pattern. The combination of the two can be called Creation Systematics.[3] It is the scientific study and explanation of biological creation. (It is the creationists' counterpart to evolutionary systematics.) Creation Systematics is not neutral or theory-free. It takes a definite point of view and scientifically pursues it.

---

[2] See the chapter, Evolutionary Illusions.

[3] The relationship between Discontinuity Systematics and Creation Systematics is like the relationship between transformed cladistics and Hennigian cladistics. Transformed cladistics aims to be neutral and theory-free, while Hennigian cladistics combines the method with a theory, namely evolutionary theory.

26

Conclusions

Testability (also known as falsifiability) is the criterion of science: Scientific theories must be vulnerable to observations. Every major scientific organization explicitly endorses this criterion, and every major evolutionist uses it as a weapon against creation theory. This chapter summarizes the book and uses the criterion of testability to overturn evolution.

The Two-model Approach

For instructional purposes many creationists adopt a two-model approach, where creation and evolution are the only two alternatives. In a two-model approach, evidence against one model is viewed as evidence _for_ the other.

Evolutionists have staunchly opposed the two-model approach. They say it is invalid because there are more than two alternatives.

> The other false dichotomy that the creationists have fostered is the so-called 'two-model' approach. In this argument there can be only one of two possibilities: either evolution is correct, or creation is correct. Hence, since no third possibility exists, anything that tends to cast doubt on one model can be cited as evidence for the other. The creationists therefore spend an inordinate amount of time looking for loopholes and unproven links in current evolutionary biology, thinking by this means they shore up their case for special and sudden creation. Rubbish! (Dickerson, 1986, p 18)

> [The creationist] goes on the unstated assumption that creation can be validated by discrediting evolution — a rationale that is acceptable neither to science nor to logic. (Weinberg, 1984b, p 6)

> Defenders of evolution often complain that the creationists spend virtually all their time attacking evolution and almost no time at all in developing a creationist model or in adducing evidence for creationist ideas. The reason for this, in large part, is that the creationists have been assuming: if not evolution, then biblical creation. In other words, if evolution is false, then creationism must necessarily be true. As we have seen, the logic of this position is utterly without merit. (Gough, 1983, p 31)

> [T]he very juxtaposition of evolution with Creation-science — what Creationists call the 'two-model approach' — is itself fallacious. One cannot prove Creationism by disproving evolution. (Ruse, 1984a, p 330)[1]

---

[1] For additional examples of evolutionists objecting to the creationist's two-model approach see Singleton, 1987, p 332; Young, 1985, p 127; Park, M. A., 1982, p 74; Stunkel, 1982, p 52; Norelli and Proulx, 1982, p 4; Gepner, 1982, p 69; Dietz, 1988, p 14; Rovner, 1988, p 23; Lyons, 1984, p 357-358; Godfrey, 1981, p 6; Steiner, 1981, p 33;

Evolutionists even convinced a federal court that the two-model approach is a "contrived dualism."

> The two model approach of the creationists is simply a contrived dualism which has no scientific factual basis or legitimate educational purpose. It assumes only two explanations for the origins of life and the existence of man, plants and animals: It was either the work of a creator or it was not. Application of these two models, according to creationists, ... dictates that all scientific evidence which fails to support the theory of evolution is necessarily scientific evidence in support of creationism (Overton, 1982, part IV(A).)

Nonetheless, evolutionists invented the two-model approach. The classic evolutionary evidences are not evidence for evolution, they are evidence against a designer. Their reasoning goes like this:

1)   Evolutionists observe a peculiar fact X in nature.

2)   Then they argue that it is senseless for a designer to have designed X.

3)   Then they arrange evolutionary theory to accommodate X.

4)   Finally, they conclude that evolutionary theory makes more sense than a designer.

Historically, fact X has been embryological "gill-slits," recapitulation, vestigial organs, odd and curious designs (the argument from imperfection), similar adaptations used for different purposes, different adaptations used for the same purpose, biologic universals, homologies, and life's nested hierarchy. All these have been used as evidence against a designer. Yet evolutionary theory did not predict them. This is the original dualism in action, a tradition traceable directly to Darwin. Evolutionists are using another double standard. They can hardly complain about the dualism of the two-model approach. They still use it.

*

Schadewald, 1983, p 25; Hanson, 1986a, p 1; Nahigian, 1990, p 4; Berra, 1990, p 139; and the New Orleans Geological Society cited in McCollister, 1989, p 44. Also, Hudson and E. C. Scott, according to *NCSE Reports*, Vol. 10, Num. 2, Mar-Apr 1990, p 2 & 3.

Scott and Cole make a six point complaint against creationist reasoning. They seem unaware that evolutionists are culpable on all six points. "The authors will have to avoid [1] 'you're wrong, so I'm right' logic [i.e., the two-model approach], [2] reliance on anomalies for evidence, and [3] unreasonable extrapolations from observations. Mostly they will have to [4] construct testable questions, and [5] give up reliance on the occasional miraculous intervention [such as miraculous chance events]. If creationists can overcome the styles of argument which they utilize, and [6] avoid unreasonable leaps beyond what the data allow, they have no less an opportunity to be published in mainline journals as other scholars." (Scott and Cole, 1985, p 28)

Evolutionists disagree among themselves about how evolution occurred, yet they insist it is a "fact" nonetheless. They distinguished between *how* evolution occurred, and *whether* it occurred. They created a false how/whether dualism.

Evolutionists arrived at their how/whether dualism through their undeclared use of the two-model approach. They cite all types of evidence against a designer, then they conclude, "It *must* be evolution," and then they debate among themselves about how it occurred.[2] Yet evolutionary theory is a smorgasbord, passively waiting to be adapted to the data. Unlike all scientific theories, it says little of significance about its central subject matter. The how/whether dualism viewed evolution as a fact while directing attention away from the theory's lack of structure.[3]

*

Gould, Luria, and Singer (1981) exemplify the above points in their college level introductory biology text.

- They point out that biological questions have "two potential resolutions" either creation or evolution (p 572). This is an endorsement of the two-model approach.

- All their evidences for evolution — whether biogeography, vestigial organs, embryology, homology, or imperfect designs — are explicit arguments against a designer, combined with plastic accommodations by evolutionary theory. (p 576-581) This is their application of the two-model approach.

- They claim, "Evolution is a fact. …. The processes and mechanisms of evolution remain a subject of lively debate." (p 575) This is the contrived how/whether dualism.

---

[2] Evolutionists often use a two-model approach in yet another way. They argue that: (1) Evidence against Lamarck's evolutionary mechanism (the inheritance of acquired characters) is evidence for Darwin's mechanism (natural selection); (2) Evidence against selective evolution is evidence for neutral evolution; (3) Evidence against Darwinian gradualism or phyletic evolution is evidence for punctuated equilibria. Evolutionists have a long history of using a two-model approach to establish their aims.

[3] Other examples of the false how/whether dualism are: National Academy of Science — Committee on Science and Creationism, 1984, p 15, 22; Gould, 1984a, p 119-120; Young, 1985, p 247-249 & 146; Fox, 1984, p 209; Asimov, 1984, p 187; Lewontin, 1983, p xxiii-xxiv; Futuyma, 1983, p 170; Hughes, 1982, p 27; Moore, 1982, p 16; Asimov, 1981, p 85-86; Steiner, 1981, p 33; Hewitt, 1988, p 298; and Berra, 1990, p 141 and 132. McCollister (1989) has resolutions, statements, and position papers from many scientific and educational organizations. Examples of the false how/whether dualism appear on pages 11, 15, 23, 24, 30, 37, 50, 52, 118, and 137.

Another example is when Gepner makes the following complaint.

> Controversies between evolutionists over technical points of theory can be magnified in the public's mind [by creationists] to the extent that doubts are raised as to the validity of the theory as a whole. .... [Creationists] obscure the distinction between evolution as a process, and mechanisms or models to explain that process. (Gepner, 1982, p 69)

Gepner makes a false distinction between the "fact of evolution" and the mechanisms used to explain it.[4]

Curious Silence

Natural selection fails to scientifically explain the adaptations of life. This is because the process operates on a fitness terrain that has contour, with peaks and canyons. The contour can easily prevent evolution from proceeding. The theory tries to get around this problem by incorporating all possible mechanisms that affect survival or warp the fitness terrain. These countless mechanisms counteract each other. As a result, the theory has no coherent structure and makes no testable predictions, so it is not science.

Some major evolutionists and philosophers of science saw the difficulties with natural selection, and occasionally drew attention to it. Their disclosures brought the wrath of the evolutionary community, in some cases compelling the discloser to publicly recant. This unfortunate circumstance revealed some of the powerful silencing forces that operate within science.

Evolutionary literature on the neutrality versus selection controversy can be closely studied without its real meaning becoming clear. The way the debate undercuts evolution was always withheld from readers. Yet, straightforward calculations show substantial problems. The genetic model prominently displayed in all evolutionary textbooks indicates that in ten million years a human-like population could substitute no more than 1,667 selectively beneficial nucleotides (or perhaps 25,000 neutral nucleotides). This is not nearly enough to account for human evolution. This fact is not widely known because evolutionary genetics textbooks successfully avoided or obscured such discussion. The textbooks continued to present the illusion that the key evolutionary processes are simple, fast, and virtually inevitable.

Cases of misinformation — such as Haeckel's recapitulation theory, human gill-slits, and vestigial organs — were taught in schools many decades after evolutionists knew these were false. Yet the entrance of creation theory into the schools got an immediate, strong, negative response from evolutionists. Why do evolutionists display such disparity in attitude toward perceived falsehoods?

---

4   In his next sentence, Gepner attacks the two-model approach of the creationists. He seems unaware that evolutionists have built their own case on a two-model approach.

459

For many decades, schools taught of "smooth gradual fossil transitions," "indisputable lineages," and "clear fossil ancestors." These errors are only recently being openly corrected by evolutionists. Yet fossils do not evaporate off museum shelves. The fossil record never did support the evolutionary claims. How can we explain this phenomenon? Why does the real fossil record surprise the public now, after all these years? Why should paleontologists have persistently kept it a secret?

For many decades, evolutionists widely published the idea that biologic universals (such as the universal use of DNA) are major evidence in their favor. It was the primary evidence that Dobzhansky used in his famous paper titled, "Nothing in biology makes sense except in the light of evolution." Simultaneously other evolutionists were studying the origin of life, and they knew that each of the known biologic universals is too complex and improbable to have been in the first life forms. So, they consequently believed that many of Earth's life forms must have contained none of the biologic universals — in direct contradiction to Dobzhansky's widely published claims. Nonetheless, these evolutionary scientists kept silent and allowed biologic universals to be used as evidence for evolution. They allowed Dobzhansky's myth to propagate.

Why did evolutionists rarely mention the process of transposition? Why was there a nearly universal silence about this process? If evolutionary scientists truly fit the classic portrait of free open-mindedness, then why did they overlook this simple possibility? What can account for this mass oversight by evolutionists young and old, good and bad, for well over a hundred years? Was it because drawing attention to simple transposition processes would contradict the "prediction" of nested hierarchy, and thereby undermine the major evidence of evolution?

The evolutionary illusion lasted so long because good scientists fell curiously silent on the critical issues.

Evolutionary Illusions

To see the data clearly, we must rid ourselves of illusions. In science, illusions hinge on using words in misleading ways. Virtually every keyword of the origins debate has been misused to foster evolutionary illusions. Altogether the misuses constitute a massive program.[5]

Many of the misuses are devoted to creating the impression that phylogeny exists, that it is clear, and that evolutionists have identified it. Yet the absence of phylogeny can be documented simply by removing the illusions and directly quoting those evolutionists who are in a position to know the real data.

Frequently, evolutionary illusions are created through equivocation, that is, by shifting the meaning of words back and forth. The major example is the evolutionists' attempts to show that natural selection is scientific. The attempts are the intellectual equivalent of a carnival three-shell game.

---

[5] For a listing of terminological misuses, see the topic "terminology, misuse of" in the index. For a listing of other illusions, see the topic "illusion."

Occasionally, illusions were created by a subtle reversal of logic. For example, evolutionists say that a particular evolutionary theory (such as natural selection, mosaic evolution, or punctuated equilibria) is scientific because it can be tested. They argue that the theory could be refuted by providing convincing evidence that evolution happened in some other way. Their no-lose proposition shows that evolutionary theory is not empirically vulnerable, and therefore is not scientific.

Illusion is often created by misdirection. For example, von Baer's laws of embryology are so difficult for evolutionists to explain that they avoided drawing any attention to the problem. Instead, they avidly used embryology as evidence against a designer. This misdirection effectively concealed the evolutionary difficulties. Few people were aware that the major features of embryology remained unaddressed by evolutionists.

Illusion is created when evolutionists claim they have experimentally demonstrated the fact of evolution. Their claim is the result of equivocation, extrapolation, and exaggeration. This can be shown by comparing the demonstrations with life's systematic pattern of large morphological gaps. The experimental demonstrations uniformly fail to span the gaps.

Some traditional fields of evolutionary evidence — vestigial organs and biogeography — have collapsed and are in disarray. Evolutionists themselves no longer agree on how these evidences can be used. Some evolutionists try to resurrect these fields by radically transforming the basic concepts. Other evolutionists flatly state that these fields are not evidence for evolution. Nonetheless, the old illusions still thrive because influential evolutionists have not clarified the matter.

There are many illusions about fossil sequence. These were created by misleading illustrations and diagrams. Illusion was also created by claiming that no fossils have been found out-of-sequence with evolutionary expectations. Since evolutionists cannot identify phylogeny from the morphological data, they traditionally used the fossil sequence itself to identify ancestors. This led to circular reasoning and to faulty claims that all fossils are in-sequence. Moreover, evolutionists have potent devices that insulate their theory from any difficulty with fossil sequence. They can claim that the fossil record is incomplete. Or more commonly these days, they simply avoid identifying ancestors and focus instead on sister groups and hypothetical common ancestors. Either device allows any fossil sequence to be acceptable.

*

One cannot talk about evolutionary illusions without discussing punctuated equilibria. It attempts to take the major features of the fossil record — abrupt appearances of new biological designs, large morphological gaps, stasis, and the absence of phylogeny — and distort these into "predictions" of evolution.

Punctuationists have been indirect about the absence of identifiable phylogeny, by referring to evolution as "bushy" and "labyrinthine." Consequently, few people recognized that the absence of phylogeny was always a central concern of the theory. Quite unlike Darwinism, punctuated equilibria was specially constructed to *destroy* the appearance of phylogeny and gradual intergradations. The theory thus tries to predict a pattern that looks just like creation.

461

While punctuated equilibria is based on accurate observations of the fossil record, the theory is evolution at its most unscientific. Punctuationists apparently sensed the awkwardness of their position. They became leading opponents of creation theory and made many arguments against a designer. This directed our attention away from the unscientific nature of evolution.

*

A major illusion about evolutionary theory is that it is scientific, that it actually has enough structure to stand firm for empirical testing. The illusion was created by offering many examples of testable evolutionary predictions. Yet in each case the so called predictions are not real. They are merely flexible accommodations to the data at hand. This is shown by the fact that evolutionists contradict each other (and often themselves) about everything that the theory supposedly predicts. Evolutionists remained silent about the true flexible, smorgasbord nature of the theory.

The illusion was aided by hierarchy theorists, who used the words and imagery of "hierarchy" to give a superficial appearance of structure to evolutionary theory.

The illusion was further expanded by the anti-reductionists. Evolutionists used testability as a weapon against creation theory, but they also tried to prevent the same criterion from overthrowing evolution. The rhetoric of anti-reductionism provided cover to achieve this double standard.

Dobzhansky coined the famous saying, "Nothing in biology makes sense except in the light of evolution."[6] But Dobzhansky got it backwards. The illumination shines in the opposite direction. *Nothing in evolution makes sense except in the light of biology.* The empirical data of biology gives shape, on a piecemeal basis, to an otherwise amorphous evolutionary theory.

The Case Against Evolution

We began this book with evolutionists asking their most poignant question: Why would a designer create life to look like evolution? Now we return to ask: Why does life look unlike evolution?

The classical evolutionary theories (such as orthogenesis, vitalism, and Lamarckism) have all been falsified, except for the one that cannot conceivably be falsified — natural selection. All the evolutionary mechanisms are now outside science. Why does nature seem to always possess counterexamples sufficient to probe any evolutionary theories, thereby exposing their lack of structure? Why is it that evolution explains life on earth only by using countless convoluted and contradictory just-so stories?

Why are life forms united by countless similarities? Why are there biologic universals such as DNA, RNA, amino acids, protein, and the genetic code? These are not predicted by evolution. In fact, evolutionists now imply that biologic universals should not exist. Evolutionists who study the origin of life have been

---

[6] Dobzhansky, 1973

462

forced to claim that many organisms, totally unlike any known, must have lived on this planet. The complete absence of such organisms refutes their claim, and is evidence against evolution.

Why have our best scientists been unable to simulate the naturalistic origin of life? Why have they been unable to create self-sustaining life, by any means whatever, from raw naturally occurring materials? This extreme difficulty is certainly not predicted by evolution.

No multicellular animal produces the enzyme necessary to digest cellulose. That fact helps make the system of life ecologically stable. Yet evolution cannot look ahead to the future, or plan for the stability of an ecological system by prohibiting designs that would be beneficial to individuals. Evolutionists therefore feel that, simply by chance, the necessary enzyme, cellulase, was not inherited by, converged on, or transposed into multicellular animals. This is awkward even for an evolutionist to believe, since cellulose is the most abundant food source on earth and the ability to efficiently digest it would be an obvious advantage to any animal. This situation is evidence for a designer and against evolution.

Why are morphological gaps plentiful, large, and systematically placed? Why are the gaps so large that they cannot be bridged by experimental demonstrations? This striking pattern is evidence against evolution.

Why does the record of life fail to show substantial patterns of lineage and phylogeny? This is evidence against evolution.

There are two methods that would have the power to establish evolution as a fact. These methods are gradual intergradations, and clear-cut phylogeny. Why does the data fail to conform to these? Why does the data fail not just in a piecemeal way, but uniformly and systematically throughout the pattern of life? Evolution does not predict that.

Why do embryological similarities commonly exist between quite different organisms said to have been separated by three to four hundred million years? Evolution does not predict this. Why does ontogeny tend to display characters in a sequence from generalized to specialized? Evolutionists are so vexed by the problem that they never explicitly addressed it. Evolution is unable to cope meaningfully with this sequence of ontogeny. Embryology is major evidence against evolution.

Why do new complex designs make their appearance in the fossil record abruptly and fully developed? Why does that usually happen in stunningly orchestrated bursts, such as the Cambrian explosion? Evolution does not predict these. In addition, the fossil sequence fails to show a vector of progress, and even Stephen Gould acknowledges this as the greatest dilemma for evolutionary study. These facts of the fossil sequence count against evolution.

The masking and unmasking of genetic libraries is a simple, powerful process that could provide for abrupt evolution of new adaptations. The results of such a process ought to be everywhere. Why has the process failed to have any significant evolutionary impact?

Why is there no available means for the inheritance of acquired characters? It is still sought by evolutionists, and it would require only a simple mechanism. Why isn't it here?

Why is it that sex *is* here, and here abundantly? The most plausible evolutionary theories predict that it should not even exist.

Evolutionists allege that a complex and implausible process of convergence has substantially affected the pattern of life. So why has the simple process of transposition somehow failed to make an impact? Evolution does not predict either situation. These count against evolution. The puzzle is amplified by the universality of DNA, RNA, and genetic code that would seem to remove a major obstacle to transposition of genetic information.

Why is there a strong nested hierarchy of similarities? Evolution does not even predict this. Simple evolutionary processes of loss, replacement, distant hybridization, anagenesis, transposition, unmasking, or multiple biogenesis would prevent a nested pattern.

These are not trivialities. These are the major features of life. *On every point, if evolutionary theory speaks with any clarity whatsoever, it favors an opinion opposite from what we observe.*

Falsified or Unfalsifiable?

When a theory is falsified by the evidence, its proponents then tinker with the theory to remedy the problem. Sometimes the tinkering helps. Frequently, however, the tinkering moves the theory from the falsified to the unfalsifiable (an equally grave problem). When this is recognized, the proponents tinker further to try to remedy this new pitfall.

So, a theory does not immediately go flying out the window when falsified. Rather, by human intervention and ingenuity, it often lingers awhile, vacillating nebulously between the nether worlds of the falsified and the unfalsifiable. In either case, the theory fails to inform us about empirical observations. The theory loses its grip on reality and becomes scientifically useless. The precise status of the theory is then an academic matter of interest only to philosophers and historians.

Evolutionary theory is like that. Is evolution falsified? Or is it unfalsifiable? Such debate could go on endlessly, depending on whose version of evolutionary theory we are talking about. May we avoid academic rancor by calling it *non-science* and leaving it at that? That approach is best. When pressed, however, we can say that evolutionary theory[7] — as practiced by its proponents — is unfalsifiable, since that is its essential character.

---

[7] There are many theories of genetics and ecology that are scientific. Most of them are entirely acceptable within a creation viewpoint. When we say evolutionary theory is non-science, we are referring to the molecules-to-man explanation—the distinguishing theory that only evolutionists embrace.

The Case For Message Theory

The essence of message theory can be given in one paragraph. Life was reasonably designed for survival. Yet life was also designed to convey a message that tells where it came from. Life was designed to look like the product of a single designer, and to resist all other explanations of origin. This simple idea explains the pattern of life in a straightforward, scientific manner.

Biologic universals at the biochemical level are ideal for uniting organisms of all types and sizes. Their presence unifies life together in an undeniable way, and makes life look like the product of a single designer.

Life is united by design, not descent. Large morphological gaps and an absence of phylogeny are precisely how you would make life look unlike evolution. This uniform pattern could not result from chance. Life had to be designed this way.

The pattern of nested hierarchy is ideal for the biotic message. (1) It allows for enormous diversity, and diversity is cumbersome for evolution to explain. (2) It unites all life together, often in a visible way. (3) It cannot be explained by a transposition process. (4) It allows the absence of phylogeny to be seen. (5) It accomplishes these goals even when the observer lacks most of the data. (6) The pattern is embedded deeply into each organism, thereby making the biotic message resistant to mutation. (7) The nested pattern cannot be the haphazard result of a single civilization, rather it must be the intentional product of a single designer.

"Convergent forms," as they are called, are especially useful in the biotic message. (1) They unify life together, often in a visible way. (2) They thwart an observer's attempts to identify phylogeny. (3) They cannot be explained by common descent. (4) They cannot be explained by transposition. These convergent designs require a special balance. To meet goals 1 and 2, they had to be similar and abundant. To meet goal 3, they had to be specially placed within the overall pattern of life. To meet goal 4, they could not be identical. Lastly, to be seen at all, they could not be so excessively abundant that the nested pattern was totally obscured. Such balanced design is precisely what we find in nature. This cannot be happenstance. It must have been designed.

The masking and unmasking of genetic libraries would be a simple, powerful evolutionary mechanism for abruptly producing new biological designs. Yet life was designed to defeat that explanation. Life's major designs appear abruptly, but they are distinctly different from anything that appeared earlier and cannot be explained as unmasked components from various ancient ancestors. This is also seen in the phenograms of life (particularly at the molecular level) which show that the mechanism could not have operated. In addition, the absence of this simple, powerful mechanism from the picture creates a puzzle for evolutionists.

The biotic message sender knew just what to leave out to be convincing. The widespread absence from multicellular organisms of a transposition pattern defeats that simplest and most powerful of evolutionary explanations. The absence also creates an evolutionary puzzle: Why isn't transposition everywhere?

The pattern of life at the molecular level of proteins and genes follows message theory precisely. It could hardly be more potent evidence. Life's many molecular phenograms and cladograms form a smooth, distinct pattern that refutes transposition and unmasking processes. That pattern allows the absences of gradual intergradation and phylogeny to take on real force as evidence against evolution. That pattern also unifies life and reveals an incredible degree of planning and design.

Odd and curious designs (that evolutionists often call "imperfections") help the biotic message. Their unique pattern lets the observer know that life had only one designer. They operate in the same way that unique quirks in penmanship allow us to recognize the work of one handwriter. They also show that the biotic message was intentional, not merely the product of an ordinary designer whose expected goal would be engineering perfection.

The pattern of embryology described in von Baer's laws is ideal for unifying organisms together in a way that is both broad and visible. It could hardly be more direct. Because of this, even the ancient Greeks were aware of life's underlying unity. The sequence of ontogeny from generalized to specialized is perfect for accomplishing that. Also, the sequence is so difficult for evolutionists to explain that they avoid any direct attempt. Embryology is major evidence for message theory.

The biotic message would have totally failed without a fossil record or if that record was viewed as seriously incomplete. The sender of the biotic message had to convince the observer that the fossil record is reasonably complete and reliable. *The only way to accomplish that task is with a fossil sequence.* The sequence has a special structure that moves the observer toward accepting the completeness of the fossil record.

Many evolutionists (especially the punctuationists) now recognize that the fossil record is significantly complete and cannot be brushed aside. That fundamental recognition is what drove them to see that life's morphological gaps and absence of clear phylogeny are real, not merely the result of an incomplete fossil record. This is a major victory for the biotic message, and is due to the fossil sequence. The fossil sequence meets essential goals that are impossible to accomplish any other way. (1) Its special structure prevents the observer from casting aside the fossil record as incomplete. (2) It bonds the pattern of life to the Earth's crust, thereby preventing the observer from taking evolutionary problems and shifting them out into Space. (3) The pattern of abrupt appearances that evolutionists call "adaptive radiation" is evidence against evolution.

The inability of multicellular animals to efficiently digest cellulose helps make the system of life ecologically stable. Moreover, this situation is quite difficult for evolution to coherently explain.

The genetic mechanisms of sex seem to be reasonable designs for maintaining the long-term genetic well-being of species. In addition, they help the biotic message. (1) The widespread distribution and similarity of sex serve to unify life (often visibly). (2) Sex strongly resists evolutionary explanation. (3) Barriers to widespread interbreeding prevent hybrids, which prevents life from looking like a smooth gradual intergradation of life forms (that could be misperceived as the result of evolution).

466

The broad absence of Lamarckian inheritance is precisely what was needed to defeat that potent evolutionary explanation. The absence of that simple mechanism also creates an evolutionary puzzle.

These are the major features of life, and message theory directly explains and predicts them. If our observations had been different (in countless possible ways), then the biotic message would have been seriously jeopardized or discredited. The features of life are finely orchestrated toward one purpose. All this cannot be sheer chance. It had to be designed. We have before us a biotic message.

Onward and Outward

William Paley proposed that a designer was necessary for the origin of life. The idea is simple, explanatory, and rationally demanded by the data. Paley's theory is also scientifically testable, and has survived countless attempts to falsify it. Yet evolutionists throw it out solely because it conflicts with naturalism. Then they replace it with nothing — they have no testable scientific theory for the origin of life. Their ideas on the problem have diverged desperately, and Nobel laureates now refer to the origin of life as a "miracle."

Most evolutionists expect that life probably exists in outer space, and they eagerly look for it. If they found it, they would use it as evidence in their favor and against creation theory. Yet if they do not find it, they can claim we have not looked hard enough. Or they can always claim that their theory did not actually predict it. In short, their position is invulnerable. They have nothing at risk from future observations.

Evolutionary illusions extend from biology to cosmology. Modern evidence shows that the universe itself seems designed for life. The universe has extraordinarily improbable properties that are necessary to support life. Such design contradicts naturalism. So, evolutionary cosmologists created the anthropic principle to explain away the design of the universe.

They also created the illusion that the anthropic principle is scientific. The illusion was produced by equivocation and by misdirecting our attention onto "man as an observer." The idea actually focuses in another direction entirely, for it requires the existence of an infinitude of other universes unlike our own. The anthropic principle is unscientific because we cannot possibly test other universes.

The Big Bang, the Conservation of Mass-Energy, and the Second Law of Thermodynamics our among most firmly established science. Yet evolutionary cosmologists discard these because *in combination* these are inconsistent with naturalism. Evolutionists throw out our best science for no other reason than to protect their philosophical commitment to naturalism.

467

Evolutionists use 'Natural' selection, that is, they select whatever natural mechanisms they need to 'explain' the data. They now have a comprehensive program for explaining everything: the design of the universe; the many special properties of Earth; the origin of life; the adaptations of organisms; the curious pathways of embryology; and the overall pattern of life and its fossils. In each case their explanation runs contrary to a straightforward reading of the available observations. And in each case their explanations are invulnerable to future observations. In short, their program is not science. From beginning to end, their program is driven by an unrelenting commitment to naturalism, at the expense of science.

*

Unlike evolutionists, the creationist can embrace science whole-heartedly. The Big Bang, the Laws of Thermodynamics, and Paley's theory represent our best science, and the creationist (unlike the evolutionist) is not compelled to reject them offhand on philosophical grounds.

Moreover, when combined together they have a logical *scientific* conclusion. They indicate that a supernatural agent has performed a creative act in this universe. The universe seems intentionally designed to signal this.

That deduction is further supported by the fact that the Earth and the universe have extraordinarily improbable features necessary for life. They seem intricately designed for life's survival. (These are the features that the anthropic principle tries to explain away.)

In addition, the Earth and the universe have features necessary for the success of the biotic message. (1) The Earth has a peculiar ability to preserve and display its fossil record that is essential to the biotic message. (2) The universe seems designed to not yield a naturalistic origin of life. (3) The absence of extraterrestrial life effectively thwarts many evolutionary scenarios and points toward the supernatural as the only remaining possibility for life's designer.

In short, the design of life, the Earth, and the universe meet the goals predicted by message theory. They are designed for life's survival and to convey a message that tells where life came from.

These are not matters of whim or philosophy. Even a reluctant observer must admit these matters are real, logical, and scientific. On every major point — from biology to cosmology — from fossils, to experiments, to extraterrestrials — this creation theory is vulnerable to future observations. It takes risks. It exposes itself to observational danger. This testability is why it is scientific, and evolution is not. Creation is not merely our best science. It is our only science.

*

William Paley showed that we can recognize attributes of a watchmaker by examining a watch. In the same way, we can deduce attributes of life's designer. The designer pursued a consistent and credible goal. The designer employed logic, reason, intellect, purpose, intent, technology, and craft. The designer understood empirically based thinking (that we call Science). The designer could mentally project into various potential situations to envision how other observers might misperceive. The designer then constructed a vital message, resistant to all other interpretations. The designer has shown a desire and capacity to communicate.

Appendix to Survival of the Fittest

The chapter on *Survival of the Fittest* contains the analysis of interest to most readers. It explains what natural selection is, and precisely why it is not science. This appendix goes further to document examples and discuss the fine points. It may be skipped or skimmed without serious loss of continuity.

The appendix examines the diverse formulations of natural selection offered by leading evolutionists. These formulations all fail as science essentially for the reasons discussed in the chapter. These are variations on the themes of tautologies, special definitions, metaphysics, and lame formulations (T, SD, M, and L).

The key insights may be gleaned from the first four sections:

- Tautology once removed (T)—a particularly evasive form of tautology.

- Mathematical "derivations" of natural selection — said to be like mathematical proofs in Euclidean geometry (T ... but also SD,M,L).

- Natural selection as the sum total of good and valid reasons for survival (M).

- Fitness is determined by an engineer's criterion (M).

*

The four sections after those focus on leading proponents of natural selection. These sections are largely documentary, though each has unique interest.

- Micheal Ruse — the foremost philosopher of science to testify against creation at the 1981-1982 Arkansas creation-science trial (Act 590).

- Ernst Mayr—the renowned Harvard evolutionary theorist and historian of science. We will examine the variety of approaches he takes in one book.

- Elliot Sober — a philosopher of science. We will examine his book-length defense of natural selection. His major contribution to the debate is the idea of supervenience.

- Sir Karl Popper—the renowned authority on testability as the criterion of science. He has publicly said that Darwinism does not pass muster.

The final four sections document (and refute) the most radical tactic used in defense of natural selection: the assault on the philosophy of science. The assault subtly tries to dispose of the criterion of testability, so as to allow natural selection to count as science.

- The criterion of falsifiable predictions — Riddiford and Penny

- Fitness undefined — Mary Williams

- Schematic science — Robert Brandon

- Direct assault on testability — Philip Kitcher

Tautology Once Removed

A tautology is a circular definition pretending to be an explanation, like this:

> Survivors survive.

Such simple statements are easy to spot as tautologies. So, we rarely see tautologies offered in this simple way. Instead, the typical loop of circularity is two statements in length, like this:

> The survivors are determined by their fitness.
>
> Fitness is identified by survival.

That pair of statements is more difficult to detect as a tautology. The difficulty is due to the increased length of the circular loop. In the same way one can create longer loops of circularity, like this:

> The survivors are determined by their fitness.
>
> Fitness is determined by the genetic constitution of the individuals.
>
> Genetic constitution is identified by survival.

In this way, one can create long loops of tautology that are more difficult to detect.

This is commonly done by removing the tautology from one situation and placing it into another *identical* situation. It is still a tautology. It has only been removed once from the original situation. I call it a **tautology once removed**. It is done like this:

> The survivors are determined by their fitness.
>
> Fitness is identified by survival in another identical situation.

The reference to an "identical situation" does not solve the tautology problem. It only increases the complexity of these statements, making the tautology more difficult to detect.

A tautology once removed is like the doctor saying, "The cause of your father's deafness is identical to Miss Smith's situation — in her case it was caused by hearing impairment."

*

Chapman uses this approach in his attempt to rebut the charge that natural selection is a tautology.

> Fitness, however, can be estimated not just after natural selection has operated, but before. Genetically similar organisms can be studied and demographic tables can be constructed that give average measures of such factors as number of viable offspring and the ability to survive in certain environments. With this information, evolutionary fitness can to some extent be predicted, and thus the tautology disappears. (Chapman, 1983, p 109)

Chapman says fitness can be estimated because "Genetically *similar* organisms can be studied" for their "*ability to survive* in certain environments." (My italics). Fitness is still measured by survival (by the survival of other similar or identical organisms). The idea hinges on the "other organisms" being similar or identical. The tautology has not disappeared. Instead the tautology is removed to a similar or identical situation. It is a tautology once removed.

*

Riddiford and Penny try this approach using a clone. (A clone is an offspring genetically identical to a parent.) They try to show that natural selection is testable. Toward this end they indicate that survival of a clone can be predicted, based on survival of its identical parent in the same environment. This turns natural selection into a tautology once removed.

> There are many known mechanisms for genetic variants affecting the probability of survival of an organism. There are countless examples from biochemical genetics ... It could be objected that with most of these biochemical examples, there was no *prediction* that a particular mutant would or would not survive, because the discovery of an altered macromolecule was made after the mutant had been selected. However, this is a trivial objection because it is always possible, in principle, though in practice tedious, to establish a clone, test whether a particular group of enzymes is present, make a prediction about the survival of the clone in a particular environment, and then carry out the test. (Riddiford and Penny, 1984, p 21)

*

If we point out the tautology once removed, then a theorist might remove it to yet another identical situation or another clone. This would be a tautology *twice* removed. That process could be continued indefinitely, but the tautology is not thereby eliminated. It is only removed farther from the original situation. Such attempts do not solve the tautology problem.

False Derivations of Natural Selection

Some authorities attempt to derive natural selection from basic propositions, as one would a mathematical formula. They try to prove natural selection to be true, and give it mathematical respectability. The derivations all have errors.

Colin Patterson takes this approach.

> [N]atural selection theory can be presented in the form of a deductive argument, for example:
>
> 1) All organisms must reproduce;
>
> 2) All organisms exhibit hereditary variations;
>
> 3) Hereditary variations differ in their effect on reproduction;
>
> 4) Therefore variations with favourable effects on reproduction will succeed, those with unfavourable effects will fail, and organisms will change.
>
> In this sense, natural selection is not a scientific theory, but a truism, something that is proven to be true, like one of Euclid's theorems: if statements 1-3 are true, so is statement 4. This argument shows that natural selection must occur, but it does not say that natural selection is the only cause of evolution, and when natural selection is generalized as the explanation of all evolutionary change, or of every feature of every organism, it becomes so all-embracing that it is in much the same class as Freudian psychology and astrology. (Patterson, C., 1978, p 147)[1]

Patterson incorrectly claims that natural selection is derived and "proven to be true." The derived statement #4 says organisms will change, yet the three propositions do not guarantee change. There are cases in nature where the three propositions are true yet organisms do *not* change. Many 'living fossils' have remained unchanged for hundreds of millions of years. The conclusion that organisms will change does not follow from the three propositions and must be removed.

The remainder of statement #4 also cannot be derived from the propositions. Given the three propositions, the correct conclusion is this:

> All organisms must reproduce and exhibit hereditary variations that differ in their effect on reproduction.

This correctly derived statement is quite different from #4. It shows that at Patterson's conclusion, new material was brought into the derivation: the idea that favorable effects will succeed and unfavorable effects will fail. These

---

[1] Colin Patterson gave insight when he wrote, "natural selection is not a scientific theory but a truism", and by his apt comparison of natural selection with Freudian psychology and astrology. He is not the only well-known evolutionist to make this comparison. On other occasions he has been vocal in his criticism of natural selection.

concepts are not mentioned in the propositions, so where did they come from? Why are we not instantly alerted by the sudden appearance of this new material?

These are tautologies that Patterson inserted here to form the heart of his conclusion. They slip past us. Favorable effects always succeed better than unfavorable effects (in anything, not just biology). How do we know favorable effects? Answer: By the way they succeed.

So, Patterson's derivation was entirely unnecessary. "ABCs with favorable effects on XYZ ... will have favorable effects on XYZ" is a true statement in any possible universe *by definition.* No derivation is necessary, or possible, to establish this point. It is true by definition, not by derivation.

Compare this with mathematically derived truth, such as the Euclidean Theorem stating that the sum of three angles of a triangle equals 180 degrees. This truth is not obvious from the start, nor is it true by definition. Just as importantly, it is *not* true for all possible geometries, all possible universes. (It does not hold true for spherical geometry.) Euclid's Theorems convey unobvious information about the structure of plane geometry.

In addition, Patterson's formulation has ambiguous references to "favourable," "reproduction," and "success." These allow ample latitude for alternative interpretations (T,SD,M). Evolutionists pack these multiple interpretations into a Trojan Horse and wheel it past the Gates of Science under the guise of a derivation. Once the horse is accepted within the fortress, the alternate interpretations can be made manifest.

*

Gould also tries a derivation:

> [T]he basis of natural selection is simplicity itself — two undeniable facts and an inescapable conclusion:
>
> 1) Organisms vary, and these variations are inherited (at least in part) by their offspring.
>
> 2) Organisms produce more offspring than can possibly survive.
>
> 3) On average, offspring that vary most strongly in directions favored by the environment will survive and propagate. Favorable variation will therefore accumulate in populations by natural selection. (Gould, 1973, p 11)

Statement #1 says organisms vary, and #2 says not all organisms can survive, but statement #3 tries to identify which organisms will survive. The conclusion (statement #3) cannot be derived from statements #1 and #2. As in Patterson's case, new material has been introduced to form the conclusion.

*

Mayr presents a derivation he attributes to Darwin:

1) There is a struggle for existence.

2) No two individuals are exactly the same; rather, every population displays enormous variability.

3) Much of this variation is heritable.

Therefore:

4) Survival in the struggle for existence is not random but depends in part on the hereditary constitution of the surviving individuals. This unequal survival constitutes a process of natural selection. (Mayr, 1982, p 479-480)

The conclusion (statement #4) makes a vague attempt to identify the survivors. It cannot be derived from the three assumptions because they make no mention of the survivors. Again new material has been brought in to form the conclusion.

Notice also the conclusion (statement #4) has an undefined reference to the keyphrase "hereditary constitution." The ambiguity allows multiple interpretations (T,SD,M).

As an alternative interpretation, notice that none of the statements clearly identifies *which* organisms will survive. A process constituted merely of "unequal survival" fails to identify the survivors. So, it cannot explain adaptation, and is a lame formulation (L).

To illustrate the non-scientific status of Mayr's formulation, we offer a theory of motion similarly.

> Motion in the material universe is not random but depends in part on the 'innermost essence' of the moving objects. This relative motion constitutes a process of kinetics.

This theory of motion, and Mayr's derivation of natural selection are not science.

*

In summary, evolutionists try to derive natural selection from basic starting assumptions. In each case, however, there are errors.

- The derivations are erroneous because the conclusion cannot be derived from the starting assumptions.

- New concepts are brought into the derivations to form the heart of the "derived" conclusion. That escapes our notice because the new concepts are tautologies we intuitively recognize as true by definition.

- The "derived" conclusions are stated so ambiguously that multiple interpretations (T,SD,M,L) can be made.

Good and Valid Reasons

Some theorists defend natural selection as follows: There are 'good and valid reasons' why organisms survive or perish — natural selection is the sum of all these reasons for survival.

Micheal Ghiselin gives an example.

> Natural selection is differential reproduction with its causes, nothing more. (Ghiselin, 1969, p 74)

Ghiselin's formulation is thoroughly unspecific about the very 'causes' that natural selection is intended to specify. It is like proposing:

> My theory of kinetics is relative motion with its causes, nothing more.

These are not scientific theories because there is nothing to test — they are metaphysical.

*

Lewontin offers a similar approach in a long-winded way. He acknowledges that the falsificationist criterion of science is "widely believed in by practising scientists who bother to think about the problem." Yet he also acknowledges that natural selection is not falsifiable. Lewontin reviews for his readers the charge against natural selection.

> Such a theory can never be falsified, for it asserts that some environmental difference created the conditions for natural selection of a new character. ... the failure to find the environmental factor proves nothing, except that one has not looked hard enough. .... The theory of natural selection is then revealed as metaphysical rather than scientific. Natural selection explains nothing because it explains everything. (Lewontin, 1972, p 181)

Lewontin then responds to the argument. He does not deny the charge of unfalsifiability, rather he confirms it:

> The trouble with this analysis is that even though *natural selection might not be an epistemologically satisfactory hypothesis,* it might nevertheless be true. Very inconvenient, but there you are. (Lewontin, 1972, p 181, my italics)

The solution he offers is to reject testability (Popper's criterion), at least for the theory of evolution. He then offers an alternative criterion of science, which he calls "confirmation of hypotheses." In particular, he affirms that natural selection is not falsifiable.

> *The way out, taken by evolutionists, is to go back to older ideas of confirmation of hypotheses, rather than Popperian falsification,* and to notice that there are two different sorts of theories, with respect to confirmation, that are indistinguishable from the point of view of falsification. The first sort, ... is not only not falsifiable, but every observation about nature is a positive confir-

mation and necessarily so. .... *The second sort, to which Darwin's theory belongs, although not falsifiable* because not universally quantified, could fail of confirmation in any number of cases, indeed always. (Lewontin, 1972, p 181, my italics)

Lewontin uses his criterion of science — confirmation of hypotheses — in an attempt to show that natural selection is science.

[I]f we chose 100 examples of variation between organisms in space or time and tried to pin down the environmental circumstances responsible, we might succeed, after immense effort, in producing only two reasonably convincing cases. Then ... we could not know whether natural selection was in fact a rare cause of evolution, or whether it was a common cause but damned hard to demonstrate. Everyone would have wasted his time. But suppose, instead, that ninety-eight good confirmations resulted. Then, if the cases were chosen without bias, every reasonable person would be forced to admit the rule of natural selection amid joyous cries of 'No Poppery!' (Lewontin, 1972, p 181)

Lewontin is really offering a round-about way of stating another version of the theory: There are environmental circumstances responsible for survival, and when we pin down these environmental circumstances we have "confirmations" of natural selection. It is just another way of saying: There are good and valid reasons why organisms survive and perish. This is a metaphysical formulation.

An Engineer's Criterion

Stephen Jay Gould tries to refute the tautology objection by proposing a different formulation. He suggests that fitness is determined by an engineer's criterion. An organism is more fit if it is closer to how a human engineer would design it.

[C]ertain morphological, physiological, and behavioural traits should be superior *a priori* as designs for living in new environments. These traits confer fitness by an engineer's criterion of good design, not by the empirical fact of their survival and spread. It got colder before the woolly mammoth evolved its shaggy coat. (Gould, 1983b, p 143)

Gould's criterion for survival can be rephrased: An organism will survive in an environment if it meets an 'engineer's criterion' of good design for survival in that environment.

Let us hope engineers never accept Gould's criterion literally as their own because if they simultaneously accept it and attempt to apply it, they must replace engineer's criterion with 'Gould's criterion' repeatedly. They will forever be recursively replacing without ever arriving at an answer. This is because Gould's idea does not provide answers. It merely says, "For the answer go ask an engineer."

Here are two proposals analogous to Gould's:

> A bridge will support weight if it meets the engineer's criterion for supporting weight.

> An object will move if it meets the physicist's criterion for motion.

Such proposals are not scientific theories because they have no innards, nothing to test.[2] We must read between the lines of Gould's idea if we are to get anywhere with it.

Take the case of intelligence. Intelligence is a difficult thing to quantify. There are many methods used to measure it. These methods do not arrive at the same results, and the field of psychology is forever debating their significance.

Gould's book, *The Mismeasure of Man*, deals with intelligence measurement in humans. He discusses two great fallacies of intelligence testing: (1) the fallacy of reification — the attempt to convert abstract concepts (such as intelligence) into single measurable entities; and (2) the fallacy of ranking — our propensity for ordering complex variation as a gradual ascending scale.[3]

The intelligence of an organism is difficult to measure. Yet, the task is compounded infinitely when one must also measure the metabolism, fecundity, coloration, behavior, mating, migration, habitat, food supply, of the organism, plus similarly measure the attributes of all the other organisms and factors in the environment, plus interpret all these measurements (in some way) to obtain a single, reified, rankable 'predictor of survival' — fitness.

This problem is further aggravated by the fact that natural selection supposedly operates on slight, small differences between these highly reified quantities. Yes, we see design in nature, in fact we are overwhelmed with it. Gould has not shown that the evaluation required by his idea can be made with any signifi-

---

[2] Kitcher attempts arguments (against creation) that are effective here against Gould's concept of natural selection. "Invocation of the word 'design,' or the passing reference to the satisfaction of 'need,' explains nothing. The needs are not given in advance of the design of structures to accommodate them, but are themselves encompassed in the design." … "to invoke 'design' without saying what counts as good design is not only vacuous but blasphemous." (Kitcher, 1982, p 137-138) In the last quote Kitcher is referring, with favor, to a viewpoint expressed by Leibniz.

[3] "We … give the word 'intelligence' to this wondrously complex and multifaceted set of human capabilities. This shorthand symbol is then reified and intelligence achieves its *dubious status as a unitary thing*." (Gould, 1981, p 24, and 25, my italics)

"Thus, the common style embodying both fallacies of thought has been quantification, or the measurement of intelligence as a single number for each person." (Gould, 1981, p 159)

cance, certainly not enough significance to test it. Gould's formulation is not tautological, but it is metaphysical.[4]

*

Another factor undermines Gould's idea. Most evolutionists, Gould foremost among them,[5] argue that nature often does *not* have designs a capable engineer would employ. They use this argument from imperfection as evidence against a designer. Then they try to claim that natural selection actually predicts this situation.

> [I]f natural selection were the cause of the appearance of design, we should expect animals and plants not to conform to engineering principles in any optimal way. (Futuyma, 1983, p 126)

> [I]deal design is a lousy argument for evolution, for it mimics the postulated action of an omnipotent creator. Odd arrangements and funny solutions are the proof of evolution — paths that a sensible God would never tread but that a natural process, constrained by history, follows perforce. (Gould, 1980, p 20, 21)

Thus, Gould argues that fitness is determined by an engineer's criterion of good design, yet he and other evolutionists also argue that nature's adaptations frequently do not conform to an engineer's criterion of good design. Gould's position is either self-contradictory, or it is intolerably vague, flexible, and un-testable. In either view, it is not science.

---

[4] The *ceteris paribus* assumption is a fancy name for the assumption that "all other things are equal." (It is rarely mentioned by that name.) Newton's theory of gravity would use the assumption like this: If a leaf comes loose from a tree it will fall to the ground, assuming *ceteris paribus*. Yet *ceteris paribus* does not always apply — the wind may instead blow the leaf up and away. We would say that instead of the theory being at fault, the *ceteris paribus* assumption simply did not apply to this case. In this way, experimental failures can sometimes be blamed on the *ceteris paribus* assumption. However, there is nothing about *ceteris paribus* that can alter the status of a metaphysi-cal theory. If a theory is untestable, then *ceteris paribus* cannot help it.

Lewontin (1978, p 222-225) tries to defend against the tautology objection by using a formulation that involves engineering analysis (similar to Gould's concept) together with the *ceteris paribus* assumption. His concept, like Gould's, is not science because it is not testable.

[5] Gould is noted for making the argument from imperfection. He often refers to it as the "panda principle" after his favorite example the panda's thumb.

Ruse

Michael Ruse writes that, "there is an empirical, nontautological, falsifiable basis to the mechanism cherished by Darwinians." He provides a formulation that he says contains three testable claims.

1) There is a struggle for reproduction.

2) Success in the struggle is, on average, not random, but a function of the distinctive characteristics possessed by organisms.

3) What selection favors in one situation will be what selection favors in identical situations. (Ruse, 1982, p 140)

Notice the undefined reference to *distinctive characteristics*, which replaces the position usually reserved for *fitness*. Both these terms suffer from the same ambiguity problems and are open to the same types of interpretation (T,SD,M).

Alternatively, his formulation can be viewed as lame (L) because, taken literally, it makes no attempt to identify *which* organisms will survive. Without such an attempt it cannot explain adaptation.

Ruse also offers an interesting form of tautology. How do we identify fitness? His statement #3 seems to provide the answer: We may identify fitness by the way it increases survival *in identical situations.* With this interpretation survival of the fittest becomes a tautology once removed from the particular situation.[6] Yet, it is still a tautology.

To show testability, Ruse offers special definitions. He provides three examples of empiric falsifiability: the arctic mammal with a white coat; protective coloration of snails against predation by thrushes; and human sickle-cell genes in malarial regions of the world. As they are all special definitions, these incarnations of natural selection are falsifiable (and are falsified for the general case). Yet he does not discuss whether *his formulation* is falsifiable. He gives these special definitions and mistakenly concludes, "the charge of unfalsifiability merits no more attention." (p 140-142)

---

[6] This interpretation is confirmed by Ruse's additional emphasis, "A characteristic that helps an organism at one time and place can be expected to offer similar help in the same circumstances at different times and places." (Ruse, 1982, p 140) When viewed this way his formulation is not a scientific theory. It is guidance, a helpful hint as it were, to conducting research. It first invites you to go out and find a situation ("a characteristic that helps an organism at one time and place"), then it exhorts you to go find an *identical* situation, then it predicts similar effects in both situations.

The idea that natural causes will have the same effect in identical situations is not a scientific theory. It is one of the axioms of science: an idea so fundamental it cannot be tested, yet so necessary it is assumed to be true. It is of fundamental importance in science because it is combined with genuine theories to make testable predictions.

One could view his formulation as a tautology once removed or as a fundamental axiom. I view it as the former because he specifically offers it as a definition of natural selection, and it therefore collapses to a tautology. In either view his formulation contains no explanation of adaptation.

To help show the non-scientific status of Ruse's formulation, consider a theory of motion framed in a similar way:

1)   Some objects move more than others.

2)   The movement of objects is, on average, not random, but a function of the 'distinctive characteristics' possessed by the objects.

3)   The way objects move in one situation will be the way objects move in identical situations.

This theory of motion is as unscientific as Ruse's formulation of natural selection.

Flexibility

This section examines the variety of flexible approaches taken in a single book by a single authority, Ernst Mayr (1982).

Mayr wrote that the phrase survival of the fittest is "rather unfortunate, because now the objection was raised that the entire theory of natural selection rested on a tautology." (p 519). Apparently to avoid a tautology, he defines natural selection as:

> ... the differential reproduction of individuals that differ uniquely in their adaptive superiority. (Mayr, 1982, p 57)

Survival of the fittest was replaced with differential survival of the differentially fit. That can still be a tautology, depending on the definition of the *fit*. If the fit are determined by their survival, then there is a tautology (T).

Nonetheless, this formulation is always lame (L) because it fails to identify the survivors. Suppose two organisms differ in their adaptive superiority. The formulation says that one will survive better than the other, but it does not say *which* of the two will survive better. Without identifying the survivors it cannot explain adaptation.

*

Mayr (p 491) quotes one of Darwin's classic definitions of natural selection involving "favorable" and "injurious" variations. These ambiguous keywords provide ample latitude for T,SD,M.

Historically, that concept has been attacked as a tautology. So, Mayr tries to defend Darwin against the tautology objection by quoting Darwin's words:

> All [Darwin] said was that among the countless variations that occur in every species, some that are *'useful in some way* to each being in the *great and complex battle of life* should sometimes occur in the course of thousands of generations', and 'that *individuals having any advantage, however slight,* over others, would have the best chance of surviving and of procreating their kind'. There is nothing circular in this statement. (Mayr, 1982, p 519, my italics)

Mayr is correct. There is no tautology here, for here he has quoted Darwin's *metaphysical* formulation. We cannot empirically test "useful in some way," "great and complex battle of life," and "individuals having any advantage, however slight." These concepts are metaphysical and cannot be evaluated. So, this formulation is untestable.

Mayr then tries to defend against the objection that natural selection is untestable.

> Several philosophers opposed to *natural selection* have stated that it is impossible to falsify any claims made on behalf of *natural selection*. Here one must make a distinction between the theory of *natural selection* as such and the application of *natural selection* to specific cases. As soon as one deals with specific cases, one can make predictions that can be falsified in principle, by testing them against various assumptions. (Mayr, 1982, p 523, my italics)

To show their theory is testable, Darwinians often employ special definitions. Mayr's statement does this by invoking many "applications" for "specific cases." He indicates that natural selection makes predictions only after one deals with specific cases. This seems to endorse an unnamed multitude of special definitions, thereby giving a mistaken appearance of testability.

Yet Mayr's statement does not actually name a specific special definition, and without that it cannot name a specific test. Without a specific test, it fails to show that natural selection is testable. This is easy to demonstrate. Merely change *natural selection* to "astrology" and his paragraph still reads true. Mayr's defense is equally effective (or ineffective) for astrology.

*

Mayr tries yet another approach to refute the nonfalsifiability of Darwinian theory:

> Finally, since few if any neo-Darwinians claim that every component of the phenotype and every evolutionary change is the result of ad hoc selection, the nonfalsifiability argument has not much force.

His statement shows another dimension of the nonfalsifiability of natural selection. The theory is not invoked in every evolutionary change, rather it is invoked at the whim of evolutionary speculation. This provides boundless flexibility, and the theorists use that flexibility to protect their theory. Theorists can keep the theory from being inconvenienced by contrary data simply by not invoking the theory for that case.

By analogy, an astrologer would defend astrology in this way:

> Since few if any astrologers claim that every component of the psyche and every daily event is the result of astrological causes, the nonfalsifiability argument has not much force.

Astrology and natural selection are both extremely flexible. Their proponents can use this flexibility to avoid any test.

Supervenience

Elliot Sober wrote a lengthy book on natural selection in which he devoted an entire chapter to the defense against the tautology objection. In it, he said:

> I very much doubt that any bad consequences would follow about evolutionary theory, even if certain characterizations of fitness were nonempirical. (Sober, 1984a, p 63)

The above statement represents Sober's approach. In his view a theory is not so bad if it is sometimes nonempirical so long as it is sometimes empirical. He argues similarly against charges that the theory is tautological and non-explanatory.

He allows many alternate formulations of natural selection. For example, he explicitly endorses the use of special definitions.

> The other possibility is to regard each model of selection process as stipulating its own special definition of fitness. (Sober, 1984a, p 70)

Sober claims it is very hard to show the tautological nature of a theory because:

> One must not only examine the structure of the theory as it now stands *but must also have some way of foreseeing how alternatives to the theory might be structured.* (Sober, 1984a, p 73, my italics)

This is erroneous. Opponents of a theory are under no obligation to foresee how alternatives might be structured. They only need show that the theory, as it now stands, is not science.

*

Sober sees the difficulty of getting a useful formulation that is simultaneously both general and empirical. Therefore, he suggests this requirement of science should be abandoned.

> But no argument was ever offered for why there must be a part of the story that is both general and empirical at once. I suggest that this requirement on explanation should be discarded. (Sober, 1984a, p 80)

His suggestion would allow survival of the fittest to have multiple formulations, some that are general (T,M) and others that are empirical (T,SD). Tautology stands alone as the only formulation meeting both criteria at once.

> [N]o perfectly general *physical* characterization of fitness is available [M]. When it comes to saying what fitness is *in general*, the characterization given in terms of survival [T] and reproduction [RC] seems to stand alone. (Sober, 1984a, p 82-83)

Having provided a tautology, Sober then immediately gives a metaphysical formulation. He does this with new unfamiliar terminology: supervenience. He argues that fitness is supervenient. These terms have the same meaning as *metaphysical*, as shown in the following three examples.

> All supervenience implies is that no *single* physical characteristic will be the *universal* key to fitness [M]. (Sober, 1984a, p 83)

Supervenience excludes evolutionary theory from finding a single physical characterization of the basis of fitness [M]. (Sober, 1984a, p 84)

[N]o physicalistic account can be offered of *what fitness is*. The reason is simply that fitness is not a physical property [M]. (Sober, 1984a, p 50)

*

He also offers bootstrapping as an independent criterion for fitness. Bootstrapping turns natural selection into a tautology once removed.

Another strategy for obtaining an independent criterion for fitness differences in a population involves 'bootstrapping.' One may begin ... by looking at differences in survival and reproductive success in one population .... Then, when confronted with a second, similar population, one may be able to use one's previous experience to reason in the opposite direction. The hypothesis would be that the characteristics that determined fitness differences in the first population also do so in the second. (Sober, 1984a, p 81-82)

*

Sober's chapter also discusses how fitness is the probability or propensity for survival and reproduction (Sober, 1984a, p 74-77). This is the probability conundrum (PC). As already discussed, the probability conundrum does not solve the problems (T,SD,M,L) with the theory.

*

Sober also tries to defend against the tautology objection by endorsing Gould's metaphysical concept of fitness as "design by an engineer's criterion." (Sober, 1984a, p 81 and 84)

*

Sober also gives many examples of lame formulations (L) and special definitions (SD) from population genetics (Sober, 1984a, p 79, 83, 84). (Evolutionists often use population genetics to display natural selection as real science. That attempt is refuted in the chapter on population genetics.)

*

In summary, Sober gives multiple formulations from all four groups (T,SD, M,L). He gives a tautology once removed (he calls it bootstrapping). He gives formulations that are metaphysical (he calls it supervenient). In his entire book he does not give a single immovable statement of natural selection and defend it as explanatory, testable, science.[7]

---

[7] Sober sometimes uses unsuitable definitions of the terms "tautology" and "*a priori.*" He also tries to replace the former term with the latter and further confusion results. One example is his implication that the whole of mathematics is *a priori* (Sober, 1984a, p 79-80). The attempt is, I think, to persuade readers that natural selection at its worst is no worse than the whole of mathematics. His argument is false, since mathematics is neither tautological (i.e., a definition masquerading as greater knowledge) nor *a priori* (i.e., assumed to be true).

Sir Karl Popper

> I have come to the conclusion that Darwinism is not a testable scientific theory but a *metaphysical research programme* — a possible framework for testable scientific theories … (Popper, 1974, p 134)

In 1974 the renowned philosopher of science, Sir Karl Popper, proclaimed, "Darwinism is not a testable scientific theory."

That proclamation won him the outrage of evolutionists worldwide. Four years later Popper publicly recanted.[8] Since then evolutionists have quoted his change of mind as the final verdict that their theory is science. Now they approvingly cite Popper's authority as the definitive answer to any criticism.

However, we must reject Popper's recantation as inadequate. This section explains why.

In his recantation, Popper gave two examples as tests of the theory. The first one is the case of industrial melanism. Let me explain this classic case before we get to Popper's discussion.

Around the 1900s certain communities in England experienced a dramatic increase in airborne soot caused by pollution from the industrial revolution. This soot coated the bark of trees making them dark. Previously the moths in the region tended to be light in color, while some were dark (or melanic, after the dark pigmentation called melanin). As the trees became dark, the dark moths became camouflaged, while the light moths became visible against the new dark background. Since the light moths were more visible, predators ate them in greater abundance. Meanwhile, the dark moths enjoyed an increased survival rate because they were harder to detect. Thus, over a few decades the population of moths became darker.

A few things should be noted about this case. Modern efforts to clean up the environment have reduced the soot pollution, and recent decades have seen the moth population return to the light colored form. The moths themselves never changed very much.

> [N]o new species of moth were created and certainly no new kind of organism was produced. All that occurred was an alteration of gene frequencies. (Thompson, 1989, p 9)

Here we return to Popper's discussion.

> Darwin's own most important contribution to the theory of evolution, his theory of natural selection, is difficult to test. There are some tests, even some experimental tests; and in some cases, such as the famous phenomenon known as 'industrial melanism', we can observe natural selection happening under our very eyes, as it were. Nevertheless, really severe tests

---

[8] "The theory of natural selection may be so formulated that it is far from tautological. In this case it is not only testable, but it turns out to be not strictly universally true." (Popper, 1978, p 339-355)

485

of the theory of natural selection are hard to come by, much more so than tests of otherwise comparable theories in physics or chemistry. (Popper, 1978)

As usual, the ability of natural selection to shift its basis confounds our ability to see through the confusion. Theories about industrial melanism may be falsifiable, but they are not the theory of natural selection. They are merely special definitions. Industrial melanism fails to show that natural selection is falsifiable.

*

Popper continues with his second example.

In its most daring and sweeping form, the theory of natural selection would assert that *all* organisms ... have evolved as the result of natural selection; ... If formulated in this sweeping way, the theory is not only refutable, but actually refuted. For *not all* organs serve a *useful* purpose: as Darwin himself points out, there are organs like the tail of the peacock, and behavioural programmes like the peacock's display of his tail, which cannot be explained by their *utility*, and therefore not by natural selection. Darwin explained them by the preference of the other sex, that is by sexual selection. .... It seems far preferable to admit that *not* everything that evolves is *useful*, though it is astonishing how many things are; ... In other words, it seems to me that like so many theories in biology, evolution by natural selection is not strictly universal, though it seems to hold for a vast number of important cases. (Popper, 1978, his italics)

The untestability of natural selection is not altered by the presence or absence of rival theories. Nonetheless, discussion of rival theories can create confusion, leading to erroneous conclusions. This happened to Popper here. He creates two rival theories by splitting natural selection[9] into two parts: (1) sexual selection; and (2) a "sweeping form" (natural selection minus sexual selection). This change in terminology causes the confusion from which he draws an erroneous conclusion.[10]

---

[9] Since Darwin's time, the theory of natural selection has included sexual selection.

"Darwin's effort to keep sexual selection distinct from natural selection encountered strenuous objections." and "The recognition of sexual selection was entirely rejected by the population geneticists" who define their terms such that "any distinction between the two kinds of selection is obliterated." (Mayr, 1982, p 596) Sexual selection "came to be regarded as an integral part of natural selection rather than separate from it." (Merrell, 1981, p 73)

[10] Some illusions about natural selection are created by comparing it with a 'rival.' Here Popper artificially creates a rival by splitting natural selection into two parts. Often evolutionists use Lamarck's theory as the rival. Their error is simple. The presence or absence of rivals has no bearing on the untestability of natural selection.

This can be understood with an analogy. An astrologer might argue that astrology is testable, by dividing it into two parts as follows:

> If formulated in a sweeping way, the astrological theory is not only refutable, but actually refuted. For *not all* personality characteristics are shaped by the motion of planets and moons, asteroids and comets. There are personality traits which are so constant and unchanging that they cannot be explained by such transitory phenomena. Many of these personality traits are explained *by the astrological theory of constellations*. In other words, it seems that like so many theories of psychology, astrology is not strictly universal, though it seems to hold for a vast number of important cases.

The logic goes like this. Theory A is divided into two subsidiary theories B and C, and the discussion revolves around the inability of theory B to *explain* certain empirical facts that are *explained better* by theory C. The issue of falsifiability gets lost in the confusion. The falsifiability of theories A, B, or C is never established.

Popper's recantation tried to defend natural selection as a testable scientific theory, but his arguments misapply his own well-established criterion. This is a lackluster showing by an otherwise great thinker. It may perhaps be attributed to the strong criticism he received from the evolutionary community as a result of his earlier pronouncement.[11]

---

11   Even evolutionists doubt the candor of Popper's recantation. "[Since Popper made his original charges against natural selection] Popper himself has modified his position somewhat; *but, disclaimers aside, I suspect that even now he does not really believe that Darwinism in its modern form is genuinely falsifiable.*" (Ruse, 1982, p 133, my italics)

The Criterion of Falsifiable Predictions

Anyone can make predictions. Even astrologers and tarot card readers make predictions. Some predictions will be true and some will be false, but no one profits when the predictions remain isolated instances.

In science we construct a *hypothesis* and then test it by testing the predictions that follow logically from it. So, if your predictions are not drawn from a hypothesis, then you are not doing science, you are merely casting predictions. No matter how much you believe your predictions, they are not science until a hypothesis is found clearly embodying them.

Some evolutionists are trying to redefine science. *They want to rid science of the requirement that theories must be testable.* Riddiford and Penny attempt it. They propose a new criterion of science: the criterion of falsifiable predictions.

> "We do not accept the criterion that a theory must be directly falsifiable. In its place we propose to use the ability of a theory to lead to testable predictions as the criterion of a theory's scientific adequacy. ....
>
> The problem of defining relative adaptedness prevents quantitative predictions that could then be thoroughly tested. However, ... it is still usually possible to make qualitative predictions, or predictions of a statistical nature [PC]. These are not so easy to test as thoroughly as quantitative tests, but as long as they can be disproved, they belong to the realm of science rather than metaphysics. ....
>
> It is predictions that can be tested rather than the theories themselves."
> (Riddiford and Penny, 1984, p 14, 29, and 32)

Evolutionists are attempting to get around the criterion of testability. They are trying to remove the burden of testability from the theory and place it somewhere else. Here they place the burden onto predictions. Riddiford and Penny argue that predictions must be testable *rather than the theory itself*. Their criterion would then allow anything to count as science, for even astrology makes individual predictions that are falsifiable.

Fitness Undefined

Mary Williams acknowledges, "The phrase 'survival of the fittest' is a source of nagging embarrassment to evolutionists." (Williams, M., 1984, p 83-98)[12]

> [I]t is clearly ambiguous, purportedly tautological, and (so far) impossible to translate into a statement that is nontautological and nonambiguous, and captures the essence of natural selection … (Williams, M., 1984, p 83)[13]

She realizes there has been a problem in defining *fitness*.

> … 'superior', 'adaptively superior', 'adaptively complex', 'greater ability of phenotypes to obtain representation in the next generation', 'adaptedness', etc. are all simply disguised ways of saying 'fitter.' (Williams, M., 1984, p 88)

She also acknowledges that evolutionists have been sneaking in undefined terms.

> [Many biologists have been led] into the inconsistent position of advocating that all terms be defined while at the same time *sneaking in undefined terms*. (Williams, M., 1984, p 96)

Williams identified many problems with natural selection.

She admits, "The belief that all (nonobvious) terms must be defined is common among scientists" — she then calls this fundamental tenet a "fallacious metaphysical doctrine."

She then provides a novel solution. She refuses to define fitness and defends this as scientifically acceptable. She says, "Fitness is a theoretical term which cannot be explicitly defined."

Her discussion uses many vague references: "intuitively stated theory," "intuitive definition," "abstract term," "deepest law," "abstract concept," and "the theory is deep." For example, "In any deep theory some of the terms will be so abstract that the lack of adequate definitions will be painfully obvious."

> The difficulty that ambushes fitness is that abstract terms which are not close to experience (i.e., to direct observation) are *not amenable to definition in terms of direct observation*. (Williams, M., 1984, p 90)

*

---

12 Williams proposes the phrase "expansion of the fitter subcland" to replace "survival of the fittest."

13 Williams attempts a formulation involving "superior in fitness" which, due to lack of definition, fails to be testable.

She claims, "it is logically impossible to define all words used" and that, fitness is a "primitive term" which we cannot explicitly define.

> [I]ts meaning in the theory is *completely* given by the statements that the theory makes about it [T]. After the theory has been axiomatized, the various *successful* interpretations [SD] of the primitive term give the most comprehensive possible statement about its meaning in the real world. (Williams, M., 1984, p 91)

Perfect definitions are often difficult to give, but her claim that 'they cannot or need not be given' is mistaken.[14]

Notice her usage of the key word *successful,* which usually refers to 'the success of organisms in an environment.' She uses the word at a higher metaphysical level. Here it refers to 'the success of interpretations in explaining survival.' Apparently, the unsuccessful interpretations are to be ignored but the successful interpretations are to be culled together into a collection of special definitions giving a comprehensive statement about the metaphysical concept of fitness.

*

Williams sees that some people are trying to throw away the Darwinian insight.

> The controversy, then, is between those who, *relying on the deep intuitive knowledge* that Darwinian theory is far from being vacuous, save the Darwinian insight by reintroducing a term equivalent to fitness without explicitly defining the new term, and those who, *relying on logical reasoning* from the accepted definition of fitness, throw away the Darwinian insight. (Williams, M., 1984, p 89, my italics)

No one is throwing away the Darwinian insight, we merely say it is not a scientific theory. There is a difference.

*

In summary, Williams tries to defend natural selection by intentionally leaving its central concept — *fitness* — undefined. Her approach is really an undeclared assault on the criterion of testability.[15] A theory that isn't defined is untestable and would allow multiple formulations (T,SD,M,L).

---

[14] "On pain of circularity we cannot formally define all the terms of a theory *within* the framework of a theory, but this fact does not prevent us from stepping outside the theory and explaining the meaning of the terms in a broader linguistic framework." (Mills and Beatty, 1984, 41.) They emphasize that fitness is a *propensity*: "the fitness of an organism is its *propensity* [PC] to survive [T,SD,M] and reproduce [RC] in a particularly specified [SD] environment and population."

[15] Rosenberg (1985, p 136-152) uses a formulation which endorses Mary Williams' attempt to leave fitness undefined, while also using the concept of *supervenience.*

490

Schematic Science

Robert Brandon correctly points out that current definitions of natural selection fail to meet the criterion of science. He then proposes the concept of "schematic law" as a new defense.

> "[Examination of the theory shows] a conflict between testability and systematic unification. I have suggested adopting [natural selection] as a schematic law as the best possible solution to this dilemma. ...
>
> [N]o definition of relative adaptedness can render [natural selection] non-tautological, general, testable, and true. [Natural selection] as a schematic law is not testable; instantiations of [natural selection] are not general. ...
>
> Darwinian evolutionary theory has as its foundation what I called a schematic law; thus *its structure does not fit any existing philosophical paradigms for scientific theories.* Heretofore, schematic definitions and schematic laws have not been recognized or investigated by philosophers of science." (Brandon, 1984, p 80, 81, my italics)

Brandon does not say much about schematic laws, nor does he rigorously defend them as science, rather suggests adopting his position as the "best possible solution to this dilemma."

Keep in mind that philosophers, theologians, politicians, and religious persons of all stripes have their 'schematic laws' too, which they are eager to have adopted as science. Brandon's idea would allow all these to be called science.

Direct Assault on Testability

Nearly all anti-creationists explicitly endorse Popper's criterion of testability, and use it as a major weapon against creation theory.

Philip Kitcher seems to be the only anti-creationist who takes lengthy, explicit exception with the criterion. His motive is evident. He sees that testability is a weapon against evolution.[16]

> Once upon a time there was an easy way to respond to challenges to scientific orthodoxy. When some crackbrained idea was paraded before a gullible public, its deluded defenders could be dismissed with one word. The magic word, more honored in the use than in the understanding, was "unfalsifiable." By pronouncing it at the right time, scientists turned many potential dragons into harmless pussycats. One day, however, there arose a band of committed dissidents who called themselves "creation scientists." The usual magic spell did not transform them into quiet conformists. Instead, they simply retorted, "Unfalsifiable yourself," and proceeded to complain loudly that some card-carrying members of the community of

---

[16] See also Kitcher, 1982, p 38-39

scientists had been unfaithful to their vows. .... Creationists have seen that it is possible to turn the appeal to Popper back upon evolutionary theory ... (Kitcher, 1984, p 168)

Kitcher's views on falsifiability are varied and confusing. We will examine them here.

*

Kitcher says the criterion of falsifiability is naive, since *all* scientific theories can be difficult (or impossible) to falsify in practice. He argues that all theories are essentially unfalsifiable, and that loosening up the criterion only allows *everything* to count as science. He concludes that the criterion is no help in discriminating between science and non-science.

As an example he compares Newtonian mechanics with the preposterous idea that "Quietness is wholeness in the center of stillness." He claims that with the criterion of testability, either they both pass as science or they both fail.[17] He concludes the criterion is ineffectual at telling the difference.

His attack on the criterion of falsifiability can be analyzed as follows:

- He over-exaggerates the tentative nature of science to make it seem largely uncertain.

- Then, he demands absolute formal certainty from the criterion of falsifiability. He demands that the criterion discriminate with perfect certainty between science and non-science. Since the criterion cannot provide this certainty, Kitcher erroneously concludes it cannot discriminate *at all*.

Kitcher is wrong through exaggeration and distortion. Science is tentative about the proving and falsifying of theories. To the same extent it is tentative when applying the criterion of falsifiability. We cannot be perfectly certain of a theory's falsifiability. Yet this does not mean we are totally uncertain, as Kitcher's argument would suggest.

In short, while science is tentative, it is not flimsy. It can give results that warrant our confidence. The tentative nature of science does not cancel falsifiability as the demarcation between science and non-science.

*

---

[17] Kitcher, 1982, p 42-43

Despite Kitcher's attack on the criterion of falsifiability, he endorses something much like it.

> [T]here is surely something right in the idea that a science can succeed only if it can fail. *An invulnerable 'science' would not be science at all.* (Kitcher, 1982, p 45, my italics)

Here he replaces the criterion of falsifiability with a similar, if not identical, criterion of *vulnerability*. Kitcher does not show any essential difference between the two.

Kitcher endorses a novel version of testability. He believes testability must be applied, not to a theory, but to its auxiliary hypotheses. (It is not clear what he means by auxiliary hypothesis.)

> An auxiliary hypothesis ought to be testable independently of the particular problem it is introduced to solve, independently of the theory it is designed to save.[18] (Kitcher, 1982, p 46)

Kitcher would replace the criterion of testability with an identical criterion to be met by an auxiliary hypothesis. A burden of testability remains, he has only shifted it away from the theory.

Kitcher has an unusual viewpoint, and the context explains why. He offers his unusual criterion of science in close association with his defense of natural selection. Kitcher's criterion of science would shift the burden of testability away from the theory. This results in a philosophy of science tailor-made for natural selection, one in which the theory is untestable, and the auxiliary hypotheses can be special definitions which are testable. Kitcher's philosophy of science is inconsistent.

*

Despite Kitcher's disagreements with the criterion of testability, he does not abstain from using it as a weapon *against* creation and *for* evolution.

> [E]volutionary theory ... has lent itself to testing from a number of different directions .... Creation 'science,' by contrast has been ... putting together a hodgepodge of vague suggestions that are explicitly designed to avoid any serious test. (Kitcher, 1984, p 173)

Again this shows Kitcher's arguments against testability are groundless.

*

Kitcher tries yet another line of defense for natural selection. Unlike most evolutionists, he does not call natural selection a theory. Instead he repeatedly and emphatically calls it the "principle" of natural selection.[19]

---

18 Kitcher highlights three characteristics of successful science, one of which is "independent testability." He intends his three characteristics as a criterion of science — he says if doctrines fall short on these criteria then "they fail to count as science at all." (Kitcher, 1982, p 48)

19 Kitcher, 1982, p 57-60

He does not say what a *principle* is, nor does he show how principles can be recognized as scientific or unscientific. After Kitcher asserts the importance of the principle, he then appears to take it all back.

> [E]xcellent and thorough textbooks in evolutionary theory have lengthy entries for natural selection, but no entry for the principle of natural selection. That is, the phrase 'natural selection' occurs many times in presenting evolutionary biology, but there is no one general statement given pride of place as the principle of natural selection. ....

> [N]o reputable biologist accounts for an evolutionary development by asserting the principle of natural selection. ....

> The main point is that the *concepts* of fitness and natural selection, not the *principle* of natural selection, play a central role in Darwinian evolutionary biology. (Kitcher, 1982, p 57-60, his italics throughout)

His defense of natural selection is unusual:

- He refrains from defending natural selection as a theory, instead calling it a principle without saying what a principle is.

- He says there is no one general statement of the "principle" of natural selection, nor does he provide one.

- Finally, he says the *concept* of natural selection (not the principle of natural selection) plays a central role in Darwinism.

In short, he demotes natural selection from a theory to a principle, then from a principle to a mere concept.

Finally, Kitcher notes that "sciences employ distinctive concepts ... and they deploy these concepts in distinctive ways to solve problems." He argues that reputable evolutionary biologists use the concepts of natural selection in a manner analogous to other sciences.

Kitcher's argument errs over two points.

First, the fact that science uses concepts does not mean all concepts are scientific. Kitcher offers an analogy between the concepts of natural selection and those of other sciences, but the analogy fails to show that natural selection is scientific.

Second, and more importantly, evolutionists claim natural selection is a scientific explanation of adaptation, i.e., a scientific *theory*. Therefore, it is inadequate to defend natural selection as merely a principle or concept.

Appendix to Population Genetics

This appendix provides additional background on population genetics.

Terminology

Evolutionists misuse the term "fitness" in population genetics. What they call "fitness" is, in reality, determined solely by measuring population growth rates. I strive to make this clear because evolutionary genetics texts do not. They mystify the term and create the illusion that survival of the fittest is within the machinery of population genetics. But the field can be rid of the term completely, without any loss of science.

In nature, many things tend to increase at a constant percentage rate. Such growth accumulates exponentially, like money in bank accounts. Malthus found that populations tend to grow this way. The population at time t is P(t), and is given by:

$$P(t) = P(0) \cdot e^{mt}$$
(where m is the Malthusian growth rate)

When $m = 0.03$ per year, the rate of population increase at any given instant is 3 percent per year.

If a population is comprised of groups, each with its own distinct growth rate, then we can predict the consequences of the differential growth. The equations of population genetics sometimes use the Malthusian growth rate, but more often they express growth in a slightly different form, as follows.

For group i, the population size at t=0 is $P_i(0)$, and later at time T it is $P_i(T)$. (Time T is arbitrarily chosen, typically as the length of one generation.) We then define the ratio:

$$W_i = \frac{P_i(T)}{P_i(0)}$$

W_i is the absolute selective value of the i-th group. (Evolutionists often call this the "absolute fitness.")

We want to know the selective values *relative to* a reference group. So, we divide by a reference, here called W_{ref}, typically chosen as the highest absolute selective value from any group.[1] The result is called the selective value w_i.

$$w_i = \frac{W_i}{W_{ref}}$$

---

[1] The reference group always ends up with a selective value of 1.

Selective values are population growth rates, peculiarly formulated perhaps, but growth rates nonetheless. They are obtained by measuring population sizes over time, nothing more.

Evolutionists often refer to selective values as *fitness, relative fitness, Darwinian fitness,* or *adaptive values.* Those terms are misleading. The values do not measure design, fitness, or adaptation. They do not measure the length of bones, the chambers of the heart, or convolutions of the brain. Much of population genetics can be de-mystified by referring to fitness values as population growth rates.

The only time this causes confusion is when a selective value is zero. Then, if you think of it as a Malthusian growth rate, you would conclude that the population is not changing size. In reality, the population goes to zero. The confusion is easily resolved by recognizing that selective values merely state growth rates in a peculiar form. The conversion from Malthusian rates is given by:

$$w_i = e^{(m_i - m_{ref})T}$$

The m_{ref} term is a reference growth rate. It is arbitrarily chosen, typically as the highest Malthusian growth rate of any group. Or it is given by:

$$m_{ref} = \frac{1}{T} \log_e(W_{ref})$$

Thus, the Malthusian rate is proportional to the logarithm of the selective value. (Evolutionists sometimes refer to selective values as "linear fitness," and by analogy with the above formula, they refer to Malthusian growth rates as "logarithmic fitness.")

*

Frequently we are interested in the difference between two specific selective values. (Usually one of them is arbitrarily chosen as 1, or as the average, the maximum, or the minimum selective value in the population.) The difference is called a selective differential, selection coefficient, or s-value.

$$s = w_i - w_k$$

Selection coefficients are differences in population growth rates.

*

All of the science in population genetics can be accomplished without ever mentioning survival of the fittest, natural selection, or fitness. Other appropriate terminology is already in place.

Derivation of Fisher's Theorem

Evolutionary genetics texts use Fisher's (misnamed) "Fundamental Theorem of Natural Selection," to create the illusion that natural selection is science. Using approximations, they give awkward derivations that shoehorn the theorem into various genetic models.[2] They further embed the theorem in discussions of fitness, natural selection, and genetic minutiae. This creates the impression that the theorem is genetical, biological, and evolutionary, and that natural selection is scientific. Their treatment confuses students about the true nature of the theorem. Fisher's theorem is actually quite simple, and can easily be derived by first quarter calculus students without any knowledge of genetics, biology, evolution, or natural selection. This section shows how.

Suppose a population has N groups, each with its own constant growth rate. The i-th group has a Malthusian growth rate m_i which can be any real number (including negative numbers and zero). The population of group i at time t is given by:

$$P_i(t) = P_i(0) \cdot e^{m_i t}$$

Thus, the theorem assumes that the N groups each have a pure Malthusian growth. If that assumption is true, then the following theorem will also be true.

By definition, the *mean growth rate* is:

$$\overline{m(t)} = \frac{\sum P_i(t) \, m_i}{\sum P_i(t)}$$

where the summations include all groups, from i=1 to N.

We want to know the *instantaneous rate of change* in the mean growth rate. This is given by the time derivative of the above equation.

To solve this we use a chain rule: The derivative of a summation equals the summation of the derivatives. We also use a chain rule for taking the derivative of a quotient.

$$\frac{d}{dt}\left(\frac{u}{v}\right) = \frac{1}{v}\frac{du}{dt} - \frac{u}{v^2}\frac{dv}{dt}$$

Also, in the case at hand:

$$\frac{dP_i(t)}{dt} = P_i(t) \, m_i$$

Combining these, we immediately arrive at Fisher's theorem:

---

2   For example, see Crow, 1986, p 83-85

$$\frac{d \ \overline{m(t)}}{dt} \ = \ \frac{\sum P_i(t) \ m_i^2}{\sum P_i(t)} \ - \ \left(\frac{\sum P_i(t) \ m_i}{\sum P_i(t)} \right)^2$$

The term on the left is the instantaneous rate of change of the mean m at time t. On the right side of the equation is the variance of m at time t.

We can write it in a simpler notation by using the concept of expected value (denoted by E[x]).

$$\frac{d \ \overline{m}}{dt} \ = \ E[m^2] - (E[m])^2$$

Thus, Fisher's Theorem is about differential growth rates — not genetics, biology, evolution, or natural selection. In fact, natural selection and evolution require that Fisher's theorem seldom applies.

Appendix to Haldane's Dilemma

This appendix provides additional background on Haldane's Dilemma. The material is more technical, subtle, or mathematical than the chapter, yet is kept as simple as possible.

Derivation of Cost

Evolutionary literature occasionally derives formulas for the cost of substitution. The derivations: (1) are shoehorned into various genetic models; (2) they make needless assumptions about the environment and selection; and (3) they are generally confusing. Such derivations are opaque to most people. The confusion also provided the cover for evolutionists to brush aside the cost of substitution.

I will here derive the fundamental formula in a manner that avoids genetics, selection, and the environment. The derivation focuses instead on survivors and their reproductive capacity. By so doing, I will show that the cost of substitution is simple in concept, and unavoidable.

Suppose a population of size S has a few individuals, P in number, who have a new rare trait. Let us refer to such individuals as the "survivors." Suppose the remaining majority, Q in number, have the old trait:

$$S = Q + P$$

To substitute the new trait, all the Q individuals must have their line of inheritance terminated, either in this generation or in some future generation. We will here simply forget about their actions, as they have no effect on our analysis.

If evolution is to be an on-going, long-term process, then ultimately the entire population must be regenerated by the few P individuals. The substitution incurs a cost defined in terms of the genetic deaths per survivor. It is the excess reproduction (in births per parent) that must be produced for the specific purpose of replacing the genetic deaths. If the replacement is accomplished in one generation, then the cost is given by:

$$\text{Cost} = \frac{Q}{P}$$

$$= \frac{\Delta P}{P} \text{ (where we define } \Delta P \text{ as } S - P)$$

In this case, the cost is large because the population is regenerated in one generation, by only P individuals. This small number of individuals bears the entire reproductive cost.

The cost can be reduced by spreading the substitution out over many generations. The survivors must ultimately increase their numbers by an amount equal
to ΔP. Suppose, however, that ΔP is subdivided into N portions of roughly
comparable size.[1] Let us call these portions ΔP_i, where i=1,2,...,N. Suppose the
substitution is accomplished in N steps, as follows. The number of survivors
starts at P_1 and increases by ΔP_1 during the first interval. This leaves P_2 survivors,
who then increase by ΔP_2 during the second interval. This leaves P_3 survivors.
And so forth. After N intervals there are S survivors and the substitution is
complete. This accomplishes the substitution in N intervals, each with its own
cost. The total cost of the substitution is just the sum of these N partial costs.

$$\text{Cost} \quad = \frac{\Delta P_1}{P_1} + \frac{\Delta P_2}{P_2} + ... + \frac{\Delta P_N}{P_N}$$

When N is small the cost is large, because a smaller number of survivors is available to pay the cost. When N is large, the cost is smaller because any slight
increase in the survivors quickly becomes available to help give birth and pay the
reproductive costs.

The cost is minimized as N goes to infinity. This is because, at any given
instant, *all* the survivors are helping pay the cost. There is effectively no delay
between birth and reproductive maturity. The substitution process is so slow that
when individuals are born they are, in effect, immediately able to reproduce and
help pay the cost.

When N goes to infinity, the summation becomes an integral, and the cost
becomes an absolute minimum.

$$\text{Cost} \quad = \int_{P_1}^{S} \frac{dp}{p}$$

(Where p is a dummy variable of integration.) Evaluating this definite integral
gives:

$$\text{Cost} \quad = \log_e\left(\frac{S}{P_1}\right)$$

$$= \log_e\left(\frac{1}{p_0}\right)$$

Where p_0 is the frequency of the trait at the beginning of the substitution.

This is the formula Haldane used for the cost of a dominant gene. It is still
used by evolutionary geneticists. It gives the minimum possible cost of a single
substitution under any conditions. This minimum requires that the substituted
trait increase slowly, smoothly, and monotonically (without decrease). If these
conditions are not met, then the cost is greater.

---

[1] The N portions can be different in size. However, as N goes to infinity, they must each
become infinitesimally small. This is what I mean by "roughly comparable size."

*

Let us take an example to make the idea more concrete. Suppose the N intervals mentioned above are generations. Suppose that each generation increases its survivors by a constant percentage k. This type of growth is typical of bank accounts and biological populations.[2] These assumptions mean that:

$$\Delta P_i = k \, P_i$$

If the substitution takes N generations, then $P_1(1+k)^N = S$. So k is given by:

$$k = \sqrt[N]{\frac{S}{P_1}} - 1$$

By the above equations, the cost of substitution is:

$$Cost = N \, k$$

Suppose the population size is S=100,000, and the substitution begins with one individual having the new trait. The following table shows how the substitution cost varies with N.

N	Cost
1	99,999.0
2	630.5
3	136.2
4	67.1
5	45.0
6	34.9
7	29.3
10	21.6
30	14.0
100	12.2
300	11.7
1000	11.6
∞	11.5

As expected, if the substitution occurs in one generation, then the cost is 99,999. The one survivor must reproduce an excess of 99,999 individuals.

The cost rapidly drops as N increases. If N is seven generations, then the species must be capable of reproducing an excess of 29.3 births per individual. And as N goes to infinity the cost goes to its theoretical minimum of 11.51.

---

[2] It can be proven that this type of growth (known as "constant percentage" growth) results in the minimum cost possible for any given value of N. If the percentage growth is not constant, then the cost is greater.

*

Several points should be made here. The derivation did not require that the population remain a constant size throughout the substitution process. It only assumed that the population is nominally the same size at the beginning and end of the substitution process. That assumption was made to allow evolution to be a long-term, on-going process.

Also, the derivation assumed that the trait increases monotonically — in a deterministic fashion. The cost is greater if the substitution does not increase monotonically. This is due to two non-deterministic effects. First, as the trait increases and decreases, back and forth, then the species must keep repaying the additional costs of territory already traversed earlier. In nature, substituted traits do not increase monotonically. This incurs additional costs that were not included in the above formula.

Second, most beneficial traits are eliminated by genetic drift, and incur a partial cost of substitution before they exit. This effect raises the average cost of substitution, and was not included in the above formula.

Thus, the above formula represents the absolute minimum cost under theoretically optimal conditions that do not exist in nature. The average cost in nature will always be greater.

Recessive Substitutions

The formula derived above assumed the most efficient possible substitution process. Therefore, it did not represent recessive mutations, which are inefficient to substitute into a population. When a beneficial gene is recessive, then it selects against itself. The selective advantage of a recessive gene is masked when in heterozygous form. So, the recessive gene (in homozygous form) selects against itself (in heterozygous form), thus causing its own genetic deaths. This effect greatly increases the cost of recessive genes.

Here is the formula for the cost of recessive substitutions:

$$\text{Cost} \quad = \log_e\left(\frac{1}{P_0}\right) + \frac{1}{P_0} - 1$$

This formula assumes that the population remains nominally the same size throughout the substitution, that mating is random concerning the substituted trait, and that the trait increases slowly and continually. The formula does not include the cost incurred by unsuccessful substitution attempts.

The Super-gene Scenario

Some theorists argue that substitution cost can be reduced by substituting several genes together as one unit, thereby incurring only one cost of substitution — several genes for the cost of one.

The first problem with this is sex: the genetic shredding machine. Sex constantly breaks up combinations of genes. Suppose a parent has a beneficial combination of five rare genes. There is one chance in 32 they will be together in a progeny. This continues generation after generation. Sex rapidly fragments and disperses uncommon collections of genes.

Theorists suggest a way around this. They suggest that several genes fortuitously become linked together, perhaps by an inversion. Sex has trouble unlinking genes that are tightly linked. The theorists say these tightly linked genes — known as super-genes — can solve Haldane's Dilemma.

Haldane himself doubted this solution and pointed out the problem.[3] The following argument is based on his.

The cost of a dominant gene depends on the starting frequency p_0, and is given by the following formula.

$$C_S = \log_e\left(\frac{1}{p_0}\right)$$

This is the minimum possible cost of substituting anything. Nothing can possibly be substituted at a lower cost. So we can use this equation to calculate the minimum cost of a super-gene.

Suppose there are three genes with frequencies p_1, p_2, and p_3. Then all three genes occur together (in the same individual) at a frequency that is the product of the three gene frequencies. Occasionally when the three genes occur together, imagine that a fortunate mutational event occurs: they all link up as one super-gene. Suppose this occurs with probability r. Thus, on average the starting frequency p_0 of the super-gene is:

$$p_0 = p_1 \, p_2 \, p_3 \, r$$

Imagine the super-gene is substituted into the population as one "gene." Let us calculate the actual cost:

$$C_S = \log_e\left(\frac{1}{p_1 \, p_2 \, p_3 \, r}\right)$$

This can be rewritten as:

$$C_S = \log_e\left(\frac{1}{p_1}\right) + \log_e\left(\frac{1}{p_2}\right) + \log_e\left(\frac{1}{p_3}\right) + \log_e\left(\frac{1}{r}\right)$$

---

3   Haldane, 1957, p 522

Therefore, the average cost of substituting the three genes as one super-gene cannot be less than the cost of substituting the three separately. This analysis can be applied to any number of genes. Viewed over the long-run the super-gene scenario does not lessen Haldane's Dilemma.[4]

Theoretical Arguments

David Merrell summarized the theoretical arguments against Haldane's calculations:

> Various suggestions have been made in an effort to resolve Haldane's dilemma, of which, incidentally, he was quite aware. One is that most gene substitutions are neutral and have no cost. Another is that, as cost depends on gene frequency, genes of relatively high frequency (and thus those with rather minor deleterious effects) would more often be involved. Another is that Haldane's argument assumes that the genes act independently, whereas this may not, in fact, be the case. Here, ... truncation selection has been suggested as a possibility, which is, in effect, the equivalent of strong epistasis. With truncation selection, the number of loci on which selection could act simultaneously with the same total effect is greatly increased. Last, it should be noted that the lowest cost is associated with the substitution of a fully dominant allele. This finding supports the ... possible importance of the evolutionary role of dominant genes. (Merrell, 1981, p 189)

The evolutionary arguments are as follows: (1) Most substituted genes begin the selective process at a higher frequency than Haldane assumed. (2) Strong positive epistasis (such as truncation selection) is prevalent in nature. (3) Most substituted genes are neutral. (4) Most substituted genes are dominant. The first two are discussed in the chapter. The third is handled in the chapter on the neutral theory. The last will be handled here next.

---

[4] "To the high cost of selection for multiple-gene substitutions is added the continual breaking-up of the favored gene combination by the sexual process. Both of these factors are especially strong in their restrictive effects when the component alleles of the new gene combination are still rare in the population." (Grant, 1985, p 167)

Gene Dominance

To reduce the cost of substitution, theorists suggest that most substituted genes are dominant. They obviously wish to disregard the high cost of substituting recessive genes. They are willing to rely primarily on dominant genes in their explanation of origins.[5]

> [I]t should be noted that the lowest cost is associated with the substitution of a fully dominant allele. This finding supports the ... possible importance of the evolutionary role of dominant genes. (Merrell, 1981, p 189)

Even if their argument were totally successful, it could only reduce the cost by perhaps a factor of two — not enough to resolve Haldane's dilemma.

Haldane's cost (C_s=30) is already heavily weighted toward dominance. If only one substitution in 475 is recessive (and the rest are dominant), then the average cost is at least 30 (for population sizes as low as 10,000). It is doubtful whether recessives may properly be ignored this much.

Recessive mutations need not be so obliging. They will not necessarily allow themselves to be ignored. Mutations are not up for auction so theorists can bid on inexpensive ones and hold back on the pricey ones. The recessives must be accepted along with the dominants, whatever their cost — and recessives are common in nature. Recessive mutations can be substituted into a population, and they will incur their cost.

*

Beneficial mutations are usually eliminated by drift — but they do not exit peaceably, they put up a fight. They offer increased survival and thereby cause selective elimination of other less endowed individuals. So, some cost is incurred without the population actually achieving a substitution. This is the typical outcome for beneficial mutations.

Haldane used a deterministic model that only included the cost for *successfully* substituted genes. He failed to include the hidden cost of unsuccessful substitution attempts.[6] Recessive genes cannot simply be ignored. Even if every beneficial recessive were eliminated by drift, they would still incur a cost on their way out.

*

Some theorists claim that dominance modifiers might solve Haldane's Dilemma. When linked to a gene, these modify the gene's dominance (hopefully from recessive to dominant), thereby reducing the cost.

---

[5] Some evolutionary theorists say they are willing to forego any reliance on recessive mutation. However, since mutation is usually recessive, they would be giving up most of their supply of new beneficial mutations.

[6] Non-deterministic models show that the added cost of unsuccessful substitution adds 2 to the cost of a semi-dominant allele. (Kimura, 1983, p 26) Kimura and Ohta used a non-deterministic model to provide a formula that must be numerically integrated to obtain the cost of substitution. However, they did not provide calculated values for cases other than semi-dominance. (Kimura and Ohta, 1971, p 72-88)

There are three problems with this:

1) The dominance modifier itself incurs a cost of substitution. So, this approach merely reduces the cost of one trait at the expense of adding the cost of another.

2) Most of the substitution cost is already incurred before a gene reaches moderate frequencies. Most of the cost is incurred before a dominance modifier could evolve. So, dominance modifiers are unlikely to evolve soon enough to give a cost reduction.

3) There is doubt that dominance modifiers are prevalent and successful in natural populations:

> As we have already seen with melanism and insecticide resistance, in many cases the newly favored alleles appear to have been dominant from the outset. Similarly, the many experiments demonstrating the existence of modifiers of dominance, or the success of selection in enhancing dominance, are suggestive, but do not prove how dominance of the wild type is actually achieved in natural populations. (Merrell, 1981, p 102)

*

A reliance on dominant genes and dominance modifiers does not solve Haldane's Dilemma.

Testability Revisited

Perhaps I will be criticized for saying that natural selection is untestable, when it seems I have provided Haldane's Dilemma as just such a test. But that is inaccurate.

If evolutionists were to solve Haldane's Dilemma, then the solution must come from new genetic models, or a re-analysis of costs and payments, or a re-assessment of the available time. Natural selection cannot provide the saving insight because it has no empirical bearing on Haldane's Dilemma. Natural selection is an unfathomable function of a theoretical smorgasbord and the unpredictable fitness terrain.

Natural selection never did claim it could turn apes into humans in ten million years. It does not claim adaptations are inevitable, nor even possible. These claims are made by evolutionists, not natural selection theory — there *is* a difference.[7]

---

[7] Remember that evolutionists *select* their claims to coincide with the available data, in this case, fossil sequence data. Their claims do not arise from the predictions of a testable scientific theory.

Natural selection could even be true. Acting over a billion-billion years, it might actually create major adaptations ... or it might not. No one knows, and the theory itself does not say. Natural selection is untestable, and Haldane's Dilemma does not test it.

Instead, Haldane's Dilemma tests precisely what it says it does. It tests the ability of a species (with its limited reproductive excess) to supply a *super-abundance* of selective traits (via differential survival) within the available time. It says nothing about the ability (or inability) of natural selection to assemble these into complex adaptations. It says nothing about the existence (or non-existence) of suitable paths across the fitness terrain.

Let me put this another way. The Darwinian vehicle is a metaphysical machine. We cannot examine the innards of its engine, its cornering power, its stability, or its ability to traverse up and down the hills and valleys of the labyrinthine fitness terrain. We have only a wavering vision of the terrain itself with its copious complexities and deformations. Rather, Haldane's Dilemma looks at starting point A, ending point B, and the available time. It shows that the construction of the Darwinian vehicle is irrelevant: there is not enough gas.[8]

*

Haldane's Dilemma tests the plausibility of claims made by evolutionists, while entirely sidestepping a test of natural selection theory itself. Natural selection may be true or false, independently of Haldane's Dilemma.

---

[8] This analogy is a close one. Suppose that ending point B is higher than starting point A, and separated by a convoluted terrain. We could argue that there is not enough energy in the available gas to take the vehicle upward from A to B, no matter what the route, no matter how efficient the engine. In this way, we may rebuff the extravagant claims of the inventor without actually testing the contraption itself. (Yet we are scientists; we are willing to stand corrected should the inventor ever demonstrate this feat.)

Appendix to Discontinuity Systematics

This appendix gives further insight into the background and rationale of the methodology.

Additional Justification

Message theory predicts that life should have a specific type of pattern. No traditional systematic method was adequate for studying that pattern, so a new one had to be invented. Discontinuity Systematics was specifically designed to probe the debate between message theory and evolution.[1]

Discontinuity Systematics seeks to identify the boundaries of common descent, with two explicit restrictions: one against phenetic and cladistic patterns, and the other against any greater involvement of creation theories. These restrictions are explained next.

*

Discontinuity Systematics, by definition, ignores phenetic and cladistic patterns. The chapter gave several reasons sufficient for that. Another is given here. Message theory predicts that phenetic and cladistic patterns should be abundant because they are key evidence against evolution. They are evidence for message theory, not evolution. Evidence for evolution must come from other sources.

This discussion was not given in the chapter because Discontinuity Systematics aims to be neutral and reasonably theory-free.[2] It aims to be usable by anyone, regardless of personal persuasion. Use of the method does not require the systematist to agree with (or have knowledge of) message theory. The chapter was written to neutrally define the method, so references to message theory were left out.

*

---

[1] The invention of Discontinuity Systematics was driven by message theory. The theory strongly suggested the systematic method. Such a situation is reasonable. For example, the theory of common descent moved Darwin to modify Linnaean taxonomy and develop a new systematic method, now appropriately called evolutionary systematics or Darwinian taxonomy.

[2] The methodology strives to be neutral and "theory-free." Yet no observational system can be entirely free of theory. Discontinuity Systematics explicitly contains lots of theory, *and all of it is evolutionary.* It has concepts of phylogeny, gradual intergradation, biological change, and interbreeding. The methodology seeks to identify their boundaries.

The restriction against creation theory arose from two sources: (1) previous conceptions of creation; and (2) message theory itself.

Creation systematists have been at a standstill since the mid 1800s. Their attempt to identify "kinds" stalled because they focused on that one word. They lacked a realistic set of terms and methods. So, I approached some leading creationists with the practical terminology and knowledge constructing methods discussed in the chapter. They warmly welcomed this development and offered helpful suggestions. Nonetheless, they were still reluctant to aggressively proceed with the business of systematics.

Their conception of creation was holding them back. They had no coherent theory of morphological pattern. They allowed, for example, that the designer may have created virtually identical kinds. So, they were reluctant to classify virtually identical organisms as common descendants! Their conceptions (or misconceptions) of creation were hindering them from seriously doing systematics.

To prevent such theoretical holdups, Discontinuity Systematics has a restriction against creation theories. Discontinuity Systematics is an *observational* enterprise, not an exercise in speculative creation theorizing. If the data indicates that organisms are credible common descendants, then they are classified as common descendants. The classification might be altered by new scientific findings, but not by ill-formed notions of what the designer "may have" done. This removes a conceptual obstacle that had kept creationists from making headway.

Also, creationists traditionally used reproductive viability as the definitive evidence that organisms are the same kind. This caused them to view "kinds" too narrowly. Without a full scientific set of continuity criteria they could not recognize discontinuity, so they were missing a major scientific evidence for creation. To correct that shortcoming, Discontinuity Systematics approaches the data as a neutral scientific observer possessing a reasonable set of scientific tools. The results are not tainted by a presupposition of creation, so they can count as legitimate scientific evidence for creation.

In short, the restriction against creation theories seems anti-creationary, but it clears the way for creationists to make real scientific progress.

Lastly, message theory says that life was designed to convey a message to an observer. The message is not encrypted such that specially revealed decoding procedures would be required for decryption. The message is in clear text, and no special theories or revelations are necessary to read it. The message (and the pattern of discontinuity) should be reasonably discernible by a neutral scientist. This is another reason why Discontinuity Systematics has a restriction against further involvement of creation theories. The methodology merely takes the point of view of the observer.

Directly Created Organisms

Directly created organisms have no ancestors, they are created by the direct action of a designer. Discontinuity Systematics does not allot any special status to them. There are two reasons for this: (1) They foster an entanglement with creation theory that is unproductive to the systematic method. (2) Specimens of directly created organisms cannot be observed. These points are explained next.

A creation theorist could argue as follows. The designer may have created a given kind as a population of any size. If the population was two or more, then the directly created organisms theoretically cannot be in the same holobaramin since they are not related by common descent. Such a theorist is then reluctant to classify virtually identical organisms as common descendants. (This conundrum is even more pronounced for asexual organisms.) In this way, the concept of directly created organisms erects an artificial obstacle in identifying the boundaries of common descent. This is especially unfortunate because we cannot observe directly created specimens anyway. We have no way of recognizing them, even if we held them in our hands.

To remove that theoretical obstacle, Discontinuity Systematics de-emphasizes the theoretical concept of directly created organisms. (The terminology is therefore defined without referring to them.) Discontinuity Systematics is an observational enterprise, not an exercise in speculating about what a designer "may have" done. The terminology is defined from the observer's point of view. If organisms are so similar that they are credible common descendants, then they are classified as common descendants. Again, this de-emphasis of creation theory is intended to clear the way for creationists to make real progress in systematics.

In Discontinuity Systematics, directly created organisms get classified together with other members of their holobaramin, without distinction. Such an individual distinction is not essential to fruitful research. We focus instead on the holobaramin since it is directly identifiable through known specimens (fossil or living). The members of a holobaramin have a variety of characters that span its morphology space, which in turn gives an idea of the characters of its directly created life forms. We can learn about the directly created organisms by studying a holobaramin and especially it earliest known members.

Definitions versus Derived Meanings

Each term in Discontinuity Systematics has a definition and a derived meaning. (The derived meanings are deduced from the four definitions in combination.)

The definitions apply easily to nature. A monobaramin, for example, is defined as a group containing only organisms related by common descent. A systematist can use this directly.

The systematist is concerned with the systematic construction of empirical knowledge. The derived meanings are inconvenient for the systematist because they cannot be directly applied to nature. For example, the derived meaning of monobaramin is "A group comprising one entire holobaramin or a portion thereof." The inappropriate use of this meaning would require the systematist to first identify a holobaramin, and then identify a monobaramin as a subset of that holobaramin. This reverses the process of identification. Monobaramins must be identified first, as a step toward identifying a holobaramin.

Unlike the systematist, the theorist is concerned with using empirical knowledge in theoretical explanations. (The explanation of holobaramins is the special task of the theorist.) The theorist, therefore, will typically use the derived meanings of the terminology since these are readily understood theoretically.

The terminology of Discontinuity Systematics is defined for the convenience of the observer or systematist, not the theorist. This advances its goal of being an observational enterprise first.

The Creationist Orchard

The rest of this appendix discusses the history of the creationists' attempts at systematics, and why a new systematic method was needed.

Before Darwin, in the times of the creationist taxonomist Carl Linnaeus, creationists held that species were fixed and immutable — each species had been separately created, remaining virtually unchanged thereafter. The creationist Kurt Wise calls this view the "Linnaean lawn." In that metaphor, each species is like a distinct blade of grass in a lawn — each blade has its own root (or origin) and continues upward, unchanged, as one sprig of grass among many.

Darwin challenged the Linnaean lawn with a new metaphor, the evolutionary tree. In his metaphor there is one common ancestor at the trunk of the tree, and the tree continues upward, with branching limbs, to encompass all life's diverse life forms. Darwin's evolutionary tree largely displaced the creationists' idea of a Linnaean lawn.

Modern creationists pose a metaphor midway between the two. Kurt Wise aptly calls the new metaphor the "creationist orchard." Numerous life forms were separately created, yet they did not remain entirely unchanged. They varied and branched, like an evolutionary tree on a smaller scale. Considerable variation occurs within the originally created life forms. In the creationist orchard, the trees are separate and distinct. There are no branches going tree to tree. Each tree is disconnected from others.

Species

By the time of Aristotle (circa 350 B.C.), people realized that the system of life has an ordered pattern. Systematists began to study the natural order and identify its smallest, most basic unit of structure. They began looking for natural groups, that is, groups that are not artificial or arbitrary collections of organisms. They sought groups spoken by the data rather than imposed by the human mind. From this search arose terms like "species" and "kinds," terms intended as the most fundamental natural groupings of organisms.

Historically, scientists selected the word "species" because it is the Latin word for kinds. The anti-evolutionary author von Baer (1828) defined the species as "the sum of the individuals that are united by common descent."[3] This shows that before Darwin's influence scientists used the term species in the same sense that modern creationists use kinds. The two terms were substantially synonymous.

With the rise of evolutionary theory the word species was defined in ever more diverse ways, and many of these definitions conflicted. Today the species definition remains a problem that defies any consensus of solution.

> In biology there is at present no general agreement on an explicit definition of the term 'species,' or on what counts as a logically or causally sufficient condition for a set of organisms to constitute a species, or for that matter on a necessary condition for species membership. Nor is there any agreed-upon operational mark of species membership. Most of the available definitions of species and the theories of speciation in which they figure are incompatible and, what is worse, inadjudicable. (Rosenberg, 1985, p 181)

> The entity designated by the term 'species' would, at first sight, seem obvious, simple, and easily defined. But this is not the case. There is probably no other concept in biology that has remained so consistently controversial as the species concept. (Mayr, 1982, p 251)

> Biologists still have difficulty in formulating a satisfactory, workable definition of a species. That a concept so central to biological thought and so crucial to biological research should still be rife with uncertainties and ambiguities is a commentary on the difficulty of the problem. (Merrell, 1981, p 359)

Because the two terms had originally been linked, the confusion over "species" created confusion for "kinds."

---

[3]   As noted by Mayr, 1982, p 257

Kinds

Modern anti-creationists have complained about the term kinds, arguing that it is ambiguous and ill-defined.[4]

Anti-creationists often equate kinds with "species" (a word now guaranteed to foster ambiguity). Then, by using a modern definition of species, they show examples where species have evolved into new separate species. They claim this as evidence that kinds have evolved into new separate kinds — in contradiction to creation theory. Their argument is mistaken. Life did not evolve, but the terminology has. Species no longer means what it once did. Species and kinds are not the same.[5]

Alternatively, some anti-creationists try to arbitrarily assign the term kinds to a rigidly fixed level of the Linnaean hierarchy such as the genus, family, or super-family. Then, by citing examples they argue that this results in inconsistency. They argue that *kind* is an arbitrary concept, erratic and unintelligible in its application to the empirical world.

The difficulty disappears by realizing that the Linnaean hierarchy itself is somewhat arbitrary. The levels of genus, family, superfamily, and so forth are arbitrarily set by systematists for convenience, and there is no fixed constancy of these levels throughout the Linnaean classification. There is no mapping of kinds onto any fixed level of the Linnaean hierarchy. In some portions of the Linnaean system kinds are individual species, while in other portions kinds are Linnaean families.

For better or worse, the word "species" is firmly embedded in everyone's vocabulary, therefore some creationists used it in their tutorial explanations. They wanted to communicate, and the use of commonly understood words was understandable for that purpose.

Yet the term *species* lacks the precision necessary for detailed discussion of creation theory. Species carries its own baggage of ambiguity and confusion, while providing no indelible correspondence with the creationists' concept of kinds. That is why many creationists begin their tutorial explanations by focusing on kinds. It communicates creation theory with less confusion.[6] (Especially, since "species" has been co-opted and redefined in so many conflicting ways by evolutionists.)

---

[4] For example see Eldredge, 1982, p 115-119; Kitcher, 1982, p 151-155; Awbrey, 1983, p 278-284; Cracraft, 1983a, p 164-169; Futuyma, 1983, p 187; Gepner, 1982, p 71; Strahler, 1987, p 361-363, 430, 74; Godfrey, 1983b, p 208-209.

[5] Modern evolutionists tend to define species narrowly as a group of organisms that commonly interbreed in the wild. Interfertile organisms that do not usually interbreed are viewed as separate species. Foxes, wolves, and jackals (which are interfertile) are viewed as separate species, as are interfertile squirrels that live on opposite sides of the Grand Canyon.

[6] The term "kinds" is not required to make the case for creation. The book put off the term until now, precisely to make this point. Discontinuity is the key issue, and there is already ample evidence for its widespread occurrence. The existence of discrete created kinds follows from that.

Many creationists now recognize that "kinds" is an inadequate term. First, it is too commonplace. It is used too often where its technical meaning is not intended, and this led to ambiguity. Creationists recognize the need for a more distinctive terminology.

More importantly, *kind* no longer meets the needs of creation systematists. The term was adequate for the Linnaean lawn, where each blade of grass in the lawn was a unique kind. The modern metaphor of the creationist orchard requires several terms to communicate subtly different meanings and construct knowledge. A single word, like "kinds," is inadequate for doing systematics in the creationist orchard.[7]

---

[7] The word baramin was coined by creationist Frank L. Marsh in 1941. He constructed it from two Hebrew roots: *bara* meaning created, and *min* meaning kind. It suffered from the same technical problems as "kind," so it was not used effectively. It now serves as the root for the practical terminology of Discontinuity Systematics.

References

Abell, G. O., 1985, "The Origin of the Cosmos and the Earth," in Godfrey (editor), 1985, p 223-242

Ager, D., 1981, The Nature of the Stratigraphical Record, Macmillan Press Ltd., Second edition

-------1983, "Fossil frustrations," *New Scientist*, November 10, p 425

Allen, K. C. and Briggs, D. E. G., (editors), 1989, Evolution and the Fossil Record, Smithsonian Institution Press, Washington, D.C.

Allin, E. F., 1975, "Evolution of the Mammalian Middle Ear," *Journal of Morphology*, Vol. 147, p 403-438

Anderson, N., 1970, "Evolutionary Significance of Virus Infection," *Nature*, Vol. 227, September 26, p 1346-1347

Aquillard v. Edwards, 1986, "*Amicus Curiae* Brief of 72 Nobel Laureates, 17 State Academies of Science, and 7 other scientific organizations"

Arduini, F. J., 1987, "Design, Created Kinds, and Engineering," *Creation/Evolution*, Issue XX, Spring 1987, p 19-24

-------1988, Letter to the editor, *Creation/Evolution*, Issue XXII, Winter 1987-1988, p 37-39

Arthur, W., 1987, Theories of Life: Darwin, Mendel and Beyond, Penguin Books, Middlesex, England

-------1988, A Theory of the Evolution of Development, John Wiley & Sons, New York

Asimov, I., 1981, "The Genesis War," a magazine debate between Isaac Asimov and Duane Gish, *Science Digest*, October, p 82-87

-------1984, "The 'Threat' of Creationism," in Montagu (editor), 1984, p 182-193

Awbrey, F. T., 1983, "Defining 'Kinds' — Do Creationists Apply a Double Standard?," in Zetterberg (editor), 1983, p 278-284

Awbrey, F. T., and Thwaites, W. M. (editors), 1984, Evolutionists Confront Creationists, Proceedings of the 63rd annual meeting of the Pacific Division, American Association for the Advancement of Science

Ayala, F. J., 1982, Population and Evolutionary Genetics: A Primer, Benjamin/Cummings Publishing Company, Inc.

-------1985, "Reduction in Biology: A Recent Challenge," in Depew and Weber (editors), 1985, p 65-80

Ayala, F. J. and Valentine, J. W., 1978, Evolving: The Theory and Processes of Organic Evolution, Benjamin/Cummings Publishing Company

Bakken, G. S., 1987, "Bakken/Gish debate transcript," 19 pages, available from the National Center for Science Education, Berkeley, CA

Ballard, W. W., 1976, "Problems of Gastrulation: Real and Verbal," *BioScience*, Vol. 26, No. 1, January, p 36-39

Barash, D., 1979, The Whisperings Within, Penguin, London

Barkow, J. H., 1980, "Sociobiology: Is this the new theory of human nature?," in Montagu (editor), 1980, p 171-197

Barrow, J. D. and Tipler, F. J., 1988, The Anthropic Cosmological Principle, Oxford University Press, New York, (paperback edition revised from the hardbound edition of 1986)

Barrow, J. D. and Silk, J., 1980, "The Structure of the Early Universe," *Scientific American*, April, p 118-128

Bell, G., 1982, The Masterpiece of Nature: The Evolution and Genetics of Sexuality, University of California Press

-------1988, "Uniformity and Diversity in the Evolution of Sex," in Michod and Levin (editors), 1988, p 126-138

Bellig, R. and Stevens, S. (editors), 1988, The Evolution of Sex: Nobel Conference XXIII, Harper & Row, Publishers, San Francisco

Bennetta, W. J. (editor), "Scientists Decry a Slick New Packaging of Creationism," *The Science Teacher*, Vol. 54, No. 5, p 36-43

Berra, T. M., 1990, Evolution and the Myth of Creationism: A Basic Guide to the Facts in the Evolution Debate, Stanford University Press, Stanford, California

Berry, R. J., 1980, "A Geneticist faced with Enzyme Variation," in Bisby, Vaughan, and Wright (editors), 1980, p 147-166

Birx, H. J., 1991, Interpreting Evolution: Darwin & Teilhard de Chardin, Prometheus Books, Buffalo, New York

Bisby, F. A., Vaughan, J. G., and Wright, C. A. (editors), 1980, Chemosystematics: Principles and Practice, Proceedings of an International Symposium held at the University of Southampton, The Systematics Association Special Volume No. 16, Published for the Systematics Association by Academic Press

Boslough, J., 1992, Masters of Time: Cosmology at the End of Innocence, Addison-Wesley Publishing Company, Reading Massachusetts

Boulter, D., 1980, "The Evaluation of Present Results and Future Possibilities of the Use of Amino Acid Sequence Data in Phylogenetic Studies with Specific Reference to Plant Protein," in Bisby, Vaughan, and Wright (editors), 1980, p 235-240

Bower, J., 1983, "The Origin and Evolution of Humankind," in Wilson, D. B. (editor), 1983a, p 114-126

Bowler, P. J., 1984, Evolution: The History of an Idea, University of California Press

-------1988, The Non-Darwinian Revolution: Reinterpreting a Historical Myth, Johns Hopkins University Press, Baltimore

Brady, R. H., 1979, "Natural Selection and the Criteria by which a Theory is Judged," Systematic Zoology, 28:600-620

Brams, S. J., 1983, Superior Beings: If They Exist, How Would We Know? — Game Theoretic Implications of Omniscience, Omnipotence, Immortality, and Incomprehensibility, Springer-Verlag

Brandon, R., 1984, "Adaptation and Evolutionary Theory," in Sober (editor), 1984, p 58-82

Brooks, D. R., and Wiley, E. O., 1984, "Evolution as an entropic phenomenon," in Pollard (editor), 1984, p 141-171

Brues, A. M., 1969, "Genetic Load and Its Varieties," Science, Vol. 164, p 1130-1136

Bull, J. J., 1983, Evolution of Sex Determining Mechanisms, Benjamin/Cummings Publishing Company, Inc.

Butler, P. M., 1982, "Directions of Evolution in the Mammalian Dentition," in Joysey and Friday (editors), 1982, p 235-244

Cain, A. J., 1982, "On Homology and Convergence," in Joysey and Friday (editors), 1982, p 1-19

Cairns-Smith, A. G., 1985, Seven Clues to the Origin of Life: A Scientific Detective Story, Cambridge University Press

Campbell, J. H., 1982, "Autonomy in Evolution," in Milkman (editor), 1982, p 190-202

Caplan, A. L., 1985, "The Nature of Darwinian Explanation: Is Darwinian Evolutionary Theory Scientific?", in Godfrey (editor), 1985, p 24-39

-------1988, "Rehabilitating Reductionism," Amer. Zool., 28:193-203

Carr, B. J., and Rees, M. J., 1979, "The anthropic principle and the structure of the physical world," Nature, Vol. 278, p 605-612

Chapman, R. H., 1983, "The Evolution of Life," in Wilson, D. B. (editor), 1983a, p 103-113

Charig, A. J., 1982a, "Cladistics: a different point of view," in Maynard-Smith (editor), 1982, p 121-124

-------1982b, "Systematics in Biology: A Fundamental Comparison of Some Major Schools of Thought," in Joysey and Friday (editors), 1982, p 363-440

Cherfas, J., 1984, "The difficulties of Darwinism," New Scientist, May 17, p 28-30

Christensen, K., 1984, Book review, in Weinberg (editor), 1984, p 66-68

Colbert, E. H., 1980, Evolution of the Vertebrates, A Wiley-Interscience Publication

Colinvaux, P., 1978, Why Big Fierce Animals Are Rare, Princeton University Press, Princeton, New Jersey

Cracraft, J., 1983a, "Systematics, Comparative Biology, and the Case against Creationism," in Godfrey (editor), 1983a, p 163-191

-------1983b, "The Scientific Response to Creationism," in La Follette (editor), 1983, p 138-149

-------1984, "The Significance of the Data of Systematics and Paleontology for the Evolution-Creationism Controversy," in Awbrey and Thwaites (editors), 1984, p 189-205

-------1984a, Book review, in Weinberg (editor), 1984, p 62-63

Creation Research Society, 1970, Biology: A Search for Order in Complexity, edited by J. N. Moore and H. S. Slusher, Zondervan Publishing House, Grand Rapids, Michigan

Crick, F., 1981, Life Itself: Its Origin and Nature, Simon and Schuster

-------1988, "Lessons from Biology," Natural History, Nov., p 32-39

Cristofolini, G., 1980, "Interpretation and Analysis of Serological Data," in Bisby, Vaughan, and Wright (editors), 1980, p 269-288

Cronquist, A., 1980, "Chemistry in Plant Taxonomy: an Assessment of Where We Stand," in Bisby, Vaughan, and Wright (editors), 1980, p 1-28

Crow, J. F., 1968, "Evolution and Genetic Loads," Haldane and Modern Biology, K. R. Dronamraju (editor), Johns Hopkins Press

-------1986, Basic Concepts in Population, Quantitative, and Evolutionary Genetics, W. H. Freeman and Company, New York

-------1988, "The Importance of Recombination," in Michod and Levin (editors), 1988, p 56-73

-------1990, "Fisher's Contributions to Genetics and Evolution," Theoretical Population Biology, Vol. 38, p 263-275

-------1992, "Genetic Load," in Keller and Lloyd, (editors), 1992, p 132-136

Crow, J. F., and Kimura, M., 1970, An Introduction to Population Genetics Theory, Harper and Row Publishers, New York

Crowson, R. A., 1982, "Computers Versus Imagination in the Reconstruction of Phylogeny," in Joysey and Friday (editors), 1982, p 245-255

Cuffey, R. J., 1984, "Paleontologic Evidence and Organic Evolution," in Montagu (editor), 1984, p 255-281, originally published in the *Journal of the American Scientific Affiliation*, Vol. 24, No. 4

Darwin, C., 1959, <u>The Origin of Species</u>, first edition, (the copy I have referenced was published by Avenel Books in 1979 and has page numbers which may be different from other published versions).

Davidson, E. H., 1990, "How embryos work: a comparative view of diverse modes of cell fate specification," *Development*, vol 108, p 365-389

Davis, B. D., 1985, "Molecular Genetics and the Foundations of Evolution," *Perspectives in Biology and Medicine*, Vol. 28, No. 2, page 251-268

Dawkins, R., 1976, <u>The Selfish Gene</u>, Oxford University Press, New York

-------1986, <u>The Blind Watchmaker: Why the evidence of evolution reveals a universe without design</u>, W W Norton & Company, New York

Denton, M., 1986, <u>Evolution: A Theory in Crisis</u>, Adler and Adler, Bethesda

Depew, D. J., and Weber, B. H., 1985, (editors), <u>Evolution at a Crossroads: The New Biology and the New Philosophy of Science</u>, Bradford Books, MIT Press, Cambridge

-------1985a, "Innovation and Tradition in Evolutionary Theory: An Interpretive Afterword," in Depew and Weber (editors), 1985, p 227-260

DeWiel, J. E. F., 1983, "Astronomy and creationism — II," letter, *The Skeptical Inquirer*, Vol. VII, No. 3, Spring, p 87-88

Dickerson, R. E., 1986, "Letter to Dr. Charles B. Thaxton," *Creation/Evolution Newsletter*, Vol. 6, No. 3, May/June, p 17-18

Dietz, R. S., 1988, "Might the Ark Have Contained Only Four Beetles?", *Creation/Evolution Newsletter*, Vol. 8, No. 5, September/October, p 11 and 14

Discover, 1986, June, Vol. 7, No. 6, "An Open or Shut Case," anonymous, p 12

Dobzhansky, T., 1962, <u>Mankind Evolving: The Evolution of the Human Species</u>, Yale University Press, New Haven and London

-------1973, "Nothing in Biology Makes Sense Except in the Light of Evolution," in Zetterberg, (editor), 1983, p 18-28, (originally in *American Biology Teacher*, Vol. 35, March 1973)

-------1975, Book review in *Evolution*, Vol. 29, p 376-378

Dolphin, W. D., 1983, "A Brief Critical Analysis of Scientific Creationism," in Wilson, D. B. (editor), 1983a, p 19-36

Doolittle, R. F., 1984, "Some Rebutting Comments to Creationist Views on the Origin of Life," in Awbrey and Thwaites (editors), 1984, p 153-163

Dover, G. A., 1980, "Problems in the use of DNA for the Study of Species Relationships and the Evolutionary Significance of Genomic Differences," in Bisby, Vaughan, and Wright (editors), 1980, p 241-268

Drake, F. D., 1982, "Will the real SETI please stand up?", *Physics Today*, June, p 9

Dyson, F., 1979, <u>Disturbing the Universe</u>, Harper & Row Publishers, New York

-------1985, <u>Origins of Life</u>, Cambridge University Press

Edey, M. A., and Johanson, D. C., 1989, <u>Blueprints: Solving the Mystery of Evolution</u>, Little, Brown and Company, Boston

Edwords, F., 1982a, A book review of "Life Itself: Its Origin and Nature by Francis Crick," *Creation/Evolution*, Issue X (Fall), p 41-42

-------1983, "An Answer to Dr. Geisler — From the Perspective of Philosophy," *Creation/Evolution*, Issue XIII (Summer), p 6-12

-------1984, "Apples and Oranges: A Response to Geisler," *Creation/Evolution*, Issue XIV, p 40-43

-------1986, "The Mystery Behind the Mystery," in *Creation/Evolution*, Issue XVII, Vol. 6, No. 1, p 41-42

Eldredge, N., 1981a, "Do Gaps in the Fossil Record Disprove Descent with Modification?", *Creation/Evolution*, Issue IV (Spring), p 17-19

-------1981b, "Misquoted Scientists Respond," edited by J. R. Cole, *Creation/Evolution*, Issue VI (Fall), p 36-38

-------1982, <u>The Monkey Business: A Scientist Looks at Creationism</u>, Washington Square Press

-------1985, <u>Time Frames: The Rethinking of Darwinian Evolution and the Theory of Punctuated Equilibria</u>, Simon and Schuster, New York

-------1985a, "Evolutionary Tempos and Modes: A Paleontological Perspective," in Godfrey (editor), 1985, p 113-137

-------1985b, <u>Unfinished Synthesis: Biological Hierarchies and Modern Evolutionary Thought</u>, Oxford University Press, New York

-------1987a, <u>Life Pulse: Episodes from the Story of the Fossil Record</u>, Facts on File Publications

-------1987b, Book Review, *Creation/Evolution*, Issue XX, Spring 1987, p 31-33

-------1989, <u>Macro-Evolutionary Dynamics: Species, Niches, and Adaptive Peaks</u>, McGraw-Hill Publishing Co., New York

-------1991, <u>The Miner's Canary: Unraveling the Mysteries of Extinction</u>, Prentice Hall Press, New York

Eldredge, N. and Cracraft, J., 1980, <u>Phylogenetic Patterns and the Evolutionary Process: Method and Theory in Comparative Biology</u>, Columbia University Press

517

Eldredge, N. and Gould, S. J., 1972, "Punctuated Equilibria: An Alternative to Phyletic Gradualism," reprinted in the Eldredge's 1985 book, Time Frames, p 193-223. (First published in Models in Paleobiology, 1972)

Eldredge, N. and Tattersall, I., 1982, The Myths of Human Evolution, Columbia University Press

Ewens, W. J., 1979, Mathematical Population Genetics, Springer-Verlag, Berlin

Felsenstein, J., 1971, "On the Biological Significance of the Cost of Gene Substitution," American Naturalist, Vol. 105, No. 941, p 1-11

------1988, "Sex and the Evolution of Recombination," in Michod and Levin (editors), 1988, p 74-86

Findlay, S., 1990, "Fundamental Theorem of Natural Selection in Biocultural Populations," Theoretical Population Biology, Vol. 38, p 367-384

Fisher, R. A., 1930, The Genetical Theory of Natural Selection, Dover revised and enlarged edition

Forey, P. L., 1982, "Neontological Analysis Versus Palaeontological Stories," in Joysey and Friday (editors), 1982, p 119-157

------1988, "Golden jubilee for the coelacanth Latimeria chalumnae," Nature, Vol. 336, 22/29 December, p 727-732

Fortey, R. A. and Jefferies, R. P. S., 1982, "Fossils and Phylogeny — A Compromise Approach," in Joysey and Friday (editors), 1982, p 197-234

Fox, S. W., 1984, "Creationism and Evolutionary Protobiogenesis," in Montagu (editor), 1984, p 194-239

------1988, The Emergence of Life: Darwinian Evolution from the Inside, Basic Books, Inc., New York

Fracassini, M., et al, "Fermi Paradox and Alternative Strategies for SETI Programs: The Anthropic Principle and the Search for Close Solar Analogs," Astrophysics and Space Science, Vol. 146, No. 2, p 321-331

Franklin, I. R., 1987, "Population biology and evolutionary change," p 156-174 in Rates of Evolution, edited by Campbell, K. S. W., and M. F. Day, published by Allen and Unwin, Boston

Freudenthal, H., 1985, "Excerpts from LINCOS: Design of a language for cosmic intercourse," in Regis (editor), 1985, p 215-228

Friday, A. E., 1980, "The Status of Immunological Distance Data in the Construction of Phylogenetic Classifications: a Critique," in Bisby, Vaughan, and Wright (editors), 1980, p 289-304

Futuyma, D., 1983, Science On Trial: The Case for Evolution, Pantheon Books

------1986, Evolutionary Biology: Second Edition, Sinauer Associates, Inc., Sunderland, Mass.

Gale, G., 1981, "The Anthropic Principle," Scientific American, Vol. 245, No. 6 (Dec.), p 154-171

Gans, C., and Northcutt, R. G., 1983, "Neural Crest and the Origin of Vertebrates: A New Head," Science, Vol. 220, p 268-274

Gayon, J., 1989, "Critics and Criticisms of the Modern Synthesis: The Viewpoint of a Philosopher," Evolutionary Biology, vol. 24, p 1-49, edited by M. Hecht et al.

Gepner, I., 1982, "The Fallacy of Kinds," in Pastner and Haviland (editors), 1982, p 69-72

Ghiselin, M. T., 1969, The Triumph of the Darwinian Method, University of California Press

------1988, "The Evolution of Sex: A History of Competing Points of View," in Michod and Levin (editors), 1988, p 7-23

Gingerich, P. D., 1984, "Darwin's gradualism and empiricism," Nature, Vol. 309, May 10, p 116

Glenister, B. F., and Witzke, B. J., 1983, "Interpreting Earth History," in Wilson, D. B. (editor), 1983a, p 55-84

Godfrey, L. R., 1981, "The Flood of Antievolutionism," Natural History, June, p 4,6,9-10

------(editor), 1983a, Scientists Confront Creationism, W. W. Norton and Company

------1983b, "Creationism and Gaps in the Fossil Record," in Godfrey (editor), 1983a, p 193-218

------1984, "Scientific Creationism: The Art of Distortion — Where is the science in 'scientific creationism'?", in Montagu (editor), 1984, p 167-181

------(editor), 1985, What Darwin Began: Modern Darwinian and Non-Darwinian Perspectives on Evolution, Allyn and Bacon, Inc.

Gough, J. B., 1983, "The Supposed Dichotomy between Creationism and Evolution," Creation/Evolution, Issue XII, Spring, p 26-32

Gould, S. J., 1973, Ever Since Darwin, W. W. Norton and Company Publishers

------1974, Evolutionary Theory and the Rise of American Paleontology, "Edited text of the first Alexander Winchell Distinguished Lecture given at Syracuse University on March 8, 1973," Dept. of Geology, Syracuse University, Syracuse, New York, 16 pages

------1977, Ontogeny and Phylogeny, Belknap Press of Harvard University Press

------1978, "Sociobiology: the art of storytelling," New Scientist, November 16, p 530-533

------1980, The Panda's Thumb, W. W. Norton and Company Publishers

------1981, The Mismeasure of Man, W. W. Norton and Company Publishers

continued ...

Gould, S. J., *continued*

-------1982a, "Is a new and general theory of evolution emerging?", in Maynard-Smith (editor), 1982, p 129-145

-------1982b, "Darwinism and the Expansion of Evolutionary Theory," *Science*, Vol. 216, April 23, p 380-387

-------1982c, "The Meaning of Punctuated Equilibrium and Its Role in Validating a Hierarchical Approach to Macroevolution," in Milkman (editor), 1982, p 83-104

-------1982d, "Fascinating Tails," *Discover*, Sept., p 40-41

-------1982e, "Punctuated equilibrium — a different way of seeing," *New Scientists*, April 15, p 137-141

-------1983a, Hen's Teeth and Horse's Toes, W. W. Norton and Company Publishers

-------1983b, "Darwin's Untimely Burial — Again!", in Godfrey (editor), 1983a, p 139-146. Also in "Darwin's Untimely Burial," *Natural History*, 85:24-30. Also in Gould, 1973, p 39-45

-------1983c, "In Praise of Charles Darwin," in Hamrum (editor), 1983, p 1-10, originally published in the February 1983 issue of *Discover*

-------1983d, "The hardening of the modern synthesis," in Grene (editor), 1983, p 71-93

-------1984a, "Evolution as Fact and Theory," in Montagu, 1984, p 117-125, originally published in *Discover*, May, 1981

-------1984b, "Creationism: Genesis Vs. Geology," in Montagu (editor), 1984, p 126-135

-------1985, The Flamingo's Smile: Reflections in Natural History, W. W. Norton and Company, New York

-------1985a, "The paradox of the first tier: an agenda for paleobiology," *Paleobiology*, Vol. 11, No. 1., p 2-12

-------1986, "Linnaean Limits," *Natural History*, Vol. 95, No. 8, p 16-23

-------1986a, "Punctuated Equilibrium: Empirical Response," (Letters), *Science*, Vol. 232, p 539

-------1987, Time's Arrow Time's Cycle: Myth and Metaphor in the Discovery of Geological Time, Harvard University Press

-------1987a, "The Panda's Thumb of Technology," *Natural History*, Vol. 96, No. 1, p 14-23

-------1987b, "Life's Little Joke," *Natural History*, Vol. 96, No. 4, p 16-25

-------1987c, "Empire of the Apes," *Natural History*, Vol. 96, No. 5, p 20-25

-------1987d, "Bushes All the Way Down," *Natural History*, Vol. 96, No. 6, p 12-19

continued ...

Gould, S. J., *continued*

-------1987e, "Justice Scalia's Misunderstanding," *Natural History*, Vol. 96, No. 10, p 14-21

-------1987f, An Urchin in the Storm: Essays about Books and Ideas, W. W. Norton & Company, New York

-------1987g, "The Verdict on Creationism: The Supreme Court's ruling is a victory not only for evolution but for teachers," *Creation/Evolution Newsletter*, Vol 7 Number 5, September/October. This article also appeared in New York Times Magazine originally, and in *The Skeptical Inquirer*, Vol. 12, Winter 1988, p 184-187

-------1988a, "Trends as Changes in Variance: A New Slant on Progress and Directionality in Evolution," *Journal of Paleontology*, V. 62, No. 3, p 319-329

-------1988b, "Ten Thousand Acts of Kindness," *Natural History*, Vol. 97, No. 12., December, p 12-17

-------1989, Wonderful Life: The Burgess Shale and the Nature of History, W. W. Norton & Company, New York

-------1990, "Enigmas of the Small Shellies," *Natural History*, Oct., p 6-17

-------1990a, "The Individual in Darwin's World," The Second Edinburgh Medal Address, Edinburgh University Press

-------1990b, "Speciation and Sorting as the Source of Evolutionary Trends, or 'Things are Seldom what they seem'", in Evolutionary Trends, edited by Kenneth J. McNamara, University of Arizona Press, Tucson

-------1991, "Eight (or Fewer) Little Piggies," *Natural History*, Jan., p 22-29

-------1991a, "Opus 200," *Natural History*, Aug., p 12-18

-------1991b, "The Smoking Gun of Eugenics," *Natural History*, Dec., p 8-17

-------1991c, Bully for Brontosaurus: Reflections in Natural History, W. W. Norton & Company, New York

-------1991d, "What the Immaculate Pigeon Teaches the Burdened Mind," *Natural History*, April 1991, p 12-21

-------1992c, "The Reversal of *Hallucigenia*," *Natural History*, Jan., p 12-20

-------1992d, "Impeaching a Self-Appointed Judge," (a review of Phillip E. Johnson's anti-Darwinian book, Darwin on Trial), *Scientific American*, July 1992, p 118-121

-------1992e, "Magnolias from Moscow," *Natural History*, Sep. p 10-18

-------1992f, "Heterochrony," in Keller and Lloyd (editors), 1992, p 158-165

-------1993, "Cordelia's Dilemma," *Natural History*, Feb, p 10-18

Gould, S. J. and Eldredge, N., 1988a, "Punctuated equilibrium prevails," Scientific correspondence in *Nature*, Vol. 332, p 211-212

------1988b, "Species selection: its range and power," Scientific correspondence in *Nature*, Vol. 334, p 19

Gould, S. J. and Lewontin, R. C., 1984, "The Spandrels of San Marco and the Panglossian Paradigm: A Critique of the Adaptationist Programme," in Sober (editor), 1984, p 252-270

Gould, S. J., Luria, S. E., and Singer, S., 1981, <u>A View Of Life</u>, The Benjamin/Cummings Publishing Company, Inc., Menlo Park, California

Grant, V., 1985, <u>The Evolutionary Process: A Critical Review of Evolutionary Theory</u>, Columbia University Press, New York

Greenwood, P. J., Harvey, P. H., and Slatkin, M., (editors), 1985, <u>Evolution: Essays in honour of John Maynard Smith</u>, Cambridge University Press, Cambridge

Grene, M., (editor), 1983, <u>Dimensions of Darwinism: Themes and Counterthemes in Twentieth-Century Evolutionary Theory</u>, Cambridge University Press, New York

------1987, "Hierarchies in Biology," *American Scientist*, Vol. 75, p 504-510

Gribbin, J. and Cherfas, J., 1982, <u>The Monkey Puzzle: Reshaping the Evolutionary Tree</u>, McGraw-Hill Book Company, New York

Gribbin, J. and Gribbin, M., 1988, <u>The One Per Cent Advantage: The Sociobiology of Being Human</u>, Basil Blackwell, New York

Hadow, H., 1984, Review of <u>Origin of Life/Evolution: Creation</u>, in Weinberg (editor), 1984, p 10-12

Haldane, J. B. S., 1957, "The Cost of Natural Selection," *J. Genet*, Vol. 55, p 511-524

------1961, "More Precise Expressions for the Cost of Natural Selection," *Journal of Genetics*, Vol 57., Nos. 2 & 3, p 351-360

------1985, <u>On Being the Right Size and Other Essays</u>, edited by John Maynard-Smith, Oxford University Press, New York

Halstead, L. B., 1982, "Evolutionary Trends and the Phylogeny of the Agnatha," in Joysey and Friday (editors), 1982, p 159-196

------1984, "Evolution — The Fossils Say Yes!", in Montagu (editor), 1984, p 240-254

Hamrum, C. L., (editor), 1983, <u>Darwin's Legacy</u>, Nobel Conference XVIII held at Gustavus Adolphus College in St. Peter, Minnesota, Hamrum (editor), Harper and Row, Publishers

Hanson, R. W., (editor), 1986, <u>Science and Creation: Geological, Theological, and Educational Perspectives</u>, AAAS, Macmillan Publishing Company, New York

------1986a, "Introduction: Science or Belief, A False Dichotomy," in Hanson (editor), 1986, p 1-9

Hartl, D. L., 1980, <u>Principles of Population Genetics</u>, Sinauer Associates, Inc. Publishers

Harris, E. E., 1991, <u>Cosmos and Anthropos: A Philosophical Interpretation of the Anthropic Cosmological Principle</u>, Humanities Press International, New Jersey

Harris, J. A., and Bisby, F. A., 1980, "Classification from Chemical Data," in Bisby, Vaughan, and Wright (editors), 1980, p 305-328

Hastings, R., 1991, "Pandering to Fears of Texas Textbooks," *National Center for Science Education Reports*, Volume 11, No. 2, Summer, 1991, p 22.

Hawking, S. W., 1988, <u>A Brief History of Time: From the Big Bang to Black Holes</u>, Bantam Books, New York

Hewitt, G. C., 1988, "Misuses of biology in the context of the paranormal," *Experientia*, Vol. 44, p 297-303

Hill, A., 1984, Book review, *American Scientist*, Vol. 72, p 188-189

Hill, C. R. and Crane, P. R., 1982, "Evolutionary Cladistics and the Origin of Angiosperms," in Joysey and Friday (editors), 1982, p 269-361

Hitching, F., 1982, <u>The Neck of the Giraffe: Where Darwin Went Wrong</u>, Published by Ticknor and Fields

Ho, M., and Saunders, P. T. (editors), 1984, <u>Beyond Neo-Darwinism: An introduction to the new evolutionary paradigm</u>, Academic Press

Hofstadter, D., 1979, <u>Godel, Escher, Bach: An Eternal Golden Braid</u>, Vintage Books

Horgan, J., 1991, "In the Beginning...," *Scientific American*, February, p 116-125, staff writer for *Scientific American*

Hoyle, F. and Wickramasinghe, C., 1981, <u>Evolution from Space: A Theory of Cosmic Creationism</u>, Simon and Schuster, Inc., New York

Hughes, S. W., 1982, "The Fact and the Theory of Evolution," *American Biology Teacher*, Vol. 44, No. 1, p 25-32

Hull, D. L., 1989, <u>The Metaphysics of Evolution</u>, State University of New York Press, Albany

Humphries, C. J. and Richardson, P. M., 1980, "Hennig's Methods and Phytochemistry," in Bisby, Vaughan, and Wright (editors), 1980, p 353-378

Hunkapiller, T., Huang, H., Hood, L., and Campbell, J. H., 1982, "The Impact of Modern Genetics on Evolutionary Theory," in Milkman (editor), 1982, p 164-189

Janvier, P., 1984, "Cladistics: Theory, purpose, and evolutionary implications," in Pollard (editor), 1984, p 39-75

Jeffreys, A. J., 1982, "Evolution of Globin Genes," in Maynard-Smith (editor), 1982, p 76-89

Johnson, B. C., 1981, The Atheist Debater's Handbook, Prometheus Books, Buffalo, New York

Johnson, C., 1976, Introduction to Natural Selection, University Park Press

Joysey, K. A., 1980, "Principles and Practice in Chemosystematics: a Summing Up," in Bisby, Vaughan, and Wright (editors), 1980, p 419-425 Press

Joysey, K. A., and Friday, A. E. (editors), 1982, Problems of Phylogenetic Reconstruction, Proceedings of an International Symposium held in Cambridge, The Systematics Association Special Volume No. 21, Published for the Systematics Association by Academic Press

Jukes, T. H., 1983, "Molecular Evidence for Evolution," in Godfrey (editor), 1983a, p 117-138

Keller, 1986, "One woman and her theory," New Scientist, July 3, p 46-50

Keller, E. F., and Lloyd, E. A., (editors) 1992, Keywords in Evolutionary Biology, Harvard University Press, Cambridge, Mass.

Kemp, T. S., 1982, Mammal-like Reptiles and the Origin of Mammals, Academic Press, New York

Kent, G. C., 1987, Comparative Anatomy of the Vertebrates, Times Mirror/Mosby College Publishing, St. Louis

Kerr, R. A., 1980, "Origin of Life: New Ingredients Suggested," Science, Vol. 210, p 42-43

Kimura, M., 1968, "Evolutionary Rate at the Molecular Level," Nature, Vol. 217, p 624-626

-------1983, The Neutral Theory of Molecular Evolution, Cambridge University Press, Cambridge

-------1985, "Natural Selection and Neutral Evolution," in Godfrey (editor), 1985, p 73-93

-------1987, "Molecular Evolutionary Clock and the Neutral Theory," Journal of Molecular Evolution, Vol. 26 p 24-33

-------1990, "Some Models of Neutral Evolution, Compensatory Evolution, and the Shifting Balance Process," Theoretical Population Biology, Vol. 37, p 150-158

Kimura, M., and Ohta, T., 1971, Theoretical Aspects of Population Genetics, Princeton University Press

Kimura, M., and Takahata, N. (editors), 1991, New Aspects of the Genetics of Molecular Evolution, Springer-Verlag, Berlin

King, G. E., 1982, "Delineation of Fallacies: A Critical Approach to Creationism," in Pastner and Haviland (editors), 1982, p 61-68

King, J. L., and Jukes, T. H., 1969, "Non-Darwinian Evolution," Science, Vol. 164, p 788-798

Kirsch, J., 1983, Book review of Mammal-like Reptiles and the Origin of Mammals, in American Scientist, 1983, March-April, p 197-198

Kitcher, P., 1982, Abusing Science: The Case Against Creationism, MIT Press

-------1984, "Good Science, Bad Science, Dreadful Science, and Pseudoscience," Journal of College Science Teaching, December 1984/January 1984, p 168-173

-------1985, Vaulting Ambition: Sociobiology and the Quest for Human Nature, MIT Press, Cambridge

Klemke, E. D., Hollinger, R., and Kline, A. D. (editors), 1980, Introductory Readings in the Philosophy of Science, Prometheus Books, Buffalo, NY

Kline, A. D., 1983, "Theories, Facts, and Gods: Philosophical Aspects of the Creation-Evolution Controversy," in Wilson, D. B. (editor), 1983a, p 37-44

Kondrashov, A. S., 1988, "Deleterious mutations and the evolution of sexual reproduction," Nature, Vol. 336, December 1, p 435-440

Krimbas, C. B., 1984, "On Adaptation, Neo-Darwinian Tautology, and Population Fitness," in Hecht, M. K., Wallace, B., and Prance, G. T. (editors), Evolutionary Biology: Volume 17, Plenum Press

Kuhn, T., 1970, The Structure of Scientific Revolutions, second edition, enlarged, The University of Chicago Press

-------1977, The Essential Tension: Selected Studies in Scientific Tradition and Change, The University of Chicago Press

Kurten, Bjorn, 1984, Not From the Apes: A History of Man's Origins and Evolution, Columbia University Press

Laferriere, J. E., 1989, "Certainty and Proof In Creationist Thought," The Skeptical Inquirer, Vol. 13, No. 2, Winter, p 184-188

La Follette, Marcel C. (editor), 1983, Creationism, Science, and the Law: The Arkansas Case, Follette, MIT Press

-------1983a, "Creationism in the News: Mass Media Coverage of the Arkansas Trial," in La Follette (editor), 1983, p 189-207

Lande, R., 1982, "Microevolution in relation to macroevolution," in Maynard-Smith (editor), 1982, p 146-153

Langman, J., 1975, Medical Embryology, third edition.

Laurent, R. F., 1983, "Irreversibility: A Comment on Macbeth's Interpretations," Systematic Zoology, 32(1), p 75

Lazlo, E., 1987, Evolution: The Grand Synthesis, New Science Library, Shambhala Publications, Boston

Ledley, F. D., 1982, "Evolution and the Human Tail: A Case Report," The New England Journal of Medicine, May 20, p 1212-1215 (Note: Stephen Jay Gould reviewed the article prior to publication.)

Leslie, J., 1989, Universes, Routledge, New York

Levin, B. R., 1984, "Science as a Way of Knowing — Molecular Evolution," *American Zoologist*, 24:451-464

Levy, E. H., 1985, "Protostars and Planets: Overview from a Planetary Perspective," p 3-16 in Protostars and Planets II, edited by D. C. Black and M. S. Matthews, University of Arizona Press, Tucson

Lewin, R., 1982, The Thread of Life: The Smithsonian Looks at Evolution, Smithsonian Books, Washington DC

-------1985, "Red Queen Runs into Trouble?", *Science*, January 25, p 399-400

-------1987, Bones of Contention: Controversies in the Search for Human Origins, Simon and Schuster, New York

Lewontin, R., 1972, "Testing the Theory of Natural Selection," *Nature*, Vol 236, March 24, 1972, p 181-182

-------1974, The Genetic Basis of Evolutionary Change, Columbia University Press

-------1978, "Adaptation," *Scientific American*, Vol. 238, No. 8, September 1978, p 212-230. Also in Genetics: Readings from Scientific American, 1981, p 252-263, published by W. H. Freeman and Company

-------1983, "Introduction," in Godfrey (editor), 1983a, p xxiii-xxvi

-------1985, "Population genetics," in Greenwood, Harvey, and Slatkin, (editors), 1985, p 3-18

Lewontin, R. C., Rose, S., and Kamin, L. J., 1984, Not in Our Genes: Biology, Ideology, and Human Nature, Pantheon Books, New York

Loftin, R. W., 1988, "Caves and Evolution," *Creation/Evolution*, Issue XXIII, p 21-28

Lovtrup, S., 1987, Darwinism: The Refutation of a Myth, Croom Helm, London

Lowenstein, J. and Zihlman, A., 1988, "The invisible ape," *New Scientist*, December 3, p 56-59

Lyons, G., 1984, "Repealing the Enlightenment," in Montagu (editor), 1984, p 343-364

Macbeth, N., 1971, Darwin Retried: An Appeal to Reason, Gambit Ipswich Massachusetts

Maddox, J., 1984, "New twist for anthropic principle," *Nature*, Vol. 307, p 409

Margulis, L., and Sagan, D., 1986, Origins of Sex: Three Billion Years of Genetic Recombination, Yale University Press, New Haven

Max, E. E., 1991, "The Evolution of Improved Fitness by Random Mutation Plus Selection," *Creation/Evolution*, Issue XXVIII, Winter 1990-1991, p 21-31

Maynard Smith, J., 1968, "Haldane's Dilemma and the Rate of Evolution," *Nature*, Vol. 219, p 1114-1116

-------1969, "The status of neo-Darwinism," in Waddington, C. H., (editor), Towards a Theoretical Biology, Vol. 2,, Edinburgh U. P., Edinburgh

-------1972, On Evolution, Edinburgh University Press

-------(editor), 1982, Evolution Now: A Century after Darwin, edited by John Maynard-Smith in association with *Nature*, W. H. Freeman and Company

-------1986, The Problems of Biology, Oxford University Press

-------1987, "Darwinism stays unpunctured," Scientific correspondence in *Nature*, Vol. 330 p 516

-------1988, "Punctuation in perspective," Scientific correspondence in *Nature*, Vol. 332 p 311-312

-------1988a, Did Darwin Get it Right? Essays on Games, Sex and Evolution, Chapman and Hall, New York

-------1988b, "The Evolution of Recombination," in Michod and Levin (editors), 1988, p 106-125

-------1989, Evolutionary Genetics, Oxford University Press, New York

Mayo, O., 1983, Natural Selection and Its Constraints, Academic Press

Mayr, E., 1963, Animal Species and Evolution, Belknap Press of Harvard University Press, Cambridge, Mass.

-------1977, "Darwin and Natural Selection," *American Scientist*, May-June, p 321-327

-------1982, The Growth of Biological Thought: Diversity, Evolution, and Inheritance, The Belknap Press of Harvard University Press

-------1984, *BioScience*, Vol. 34, No. 4, p 252

-------1985, "How Biology Differs from the Physical Sciences," in Depew and Weber (editors), 1985, p 43-64

-------1988, Toward a New Philosophy of Biology: Observations of an Evolutionist, Belknap Press of Harvard University Press, Cambridge

-------1991, One Long Argument: Charles Darwin and the Genesis of Modern Evolutionary Thought, Harvard University Press, Cambridge, Massachusetts

McCollister, B., (editor), 1989, Voices for Evolution, The National Center for Science Education, Inc., Berkeley, CA, A compilation of anti-creation position statements from numerous scientific, educational, and religious organizations.

McGowan, C., 1984, In the Beginning... A Scientist Shows Why the Creationists are Wrong, Prometheus Books

McKenna, M. C., 1987, "Molecular and morphological analysis of high-level mammalian interrelationships," in Patterson (editor), 1987, p 55-93

McKown, D. B., 1993, The Mythmaker's Magic: Behind the Illusion of "Creation Science", Prometheus Books, Buffalo, NY

McMenamin, M. A. S., 1989, "The Origins and Radiation of the Early Metazoa," in Allen and Briggs (editors), 1989, p 73-98

Medawar, Sir Peter, 1983, "The Evidences of Evolution," in Hamrum (editor), 1983, p 45-52

Meeuse, A. D. J., 1982, "Ecological Aspects of Phylogenetic Approaches to Taxonomic Classification," in Joysey and Friday (editors), 1982, p 257-268

Merrell, D. J., 1981, Ecological Genetics, University of Minnesota Press

Michod, R. E., and Levin, B. R., (editors), 1988, The Evolution of Sex: An Examination of Current Ideas, Sinauer Associates, Inc., Sunderland Massachusetts

Midgley, M., 1985, Evolution as a Religion: Strange hopes and stranger fears, Methuen & Co., New York

Milkman, R. (editor), 1982, Perspectives on Evolution, Sinauer Associates

-------(editor), 1983, Experimental Population Genetics, Hutchinson Ross Publishing Co., Stroudsburg, Pennsylvania

Miller, J., Illustrated by Borin Van Loon, 1982, Darwin for Beginners, Pantheon Books

Miller, K., 1982, "Answers to the Standard Creationist Arguments," Creation/Evolution, Issue VII (Winter), p 1-13. Also, in Zetterberg, (editor), 1983, p 249-262

-------1982a, "Special Creation and the Fossil Record: The Central Fallacy," American Biology Teacher, Vol. 44, No. 2, p 85-89

Mills, S. and Beatty, J., 1984, "The Propensity Interpretation of Fitness," in Sober (editor), 1984, p 37

Milner, R., 1990, The Encyclopedia of Evolution: Humanity's Search for Its Origins, Published by Facts On File, New York

Minkoff, E. C., 1983, Evolutionary Biology, Addison-Wesley Publishing Company

Montagu, A. (editor), 1980, Sociobiology Examined, Oxford University Press

-------(editor), 1984, Science and Creationism, Oxford University Press

Moore, J. A., 1982, "Countering the Creationists," Academe, March-April, p 13-17

-------1983, "Evolution, Education, and the Nature of Science and Scientific Inquiry," in Zetterberg, (editor), 1983, p 3-17

-------1984, "Science as a Way of Knowing — Evolutionary Biology," in American Zoologist, 24:467-534

Morowitz, H. J., 1985, "The Origin of Life," in Godfrey (editor), 1985, p 243-257

Munitz, M. K., 1981, Space, Time and Creation: Philosophical Aspects of Scientific Cosmology, Dover Publications, Inc., New York

Nahigian, K. E., 1990, "Nontheistic Miracles," NCSE Reports, Vol. 10, No. 1, Jan-Feb, p 4

-------1991, Letter to the Editor, Creation/Evolution, Issue XXVIII, Winter 1990-1991, p 45-46

National Academy of Sciences, Committee on Science and Creationism, 1984, Science and Creationism: A View from the National Academy of Sciences, 1984, National Academy Press, Washington, D. C.

Nelson, G., and Platnick, N., 1981, Systematics and Biogeography: Cladistics and Vicariance, Columbia University Press

-------1984, "Systematics and Evolution," in Ho and Saunders, (editors), 1984, p 143-158

Newell, N. D., 1982, Creation and Evolution: Myth or Reality?, Columbia University Press

-------1984, "Why Scientists Believe in Evolution," a 14 page pamphlet from the American Geological Institute, Alexandria, VA

Ninio, J., 1983, Molecular Approaches to Evolution, Princeton University Press

Nitecki, M. H. (editor), 1988, Evolutionary Progress, University of Chicago Press, Chicago

-------(editor), 1990, Evolutionary Innovations, University of Chicago Press, Chicago

Norelli, R. J. and Proulx, R. R., 1982, "Anti-Science as a Component in the Growing Popularity of Creationism," in Pastner and Haviland (editors), 1982, p 4-11

O'Donald, P., 1968, "Measuring the Intensity of Natural Selection," Nature, Vol. 220, p 1967-1968

-------1969, "Haldane's Dilemma and the Rate of Natural Selection," Nature, Vol. 221, p 815-816

Orgel, L. E., 1982, "Darwinism at the very beginning of life," New Scientist April 15, 1982, p 149-151

Orgel, L. E. and Crick, F. H., 1982, "Selfish DNA: the ultimate parasite," in Maynard-Smith (editor), 1982, p 66-75

Overton, W. R., 1982, "McLean v. Arkansas. Opinion of William R. Overton, U.S. District Judge, Eastern District of Arkansas, Western Division," in La Follette (editor), 1983, p 45-73; Montagu (editor), 1984, p 365-397; and Wilson, D.B. (editor), 1983, p 206-222.

Padian, K., 1991, "The Origin of Turtles: One Fewer Problem for Creationists?" National Center for Science Education Reports, Volume 11, No. 2, Summer, p 18-19

Pagels, H. R., 1985, "A Cozy Cosmology: The Anthropic Principle Is Convenient, but It's Not Science," *The Sciences*, Vol. 25, No. 2, p 34-38

Park, M. A., 1982, "Debating with Duane," in Pastner and Haviland (editors), 1982, p 73-76

Parrish, F. K., 1991, "Parrish/Gish debate transcript," 24 pages, available from the National Center for Science Education, Berkeley, CA

Pastner, S., and W. Haviland (editors), 1982, <u>Confronting The Creationists</u>, Northeastern Anthropological Association Occasional Proceedings No. 1

Patterson, C., 1978, <u>Evolution</u>, British Museum (Natural History) Cornell University Press

-------1982a, "Cladistics," in Maynard-Smith (editor), 1982, p 110-120

-------1982b, "Morphological Characters and Homology," in Joysey and Friday (editors), 1982, p 21-74

-------1983, "Aims and Methods in Biogeography," in <u>Evolution, Time and Space: The Emergence of the Biosphere</u>, edited by Sims, Price and Whalley, Academic Press, p 1-28

-------(editor), 1987, <u>Molecules and Morphology in Evolution: Conflict or Compromise?</u>, Cambridge University Press, Cambridge

Patterson, J. W., 1984, "Thermodynamics and Probability," in Awbrey and Thwaites(editors), 1984, p 132-152

Paul, C. R. C., 1982, "The Adequacy of the Fossil Record," in Joysey and Friday (editors), 1982, p 75-117

-------1989, "Patterns of Evolution and Extinction in Invertebrates," in Allen and Briggs (editors), 1989, p 99-121

Pine, R. H., 1984, "But Some of Them *Are* Scientists, Aren't They?", *Creation/Evolution*, Issue XIV, p 6-18

Pollard, J. W. (editor), 1984, <u>Evolutionary Theory: Paths into the Future</u>, A Wiley-Interscience Publication

Popper, K., 1978, "Natural Selection and the Emergence of Mind," *Dialectica*, Vol. 32, No. 3, p 339-355

-------1980, "Science: Conjectures and Refutations," in Klemke, Hollinger, and Kline (editors), 1980, p 19-34

Press, W. H., 1986, "A place for teleology?", (Book review of Barrow and Tipler's 1986 book: The Anthropic Cosmological Principle), *Nature*, Vol. 320, p 315-316

Provine, W. B., 1988, "Progress in Evolution and Meaning in Life," in Nitecki (editor), 1988, p 49-74

Raff, R. A., and Kaufman, T. C., 1991, <u>Embryos, Genes, and Evolution: The Developmental-Genetic Basis of Evolutionary Change</u>, Indiana University Press

Raup, D. M., 1979, "Conflicts Between Darwin and Paleontology," *Field Museum of Natural History Bulletin*, Vol. 50, No. 1

-------1981, "Evolution and the Fossil Record," *Science*, July 17, p 289

-------1983, "The Geological and Paleontological Arguments of Creationism," in Godfrey (editor), 1983a, p 147-162

-------1988, "Testing the Fossil Record for Evolutionary Progress," in Nitecki (editor), 1988, p 293-317

-------1991, <u>Extinction: Bad Genes or Bad Luck?</u>, W. W. Norton & Company, New York

Raup, D. M., and Valentine, J. W., 1983, "Multiple origins of life," *Proc. Natl. Acad. Sci. USA*, Vol. 80, p 2981-2984

Rees, M., 1987, "The anthropic Universe," *New Scientist*, August 6, p 44-47

Regis, E., Jr., (editor), 1985, <u>Extraterrestrials: Science and Alien Intelligence</u>, Cambridge University Press, Cambridge

ReMine, W. J., 1990, "Discontinuity Systematics: A New Methodology of Biosystematics Relevant to the Creation Model," <u>The Proceedings of the Second International Conference on Creationism</u>, (Vol. II, Technical symposium session), p 207-216, published by Creation Science Fellowship, Inc., 362 Ashland Ave., Pittsburgh, PA

Riddiford, A., and Penny, D., 1984, "The scientific status of modern evolutionary theory," in Pollard (editor), 1984, p 1-37

Ridley, M., 1985, <u>The Problems of Evolution</u>, Oxford University Press

-------1986, <u>Evolution and Classification: The Reformation of Cladism</u>, Longman Group Limited

Riedl, R., 1978, <u>Order in Living Organisms</u>, A Wiley-Interscience Publication, translated by R. P. S. Jefferies

Rollinson, D., 1980, "Enzymes as a Taxonomic Tool: a Zoologist's View," in Bisby, Vaughan, and Wright (editors), 1980, p 123-146

Root-Bernstein, R., 1984, "On Defining a Scientific Theory: Creationism Considered," in Montagu (editor), 1984, p 64-94

-------1984a, "Ignorance Versus Knowledge in the Evolutionist-Creationist Controversy," in Awbrey and Thwaites (editors), 1984, p 8-24

Root-Bernstein, R. and McEachron, D. L., 1982, "Teaching Theories: The Evolution-Creation Controversy," *American Biology Teacher*, Vol. 44, No. 7, p 413-420

Rose, S., 1980, "It's Only Human Nature: The Sociobiologist's Fairyland," in Montagu (editor), 1980, p 158-170

Rosen, D. E., 1984, "Hierarchies and history," in Pollard (editor), 1984, p 77-97

Rosen, J., 1985, "The anthropic principle," *American Journal of Physics*, Vol. 53, No. 4, p 335-339

-------1985a, "The anthropic principle II," *American Journal of Physics*, Vol. 56, No. 5, p 415-419

Rosenberg, A., 1985, The Structure of Biological Science, Cambridge University Press, Cambridge

Roughgarden, J., 1979, Theory of Population genetics and Evolutionary Ecology: An Introduction, Macmillan Publishing Co.

Rovner, H., 1988, "We Need More Plimers," letter to the editor, *Creation/Evolution Newsletter*, Vol 8, No. 6, p 23

Rucker, R., 1982, Infinity and the Mind

Ruse, M., 1982, Darwinism Defended: A Guide to the Evolution Controversies, Addison-Wesley Publishing Company

-------1983a, "Creation-Science Is Not Science," in La Follette (editor), 1983, p 150-160

-------1983b, "Response to Laudan's Commentary: Pro Judice," in La Follette (editor), 1983, p 167-173

-------1984, "Is There a Limit to Our Knowledge of Evolution," Commentary in *BioScience*, Vol. 34, No. 2. Also reprinted in Ruse (editor), 1988, p 116-126.

-------1984a, "A Philosopher's Day in Court," in Montagu (editor), 1984, p 311-342)

-------1985, "Is rape wrong on Andromeda? An introduction to extraterrestrial evolution, science, and morality," in Regis (editor), 1985, p 43-78

-------(editor), 1988, But Is It Science? The Philosophical Question in the Creation/Evolution Controversy, Prometheus Books, Buffalo, New York

-------1988a, Philosophy of Biology Today, State University of New York Press, Albany

-------1989, The Darwinian Paradigm: Essays on its history, philosophy, and religious implications, Routledge, New York

Ruse, M., and Wilson, E. O., 1985, "The Evolution of Ethics," *New Scientist*, October 17, p 50-52

Sagan, C., 1973, (editor) Communication with Extraterrestrial Intelligence, MIT Press, Cambridge

-------1973b, The Cosmic Connection: An Extraterrestrial Perspective, Anchor Press, Doubleday, Garden City, New York

-------1979, Broca's Brain: Reflections on the Romance of Science, Ballantine Books, New York

-------1982, "Extraterrestrial Intelligence: An International Petition," *Science*, Vol. 218, No. 4571, June 29, p 426

Saladin, K. S., 1984, "Evolution vs. Creationism I — Saladin-/Gish debate transcript," 72 pages, available from the National Center for Science Education, Berkeley, CA

-------1988, "Evolution vs. Creationism II—Saladin/Gish debate transcript," 91 pages, available from the National Center for Science Education, Berkeley, CA

Satta, Y., and Chigusa, S. I., 1991, "Mitochondrial DNA in *Drosophila*: the Genetics and Evolution," in Kimura and Takahata (editors), 1991, p 117-134

Saunders, S. R., 1985, "The Inheritance of Acquired Characteristics: A Concept That Will Not Die," in Godfrey (editor), 1985, p 148-161

Scadding, S. R., 1981, "Do vestigial organs provide evidence for evolution?", *Evolutionary Theory*, vol. 5, p 173-176

Schadewald, R., 1983, "Creationist Pseudoscience: Scientific creationism is a classical pseudoscience in every way," *The Skeptical Inquirer*, Vol. VIII, No. 1, Fall, p 22-35

Schafersman, S. D., 1983, "Fossils, Stratigraphy, and Evolution: Consideration of a Creationist Argument," in Godfrey (editor), 1983a, 219-244

-------1985, "Anatomy of a Controversy: Halstead vs. the British Museum (Natural History)," in Godfrey (editor), 1985, p 186-219

Scherer, S., 1990, "The Protein Molecular Clock: Time for a Reevaluation," in *Evolutionary Biology*, Vol. 24, edited by Hecht, Wallace, and Macintyre, Plenum Press, p 83-106

Schoch, R. M., 1983, "Evolution Debate," Letter in *Science*, April 22, p 360

-------1986, Phylogeny Reconstruction in Paleontology, Van Nostrand Reinhold Company, New York

Schopf, T. J. M., and Hoffman, A., 1983, "Punctuated Equilibrium and the Fossil Record," Letter in *Nature*, Vol. 219, Feb. 4, p 438-439

Scott, A., 1985, "Update on Genesis," *New Scientist*, May 2, 1985, p 30-33

-------1986, The Creation of Life: Past, Future, Alien, Basil Blackwell Inc., New York

Scott, E. C., 1990, Review of the book Of Pandas and People, *NCSE Reports*, Vol. 10, No. 1, Jan-Feb, p 16-18, Scott wrote the article as executive director of NCSE (the National Center for Science Education), a staunchly anti-creation/pro-evolution organization.

Scott, E. C. and Cole, H. P., 1985, "The Elusive Scientific Basis of Creation 'Science'," *The Quarterly Review of Biology*, Vol. 60, No. 1, p 21-30

Selander, R. K., 1982, "Phylogeny," in Milkman (editor), 1982, p 32-59

Shapiro, R., 1986, Origins: A Skeptic's Guide to the Creation of Life on Earth, Summit Books, New York

Shipman, P., 1986, "Baffling Limb on the Family Tree," *Discover*, Vol. 7, No. 9

Shotwell, D. A., 1987, "Is the Universe Improbable?", *The Skeptical Inquirer*, Vol. 11, Summer, p 376-382

Silk, J., 1986, "Teleological Cosmology," (Book review of Barrow and Tipler's 1986 book: The Anthropic Cosmological Principle), *Science*, Vol. 232, p 1036-1037

Simpson, G. G., 1953, The Major Features of Evolution, Columbia University Press, New York

Singleton, R. Jr., 1987, "Creationists versus Evolution: A Paradigm of Science and Society Interaction," *Perspectives in Biology and Medicine*, Vol. 30, No. 3, Spring, p 324-344

Sloan, R. E., 1983, "The Transition between Reptiles and Mammals," in Zetterberg, (editor), 1983, p 263-277

Smith, G. H., 1979, Atheism: The Case Against God, Prometheus Books, Buffalo, New York

Smith, L. P., 1984, "Creationist pseudoscience," letter, *The Skeptical Inquirer*, Vol. 8, Spring, p 285

Sneath and Sokal, 1973, Numerical Taxonomy, W.H. Freeman, San Francisco

Sober, E. (editor), 1984, Conceptual Issues in Evolutionary Biology: An Anthology, MIT Press

------1984a, The Nature of Selection: Evolutionary Theory in Philosophical Focus, A Bradford Book, MIT Press, Cambridge

Sokal and Sneath, 1963, Principles of Numerical Taxonomy, San Francisco, W. H. Freeman and Co.

Sonleitner, F. J., 1990, "Molecular Nonsense in the Bible-Science Newsletter," *NCSE Reports*, Vol. 10, Num. 2, Mar-Apr 1990, p 14-15

------1991, "Natural Selection by the Numbers," *NCSE Reports*, v. 11, no. 1, National Center for Science Education

------1991a, What's Wrong with Pandas? A Closeup Look at Creationist Scholarship, A detailed critique of the book "Of Pandas and People." Approximately 250 pages. Available on disk from the National Center for Science Education, Berkeley, CA

Stanley, S. M., 1981, The New Evolutionary Timetable: Fossils, Genes, and the Origin of Species, Basic Books, Inc., Publishers, New York

------1988, "Species selection and the role of the individual," Scientific correspondence in *Nature*, Vol. 333, p 214-215

Stebbins, G. L., 1982, Darwin to DNA, Molecules to Humanity, Published by W. H. Freeman and Company

------1982a, "Modal Themes: A New Framework for Evolutionary Syntheses," in Milkman (editor), 1982, p 1-14

Steiner, R. A., 1981, "The Facts Be Damned!", *Reason*, December, p 28-33

Strahler, A. N., 1987, Science and Earth History — The Evolution/Creation Controversy, Prometheus Books, Buffalo, N.Y.

Stunkel, K. R., 1982, "Understanding 'Scientific Creationism'," in Pastner and Haviland (editors), 1982, p 51-60

Syvanen, M., 1984, "Conserved Regions in Mammalian Beta-globins: Could They Arise by Cross-species Gene Exchange?", *Journal of Theoretical Biology*, Vol. 107, p 685-696

------1985, "Cross-species Gene Transfer; Implication for a New Theory of Evolution," *Journal of Theoretical Biology*, Vol. 112, p 333-343

------1986, "Cross-species gene transfer: a major factor in evolution?", *Trends in Genetics*, March, p 63-66

------1987, "Molecular Clocks and Evolutionary Relationships: Possible Distortions Due to Horizontal Gene Flow," *Journal of Molecular Evolution*, Vol 26, p 16-23

Tarter, J. C., 1983, "SETI Program," Letter in *Science*, April 22, p 359

Templeton, A. R., 1982, "Adaptation and the Integration of Evolutionary Forces," in Milkman (editor), 1982, p 15-31

Thaxton, C. B., Bradley, W. L., and Olsen, R. L., 1984, The Mystery of Life's Origin: Reassessing Current Theories, Philosophical Library, New York

Thomson, K. S., 1988, "Ontogeny and phylogeny recapitulated," *American Scientist*, Vol. 76, p 273-275

Thompson, P., 1989, The Structure of Biological Theories, State University of New York Press, Albany

Thwaites, W. M., 1983, "An Answer to Dr. Geisler — From the Perspective of Biology," *Creation/Evolution*, Issue XIII (Summer), p 13-20

------1984, "Design: Can we see the hand of Evolution in the things it has wrought?", in Awbrey and Thwaites (editors), 1984, p 206-213

Tipler, F. J., "Anthropic-principle arguments against steady-state cosmological theories," *Observatory*, Vol. 102, April, p 36-39

Torrey, T. W., 1967, Morphogenesis of the vertebrates, second edition, John Wiley & Sons, New York

Trimble, V., 1977, "Cosmology: Man's Place in the Universe," *American Scientist*, Vol. 65, Jan-Feb., p 76-86

Underwood, B. F., 1876, "The Design Argument Refuted," originally given in an oral debate July 1875, then published by the Liberal and Scientific Publishing House of New York in 1876, and reprinted in *The American Atheist*, July 1988, p 43-45

Valentine, J. W., 1978, "The Evolution of Multicellular Plants and Animals," *Scientific American*, September, p 140-158)

-------1985, "The Evolution of Complex Animals," in Godfrey (editor), 1985, p 258-273

Van Valen, L, 1963, "Haldane's Dilemma, Evolutionary Rates, and Heterosis," *The American Naturalist*, Vol. XCVII, No. 894, p 185-190

Varisco, D. M., 1982, "The Recent Evolution of 'Scientific Creationism'," in Pastner and Haviland (editors), 1982, p 12-26

Vogel, D., 1984, Book review of *Chemical Evolution*, in Weinberg (editor), 1984, p 1-2

Waddington, C. H., 1960, "Evolutionary adaptations," in Yax, S. (editor), 1960, The evolution of life, University of Chicago Press

Walker, K. B. (editor), 1984, The Evolution-Creation Controversy: Perspectives on Religion, Philosophy, Science and Education — A Handbook, Proceedings of a Symposium Convened by R. A. Gastaldo and W. F. Tanner, The Paleontological Society, Special Publication No. 1

Weinberg, S. (editor), 1984, Reviews of Thirty-one Creationist Books, Published by the National Center for Science Education, Inc., (The Committees of Correspondence), Syosset, New York

-------1984a, Review of Fossils: Key to the Present, in Weinberg, (editor), 1984, p 7-9

-------1984b, Review of Origins: Two Models, in Weinberg, (editor), 1984, p 5-7

-------1987, "Anthropic Bound on the Cosmological Constant," *Physical Review Letters*, Vol. 59, No. 22, p 2607-2610

Wen-Hsiung, L., and Graur, D., 1991, The Fundamentals of Molecular Evolution, Sinauer Associates, Sunderland, Mass.

Wesson, R., 1991, Beyond Natural Selection, MIT Press, Cambridge, Mass.

Williams, M., 1984, "The Logical Status of Natural Selection and Other Evolutionary Controversies," in Sober (editor), 1984, p 83-98

Williams, G. C., 1975, Sex and Evolution, Princeton University Press, Princeton

-------1988, "Retrospect on Sex and Kindred Topics," in Michod and Levin (editors), 1988, p 287-298

Williamson, P. G., 1982, "Palaeontological documentation of speciation in Cenozoic molluscs from Turkana Basin," in Maynard-Smith (editor), 1982, p 154-166

Willis, D., 1989, The Hominid Gang: Behind the Scenes in the Search for Human Origins, Viking Press

Wills, C., 1981, Genetic Variability, Clarendon Press, Oxford

-------1989, The Wisdom of the Genes: New Pathways in Evolution, Basic Books, Inc., Publishers, New York

Wilson, D. B. (editor), 1983a, Did the Devil Make Darwin do it?: Modern Perspectives on the Creation-Evolution Controversy, Iowa State University Press

-------1983b, "Shaping Modern Perspectives: Science and Religion in the Age of Darwin," in Wilson, D. B. (editor), 1983a, p 3-18

Wilson, J. H., 1983, "The Origin of Life," in Wilson, D. B. (editor), 1983a, p 85-102

Woese, C. R., 1987, "Macroevolution in the microscopic world," in Patterson (editor), 1987, p 177-202

Wolpert, L. and Richards, A. (editors), 1988, A Passion for Science, Oxford University Press, Oxford

Womack, S. A., 1982, "Creationism Vs. Evolutionism: The Problem for Cultural Relativity," in Pastner and Haviland (editors), 1982, p 27-34

Wright, S., 1969, Evolution and the Genetics of Populations, (A treatise in three volumes, Vol. 2, The Theory of Gene Frequencies), University of Chicago Press

Yockey, H. P., 1986, "Materialist Origin of Life Scenarios and Creationism," in *Creation/Evolution*, Issue XVII, Vol. 6, No. 1, p 43-45

Young, W., 1985, Fallacies of Creationism, Detselig Enterprises Limited, Calgary, Alberta

Zetterberg, J. P., (editor), 1983, Evolution Versus Creationism: The Public Education Controversy, Oryx Press, Phoenix

Zindler, F., 1990, "Is Creationism Science?" Transcript of a debate between Zindler and creationist Duane Gish. 39 pages available from National Center for Science Education, Berkeley, CA

Index

An indexed topic can be located anywhere on a page: in the body text, in indented quotation paragraphs, or in footnotes. Italicized page numbers indicate that the topic is definitely located in a footnote. Also see the table of contents for additional help in locating topics of interest.

continued ...

ACKNOWLEDGMENTS: Thanks to Kurt Wise for many generous and insightful technical discussions through the years, especially on systematics. Special thanks to Bill ReMine III, Gary ReMine, Karen and Steve ReMine, and J. M. K. for detailed manuscript editing and endless encouragement.

Book Ordering Form

Now that you've seen the book you can order it for yourself or as a gift, and save handling/shipping fees by following this offer: Photocopy this page and use as an ordering form — prepaid orders only — use a personal check, cashier's check, money order, or bank draft — do not mail cash.

```
Ship to:      _____
Address:      _____
              _____
City:         _____
State (or country): _____
Zip (or postal code): _____
```

The Biotic Message (hardbound) .... QUANTITY   _____

at $44.95 (U.S.) each   × $44.95

TOTAL COST OF BOOKS   _____

Add applicable sales tax. (Currently this applies to Minnesota residents only. If the laws change, then follow the new rates.)

SALES TAX   _____

For U.S. addresses allow 3 to 6 weeks for delivery.

Foreign Shipping: For shipping to addresses outside the United States add $4 per book. ($14 maximum foreign shipping fee per order.) These are shipped at the "Book—Surface Rate" of the U.S. Post office, so accordingly allow for increased delivery time. Payment must be in U.S. funds by bank draft drawn on a bank in the U.S. Ask your banker, they usually provide this as a service.

FOREIGN SHIPPING   _____

TOTAL   _____

Make check payable to *St. Paul Science*.

Mail to: ***St. Paul Science***
                P.O. Box 28006
                Saint Paul, MN 55128

Discounts available on quantities of ten or more. Write for details.
The above prices and information are subject to change without notice.

WGPB

2 Tim 3:16 - _All_ scripture...
2 Peter 1:21 - Prophecy from God
Prov 30:5+6 - Every word His pure
Psalms 12:6 -
Psalms 119:9-16 -
1st John 5:13-15 - Know God's will Thru His word
John 8:30 -
John 14:22 -

Matt 7:21-29 Not saying Lord, Lord; but doing His will
we can come to Church & say we agree, but Then go act in the world
& go The world's way it be 'hypocrits' & Miss Heaven
James 1:22-25 - _Be doers_, Not hearers only.
→ The word is a shield, a hammer, a sword, and a mirror

VIP
A _shield_ to stop The firey darts of the wicked one
A _hammer_ to destroy strangholds of Satan

A _sword_ to divide Truth from error, to discern good from evil

A _mirror_ to see our SIN, so That we Repent

Read The Bible daily for hours, _No_ to TV & movies & anything else
That steals our time away from God, & His word. You have The time
Make good use of It for God, for Christ's sake, & your own.
Matt 7   Build on The Rock